THE
TIGER'S
WOMAN

THE
TIGER'S
WOMAN

Celeste De Blasis

DELACORTE PRESS/NEW YORK

Published by
Delacorte Press
1 Dag Hammarskjold Plaza
New York, N.Y. 10017

Manufactured in the United States of America

First printing

Designed by Jo Anne Bonnell

LIBRARY OF CONGRESS CATALOGING IN PUBLICATION DATA

De Blasis, Celeste.
The Tiger's woman.

I. Title.
PS3554.E1765T5   813'.54   80-23285
ISBN 0-440-08819-4

*With love and thanks
to Uncle Joe; Aunt Donna; and my cousins,
Kemper, Craig, Scott, and Nicki,
for enriching my life in so many ways, and to R. J. P., a very special
man, for all the happy, gentle times, and for the adventures in
faraway places*

ACKNOWLEDGMENTS

Aside from my proofreader, none of the people mentioned here have read any part of *The Tiger's Woman.* The novel belongs to me alone as stories always belong to the storyteller. But I will praise here and endlessly in my heart these people who have been so generous with their time and expertise in helping me to set the fiction in fact. And the most miraculous thing of all is that many of these people I have never met face to face and probably never will, and yet, they made the space in their busy lives to answer the inquiries of a stranger. They shared their knowledge on a wide range of subjects including the problems of the deaf in a hearing world, logging, shipbuilding, sailing, care of livestock and crops, and distribution of wildlife in the Northwest. They sent me their own accounts and reference lists for further information, and they patiently completed my questionnaires. They searched through old records for weather reports and various bits of historical data unavailable in general texts. Those I did meet and interview directly were equally kind. My thanks to all of them and my apologies to anyone whose name I have inadvertently omitted:

Pat and Jim Andrews; William Blaker; Donna Campbell; Ms. Kemper Campbell; Betty Coon; Tina Cornelius; Barbara Cummings; Mary-Thadia d'Hondt of the Seattle Historical Society; Susan Dailey; Jean and Raymond De Blasis; Ralph Drew; Vi Drister; Charles Eaton of Friday Harbor Laboratories; Fred Ferguson; Jim Goble; Freida Heaman; Mildred Kaunas; Marge Klugman of GLAD; the librarians of the Victorville branch of the San Bernardino county system, particularly Alice Christiansen, Ruth Burch, and Joyce Burke, though all of the staff have been unfailingly patient and helpful; Carl and Janetta Nelson; Raymond R. Newton; Martha Okland; Sandra L. Perkins; Mr. and Ms. J. D. Pierson; Kathy Poncy; Peggy Sartor; Anna Slavick; Homer and Frieda Stewart; Dr. William C. Stokoe of Gallaudet College; Michael Thompson; Captain Webb; Carol Yandell of the Port Townsend Historical Society; and Steven Young.

Drake's Island is a mythical place, but the San Juan Islands do exist. Perhaps I was just lucky, but the people I met on my visits to the archipelago were as beautiful as their land, and the rhythm of island life was a song from another time.

Celeste De Blasis
February 1980

Mary Smith

CHAPTER

I

*I*t wasn't all her own bosom filling the low-cut bodice of the spangled dress, but her legs were fine in the black net stockings, and in this routine with the high kicks, the legs got most of the attention anyway. She sang, kicked, and strutted, and felt wearily that she'd been doing this all her life rather than only a few weeks. The heavy theatrical makeup and powder made her skin itch, and she could feel the sweat trickling down, under the curly brown wig.

Her smile wavered, and she restored it with an effort as she winked coyly over her shoulder, wiggling her flounce-covered bottom in unison with the three other girls, causing the male audience to yell their approval and some lavish obscenities.

The tinny piano notes drew to a close as the girls turned and curtseyed pertly.

Her knees were suddenly so weak; for a horrified instant, she didn't think she was going to be able to straighten up. Sheer willpower jerked her upright and allowed her to leave the little stage with the others. Frenchie stepped on after them, and her husky voice began the first of the suggestive songs she would offer, accented English leading up to unintelligible and therefore titillating French. Though Frenchie had come to San Francisco via New Orleans, she hadn't a drop of Gallic blood; she depended on her body to say everything, and Frenchmen, should any be in the audience, to say nothing.

Mary blotted her face absently until she realized she was smearing her makeup. Carefully, she repaired it in the dingy mirror with the aid of the flickering gaslight. Her face was hot, her hands ice-cold, and she wondered distractedly how that could be. Then she remembered. It had been the same that night, the same when she had looked at the stained metal in her hand.

She knew that man. Ten years ago, in 1859, she had been eight years old, and he had come to the house in New York. He had traveled all the way from San Francisco to do business with her father's bank.

She had heard about the visitor from far away, the whole house was aflutter with it, and she had crept partway down the stairs to peer through the balustrade. She had thought he would look very odd coming from the Far West. But he had been dressed in the height of fashion for a gentleman and hadn't looked at all as she had imagined. The strangeness of him was his tanned skin and the sun streaks in his heavy brown hair. Even covered in fine broadcloth, his body had looked very strong, not like most of the city dandies she had seen.

He stood quietly in the entryway, waiting for the maid to announce him, and when he glanced up, she saw eyes like no others she had known. They were brown, made tawny by shades of gold moving in them like forest light. They regarded her intently for a moment, and then the man smiled, his grave, rugged face suddenly very young and merry, acknowledging her and pledging not to betray her presence.

She nearly gasped aloud in dismay, nearly betrayed herself when her father came out to greet the man with great heartiness and to lead him to the study. The man carried no cane, and she had not seen him come in, had no warning that he was severely lame, his right leg marring the perfection of the strong body.

Even then, she had known she was no kind, soft child, but canny and perpetually angry, continually hoping that the adults around her would get what they deserved, which was unpleasant indeed. But she hadn't felt that about the lame man. She had felt outrage that such a splendid creature should be so chained. It was the only way, even then, that she could think of him without conflict. A splendid creature. Someone who stood apart from the normal ways of humankind, or at least, what she had then judged to be the normal ways.

She had never seen him again. She could not remember the name of the man from San Francisco. Ten years ago and surely he had changed. His face was lined and harsh. He must be in his thirties now. But he was the same one, she was sure of it. Even beyond the smoking lanterns of the stage lights, even in the murky, crowded saloon, she knew that when he stood he would be big and tall and when he walked he would be lame. The eyes, they were the same, and they had watched her, not one of the others, just her.

Her heart beat so furiously, she panted for breath and her surroundings blurred. How could he know? She was not the child she had been nor was her appearance that of the woman she was now. She touched the brown wig and ran her fingers carefully over the makeup on her cheek. That girl, that woman, had disappeared into the past. Mary Smith lived in her place.

Her heart steadied; her breathing slowed. She was mistaken. Fear had made her misjudge as it had so often. He did not know her. He was not particularly interested in her. He had been watching someone else.

When Frenchie had taken her last bow and tossed her last careless kiss, Mary was ready to go on again with the others.

She didn't miss a step, her smile never faltered, but now she knew the worst was true. He was watching her, no one else. She stared back even as she danced, even as she mouthed the inane words. She could not see the color of his eyes, and yet she knew the same light moved in them.

And then as she and the other girls were leaving the stage

again, the nightmare intensified. The man stood and began to lurch through the crowded space toward her, his gait even the worse for drink. But another drunk, a man Mary hadn't even noticed until now, had the same idea. The two of them collided, and she heard the solid smack of a fist hitting flesh. She gazed in frozen horror at the thrashing bodies. "I seen the bluebird first!" the drunk yowled, and Mary felt as if the blue stuff of her flimsy gown was being stripped away. The crowd was egging the fighters on, and it seemed as though a full-scale brawl was going to erupt. She saw a knife blade flash in the drunk's hand and screamed a warning without thought. The fight was in deadly earnest now, and Mary began to suspect that the lame man had been fighting simply for the hell of it before because now he fought with unleashed fury, sending the knife arching away, pummeling the man with his fists until he had knocked him senseless enough to allow him to pick the body up, carry it to the door, and heave it outside. No one tried to stop him; men moved out of his way. His halting progress added a strange menace to his strong body.

Now he was moving purposefully back toward the stage. Mary felt miserably exposed, knowing everyone was watching to see what would happen next, wanting to flee, unable to move.

A bruise was beginning on his clean-shaven jaw. His eyes were narrowed and glittering. Even though she was above him on the stage, he seemed to her to tower over her. He was the same and not at all the same. The grave kindness of the younger man was gone. She felt as if she were being stalked by a large predatory beast.

"May I see you home after you're finished here?" The overly precise words were innocuous enough, but the meaning behind them was not.

"I . . . I already have plans," she replied stiffly. She forced herself to move, to turn from him and leave the stage, expecting every second to feel him grab her.

She was shaking violently by the time she joined the other girls, but except for a few curious glances, they left her alone as they straightened their costumes and repaired their makeup. She was not close to any of them, but they felt no animosity toward her. They knew she was on the run, and they understood the multitude of circumstances which might have caused that. Without exception, they, too, had left people and places behind which they hoped never to see again.

She buried her face in her hands. She had been doing all right, keeping the past and the present apart, but the lame man was threatening to end the separation. She didn't know whether or not he meant to, didn't know if he remembered anything, knew anything. Her knowledge was enough to make him a fearsome figure.

She jumped when Frenchie touched her shoulder.

"Honey, it's only some dude wanting more than he deserves." Frenchie studied her face more closely. "Something more?"

"I don't know," Mary managed. "Do you think he'll give up now?"

Frenchie started one of her artful Gallic shrugs, then thought better of it. "I know no better than you do. He was determined enough to fight. His clothes are good. He has the look of a rich man. I wouldn't mind taking your place. But that isn't what he has in mind. He hardly looked at me." Her shrug was genuine now. "What's the difference? He persists, you refuse."

The warning bars sounded on the piano, and Frenchie grinned. "Two more rounds, and we're finished for the night. I'd better start looking if I plan to take a bed warmer home with me. Maybe I can catch your beau's eye after all, if you're sure you don't want him."

Mary shuddered involuntarily. Her voice was brittle, though she knew Frenchie only wanted to lighten her mood. "Don't call him that! I don't want him. I would to God you could distract him!"

Frenchie didn't take offense. She gave Mary a little pat to send her out with the other dancers. "Remember, all you have to do is nothing. He can't buy what you won't sell."

Mary knew that in Frenchie's world that was true, and Frenchie was tough enough to make sure the rule held. But Mary also knew that she herself belonged only to the fringes of this world, was only beginning to know how to cope. And whatever the other girls had done, she doubted they had murdered anyone. She had, or at least, she had tried. It would be better to know one way or the other. No way to find out, no way without leaving a trail to herself.

The man was still there, watching her. He did not leave until the chorus line's closing number, and Mary didn't think he'd gone far.

She waited for Frenchie to finish her last song, waited through the whistles and catcalls. Frenchie always put a little extra into her finale.

"Did you find someone to keep you warm?" She tried to make her voice worldly and casual but succeeded only in sounding desperate.

Frenchie shook her head slowly. "Your gent's gone. Only you figure not far enough. I won't fight you on the idea. I expect he's waiting outside somewhere. He has the look of a man who doesn't give up when he wants something—or someone. What do you want me to do?"

The offer, so straightforwardly and generously given by this woman who owed her nothing, brought tears to Mary's eyes, and she had to swallow hard before she found her voice. "I want you to give me your key, and I'll give you mine. If it comes to that, I don't want him to discover anything about me, and in your room, he won't." She knotted her fists and rubbed her eyes hard, glad of diffusing the inner pain. She almost laughed when she saw the smears on her knuckles. She must surely look a sight; maybe getting rid of the man was going to be easier than she thought. "Anything else I can manage."

Suddenly she believed her own words, and Frenchie heard the strength and believed her too. "It's a sure bet my style won't tell him a thing about you," she agreed without rancor.

"All right, I'll leave here first, and I'll stay in your room until you come." She picked up her bag and searched through it. The derringer was exquisite, a jewel of death with ivory and silver work on the handle. She held it out to Mary. "But I won't do any of it if you don't take this. I'll have no use for it tonight, but you might."

Knowing Frenchie meant what she said, Mary took the gun,

holding it gingerly at first, more confidently as Frenchie repeated over and over how easy it was to fire.

"It's a lethal little toy if you don't panic, and if you're close enough."

Mary wondered—was it easier the second time, the killing of another human being?

Frenchie saw the hardening of her expression and was satisfied. "I'll see you when I see you." She exchanged her key for Mary's and left without a backward glance.

Mary gave her time enough to be out of sight on the street and yet more time so that she would surely be almost to the boardinghouse. The tired sounds of the early morning cleanup were comforting for the first time, the clink of glassware being washed and bottles being straightened, the barkeep and his assistants murmuring in low voices. A few hours and the saloon would be open again with a new shift though the girls wouldn't be back until evening.

John Pike, the piano player, ventured into the back to find his coat, having had a last comforting snort of whiskey, sure that all the females had left. He was startled when he caught sight of Mary, but he gave her a friendly grin. "Waitin' for the fog to come in thicker? 'Spect that gent's long gone, but I'll walk with you a way if you want. Mary, isn't it?"

He was loose-limbed, frail looking, weary, and John Pike wasn't likely his real name. He probably wasn't thirty yet, but his eyes were ancient. He didn't know her at all; still, he was offering his help.

She felt comforted, warm, and not so alone. She smiled and said easily, "My thanks, but I don't need an escort. I'm just enjoying the quiet. My boardinghouse is a noisy place. You go along. I'll see you tomorrow."

John Pike met her smile with his own and departed thinking that just one more time it might not be so unwise to become involved with one of the dancing girls. A strange one who kept herself so aloof, but that smile, it transformed her. He went off humming.

By the time his tune had faded, Mary knew she had tarried as long as she could. Frenchie was long since at the boardinghouse. The saloon would soon be locked; another minute or so and the barkeep or one of the others would discover her just as the piano player had. She gathered her cloak around her and took a last look. So short a time ago this place had meant nothing but drudgery; now it seemed a haven she must quit. She cursed the man, surely no angel with fiery sword, but a demon with equal power.

Thick tendrils of winter fog drifted in the alley. Sounds were muted and sharp at the same time. Mary pressed herself against the wall, scenting the air, listening, the fox not ready to go to ground in this alien place.

She moved out of the alley into the street. The derringer was in her hand. A simple way to kill a man, not so close, no blood on the metal.

One step at a time, one step after the other, not so far, not so far. Other footsteps but not close, not following. She went on, feeling relief begin. He had gone away after all. He hadn't known; hadn't wanted anything more than a woman he fancied for an instant.

She froze, heart hammering against her ribs. The scattered gaslights wore misty haloes, and the sounds of other pedestrians had faded away when now she wanted legions.

The alley was like the one she had left, narrow, shadowed, but not dark enough. The growling could be from dogs fighting over refuse, but the sound of blows on flesh was human, and the shape she saw at the mouth of the alley was that of the lame man, hitting out viciously, a knife in one hand. He hadn't deigned to use it in the saloon, but he needed it now. He was trying to keep his back to the wall as three men kept rushing him like hounds trying to bring down a stag.

Mary recognized one of the men and knew instantly what had happened. After he had been thrown out he had rounded up two friends and waited to avenge himself.

The Barbary Coast was no place to call for help. If only she had walked another way. If only the lame man hadn't waited for her. If only she could go on now and let the attackers take care of her problem.

She couldn't do it. She saw again the young man smiling up at the child.

The lame man went down suddenly, his bad leg crumpling under him as one of his attackers kicked hard from the side. Before the three could spring on him, Mary stepped closer. "Stop it!" she shrieked. The derringer was in her hand. "I can't shoot all of you, but I can even the odds. Who will it be?" Her voice was savage with fear and desperation.

The men checked, one murmuring, "Jeez, ain't nothin' worse 'n a she-bear." One made as if to grab at Mary and found the gun leveled at his midsection. "Back off!" she hissed, and they did.

The lame man stood and staggered a little as he fought groggily for his footing. "All right," he said finally, "any more of this, and someone's going to be killed." There was calm menace and certainty in his voice.

"Weren't my fight to begin with," one of the men mumbled. Another added, "Looks like the lady made her choice, Will." Even Will, the one who had started the brawl, suddenly appeared to have lost interest in everything except saving his skin.

Mary felt the tension leaving them all as the men edged away, but she kept the gun steady on the retreating figures until the fog swallowed them.

She spun around at the sound of his laughter, and he took the gun out of her hand which was suddenly shaking uncontrollably.

"I'm glad the reaction was delayed, else you might have done some damage with this, and Lord knows to whom! I take it you've never fired one before?"

He was highly amused, and Mary's mood veered sharply to anger. "Of all the ungrateful creatures!" she sputtered.

"I assure you I'm most grateful," he said. "But my curiosity exceeds even my gratitude. I presume you carried this to slay the dragon, namely me. Yet you turn about and save the beast. Care to tell me why, and why you judge me less dangerous than the villains you dispersed?"

She ignored the first question and answered the second nastily, "Another good push would send you sprawling again. I hardly think I need fear you."

The cold metal of the gun pressed against one cheek as he held her head and kissed her hard.

He had moved so swiftly, so unexpectedly, she did not react until it was over, and he was towering over her again. She scrubbed her mouth violently with her hand and shuddered as a wave of revulsion swept through her.

"That bad?" he said ruefully. "I must be losing my touch."

Her hand clenched into a fist. She longed to smash it into his already bruised jaw, but then she saw the truth of what she had said. A good push would send him sprawling again. He was swaying on his feet, ready to keel over from the combined effects of alcohol and the beating he'd received. No threat at all; a task to be finished.

"Where are your lodgings?" she asked brusquely.

"On Market at Bush, and if you'll tell me which direction it is from here, I'll head that way." His words were too careful, and he rubbed his face wearily, obviously dizzy and disoriented.

"It's much too far. Come on, my room's close by. You can return to yours in the morning."

"That's all I wanted in the first place." The laughter was back in his voice, but before they reached the boardinghouse, he was leaning on her. She peered through the fog nervously and listened for footsteps, but his attackers seemed to have given up.

The boardinghouse had settled down for the night, at least enough so that no one intercepted them as she helped the man up the stairs and into Frenchie's room.

He stayed where she had left him, leaning against the wall until she had lighted the lamps, and then he allowed her to help him to Frenchie's bed where he collapsed with a sigh. He squinted his eyes, peering around the room as if he were having a good deal of trouble focusing, but his mind was still working, at least marginally. "Doesn't look like you," he said positively.

She glanced around at the chaos of Frenchie's quarters, at the feathers, shoes, beads, stockings and other lingerie, at the garish and dingy silks and satins hanging on every available hook and edge and spilling out of carelessly kept drawers. He was right; she would never be able to tolerate such a mess, and the colors were all wrong. But she steeled herself for the part, just as if she were kicking high for the men to see her legs and whatever else their luck allowed. It was why she had borrowed Frenchie's room.

"On other days it looks better and on some it looks worse, just like I do. Take it or leave it. But I'll remind you, you're in no condition to be fussy." She knew that was the sort of thing Frenchie would say.

"Doesn't sound like you either," he said, no less sure than before.

Ignoring his comment, she got a basin of water and the cleanest towel she could find from the bureau.

"I can do that," he protested, turning his head away as she began to sponge at his split lip and the blood on his chin.

"Do shut up and lie still! You're wincing every time you move. It would take you longer, and I for one want to get some sleep tonight."

He submitted meekly, and something pulled at her heart. He looked suddenly young and vulnerable. The young man come back again. Her hands were gentle as she finished washing his face. Matter-of-factly, she opened his shirt and ran cool hands over his bruised rib cage.

"Do you think anything's broken?" she asked anxiously. "I'm not very good at this sort of thing."

"Doing fine. Nothin' broken, jus' a little battered an' very drunk," he murmured, not opening his eyes. "Jason Drake. My name. Wha's yours?"

"Mary."

"Doesn't fit," he mumbled. She was glad she wasn't touching him then because her whole body twitched with fear.

She pulled off his boots and tried to suppress the memory of when she had last done this for a man; it was so important not to remember.

"What 'bout my breeches?"

"You can damn well sleep in them!"

She saw him trying to open his eyes, but sleep was too close, and a smile curved his mouth as he drifted off. "Room on th' bed for two," was the last thing he whispered.

She stood looking down at him for a moment. Even through the cloth, she could see the muscles of his lame leg knotted and pulsing. She wondered if it pained him much or if he was too accustomed to it to notice. She wondered how the injury had happened in the first place. It was such a pity that so strong a body should be crippled. She wondered why she could still feel his mouth on hers and why it no longer disgusted her. And why she could still see the brown eyes with the light moving in them even though they were closed.

A shock of fear burst inside and raced to every nerve ending. What was she doing, wondering about him, thinking like this? It was madness to lose sight of her purpose even for an instant, total insanity to do so for a man. She had a man to thank for the days of terror and the running which had brought her to this seedy boardinghouse thousands of miles from home, and now this man too to thank for the journey which must begin again.

She waited only long enough to be sure he was soundly asleep before she fled to the floor above and her own room. She knocked softly, and Frenchie answered immediately, obviously not having slept.

"Well, what happened?" she asked, concern making her voice sharp. "I've been waiting here wondering whatever possessed me to agree to your scheme."

In a low, swift voice devoid of emotion, Mary told her what had happened, and gave the derringer back.

Frenchie shook her head. "That's the worse lunacy I've ever heard of! Some rowdies offer to do your work for you, and you stop them!"

"That's not the end of it," Mary said in the same empty voice. "I must leave now, before he awakens."

"Leave? You mean find other lodgings?" Frenchie asked suspiciously.

"Other lodgings yes, and in another place." She saw the questions and pled, "Don't ask, please don't, because I can't tell you why. Just know that it is necessary." Already she was beginning to gather up clothing, folding it nervously; she had so little, it wouldn't take long.

Frenchie stayed Mary's hands with her own. "Most of the people I know came west because of hard times at home. Whatever it is, it can't be that bad!"

Mary pulled away. "Indeed it is bad, and I'm not going to stay here while it gets worse."

Frenchie opened her mouth and closed it again. She watched Mary for another minute, then muttered, "I'll be right back," and left the room.

She returned quickly. "He's still asleep. He'll sleep for hours." She held out her fist. "Take these, he owes you." A few gold coins jingled into Mary's hands.

"Don't refuse. He can afford it, and I didn't take all of it. If he notices, I'll tell him some story in the morning. I'm a good liar."

Mary tucked the money into her reticule. Frenchie was right. This was no time for moral strictures. Survival was more important.

"Do you know where you're going?" Frenchie asked, trying to be practical.

"I feel as though I'm on the edge of the world already," Mary admitted. "But I thought maybe south to Los Angeles or even further, to Mexico."

"Where the language and everything else is different. I don't know anyone there, but I do know someone, Angie Cooper, in the Washington Territory, in Seattle. Go north. It's as wild there now, I've heard, as it must have been here twenty years ago. It's hard to track people down in a place like that. And Angie will help you find a job. She's fond of sea captains and lumbermen, something to do with deep waters and deep roots." She was pleased to have coaxed the little smile from Mary. "She has a boardinghouse, captains in the lumber shipping trade bring me news of her now and then, but she used to work dance halls and saloons. One way or another, I know she can help you."

Mary agreed because she had no preference. She was numb with the burden of uprooting her life, traveling again, beginning over again. But she was touched by Frenchie who, now that she was convinced of Mary's determination, threw herself into making things easier, helping with the packing, laboriously writing notes in her childish hand to a sea captain, a friend she knew was in port and heading for Seattle, and to Angie, and checking now and then to make sure Jason Drake was still sleeping.

There was no sense in leaving before first light, and Mary did not change her clothes until the world outside was paling. When she emerged from behind the rickety dressing screen, she was unrecognizable. The brown wig of the dancing girl was covered by a dull, black-veiled bonnet which shaded most of her face. The poor stuff of the black gown covered her body so well that no soft curves showed anywhere. The high neck was particularly effective.

She smiled in satisfaction. She was eighteen, but that would be difficult to ascertain through the shrouding garments. She had gotten away before in this guise; it would work again. She stuffed the discarded blue costume into her satchel.

"It's all mad, love," Frenchie said, shaking her head in horror at the disguise.

Mary smiled suddenly and hugged her. "Thank you, Frenchie, thank you for everything. I'll miss you. If you're ever in Seattle . . ."

"Sure, if ever." Frenchie's mouth trembled for an instant and then firmed. "Won't change your mind about the derringer?"

"No, keep it with you when the man wakes up. I expect he'll be in a foul temper. But don't hurt him please; I've gone to a great deal of trouble to save his skin."

Frenchie eyed her closely and nodded. "I have better uses for a man than killing him. Maybe with you gone, he'll reconsider." She kissed Mary swiftly on the cheek. "Take care. And go quickly now before I make a fool of myself. In a few days it will be Christmas. Have a happy one," she added sadly when she knew Mary couldn't hear her.

Mary met no one on her way out, but as long as Jason Drake continued to sleep, she wasn't worried. Even meeting the proprietress wouldn't have been that bad. Mrs. Davies had seen too much in her life to carry on about a sudden departure. Mary owed her nothing, had always paid her board promptly, and was slightly ahead now; she knew that was enough to insure disinterest and even a certain loyalty. Mrs. Davies was accustomed to people who led double lives at least. Most of the dance hall girls and the so-called seamstresses who made up her clientele did other things for extra money.

Mary drew a deep breath. The air smelled of the sea. The fog was lifting, drifting away in pearly gray wisps as the sun rose. She had an absolutely certain feeling that she would find passage on the ship to Seattle.

It had begun with Uncle Tim's theatrical friends in New York on that horrible night, and it went on now from Frenchie to someone else. People living exotic, precarious lives on the edge of survival yet still willing to help someone else survive, even when it put their own existences in peril.

She was suddenly far warmer than the day's early chill allowed.

Head throbbing, Jason Drake pressed his face against the cold windowpane. Dimly he could see a figure on the street below, a woman in shapeless widow's weeds. She was obviously on her way somewhere—to other lodgings, to another town, another country. He didn't give a damn. Having made it the short distance from the bed to the window, all he could think of was crawling back to the bed. It wasn't only his head that ached, everything else did too, and he thought if he survived this, he was surely immortal. He wondered where the girl had gone— to wash, to get breakfast? Her belongings were still scattered all over the place. Mary, that was her name, or at least the name she'd given; she hadn't offered more. If he lived, and if the drum ceased beating in his head, he'd like to find out more about her. A sure sign of life. He laughed at himself, clutching his head as the drum beat harder.

The door creaked, and a woman walked in. He vaguely recognized her from the night before, the singer of faulty French. And he knew in an instant that these were her bits and pieces lying all over, this was her room.

"Where is Mary?" he asked, his throat hurting as much as his head.

"Mary? Oh, the girl who borrowed my room. I haven't the slightest idea. Any more questions?" She knew as well as Mary did that Mrs. Davies would hold her tongue too.

Jason saw the little smile, looked into her mocking, knowing eyes, and knew he had lost.

CHAPTER
2

$\mathcal{M}$ary's first sight of Seattle made her doubt Frenchie's friendship and good intentions. Never had she seen a more unprepossessing town than this jumble of shacks scattered over steep hills and huddled on the waterfront, all of it hunkered down under a cold, gray drizzle of rain.

It had been a terrible trip on the winter sea. Every time the water had shown the least ruffle of motion, her stomach had heaved with it. She had not even marked the day when 1869 became 1870, let alone joined in the ship's celebration of Christmas. She had never felt so ill in her life. Even now, on the smooth waters of Puget Sound, her stomach quivered with remembrance, and she clung to the ship's rail, her knees even less steady than the rest of her.

Captain Smythe had been disappointed. He had looked forward to her company on the voyage but had soon realized his passenger was more withdrawn and less communicative than any woman he had ever met. How she happened to be Frenchie's friend was beyond him. He hadn't even had to bark at his crew; the sad aura around the young widow and her obvious mal de mer had doused any spark of interest. Still, she

had thanked him gratefully for the efforts he had made to see
to her comfort in the barren little cabin, and he felt a kind of
fatherly protectiveness for the ghostly figure in widow's weeds.
Only once had he tried to offer his sympathy on her loss. The
sea had been fairly calm, and Mary had been well enough to take
a cautious light supper with him at his request. But when he
gently mentioned her widowhood, she had turned her head
away, offering only the low, tense words, "The war."

It was certainly a valid tragedy for thousands of women in the
United States. But the War Between the States had been over
for five years, and Captain Smythe doubted very much that Mary
was old enough to have been married back then. Her hands, the
way she moved—too many things betrayed her youth. Perhaps
she had married a man with little time left to live. The war had
broken so many who had not been killed outright. Or perhaps
she had been a child bride after all, marrying her sweetheart
early because tomorrows were impossible to promise. It was a
mystery he would probably never solve; she had not asked him
for any help beyond passage on his ship for which she had paid
in gold. And yet, it caught his heart to hear her soft, despairing,
"Dear God," as she got a closer view of Seattle.

He stood beside her and made his offer gruffly. "We'll be
heading south again in a few days after we've unloaded the cargo
and taken on lumber." He gestured toward the clouds of steam
and smoke oozing up through the rain. "That's Yesler's mill,
usually get a bit there, and more from other mills on the
Sound." He cleared his throat nervously. "What I'm trying to
say, ma'am, is that I'll give you passage back to San Francisco
if you've a mind for it. This is still pretty wild country up here,
isn't for everyone." He emphasized the word "give."

For a moment she was tempted—Seattle looked such a dreary
place—and she was touched by his offer. But the image of Jason
Drake loomed huge in her mind again. Her voice was firm.
"Thank you for your generosity, Captain, but, no, I'll stay here
for a while." Quite suddenly laughter spilled out despite all her
worries. "I wasn't born to be a sailor, that's quite clear! Even the
muddy ground of Seattle will suit me better than the roll of the
sea."

The captain grinned, charmed by the sound of her laughter,

more sure than ever she was younger than her pose. "Then I wish you well." He thought that if she ever doffed the trailing weeds, every logger for miles would come courting. He wouldn't mind himself seeing her without—he chided himself for being an old he-goat and moved off to attend to his duties.

The arrival of a ship was still a major event here, which gave Mary an even clearer idea of how small the place was; in San Francisco few would have paid any attention except the agents for the merchants. Here she guessed it was the few merchants themselves who were scurrying about for their share of the goods. Knots of people were gathering at the waterfront, simply watching. Canoes and rowboats bobbed in the water as their occupants stopped paddling to observe the activity. No one seemed to be taking any notice of the rain. But Mary's hope that the bustle on the wharf would cover her own arrival was short-lived.

"Carry your belongin's, ma'am?" "Relatives meetin' you, ma'am?" "Where're you stayin'?" Her brace of gallants seemed to have materialized out of nowhere, assorted in ages from a blushing youngster to a bewhiskered old fellow, in sizes from a few who were shorter than she to many who were enormous and loomed over her, and in dress from a dandy's waistcoat and tailored trousers to much-washed flannel shirts and work pants. But they all shared one goal—to have first chance at the widow. They didn't for the moment care whether she was young or old, good-looking or not; that could be discerned later. She was female and nothing was more important than that in this place where women were in such short supply.

Mary was acutely embarrassed and would have been frightened except that to a man they were polite and so obviously anxious to make a good impression that she began to giggle helplessly and gave up trying to dissuade them. "Mary Smith, from San Francisco," was all the information they received about the new arrival as the strange procession moved along.

Actually, it was good to have someone carrying her belongings, as the footing in the town was rough and steep. There were boardwalks here and there with steps connecting one section to the next in the ascent, but much of the way was muddy, and there were even tree stumps left inconveniently in the road. The old whiskered gentleman informed her gleefully that there were still places in Seattle where it was better to go by rowboat than on foot, but not Angie Cooper's boardinghouse, not unless the boat had wings. "And now wouldn't that be somethun', damn my soul, beg yur pardon, ma'am."

Mary felt more and more giddy. Her body was unwilling to credit that it was on solid earth once more; she could still feel the rocking motion of the ship and was unsure about each step until her shoe met the ground. It was a most uncomfortable sensation, but her escort was pressed so closely around her, she was certain someone would catch her before she hit the ground. She started to laugh again, feeling more light-headed by the second. It was all so absurd, sanity seemed to have been left back on Captain Smythe's deck.

It returned abruptly in front of the plain board house belonging to Angie Cooper.

The woman was somewhere over thirty, still firm-fleshed with a high proud bosom, a wealth of dark hair faintly touched with gray, and very blue eyes. Her features would be generous and symmetrical when they were not pulled into a forbidding frown. Her eyes were icy, her voice no warmer. "Well, boys, what's all the ruckus? You all so drunk you don't know it isn't the Fourth of July?"

"Ah, come on, Angie, ain't no cause to be so uppity."

"She just got off Capt'n Smythe's rig."

"Said she was lookin' fer yur place."

The cheerful chorus went on as Mary fumbled in her reticule for the slip of paper from Frenchie and handed it to the woman. She wished now that she had found the place on her own instead of allowing this foolish parade. She watched Angie read the note slowly, painstakingly. If the woman did let her stay here, books would not be one of the subjects they discussed. She sighed inwardly. It seemed that the further she traveled in the West, the further she was from things that mattered to her. Further from *him* too, she reminded herself, and Jason Drake had nothing to do with the thought.

Angie took her time reading the note, studying the widow

while she did so. No matter the pattern of her life now, she'd been in the business too long to mistake this one. Under those yards of black stuff, there was a young one indeed. But Frenchie had sent her, and Frenchie had been a good friend. Angie suddenly missed the riotous old days in San Francisco.

Her expression was warmer when she nodded at Mary. "Well, come on in then. No use standing in the wet." She shooed the men off. "Go about your business now, all of you. Won't have your muddy tracks all over my house."

They left good-naturedly, calling promises to visit the newcomer soon. Mary was led into a room cluttered with exotic nicknacks and even a piano but clean enough and warm from the fire crackling on the hearth. She stretched her hands toward the flames with a little sigh of pleasure.

"Yep, it's a climate that chills the bones until you get used to it, no matter all the bragging about it being so mild," Angie remarked, watching her. "Take your bonnet off and sit while I make tea. You look a mite washed out. Time enough to talk terms." With that she was gone in a rustle of skirts.

Mary removed her bonnet carefully and put her damp cloak near the fire before she sank into an overstuffed chair. Her eyes closed and she was nearly asleep when the rattle of china cups startled her back to attention.

"I'd guess ships aren't your favorite way to travel." Angie's voice was kind. There was something about this young—yes, very young—pale-faced creature that pulled at her heart.

"You'd guess correctly then," Mary laughed. "Even sitting here, I feel as if the sea is rolling beneath me. I shall be very glad when it stops." She sipped the hot tea gratefully as Angie gestured around the room.

"My man's a sea captain, takes lumber and other things to Hawaii and beyond to China and always brings back something for me. Suits me fine. I'm no sailor either." Her voice became more brisk. "I charge two dollars a week here, and that's a bargain. You won't find cleaner rooms or better food anywhere else in town. And this is a respectable house. You want to be in the business, you go talk to John Pinnell at the Illahee."

"Illahee?" Mary asked blankly.

"Means 'home away from home' in Indian talk, means the best whorehouse in these parts, Pinnell owns it. Some people call it the Mad House," Angie explained bluntly.

Color flamed in Mary's face. Did she look like that, had he left some mark on her that everyone could see, that Jason Drake had seen in San Francisco, that this woman saw now? "I'm not . . . I don't," she stammered.

Angie grinned at her. "Don't take on so. I wouldn't care if you did just as long as you don't do it in my house. This is my territory. Couldn't help wondering, Frenchie sending you and all. Funny place for a young widow to come to."

"I, well, there was trouble with a man in San Francisco, but it wasn't my fault, truly it wasn't! It just seemed better to leave."

"Don't you have any folks, your own or your husband's?"

The soft insistent questions. It was time to offer some story, Mary thought. She plunged headlong into the river of lies. "No, you see, my parents died long ago. I lived with an old aunt. She never did approve of Ja . . ." (God, she had almost said Jason because it was the first name that had come into her head.) "Jake. He was older than I and had known me from the time I was little. He was always kind to me. Then the war came and changed everything for so many. He went off to fight, and I saw very little of him until the end of it all. He came home wounded and very ill. I'd grown up a lot in the meantime, and when I saw Jake again, I knew what I wanted. Yes, I was very young, but sometimes love doesn't have much to do with years. We both knew he wasn't going to live very long. He didn't want to tie me to an ailing man, but I convinced him it was all I wanted. He knew how lonesome it can be to live with old people; he'd been raised by his grandparents, and he knew I didn't get on very well with my aunt. I think that helped. His grandparents died during the war, and I never saw my aunt from the day I ran away with Jake. I don't know whether she's alive or not, and I don't care. Jake and I were very happy, but he died nearly a year ago. The war altered many lives." Yes, that was a good finishing touch, she thought. Actually the whole fable touched her. She thought she'd told it very well; she wished it were true.

Angie listened and thought, maybe it's true. And maybe she's a good actress. Strange that she mentioned no places in her story, nothing about her hometown, not even the state. Well, it was her business. Further questions would be useless and unfair. She made the decision on the instant. She herself didn't tell everyone everything.

"I don't expect you'll stay a widow long," she said, indicating her acceptance of the story. "You heard of Mercer's belles?"

Mary shook her head.

"Well, they were the most useful goods ever shipped to Seattle. The way those men greeted you today, it's a good show of how things are. There's thousands of men out in the timber, at the sawmills, and on the ships, but there're hardly any women at all. Asa Mercer tried to fix that a few years back. He went east to New England in '64 knowing the war was ruining the prospects for a lot of women. He offered them the chance for a new life as schoolteachers, music teachers, and seamstresses, and, though it wasn't said, the almost certain promise of a husband. He lost some to San Francisco, but he brought nine women back on the first trip, and they were snatched up except for one who preferred being a schoolteacher to being a wife. So off he went again. He planned to bring back five hundred, even collected three hundred dollars a head from some of the men who wanted a chance for a bride. But it all went wrong. President Lincoln got shot, and with him went Asa's government connection. Then a New York paper got hold of the story and made a scandal of it, said Asa Mercer was bringing women out to work in brothels. Only an Eastern idiot would have thought that about Asa, him a straitlaced man. He barely made it back because of the money running out. Most of the passengers were single men or families, only forty-some single women made the trip, and Mercer married one of them himself and left Seattle. All the others married too. So, you see, that little handful of females wasn't near enough to solve the problem around here. I expect you'll be changing your name soon."

"I don't think so." She said it gently, knowing Angie meant well. "Now, if you won't think me too rude, I would like to see my room. I'm really very tired."

"Here I am nattering away when you must be dying for a bed

that doesn't rock!" Angie apologized as she rose and led the way down a hall.

The room was plainly furnished in contrast to the other clutter. After making appropriately appreciative noises and paying the first week's board, Mary saw Angie out and locked the door behind her. She took the wig off and ran her hands through the short, matted curls of her own hair. She undressed, took a sponge bath using the water Angie had provided, sank into bed, and felt herself rocked to sleep by her body's memory of the sea.

She slept through until the next morning, and the first thing she thought about on waking was the necessity of finding work and finding it quickly. The money stolen from Jason Drake would soon be completely gone. She had presented herself to Seattle as a grieving widow, so dancing in a saloon was out of the question. There was a certain safety in the disguise, and she wasn't going to give it up to find a job like the one which had gotten her into so much trouble in San Francisco.

Her stock of saleable talents was, she thought grimly, very limited, but with a bit of work here and a bit there, surely it would be possible to survive.

Angie was openly amused when Mary told her that she planned to offer her services as a seamstress and a French and music teacher. "Very genteel, oh, to be sure. Just like Mercer's girls."

Her determination faltered. "You don't think it will work?"

"I think it will." Angie was still laughing. "I think it will work better than you know and not in the way you expect."

Mary hadn't long to wait before she discovered the meaning of Angie's cryptic comments. An advertisement in *The Seattle Weekly Intelligencer* brought more than enough work to do, and not from women bringing her mending or small children to be instructed in the fine arts. Her customers were men. They brought shirts that needed buttons sewn on and rents repaired. They sat patiently listening to her while she explained the rudiments of reading music or the basics of speaking French. Most of the time they really didn't need any mending done—they could have done it themselves and often had caused the damage deliberately—and few of them had any aptitude or real interest in music or French. They came and paid their money just to have the lady's company and a chance of her acceptance of their marriage proposals.

The first proposal took her completely by surprise. She was patiently demonstrating the scale of C for the countless time to Charlie Grant, a very large logger who, despite his skill in the woods, could not seem to control his fingers on the keyboard.

He mumbled something which she assumed to be despair or anger over his lack of progress though she understood not a word of what he'd said.

"Mr. Grant, perhaps the piano just isn't the right instrument for you to play," she suggested gently.

He cleared his throat. "Mrs. Smith, er . . . Miss Mary, would you do me the honor of becoming my wife? I love you, an' I'd try real hard to take care of you."

This time she heard every word, and she felt the color rising in her own cheeks as it was in his as she stared at him.

Her silence caused him to rush on. "I got family, good family back in the States, an' my ma an' my sisters, they'd like you just like Pa would. I been out here for some time, an' I like it, but if you'd rather, we could go back to Michigan where it's a mite more settled. I work hard an' I don't drink enough to matter, so I've saved a good bit. You wouldn't need to work no more, an' I could build you a nice little house. Here or there."

Mary finally found her voice. "Oh, please stop! I can't marry you. You do me a great honor, but I can't marry you!" What miserably inadequate words, she thought, to give this big, brown-haired, brown-eyed, kindly-faced young man in return for his offer to change his life for her. She expected him to blunder away in anger and hurt, but instead, he drew a deep breath and grinned.

"Don't look so sad, ma'am. I didn't really expect you'd say yes, but I had to try. An' I won't promise I won't ask you again sometime. An' now, show me them scales again. This time I think I can keep my mind on 'em."

Her relief was so acute, she laughed aloud. "Perhaps there's hope for you and the piano coming to terms after all, Mr. Grant."

The experience of Charlie's proposal was a good one for her. He became a symbol of most of her students, the loggers, sawyers, clerks, and sailors who shared the need for female companionship of the kind they had known from their mothers, sisters, and the brides they might have taken back in the more populated lands of their origins. They didn't want to join the ranks of the squaw men even though they did sometimes satisfy their hungers on the fat, squat bodies of the Indian women at the Illahee, women who had been rented for the price of a few Hudson's Bay blankets and washed clean of their native perfume of urine and dogfish oil. For enough money, the men might even buy time with one of the Illahee's faded white whores. But Mary knew it wasn't the same. These men had left older worlds for this new one, and most were satisfied, but there were things left behind that they missed. Mary understood that as Charlie Grant had become a symbol for her, so had she become one for the men.

She made it a point to listen attentively to their stories and their troubles, and she offered sympathy and the best advice she could. They were so anxious to speak again with a woman of her kind, they didn't seem to notice that she never offered details of her own life. And though she repeated the pattern of gentle but firm refusals to marriage proposals, she knew that nearly every one of the men harbored at least a small hope that Mary Smith would finally cease grieving over her dead husband and choose a new one. But they were so kind in their attentions, she felt none of the fear or threat she had felt from Jason Drake. She was fully aware that Angie had done her work well, embroidering the story of the Widow Smith with a few flowers of her own. And that was mutually advantageous—it gave her extra dignity even as it kept Angie's house free of trouble.

Mary played her role well. Soon, she began to enjoy it. The respect accorded her was quite different from the lot of a traveling actress or a dancing girl. In the widow's guise, used longer this time than ever before, she had acquired very real protection, far sturdier than the flimsy gauze of mourning. And she was genuinely interested in the stories the men told her. She felt a kinship with them. So many had come so far, particularly the loggers who had left the thinning forests of New England and the middle states, even the woods of the Scandinavian countries, to labor in the virgin timber of Washington Territory. She became accustomed to the wide range of accents, used to the calk scars on their faces, evidence of brawls in which knives and guns were considered unsporting but stamping with the heavy spiked boots was fair and left pits as deep as the ones in Angie's wooden floors.

Most of the loggers were rough men who drank, raised hell, and spent their wages recklessly whenever they had a day or so out of the woods, but when they came to visit the Widow Smith, to a man, they behaved as well as Charlie Grant. Mary saw the loggers most often on Saturday nights and Sundays except for those who had left one camp and hadn't decided on another yet. The clerks and local sailors dropped by any time they could manage an excuse to see the Widow. The other boarders at Angie's house, all men, made it clear that they considered themselves fortunate to be living on the premises.

Mary was as careful in her handling of Angie as she was in her refusal of the marriage proposals. She wanted to give the woman no offense, no cause to evict her. She paid her board on time and tried to be helpful around the house, but she offered no confidences even when Angie had grown accustomed to her presence and treated her more kindly than their simple arrangment dictated.

"I expect growing up with your old aunt made you sort of formal and proper like," Angie ventured one day, instantly looking as if she wished she hadn't spoken.

But the words and the tone were sweet proof to Mary that whatever Angie had first thought of her story, she believed it now.

"Yes, my aunt had such prim ideas of how life should be run, I'm sure her influence still shows," she agreed cheerfully, but there was a sad little part of her that wished she could confide in Angie, whom she had grown to like quite well.

She felt safer with every passing day. That she could measure with the easing of the cramping spasms of fear. He would not find her here. The other changes were more subtle and startled her when she realized the extent of them.

She had wholeheartedly sympathized when she heard the story of Seattle's first white settlers' arrival some nineteen years before. The women had taken a good look around at the dark-forested, rain-drizzled land that was to be their reward for leaving everything familiar at home and traveling for long weary days, and they had wept. But they had stayed, and some were still here and their descendants with them, especially the members of the Boren and Denny families. The first point of settlement had been named "New York Alki," meaning "New York By and By," and causing great amusement to all the other settlers on the Sound, and those beyond, who heard the grandiose name. The place had proved an impossible anchorage during the winds of winter, so most of the people packed up and moved a bit to the north and east to the more sheltered prospects of Elliott Bay. Seattle had been born and finally named for Chief Sealth who had proven himself friendly to the whites.

Angie, whom Mary had found to be a good source of local information, snorted at the irony of the name. "Suppose he knew it was an honor, his friend Doc Maynard suggesting it and all, but he's probably turning in his grave anyway. I've heard the Indians don't like having their names used after death, ruins their chances of heaven or something. Anyway, what with whiskey and smallpox and some other nice gifts, we've pretty much got rid of the creatures, so I can't see as how the Chief would have liked this town of white folks named after him. Sure didn't do him much good. And that ugly old crone who sells clams and firewood and lives in a hut by the beach, why that's Angeline, his daughter. Lot of good it did her too!"

Angie's attitude toward the Indians was a common one, a mixture of pity and distrust. If they had once been a mighty people, Mary saw no signs of it now. The Indians who paddled their canoes and sold their catches of fish were the ragged remains, mostly living on lands specified by the government, their freedom and strength gone, their culture vanishing under the onslaught of whites who had taken their territories and bought their women.

They were a sad people, but Mary began to understand why Seattle's collective memory still marked the danger. The last

Indian war had been fourteen years before. People had been
killed in outlying settlements; more, the various coastal tribes
might have joined forces with the fiercer Indians to the east—
the greatest threat of all. But the Battle of Seattle itself hardly
deserved the name at all. The alliance of the tribes had failed to
hold. Chief Sealth had taken his people and left the area at the
urging of his white friends, not wishing to do them harm. The
whites had suffered only one casualty, a young man who had
stuck his head out at the wrong time after being told not to. The
support of a gunboat in the bay had broken all resistance. It was
the end of the Indians' brief dream of ridding themselves of the
invaders. But it was no clear victory for Seattle. Always in need
of more families, the town lost many of the precious few it had
after the battle, even though the danger was past. It had taken
years to recover; only now were settlers beginning to trickle in
in noticeable numbers. Scarcely more than a thousand people
inhabited Seattle, but those who did were doing their damnedest to supply the needs of the thousands of loggers scattered in
the camps along the Sound. So far, it had fallen far below the
promise of New York Alki, but it was filled with hope.

That was the element that had worked its subtle magic on
Mary. Seattle had its problems, but it also had its hope, endless,
overflowing hope. Elliott Bay was surely the finest deepwater
bay in the world, alive with a bounty of fish and a perfect place
for lumber ships to take on their loads. And there on one of the
hills were perched the white buildings of the University, the
main structure complete with columned portico and a belfry. It
didn't matter that there had been few students and many problems in the nine years since it had been built. While Seattle had
missed its bid to become the capital or to have the penitentiary,
it had what many of its prominent citizens considered the most
promising and prestigious establishment of all. Surely it would
grow and someday attract students from all over the Territory
and beyond.

Mary's first impression of the buildings and their use had been
that both were ridiculous. She had seen the heart of this town
lying in billows of smoke and steam from Yesler's mill, in the
road used to skid logs down to the mill, in the muddy sawdust-
filled flats that harbored barkeeps and prostitutes. But her view

had altered until she realized that now when she gazed at the University she felt the same pride and promise that others did. Now when there was talk of the Northern Pacific Railroad, and there was talk constantly, she too felt excitement, hope. Surely the railroad would choose Seattle for its terminus, surely the city would prosper beyond imagining once it was linked to the rest of the country by rail. It didn't matter that huge forests shut out the light for endless miles and threatened to take back any spot of cleared earth which was not constantly guarded against their incursion. It didn't matter that Seattle's best exchange with the outside world was at the mercy of the wind and tide. The ships would continue to ply the waters, but how great and glorious the prospects would be once the rails were laid and branch lines bloomed. The coal deposits so close by lay nearly untouched because the land was a wilderness of deep forest and inland water—with roadbeds hacked out and rails laid down, the coal could be transported out or brought to the water's edge to be loaded on ships. Supplies would come in and go out, and most important, more people would come, not just rugged loggers, but families, and if enough came, so would statehood. Seattle was poised right on the edge of joining the world.

Mary had come here just because it was isolated, but now she hoped as much as anyone that the city would grow and prosper. And she would remember forever her first clear view of her new world.

Bart and Red, loggers and hopeless students of music and French respectively, had begged for the privilege of taking her for a Sunday stroll. They had been among the first to answer her advertisement, and she was amused by their clumsy eagerness to please her and relieved that neither had made any embarrassing advances. Laughing, she'd agreed to the outing despite the fact that the day had begun with an overcast sky and a fitful wind. The two men looked as if they could use the fresh air. She suspected they'd overdone whatever they'd done the night before.

The three of them had walked along talking and then had stopped suddenly as one as the increasing light struck eyes accustomed to gray days.

Bart and Red, though they had seen it many times before,

shared Mary's silent awe as if it were the first time for them too.

The mist was lifting, torn away by the wind. The sunlight streamed down in ever increasing waves until for an instant, Mary was blind to everything but the golden flood. And then she saw the world transformed. The breathtaking magnificence lay before her. Emerald green islands rose out of the blue waters of the Sound, and on the peninsula beyond, great snow-capped peaks cut stark patterns against the sky. Mountains ruled vision, forming the boundary to the east too, immense, implacable, never free of snow and ice on their upper reaches, gleaming in the sun.

It didn't matter that the clouds and damp mist came again. Hope had begun in Mary that day. The fear had begun to ease. An unfamiliar feeling of contentment had stolen over her, and she had glimpsed the chance of a new life, something more than brief refuge. A new life in a new year.

CHAPTER
3

*A*ngie was as flustered as a schoolgirl, and Mary was amused. She was grateful to her and had developed a fondness for her, but there was a hard edge to Angie, a calculated shrewdness in everything she did that had made Mary careful. She knew that if she did anything which really offended her landlady, she'd be out in no time at all. She liked her quarters and her life at the boardinghouse and didn't want to jeopardize either. She was careful never to voice any criticism or make any judgment, though she knew Angie had been sleeping regularly with one of the boarders, a surveyor for the railroad. It wasn't any of her business anyway, but she had come to doubt Angie's devotion to the sea captain, had even come to wonder if he still existed or ever had despite the clutter of gifts Angie displayed. Perhaps he was no more real than her own Jake.

Now, observing Angie, she no longer doubted. The ship had been sighted, and Angie was completely undone by the prospect of the reunion. She had already changed her dress twice, smoothed her hair countless times, and had enough food cooking to feed an army.

"Damn and blast!" she swore suddenly and looked as if she were about to cry. "I forgot the apples! I haven't enough! And Tom does love his pie."

Mary burst out laughing. "My God, Angie, you've already got two desserts here besides everything else, but I'll go get the apples for you. Quit worrying. You look beautiful and the food's beautiful too, and I'm sure the only thing the captain wants anyway is you. Aren't you going down to meet the ship?"

Angie calmed down and smiled, her eyes looking misty and young. "No, I never do. He comes to me here and when he leaves again, I'll see him to the door and no further. It's our way. This is the house he helped me build, and this is where we belong together."

Mary felt moved to give her a sudden swift hug, she was so touched by the sudden softness and vulnerability. Then she scooped up the basket and headed for the door, grabbing her cloak and asking how much fruit Angie wanted. The answer, "enough for three pies," set her laughing again. She was beginning to picture the man as a veritable giant.

It was another misty day, but not so wet as to make footing treacherous, and though it had been very cold off and on, the temperature was mild, the damp air blowing softly and smelling of the sea and woodsmoke. Mary felt like skipping but kept to a more decorous pace thinking what a funny sight it would be for Seattle to see the Widow Smith rolling down the hill. She'd made herself a new dress, and she'd wear it tonight. It was a soft purple, still within the bounds of mourning, but so much brighter than the worn black and the murky brown of her other gowns. She thought wistfully of the few equally worn but brighter colored dresses and especially of the rose-hued one, all folded away in the wardrobe, and wondered if she'd ever wear them again.

She paused briefly to watch the activity near the water and the majestic ship swinging gracefully into the bay with the help of steam tugboats, and she gasped when she saw the name of the ship, the *Angie Cooper*. She hadn't said a word about it, but how proud Angie must be of that tribute.

Mary took time to choose the best of the dried fruit. There

were a few other customers in the store, and they nodded and smiled pleasantly at her.

"Bet Angie's near out of her head," the clerk, Henry Hadley by name and one of her better piano students, said, and Mary nodded happily. "She is, which is why I must take these to her. She's cooking enough food to feed the whole territory."

"Wait until you see Captain Tom; he *is* a whole territory!"

The laughter was still echoing behind her when she walked outside. And then she froze, her heart jabbing painfully against her ribs. The shock was so sudden, she did the worst possible thing. She lost her grip on the basket. Still she couldn't move.

The man coming toward her would undoubtedly have passed right by with a polite nod had she not drawn attention to herself, but now his dark, penetrating eyes were fixed on her.

Tall and distinguished, gray at the temples, and as sharp a financier as had ever been born. Richard Clayton. She had known him for a very long time. He was a friend and business partner of . . . No, she could not think of him, she could not. The terror would blind her. She felt her body tensing to flee, but the instinct to survive, lulled by the security of her new life, rose painfully again. Richard Clayton could not be here looking for her. It was impossible. He had to be here on business of his own; that was more than possible. His interests covered a wide range —timber, coal, the railroad, any or all could have brought him here, but not her. He would not expect to see her here. The brown wig was in place, the hood of her cloak shadowed her face, the black dress concealed her body. Careful now, careful. If she could control the panic, there was every chance he would not recognize her.

Only an instant had passed since she had dropped the basket, but Clayton was eyeing her anxiously. "Are you all right?"

"Perfectly, thank you, sir. I felt a little faint, but I'm fine now. I was in such a rush, I forgot to eat breakfast this morning. Silly of me." Her voice was high and thin but audible, and she kept her head bent as she stooped to retrieve her burden.

"Allow me," he said, gathering some of the bits that had spilled, picking them up much faster than her shaking hands could. She suppressed the hysterical laughter rising in her throat at the picture of dapper Richard Clayton on his knees scrabbling for pieces of dried apple.

The basket was set to rights again, and she thanked him, still keeping her voice in a register much above her own.

"Excuse me, ma'am, but I must ask, have we not met somewhere before?" His tone was both respectful and puzzled, but she knew that if she looked into his eyes they would be sharp with speculation.

"No, sir, we have not. I would not forget such a distinguished and kind gentleman had I met him before. And now, again, my thanks and good day. I must be home with these." Never had trite phrases cost so much effort. She could feel the sweat trickling down between her breasts, and she prayed that the mixture of coy tribute and propriety would end the encounter safely. The mock wedding band of base metal she wore beneath her glove seemed to be pulsing with her lies.

The immediate objective was gained. He stepped back and tipped his hat respectfully, allowing her to go on her way without insisting on escorting her. But what of the future? He had not recognized her yet. If he had, he would have used her name; shock at finding her here—or indeed anywhere—would have insured that. But he had sensed something familiar about her. Would he continue to think about it and wonder? Would he ask in the store she had just left? He would learn little if he did, but whether that would still his curiosity or increase it, she couldn't judge. If he did suddenly guess who she was, what would he do about it?

She was handing the basket to Angie before she even knew she was back at the boardinghouse.

"What's the matter with you? You look as if you've seen a ghost!"

The sharp concern in the voice penetrated her consciousness. "I saw someone who looked like Jake." She was careful about the name. "It did give me a start, but I'm all right." Lies on lies, thousands of miles of lies.

Angie was all solicitude. Tom would be here any minute now, and she wanted the whole world to be as happy as she. "Why don't you go and lie down for a bit?"

Mary shook her head and managed to smile. "I'd be much better off fixing these, then you can meet your captain at the door without having to tell him there won't be any apple pie." It was a lifetime ago that she had stopped to gaze at the ship, but suddenly she remembered. "I saw the *Angie Cooper*; she's a lovely lady too."

Angie blushed scarlet with embarrassed pleasure. "Oh, that. The ship's more than half Tom's and the other owners don't mind, so he would have his way."

Mary thought about the sweetness of the naming as she prepared the apples following Angie's instructions with deliberate concentration, adding a little water to boil them to softness since there wasn't time to soak them overnight. She willed herself to think of anything but Richard Clayton and all he symbolized, yet could think of little else. Her first impulse—to pack her things and flee—was foolish. She didn't even know if any ships were leaving with the tide, and she did know that her small hoard of money wasn't enough to go very far. And nothing would call more attention to the Widow Smith than if she took flight now after seeming to have made a new start in Seattle. People would talk about it, and if Richard Clayton heard, it would surely increase his curiosity and suspicion. In a big city, there was little chance he would hear; in this close world, there was little doubt that he would.

There was going to be a party in this house tonight, and she was not going to spoil it by worrying Angie. She was going to wear her new dress and join the celebration. She was going to blend into the mood—like any frightened creature seeking camouflage, going to ground.

The voice boomed like thunder through the house and Mary dropped the big spoon she was using. "I'm home, my sweet Angie, I'm home!"

She heard Angie's shriek of joy and then nothing else for quite a while. She stayed in the kitchen, not wanting to be *de trop* at the reunion, and that was where she met Captain Tom Clark when Angie towed him in, her mouth rosy and her skin pink from Tom's beard.

Mary stared at him with wide eyes as her hand disappeared in his huge paws. He was the biggest man she had ever seen, not only tall, but broad. He was in his middle forties, his hair and his beard bright sun-streaked copper flecked with gray, and his eyes were blue, surrounded by sharp creases in his weathered face. His bony nose was slightly off-center, obviously the victim of more than one fight, but Mary doubted that anyone had ever emerged the victor over him. He radiated awesome power, but there was also warmth and gentleness in his face as he looked down at her. "So my girl has gotten herself some help to feed me! Pleased to meet you, Mary Smith." His voice rumbled out in a friendly roar, bouncing off the walls of the room.

By evening, the house was filled with laughter and sound. Three of Tom's crew and several of Mary's admirers added their number to that of the residents, and Mary saw how wise Angie had been to prepare so much food. All the men ate with great gusto, but no one came close to consuming as much as Tom. And once the meal was finished, the stories began, vivid conjuring of ships, seas, and foreign ports. Since the Captain had last seen Angie, he had sailed to Hawaii, China, and back to Seattle via San Francisco. But he hadn't forgotten his love. Angie was now in possession of a shimmering length of silk the color of her eyes in addition to several pieces of fine porcelain and a carved blossom pendant of jade, the gemstone only the First Wife in China was privileged to wear, or so Tom assured her.

Angie was luminous with the pleasure of having her man home, and more, showed not the slightest embarrassment around the surveyor who had been sharing her bed. Neither did he show any constraint but laughed with the rest of them and told his own stories about some of the wild regions he had seen in his traveling work. It was doubtful that the captain, a man with an obvious and zestful appetite for life, had been celibate either in all the ports he had visited. Mary marveled at this tolerant attitude shared by the three, certain that she would make a total mess of it were she in similar circumstances.

Tom proved himself more than passable on the piano and persuaded Mary to play several duets with him once Angie had informed her that the new boarder had kept the ivory from being lonesome while he was gone. It fascinated Mary to watch the enormous hands move with such grace and precision over the keys. And when he and his crew sang some sea chanteys, his voice was rich and true. Tom Clark was indeed a man of many parts. Raised in New Bedford, part of generations that had gone to sea, still his family had the New England love of learning and had insisted he know more than currents and rigging. One of his sisters and one of his brothers were schoolteachers, and three other brothers lived under sail. He seldom saw the Atlantic anymore, having turned to the Pacific to make his fortune, but he kept track of his family through the network of news carried by other captains and by occasional meetings with one of his brothers who was still in the whaling trade.

It was no wonder that Angie awaited his visits with such joyous anticipation. For the first time, Mary understood the burden of loving a seafaring man, no matter how charming he was. Along with the tales of beauty, excitement, and danger overcome, there were the stories of ships and crews that hadn't been so lucky. Mary felt a sudden welling of compassion for Angie. Despite her independent façade, she must worry about Tom every day he was gone and wonder if she were ever going to see him again.

The irony of the comparison was inescapable. Angie had one man she longed to see every day he was gone while she, Mary, had a host of people she never wanted to see again, particularly Richard Clayton. He continued to haunt her thoughts during Captain Tom's stay despite the boisterous life and joy Tom brought to the boardinghouse and to Angie.

Mary paid attention as she never had before to the newspaper listings of vessels arriving and departing the port, hoping each of the departing ships might have been the one to take Richard Clayton away. She also checked the advertisements, dreading to find mention of the man's name indicating he was staying in the city for a time on some business or other. To her relief, no mention of him appeared. She ceased to leave the boardinghouse unless she absolutely had to, and when she was beyond its protection, her heart beat furiously until she was back in its shelter.

She did not see Richard Clayton again. Finally, Henry, the

storekeeper, volunteered the information she sought. The man
had asked after her. Henry was ashamed to admit that he hadn't
been too friendly with his answers; it was guilt that was making
him tell her now.

"After all, there's enough of us lined up now without another
one," he said, his pale skin showing his nervousness. "Doesn't
matter anyhow, he took ship from here days ago," he added with
satisfaction.

She could have kissed him. Instead, she smiled and assured
him he'd done the right thing. She was immensely relieved, but
she still had no way of knowing whether Clayton's interest would
continue, or whether the truth would occur to him. She clung
to the fact that he was gone and hoped he'd never return.

For Angie, caught up in Tom's too brief stay and unaware of
Mary's distress, the days ran too swiftly as they always did when
he was with her, and now the dawn would come even though she
would give up the sun forever if this night could go on and on.
She snuggled closer to his hard, massive body, drawing his
warmth against her own chill. Her body was satiated with lovemaking, but her heart was still hungry for reassurance from this
man who knew her better than anyone else ever had and loved
her more. "Sail safely back to me," she whispered very softly,
sure he was asleep, but his arm came around her, stroking her
back, and his beard tickled her ear. "I always will, always. A few
more voyages, and I'll be back to stay, to rock on the porch and
drive you mad."

She knew it wasn't true, and she knew she didn't want it to be.
He would die without the sea-rocked decks beneath his feet, and
he wouldn't be the same man if his life were different. With a
little sigh, she fell asleep against him.

In the morning, the old ritual steadied her. "Marry me?" Tom
asked as he always did just before leaving.

"And ruin it all. No, my captain, no sir! You're married already, to the sea, and I don't want her any more jealous than she
is." Those were the words she always added, a talisman for
warding off the evil eye.

He kissed her hard. "I'll be back before you miss me."

"I know you will." She stood out on the porch waiting for him to turn once, wave, and throw her a kiss, and then she went inside.

Mary watched the *Angie Cooper* leave the bay; Angie did not. Angie lighted a fire in the parlor and sat close to it, rubbing her hands together against the inner cold. She did not weep; she never did. It was a matter of waiting for the first great wave of emptiness to wash over and past.

She looked up gratefully when Mary brought in the tea, suddenly glad to have company and thankful that Mary offered no hollow words of comfort. There would be no comfort until Tom was safely back in her arms again.

CHAPTER
4

$\mathcal{M}$ary had been in Seattle for nearly two months, but it seemed much longer. And even with the scare of seeing Richard Clayton, her affection for the misty green, sea washed world continued to grow. She was grateful too, for the new ease between herself and Angie. Having seen the vulnerability in each other made it impossible to go back to the old more standoffish relationship even though Angie mistook the cause of Mary's episode of misery and was only glad that the girl seemed more at ease now.

Mary had no warning that the nightmare was beginning again. A sleekly graceful schooner more than seventy feet long, with gleaming wood and brass fittings, and named the *Gaiety* made port and the rumors began, rumors about the "Tiger" told with the flourish usually reserved for tall tales. She would have been better warned had someone used the man's name, but to Seattle, he was simply the "Tiger."

The Tiger had bought and sold this and that, Goddamn it all, wasn't he the one, hard and clever! The Tiger had been gone quite a while, and he was mad as hell about something, heard tell he broke up more than a few saloons this time, the Barbary Coast was going to miss him. Heard tell it was over a woman, don't that beat all, whoever knew of the Tiger having any trouble that way! Why, most skirts fall all over themselves trying to get to *him*. Angie's lips tightened a little at comments like this though she didn't deny them, and the men tended to cast covert glances at Mary as though sizing her up as the next victim.

It could not be, it simply could not, she told herself, but she did not ask the man's true name. She felt her world turning to the thinnest glass, ready to shatter at the slightest touch.

The truth did shatter it in one still-caught instant when she saw him.

The street was muddy, and she was stepping carefully on her way to buy thread. She felt the stare as if she'd been summoned and looked across the way. He was standing with another man who made no difference at all to her. Jason Drake made all the difference in the world.

She saw him take a step toward her. She ducked her head and kept walking away, expecting each second to hear a shout or feel a hand on her shoulder stopping her. She didn't know why, but she knew this was much, much worse than encountering Richard Clayton. She had felt the fierce light in Jason Drake's eyes even though she was much too far away to see his eyes at all.

This time she had not frozen in place or dropped anything; she kept moving away from the danger. She did not look as she had when Jason Drake had seen her in the brief blue costume. It did not matter. He would know. Perhaps he already did.

It was too much and too much too soon after meeting Clayton. The fragile glass of her new life lay in fragments all around her.

"What do you know about Jason Drake?"

Angie stared at Mary, unable to credit what she saw. Mary's face was white and taut, but her eyes were the most changed. The dark ring around the gray had grown darker, and the gray glowed with golden sparks—huge eyes blazing with rage in the pinched face. She would have been hard put to describe the girl's eyes before; now she would never forget them and couldn't think of anything save that she had offended her in some terrible way.

The question came again, harsh and insistent, and with another: "He is the Tiger, isn't he?"

Angie nodded, recovering her wits as she realized Mary's rage
was not directed against her. "Yes, Jason Drake is the Tiger.
Everyone here calls him that, though not to his face. I never
thought . . . what difference can it make to you? I don't understand." Her voice trailed away in confusion.

"You don't have to understand. But I need to know. What is
he doing here?" she asked frantically.

"He lives here part of the time when he's not on his island,
when he's not doing business in San Francisco, when he's not
at his logging camp or wherever else he makes money. He has
his fingers in a lot of pies. He owns timber, ships and shipyards.
The Mactavish yard, that's his even if it is called by the ship-
wright's name."

"Why is he called the Tiger?" Again the grating, changed
voice.

"Bucking the Tiger, ever heard that, testing your luck in faro?
Lots of people try it, few ever win. The house has the final edge,
and there's a good deal of cheating by the dealers besides.
Jason's luck was unbelievably good—still is—and trying to cheat
him didn't seem like a good idea to most even when he was a
lot younger. The name started in San Francisco at the faro
tables, but it means a lot of other things now to people who
know him. He's a damn savage in business, waits, stalks what he
wants and always comes out with the kill. Always. It's the same
with women; he always gets the one he wants." There was a
bitter note in Angie's voice.

"Then he's savage with women too?" Mary's throat was dry.

"Not in the same way. He pays well. He's a magnificent animal
in bed. But he never stays around for the second season." Her
eyes held Mary's. "He's out of your class. Stay away from him.
He's a hellion. He's broken up half the saloons on the Pacific
Coast and sampled most of the fanciest tail . . . including mine."

"I'm sorry," Mary murmured, her voice suddenly soft.

"For what?" Angie snapped. "Didn't have a thing to do with
you, and it's no shame to have slept with the Tiger." A small
involuntary smile of remembered pleasure appeared and was
gone.

The shame is to have loved him and to still want him, despite Tom's love, despite everything, Mary thought.

The truth was beginning to dawn on Angie even before Mary forced out the difficult words. "I left San Francisco because of him. I thought he lived there, not here. He was one thing too many. He might have recognized me today; I don't know. But even if he didn't, soon he'll hear enough to know."

"My God, it's you the Tiger lost!" Angie gasped. She shook her head slowly, thinking about it, adjusting to the knowledge. Finally, she spoke again. "Women come to him. I've only known him to be upset over one other, and he took care of that. Her name was Gaiety Dane. He married her ten years ago, and eight years ago, she died."

"Jason?" His name was a strangled whisper.

"Of course not! I didn't mean that. His habits don't run to murdering women, just to casting them off. I've painted him so black, I'll find myself apologizing for him if I'm not careful. He wasn't even in the house when the accident happened. She was near her time. She fell down the stairs. The baby lived, but she didn't. She was the first and I think the last woman who was able to tame the Tiger. She'd been a dancer and other things too in San Francisco and elsewhere, and she was willing to be his mistress, but Jason didn't care about her past. He married her and brought her north. Gaiety was fine in her way. She fit her name, always full of laughter and mischief. She was as generous in giving as in taking, and she was honest. I knew her before the marriage when I was in San Francisco too, and I came up here shortly after she did." She didn't elaborate on why she herself had left the city or how Tom had helped her. That was between the two of them and no one else. "She really loved Jason. She wasn't twenty-five when she died, and everything soft in Jason died with her."

"The child?"

"A little boy, Jamie. I only saw him once, but he was a brat even then. He lives on the island. Jason's mother lives there too, and a proper bitch she is. Ah, that's another part of Jason's life, that island. After Gaiety died, he left his mother and his new baby here, went to that island for six months, and took possession of it. And he didn't just build a cabin like most do, he started building a world, brought workmen and materials mostly from Victoria on Vancouver Island. His home has been more there than anywhere else ever since. The island is one of a group of hundreds northwest of here. There's still some question of whether they belong to the United States or to England, but that doesn't seem to bother Jason. He calls it 'Drake's Island,' but everyone else calls it 'Tiger's Island.' A stranger collection of people than those who live there you'd be hard put to find. Jason collects people nobody else wants. I was there just once. Jason never did properly collect me." There was wry self-mockery in her voice.

"I need to know, did Frenchie know Gaiety, know Jason?" The cold knot of suspicion was painful.

"Not that I know of. I knew Frenchie because we lived at the same, uh, house for a while. Gaiety lived somewhere else, but she worked where I did, dancing, and oh hell, meeting men! It's a tough business when you're independent, you know that. I knew a lot of people in those days, and there wasn't any cause for them to know each other, lots of reasons for them not to."

Mary breathed easier. Angie had obviously not seen the mistrust behind her question. She shifted her mind to the few options she had left.

Angie wondered what was going on behind Mary's suddenly blank eyes, wondered what she was planning to do. The grim set of the girl's face forbade questions. Jason and Mary, that was an odd combination to consider. But something had happened between them. Mary had fled him, and if the rumors were true, the Tiger hadn't liked it one bit.

She thought of how her own need had been met by Tom. It still made her furious to think about the injustice of it even though it had worked out for the best. The man whose heart and everything else had stopped in her bed had meant nothing special to her though he had always been as kind to her as she to him. But he had been socially prominent, and all hell had broken loose at his death, hell in the person of his heretofore coldly reserved wife who discovered heat and passion in her lust for vengeance. Suddenly there had been talk of blackmail and murder charges. Angie had known her innocence as well as she had known how doubtful it was that those in power would take her word over the wife's. She had not asked for Captain Tom's help. He had simply appeared and offered to take her out of danger. She had accepted without hesitation, glad that he was in port in her time of need. She had not seen that much of him—his profession precluded that—but she had liked what she had seen and known. And halfway between San Francisco and Seattle, she had realized she liked everything about him very much indeed. She had never before thought to commit herself so completely to one man, but she had done it on that voyage with Tom, and she had never regretted it. Nor had she ever felt any guilt for satisfying her physical needs with other men while Tom was gone—those men meant no more to her than the women Tom took in various ports meant to him. Except for Jason—he had been another matter entirely; he had been a threat simply because of the things she had felt for him. She was suddenly more relieved than she had ever been before that Jason had never truly cared for her, had only turned to her as he had to others after Gaiety's death. She would have lost so much and gained so little. She had no illusions about it. She could not have held Jason, but she might have clung to him long enough to lose Tom.

She didn't have to question Mary about what she was going to do. Seattle was too small a town to hide much for long. If Mary had any contact with the Tiger, everyone would know almost as soon as it happened. And if Mary were going to leave Seattle, Angie would be the first to know.

Only then did it occur to her that the gold in Mary's eyes was like the light in Jason's, and that maybe the match was not so odd after all.

Mary had no intention of leaving. She knew that beyond all else. She had run as far as she was going to. She could not afford another journey even if she could think of somewhere else to go.

A bargain with the Tiger. Turning the tables on him. As he had sought her, now she would seek him. A protector. What she didn't want, she now must have. Richard Clayton might well be taking word back even now. And Jason Drake surely was here, destroying her fragile new security by his mere existence.

She did not think he would say no, at least not to the first trade. It was enough—the chance of trading something worthless for some safety, some time. In the next few days, she went over and over the way she would approach him, what she would ask, and when, and she collected every bit of information she could from Angie, dropping questions here and there whenever gossip of the Tiger was mentioned, hoping she didn't sound too obvious. He still had his house in Seattle, she discovered, but her resolve was not strong enough to invade that lair after dark; he might already have a woman there. No, she would seek him out in daylight; somehow that seemed safer.

She wove her fingers tightly together, flexing them, rubbing her knuckles with her fingertips as if her life depended on it. The shipyard was Jason's, he was here, but whether or not the clerk would carry the message that the Widow Smith wished to see him was another matter.

She kept her head bowed, watching the kneading of her hands. The clerk's attitude and that of the men working in the yard had made it clear that few women had ventured into this domain looking for Mr. Drake and those that had had not been of the Widow's type. Suddenly she didn't know what she feared most—acceptance or refusal of her request to see him.

It was taken out of her hands when the clerk came back to lead her to Mr. Drake.

In the small office, he loomed over her, bigger than she remembered, staring at her, and she straightened her spine against the impulse to cower.

"I was close to knowing but not sure," he said, breaking the tense silence. "I saw the widow leaving that morning in San Francisco, very touching, the war made so many of them. And lo, she appears again in Seattle, the same sad drab, along with sure traces of a dancing girl named Mary. Have you come to pick my pockets again?"

"Surely your life is worth more than I took," she said, trying to keep her voice steadier than her knees. "May I sit down?"

"Be my guest since you seem bent on it in any case."

"Enough!" she snapped, fear and anger equal. "You've been interested enough in finding me, if the gossip holds true. Now you've done it. I came here to bargain, not to play foolish games."

His eyes widened and then narrowed as he studied her. Light and darkness moving in the eyes, the Tiger watching. "And just what do you have to trade?"

She took a deep breath and stared up at him through the protective veil she had worn so purposefully today. "Myself. To be your mistress or whatever you want to call me."

"And what do I give you in return?" This was all mad, but he could not stop himself from asking the question.

"You give me your protection. And should you want to end the bargain or should the need arise for me to travel on again, you will help me to get away safely."

When he found his voice, he was caught between the impulse to laugh at the outrageousness of it and the urge to shout at her for her presumption. "Do you think you're worth all that?"

"No," she replied promptly. "I am quite certain I'm not. But nothing less will do."

It was dangerous to have been as bored as he had been with his life lately; he knew just how dangerous. It led to taking insane risks just to feel alive. He had felt alive brawling for a chance at the dancing girl, and he had felt alive when he saw the widow here in Seattle and had scented the dancing girl's trail. It had, he thought, little to do with her. She had been simply an object more difficult to obtain than most. But now here she was, stalking him, attacking with piteously inadequate weapons, but attacking nonetheless because she feared someone or something more now than she feared him. It was intriguing, and he had a sudden urge to see her emerge from this sack of fusty widow's trappings. He remembered the brief blue costume very well. It was too tempting to resist testing her to see how far she would go.

"Agreed," he said, and she blinked at him, trying to take in the knowledge that she had won. "Have you changed your mind already?"

Her answer was low but audible. "No. What do you want me

to do now?" She thought that if he took her here in this dirty wood-smelling place with the workers and clerks so nearby, she would die of shame and be done with it, but the choice was his.

"I suggest we go to my house. It's much more private than this."

She hoped he would not always be so capable of reading her mind.

She knew everyone was staring as Jason led her out of the place. One of the men she knew, but she ignored them all as Jason announced he'd see them the next day. She followed him docilely.

He stopped abruptly. "How did you get out here?" It was a muddy distance from the center of town.

"I walked."

He looked down at her dirty shoes peeking from beneath the equally dirty hem of her dress. The weather had turned cold again, colder than usual for March, and more rain threatened. Beside him, Mary shivered, drawing her cloak more tightly around her. Faint, elusive pain moved in Jason.

"Can you ride?" he asked, more brusquely than he intended.

"Not very well," she answered honestly. "I've only been on a horse twice, and it was a pony really, fat and slow." *Dangerous, dangerous, little girls shouldn't, might get hurt.* The voice sounded in her mind and faded away.

"Come on, then, I'll take you up with me," Jason said as a man led out a big, prancing chestnut. What kind of child had she been to have had only limited access to riding? From a city? Which one? It slipped through her voice, but not plainly enough to tell him any more than that she had surely been educated on the eastern seaboard.

He swung up into the saddle and reached down for her.

The horse looked as big as a wall to her and hot-tempered as well, and she hesitated a moment before she closed her eyes and let Jason swing her up behind him. Her skirt and petticoats were every which way, and she pulled at them and her cloak, trying to cover her legs decently. She felt a little tremor running through Jason and knew he was aware of her dilemma. If he laughed aloud, she'd push him off this beast, and to hell with the consequences.

"I wouldn't, if I were you," he warned, his voice muffled, his shoulders shaking harder. "You'd probably end up hung upside down by your heels, not to mention your skirts. Seattle would talk about it for days."

"I expect Seattle's going to talk about this as it is," she snapped. "The Tiger carrying off the Widow."

"Don't call me that. My name is Jason."

The deadly quiet of his words left no doubt that he meant them. He didn't like the title given to him. It was something to think about, when she had time, if she ever thought coherently again. Now was certainly not the time. The horse moved off at a smart pace, and Mary had no choice but to cling tightly to Jason. It started to rain, and instinctively she pressed harder against his broad, warm back. How easily and skillfully he rode, freed from his own hobbling gait.

She refused to look at anything on the way. In a very short time word would be all over town about Jason and his passenger. Most would surely think this had all been prearranged and explained why the widow had refused other offers. But she knew a bad reputation was the least of her worries. So much worse was word going back and the danger coming closer—if it still existed, if *he* still existed, if she hadn't killed him. No one, not even Jason Drake, could be as dangerous.

When they stopped and Jason swung off the horse, reaching up to lift her down, she stared in surprise. They were in front of a frame house fairly high up on the back slopes, trees cut down to give a view of the water. Even on the outside, the house was far less rustic than most of the rough wood and split cedar houses which characterized the place, and it had two full stories. It said a good deal about him that he had built this when everyone else seemed to be content with one-storied houses. Buildings such as this were still rare here.

He led her inside and lighted lamps and a fire in the hearth before he went outside again to see to the horse. She glanced around. The room was a small but well-appointed parlor with a dining area on the other side of the hall they had entered by.

In the hall, she had glimpsed the dark of a staircase leading to an upper floor. *The staircase where his wife had fallen.*

She stared at the fire and stretched her hands out to it, not turning when she heard Jason come back into the house. He seemed to have business elsewhere, and she wished it would take him forever. She heard him go upstairs, heard him moving around there. She heard him come back down, and finally she turned from the fire when he came back into the parlor. He lowered himself into a chair which gave him the warmth of the fire and a view of her.

"Take everything off," he ordered pleasantly, slouched back in his chair. But he could feel the pulse beating in his temple, his heart beginning to jump against his ribs. He couldn't believe she was going to go through with this, but if anyone's bluff was going to be called, it was going to be hers.

His command given, she knew there was going to be no quarter offered, but even this was better than the wordless maneuvering which had commenced with the ride from the shipyard. It was what she had asked for, what she deserved.

She met his eyes directly. "If I do this, all of it, you will keep your part of the bargain? You will meet every condition?"

He nodded, forbearing to ask why she trusted his word. He knew he would honor it, and somehow she knew too, if it came to that.

She turned her back on him, and he did not object. Suddenly he had a distinctly queasy feeling, a gut reaction. Despite her hard bargaining, her demands, she was immensely vulnerable and her vulnerability was becoming his own. He started to tell her the deal was off, but the words never came. He had been staring at her with blind eyes as he thought, but now as she turned to face him, he saw her again, too clearly. He blinked in disbelief, and his breath left his body in a long sigh.

Without the shadowing bonnet, he could see the young glowing skin of the palest honey rose. The facial bones were delicately carved, the mouth surprisingly full. There was no veiling and no theatrical makeup now to conceal the wide gray eyes, the irises dark ringed and shimmering with gold flecks. The thick lashes and slim arching brows were deep brown, many shades darker than her hair.

He nearly exclaimed aloud. He had assumed that the curly brown locks of the dancing girl and the widow were Mary's own, but now he saw how complete the disguise had been, and how necessary for someone in hiding. Mary's hair was bright, shining silvery gold without red to tarnish it; a color usually lost in childhood. It was cropped as short as a boy's but now, uncovered, it was beginning to spring into curls as if it had a life of its own. Jason's hands ached with the need to touch it, and his body ached with stronger need as he gazed at her. She was built on long, slender lines, but her breasts were round and perfect for her figure, her waist was narrow above the gentle swell of hips, the soft curve of thighs, the long tapered legs. Not even the dancing girl's brief costume had revealed this.

He silenced his last doubt about taking what she offered. He wanted her, and better he than some other man. She needed a protector, and he had the strength and power to fit the role.

"Do I meet with your approval? Do you want to check my teeth?" she asked waspishly, tossing her head and trying to act bold and confident, a filly for sale, but she was beginning to shiver.

For answer, he went to her and drew her close, tipping her head up and brushing her lips with his own. He smoothed the silken curls, and still wordlessly, he picked her up and carried her upstairs to the master bedchamber, feeling her tremble in his arms.

She shut her eyes and kept them shut until he put her down, but she could not help but marvel at his strength. He was strong enough to carry her effortlessly despite his handicap, despite the fact that she was not a small woman. *Strong enough to hurt her.* Fear shot through her again. It always hurt. But nothing and no one could be worse than the past.

She opened her eyes, looking around the room. The bed on which she lay was large. There was a fire burning on the hearth. The low flames in the oil lamps gave the room a soft glow against the gray rain outside. For this he had come upstairs; he was well practiced even to the lighting of his lust. The furniture was fine polished wood and uncluttered, masculine without being monastic. She thought of the parlor. A small, cozy, and carefully done house. A well-kept house for well-kept women.

She shuddered and closed her eyes again. He had stripped off his clothes and was standing over her. She didn't want to look at him. Soon it would be over. She suppressed the thought of what might happen if she didn't please him. All this for naught.

It was not soon over. Jason lay down beside her, and a smile she did not see curved his mouth. He was a good lover, and he knew it. It was an art he had been practicing for a very long time now, and Gaiety had taught him most of all about how to please a woman. But if ever there was a woman set on giving herself up to an unholy sacrifice, it was this one. It was a rare challenge. He had always paid well for willing women and had seen no point in pursuing the unwilling. But for reasons he didn't even care to examine, that had changed the night he had first seen Mary and wanted her. He wanted her even more now, but there was time, and he was patient, and the desire would not be solely his before this was complete.

His mouth traced delicate patterns over her cheeks and brow, nibbled at her ears, trailed to the hollow of her throat and across the softness of her breasts, circling but not touching the nipples, returning to find her mouth, savoring the clean young scent and taste of her. His hands stroked the velvet of her belly and thighs but did not trespass further.

She wanted to scream at him to stop prolonging it, to be done with it. She did not understand what was happening to her. The fear that held her rigid was draining away, and the new sensations were in their way even more terrifying. Wherever he touched, he left a trail of delicate flame. When his mouth was on hers again, she opened to his probing tongue without knowing why she did or why she felt the stroking in the depths of her body.

When he sucked gently at first one and then the other, she felt her nipples tighten, felt as if she had been crying out to him for hours to do this just so. She shivered uncontrollably, and shame flooded through her as his mouth moved down her belly, but her legs opened and her body caught fire from the most intimate of kisses. She had never felt this before, never, this heat radiating in a wide sun from the pulsing center. His fingers now where his mouth had been, moving so skillfully. She whimpered aloud, and he was above her, staring down at her, his eyes willing hers to open. She saw the fierce light moving in his eyes, his tiger's eyes. "Say it!" he commanded. "Say you want me to take you. Say it!"

Obscene vow. She would die with it and could not live without it, her will eclipsed in his. "I do, I do want! Now, take me now!"

There was no pain in this, only pain without, her body open to him, needing him above all other things, welcoming his strong stroking manhood as if it were part of her own flesh returned to her, completing what she had not known was incomplete.

He watched her face as he thrust harder, deeper, faster, watched the fire he had kindled consuming her until he too was consumed and could wait no longer.

She could still hear the echoes of her own high-pitched cries. Jason's body was heavy on hers, yet when he rolled off, she held him for an instant, not wanting to lose the contact. She had felt her body exploding in a thousand fragments; impossible to believe she was whole again.

Her heartbeat slowed, the warmth seeped away. Bad enough that so much had been taken from her so long before, far worse now that she had given all that remained. Shattered after all.

Jason drew her against him and was startled by the chill on her flesh. He rubbed her back gently, trying to warm her. Her bones felt fine and fragile beneath the soft skin. She did not resist him; she just seemed not to be there any more.

"He was an idiot," he said suddenly.

"Who?" she asked without interest, only giving the response she thought he expected.

He drew away a little so he could see her face clearly. "Your first and I suspect only other lover." She had not been a virgin; he had not expected her to be. Dancers on the Barbary Coast rarely were. But more, an intangible quality, an ageless knowing in her eyes, a host of things he could scarcely explain had told him he would not be the first. And now he was quite sure that what he had suspected about her previous lover was equally true.

"An idiot," he repeated. "And surely a brute to have given

you such hate and reluctance for one of the best pleasures life
offers. Perhaps he never pleased you, but surely I did, and that
is somehow worse, isn't it?"

Her eyes darkened until they were dull and blind looking,
staring through Jason and far beyond. All the color had drained
from her face, leaving it blue and pinched.

Jason took her by the shoulders and shook her, his hands
biting harder than he intended because her silent withdrawal
made him uneasy. "Goddamn it, don't!" he thundered even
though he knew it was a ridiculous thing to say.

But it was effective. She focused on him again. "Never, not
now, and not ever will we speak of him."

"Another condition?" his rising anger made the words harsh.

"Yes, if you still want the bargain kept. And in return, I will
not question you about your past."

"Ah, but there's a difference." His voice was silky. "I don't
care whether you know about my past or not. I built this house
for my wife, and I still need a place here as well as my home on
Drake's Island of which I'm sure you've heard. And one or two
women have stayed here since Gaiety. I'm not ashamed of my
past."

"How fortunate and singular you are then," she returned
coolly. "I am like many people. I have much to regret, much to
be ashamed of in mine." She did not want to think of the dead
woman, had she loved this house, helped plan it? Surely she had
died here. And had Angie also lived here for a while?

He saw suddenly how pathetic it was—the tethered lamb defy-
ing the Tiger, no matter how much he rejected the name given
to him. But no quavering little bleats from this one. A small
snarling, a futile, diminutive growl of fury which could gain
nothing and lose everything.

Her past, how could it possibly contain enough to be worthy
of shame? The unvirgin virgin. He was sure he knew. A young
man, clumsy and inexperienced, had taken her for love or whatever reason and all the guilt had followed. He did not doubt that
she had been gently, even strictly, raised. She spoke too well,
and even the way she carried herself could have come from no
less than a consciously upper-class background. All her efforts

to appear otherwise were transparent to his eyes. He remembered how ill Frenchie's surroundings had suited Mary. Even then he had known. Perhaps a young lover had seemed a way out of a life she hadn't liked, perhaps for its restrictions. It did not disturb him that she had fled to the West, though he thought her obvious fear that someone might be searching so far to find her was probably unreasonable. Unless, of course, there was money involved. That was more than possible. In Jason's cynical view, people were apt to do far more for money than for blood or love. But if she had wealth, she surely had not access to it now.

She was not going to tell him. That he knew. He regarded her gravely for a minute before he kissed the darkening flesh where his hands had bruised. A little shiver rippled through her, and she watched him warily, her heartbeat visible in the quick pulsing of her breast, but she stayed where she was.

He moved away from her on the bed and lay on his back, gazing at the ceiling. "You had better go collect your things. We'll stay here until we leave for the island."

She moved, and he turned his head to look at her again. She knelt on the bed, uncaring of her nakedness, one fist pressed tightly against her mouth as if to stop a cry, her eyes enormous.

"Well, you've gotten what you wanted, haven't you?" he asked. "What did you intend to do, keep Seattle's approval of the sweet young widow while you serviced me?"

She felt the hot tide of color rising to stain her skin and could do nothing to prevent it. He was too knowing, this man. She had not thought everything through after all. Even as he guessed, she had had some dim idea of seeking his protection without having to submit so thoroughly to his presence. To live with him, to be controlled and used by him day and night. It was what she had fled from. Even as she thought it, she knew it was not true. Jason Drake was not the other man. And he did not remember the child of herself.

"I'm not so indelicate as you suppose, my dear. I can play the game of a man in love as well as any. No one will know of the bargain. Seattle will forgive anything for love. Do you want me to accompany you?"

His voice was rough and yet, at the same time, oddly gentle.

How strange that they had spoken no love words in what had seemed to her an eternity of physical joining, yet now he said "my dear" so easily she was not sure he knew or that it had any meaning at all. How many times had he said that to Angie, to the others?

"I don't want you to come with me," she said in a small voice.

She got up. She knew Jason was watching, but it made no difference. He had seen everything and savored her at his leisure.

He was still lying on the bed when she opened the door to leave.

"Come back if you will. I won't come after you," he said.

She left without looking back. She knew without doubt that he meant what he said. If she didn't return, Jason Drake would make no further effort to find her. The chase was over for him. The knowledge was strangely chilling. Perhaps what he wanted had proved worthless in the having. She knew it was, but she lost her power to bargain if he also knew.

She dressed hurriedly in the parlor and let herself out of the house. The rain had turned to sleet, but she hardly noticed the wet chill seeping into her bones. Back to Angie's, try to make a decision and quickly, Jason would not wait long if at all, for her to decide. She knew suddenly that it had cost him something to let her go like this, without an escort, back to the boardinghouse. He had given up the satisfaction of the chivalrous show to allow her full freedom of choice. Her mind leaped to consider how strange it was that in bed she had forgotten he was lame, had thrust the knowledge away. Even now she did not know how it had happened. But it only mattered because it must matter to him.

Jason lay with his eyes closed, wishing sleep would come, knowing it would not. Better this way. It wasn't so far, only about a half mile. But he hoped she wouldn't fall, hoped the poor ugly shoes wouldn't get too wet, hoped she wouldn't be too cold. To have gone with her would have decided it. Velvet warm skin, young, supple body, soft fragrance, sweet taste, naive yet knowing so much more than she realized or wanted to. So much if she were willing. His body warmed at the thought, and he swore, a long string of epithets gleaned from sailors and lumbermen who were masters at the craft. Far better to deal with those women who knew their trade and loved nothing, wanted nothing as much as gold. A sharp, renewed hunger made him hope Mary would come back, but the saner part of him hoped he would never see her again. He didn't know quite how, but he was sure the cost of her would be more than he was willing to pay and in currency far rarer than gold. And it bothered him that even with the strangeness of her and her bargain, she seemed hauntingly familiar. He knew it couldn't be; he would have remembered.

CHAPTER
5

*J*ason awakened with a sudden startled movement to the white glare of morning. It had been the longest night he could remember. The cold had turned to snow, rare enough here where mild winters were the boast, doubly strange this late, in the first week of March. But it wouldn't have bothered him at all had it not been for Mary Smith.

He had been sure she would not try to return in the storm, but not sure enough to cease worrying and sleep. It had been hours and hours, each minute stretched out by guilt he denied.

His body quickened with instinctive hunger for the woman beside him. He studied her sleeping face, and the hunger died. There were shadows beneath her eyes, marks of the decision she had made and the sliding trek through the snow. The knock on the door had been so light and timid, he had at first thought it a rustle of the storm. When it came again, he had found her there, snow clinging to her clothing and her eyelashes, her teeth chattering.

Mary opened her eyes to Jason's stare, and the night came back to her as clearly as to him.

Angie had been waiting for her. She studied Mary's face, then said, "I know where you've been. The weather's foul. Jason would wait. But I don't think you will. Go, pack what you need, I'll send the rest along when it clears. And you have time at least for a cup of tea."

Mary nodded, unable to speak for the kindness. Angie's understanding didn't falter. She pointed out that the snow that had just begun was further reason to delay, but she did not insist on it, fully aware that Mary's courage was held together by thin thread.

When Mary stood ready to depart, Angie kissed her on the cheek, hugged her, and stepped back. "Good luck, Mary Smith. I doubt there ever was a Jake or an old aunt, but it doesn't matter. Soon most of Seattle will know the romantic story of the Tiger and the Widow. I'll see to it, and it will be all right. I'll miss you. Don't stay away too long. Jason won't mind you visiting here."

Mary turned away with tears in her eyes, overwhelmed by the gifts of compassion, tolerance, and help offered so simply despite the faint pain of remembrance that continued to show in Angie's eyes at mention of Jason. She realized that Angie must have divined her intention almost at the instant she herself had known what she would attempt.

By the time she reached Jason's house, she was cold and frightened down to the marrow of her bones. When he opened the door, her knees gave way, and she would have fallen over the threshold had he not scooped her up in his arms.

Everything had been a blur of fatigue, but she remembered what he had done, and a blush touched her cheekbones as she returned his stare. He had undressed her and wrapped her in a blanket by the fire. He had heated water, prepared a warm bath, and put her in it. She had fallen asleep, beyond regret or embarrassment, beyond anything but the need for rest and warmth. She had barely roused to the knowledge that he was putting her to bed, easing down beside her, holding her against his warmth.

He had made a bargain with a woman and had had to care for a child. Her blush and her resolve deepened.

Jason watched the changing emotions with interest. His hand strayed to the silk of her hair, but his words could not have been more mundane. "I'm hungry, want to help me cook breakfast?"

She relaxed and smiled at him. "Yes, but I must warn you, I'm not a very good cook yet, even though Angie's been teaching me." She felt a twinge of sorrow for Angie; nothing changed in Jason's expression at the mention of her name. And then the sorrow was for herself, for the day when she too would be forgotten by him. It was a useless sorrow, and she tried to banish it.

Jason's thoughts were an unwieldy jumble as he shoved kindling into the stove and set out the makings of a large meal. This shared domesticity gave him an odd feeling, and he didn't know whether he liked it or not. It had been a long while since he had awakened with a woman still beside him in the morning, and not since Gaiety had he felt the urge to protect as strongly as the urge to take. It made him uneasy, as if he were stealing things from Gaiety to give to a stranger. The irony of it did not escape him. Gaiety had not needed the protection he had wanted so much to give her, had not needed it until death had come for her, and he was unable to protect, while this one, this Mary Smith, needed it so desperately, she had made a bargain with a stranger for it.

He watched her trying anxiously to follow his instructions and help with the cooking. Her claim was true, even the strangeness of a new kitchen could not account for this. She acted as if she were on an alien battlefield. Where in the world has she come from? The forbidden question.

He had a sudden image of Maggie teaching Mary housekeeping skills and realized he was already seeing Mary as part of life on the island.

Mary watched him as she tried to make herself useful. He was such an odd combination of catlike grace and lameness, every muscle, bone, and nerve quick and strong except for those in his twisted leg. She had not thought she had studied his body so carefully when he had taken her, when she had slept nestled against him, but her memory betrayed the lie. Beneath the cloth, she could see the twisted, knotted muscles of his right leg, the uneven fit of the hip socket, the scar across his thigh, nothing as it should be for a strong, straight limb.

"How did you hurt your leg?" She heard herself ask the question and was amazed at her temerity, sure he would be offended.

But he was not. He smiled ruefully. "I wish I could claim it was from some heroic effort, but actually it was the result of disobedience when I was seven. I'd been warned not to ride a neighbor's horse. It was a mean-tempered brute. But I was sure that all he needed was a well-meaning friend. He threw me against a stone wall. I'm lucky I didn't break my head instead of my leg. The doctor did his best a couple of days later. His best was to save the leg, if not its full use."

He turned his attention back to the slices of bacon sizzling in the pan and did not see the sudden whiteness of Mary's face though he heard another soft question, "Days later, how could that be?"

He shrugged, not taking his eyes from his task as he turned the meat carefully. "My fault again. I dragged myself home but I didn't want my mother to know, wanted to wait for my father because he could never stay angry for very long. The problem was that my father wasn't home and wasn't going to be for two days. I told my mother I had a bad stomach and just wanted to rest. By the time father got home and a doctor was called . . . well, I don't remember much about it."

She barely restrained her gasp of outrage. It was as if she saw what he could not remember—a little boy in agony and fever and a mother capable of such monstrous neglect and unconcern that she had not bothered to search out his true injuries until it was nearly too late. She saw it as clearly as if it were happening before her eyes. She hated the image. The last thing she needed was to think of him as vulnerable.

She searched desperately for another subject and heard her inane questions about work at the shipyard. But it succeeded, an obvious trigger to one of his major interests.

"The British are correct. The future is in iron ships and steam power. But for now, a combination of wood, steam, and sail will still do for us, and Robert Mactavish knows the shipbuilding craft as well as anyone I've ever met. He started in Scotland, but he's learned the differences between the Atlantic and the Pacific. There are differences indeed, differences in winds, currents, and differences in needs. Did you watch any ships taking on lumber along the California coast?"

Mary shook her head, not mentioning that she had been in no condition to notice anything except her own misery.

"Well, it's a skill to catch the eye. It takes a fine captain to maneuver his craft into a doghole for loading without smashing to bits on the rocks, especially if you haven't steam power, haven't any power except the wind and the tide. They call those little inlets 'dogholes' because the sailors say they're not even big enough for a dog to turn around in. But the ships do get in and out. Many of them are specially rigged for the job. There are new challenges here, and they're being met by men from Europe and New England, men used to another ocean but willing to learn."

She smiled, charmed by the enthusiasm that glowed in his eyes and rippled through his voice. "Your ship, the one you came on, does it have steam?"

He grinned back at her. "Nope. The *Gaiety* has only her sails. Some habits are hard to break and matching sail with wind and tide is one of them. The *Gaiety* is San Francisco–built of western woods; she was born to sail the Pacific."

Mary thought she was going to have to become a much better sailor if she was going to survive this new turn in her life. But even the thought of being on a ship again did not diminish her appetite for the breakfast Jason had cooked.

"You're a handy fellow to have around," she said, and her eyes glowed with sudden mischief.

For an instant she looked so young and carefree, Jason nearly choked on a mouthful of coffee. Inwardly he cursed again the shadowy figure of the man who had been in her life before, but his face did not betray his thoughts. "Oh, I'm a man of many talents," he agreed, pursing his lips and trying to look smug.

Mary blessed the snow. The white mantle lay over the town, but the beauty of it was not as important to her as the delay it would provide before she had to face Seattle again.

Jason was glad of the respite too, but not for the same reason. He was more and more intrigued by this woman he had taken into his life, and he wanted time to know her better before he took her to the island. He offered information about his own background, telling her of his father who had moved ever westward, always seeking a fortune in this or that, sometimes succeeding, sometimes failing.

"He was a dreamer and a spendthrift, but he was also an intelligent man and a charming one. And he always managed to feed his family. In some places where fortune had been kind, we were on top of the world, and in others, when all had been risked and lost, we were at the bottom. But my mother and I were never hungry. The ups and downs were hard on her. She cares, perhaps too much, for social standing. But she stayed with him. For a child, the life was wonderful. I saw more of this country than most people see in a lifetime. And even though my father had been disowned by his family as a black sheep he didn't forget the good they had given him. He came from a straitlaced New England family, prosperous merchants who had always considered money spent on education as money well spent—if only to make you better educated than your competitors. We were never in one place long enough for me to gain much from schools, but I never felt the lack. Father set out a course of study when I was very young, and somehow he always managed to gather the books and find the time to discuss them with me. It was no hardship for me. He made lessons interesting, and I was flattered by the time he spent with me. If he hadn't had the wanderlust in his blood, he would have made a fine schoolmaster, if not a merchant like the generations before him."

"You were fortunate in each other, and you still miss him. When did you lose him?" she asked softly.

"In fifty-four. I was seventeen. His fortunes were on the way down again. He'd over-invested in a ship that was lost, and he'd speculated on a load of merchandise that proved a glut on the San Francisco market. Perhaps it was one blow too many or perhaps he was just tired. He was sick for a very short time, and then he died. I was lucky; he'd taught me a considerable amount about business. Strangely, one of the things he'd tried to teach me was to be more careful than he, but it's not a lesson I ever learned. And I gambled with cards, with dice, on horses, on just about anything, and that's something he never did. All his gambles were in commerce. But I won. I won enough to take care of myself and my mother and to pay off my father's debts. I even won enough to take some business risks of my own. No one cared about my age. San Francisco was still a young town then."

He bucked the tiger and became the Tiger. She saw the reckless young man he must have been and smiled at the image even as her mind marked down the fact of his thirty-three years.

"Why did you ever come this far north?" she asked, wanting to put all the pieces together.

"In fifty-eight, thousands passed through here on their way even further north for the gold rush on the Fraser River. I was one of them. I didn't really expect to find gold, and I didn't— most didn't. But I saw this country, and I saw the islands, and I couldn't forget any of it. Have you ever heard of the Pig War?"

She shook her head, fascinated by the laughter in his eyes.

"Most haven't, but it's true—the United States and Great Britain nearly went to war again in fifty-nine, and all over a pig on San Juan Island. You see, when the treaty was signed establishing the boundaries of the two countries' western possessions, an ambiguity was included. One boundary in the treaty is stated as 'the middle of the channel which separates the continent from Vancouver's Island.' The problem is that there is more than one. There are in fact at least three major channels which fit the description. And of those three, one is to the east, one to the west, and one cuts right down the middle of the islands. There are other minor waterways which might qualify too. And nowhere in the treaty is it specified which channel was meant. You can imagine what that has led to—Americans and British both have settled on the islands. And on San Juan Island, one English pig invaded one American potato patch once too often and was shot for his trespass. And that led to a demand for payment many times the going rate for a boar which led in turn to attempts at arrest which led to the question of what country was sovereign and thus had the power of making arrests which led in turn to a sudden definition of whether one was an American or a subject of the king and to an arming of the opposing camps which even included gun ships and some tense times before word got back to the countries involved that they were about to follow the bugle for the sake of a dead boar and lack of payment for same." He drew a deep breath. "Anyway, the countries didn't go to war, but to this day there is an American camp and an English camp on San Juan Island, both staffed by soldiers who now celebrate most festivals together and include the mixed islanders who live between the two camps. But when it's all settled someday, the United States will own the islands."

"I believe you because no one could make up a story like that, or at least, I don't think anyone could, even if it does sound like the answer to a riddle." Her skeptical expression broke into a smile. "So now that I've almost decided to believe you, tell me why the United States will own the islands."

"Because the islands are in an important stretch of water and too close to our western boundaries to let them belong to anyone else. And England is too far away to want to fight a real war for them. She has enough to do now supplying and peopling the western empire she has full title to."

"Now I truly do believe you. That's far too sensible to be made up." She was still thinking about what he had just told her and what she knew from Angie about his island home, and she was thinking even more about the fact that his mouth was slightly and endearingly crooked when he smiled—the right corner pulling up just a little more than the left. Finally she heard the question and knew he had asked it for at least the second time.

"What about you?"

Her own smile faded, and she stared at him for a moment before she repeated the litany of the old aunt. She left out the fairy-tale Jake this time. "That's all, and it is more than the bargain allows."

Her eyes were the cold dark gray of a winter day without hope of sun, and her voice had the icy sting of sleet against the skin.

Sudden hot anger rose in Jason, burning against the chill of her, against the way she had ruined the ease between them. His hands knotted with the sudden urge to shake the truth out of her. She had asked questions, and he had answered them, offering his past, sure she would tell him the truth in exchange. He had been absolutely sure he could charm her into trusting him.

He rose abruptly from his chair by the fire, swaying until he found the balance of his bad leg. "I find I need a breath of fresh air after all."

She returned his glare with calm defiance until he looked away and slammed out of the house.

His first thought was to go down on the sawdust and find a bottle and other pleasures, but it was too far to go. He wasn't going to ride the chestnut on this icy footing. He laughed without mirth at the thought. His own chances of making it anywhere without falling were a lot less than the horse's, but he wasn't going to risk the beast for his own anger.

He found himself wet and cold at Angie Cooper's boarding-house.

Angie felt a fierce rush of resentment as she let him in. He greeted her politely enough but as nothing more than an old friend, no flicker of remembered passion lit his eyes or shaped his words.

And then the image of Tom was warm and comforting in her mind, blocking out the interlude with Jason when Tom had been away. The resentment was gone, her smile warm. "You're freezing. Let me get you something hot to drink before you ask questions I can't answer anyway."

As she watched him cradle the cup of steaming coffee liberally laced with rum, Angie felt sorry for him. He looked unsettled and uncertain, and all over Mary Smith. She shook her head ruefully. "Jason, I do know why you're here, and I really can't answer any questions."

"Can't or won't?"

"Can't. Not all women exchange all their secrets, and certainly not Mary Smith. Oh, I know she ran away from you in San Francisco, but you know that too. And I know that she saw someone from her past here in Seattle and was scared silly. But I don't know who he was or where he came from, so that's a useless bit of information. And what little she told me about herself, well, I don't believe one word of it anymore. Why's it so important to you? No one comes out here if he has a perfect life where he is. You planning to marry her, is that why you can't just let it be?"

He exploded in wrath at the question. "Hell, no! Gaiety was my wife, the only wife I'll ever have."

"So when you're tired of this girl, you'll go your way, she'll go hers, and that'll be the end of it. Why does it matter what came before or will come after?" She had not suspected the depth of his mourning for Gaiety, but she saw it now, and she wished she had the courage to tell him how much Gaiety would have hated it. Gaiety had been full of life and love, and the last thing she would have wanted to leave Jason was a legacy of angry sorrow.

Jason spoke slowly. "I don't know why it matters. But it does. I don't know why I've tangled myself up with Mary Smith, but I have. She's a tight-stretched rope ready to break. I want to know why. I want to know what or who frightens her so much she's willing to come to me and offer herself as the price for my protection."

Gaiety, he's going to be all right. Mary Smith, I wish you well, and I know Gaiety would too. Angie's voice was as kind as her thoughts. "Someday maybe you'll know, when she's ready, when she trusts you enough to tell you. But if you want to keep her now, you must accept her as she is, without yesterdays. I know if you push too hard, she'll run again, and this time, I doubt you'll find her. Is it worth that?"

He shook his head and stood. "No, it's not. Thank you, Angie, Tom's a lucky man."

Angie watched his precarious progress until the cold drove her back inside. Her longing for Tom cut with sudden sharpness, and she wondered how many days from home he was and on what distant sea. "Sail safely back to me," she whispered.

The cold and the sudden jolts of slipping on the snow made Jason's leg ache, but he ignored it, wanting only to get back to the house as quickly as possible, fearful that she wouldn't be there.

But she was, still crouched in her chair by the fire, eyes watchful and still defiant as he approached her.

"I'm sorry. I broke my word," he said softly. "No more questions. Bargain?"

The tension drained away, and she smiled at him. "Bargain."

As she said the word she knew how important it had been for her to win this battle, and how much she had doubted her strength was a match for his, how much she had doubted that he wanted her enough to give in. It gave her an odd sense of power. She watched him lower himself into his chair, watched the careful stretching of his leg toward the fire, watched his hand rub his thigh in an unconscious, automatic attempt to ease the pain.

She slipped to the floor beside him so swiftly, he didn't know what she was about until she pushed his hand away and began to knead the knotted muscles.

He froze in embarrassed protest, mumbling, "It's nothing, don't . . ."

"Then nothing will be less," she countered, ignoring the command, working to ease the cords she could feel beneath her hands.

He did not protest further. He put his head back and closed his eyes, giving himself up to the voluptuous pleasure, as the deep ache eased. Gaiety was the only other person who had ever done this for him. Even the slender yet strong touch of the hands felt the same. But when he opened his eyes again, it was Mary's face he saw, not Gaiety's. Wordlessly, he drew her up onto his lap, ruffling the soft curls, kissing her throat, and working at the fastenings of her clothes.

He took her in the circle of warmth cast by the fire, her body pale and slender against the rich hues of the carpet from China, an ivory figurine against enamel. The exotic image stirred his senses, and he spent his passion in a swirl of contrasting colors and textures, pale and blood rich, soft and rough silk. No yesterdays, no guarantee of tomorrows, but this, this taste and scent of her, this sight of her, this feeling of her velvet flesh beneath and sheathing his own.

It was as if the first time had been ages, not measurable hours before. All was changed now. She did not flinch from his touch but touched him back, running her hands over the strong muscles of his back and down his lean flanks, moving her body to accommodate him, rising and falling in counterpoint to his rhythm.

But it was he who cried out, and when he was complete and drifting in a golden haze, he opened his eyes, met hers, and knew what he had won and what he had lost.

The gray eyes were calm and remote. Whether he had pleased her as he had pleased himself had no importance for her this time. The bargain had been reaffirmed, and she was paying her share. He wondered why he was not satisfied with that and marked it down to injured male pride. He did not know that he had cried his dead wife's name even as he had reached the peak of his pleasure in Mary Smith's body.

She was grateful for the gift. She was separate again; mind and spirit safely severed from the actions of her body. When he had first taken her, she had recoiled in terror from the knowledge that he had touched all of her at once—flesh, spirit, mind—and moved them to his will, but now his dead wife was between them, a ghostly barrier as strong as steel, and Mary was free again.

The change in Mary frustrated Jason in the following days. He had been without a steady woman for a long time, and his hunger was intense, but he wanted her to respond to him as she had in their first joining. He succeeded only in assuaging his body and making hers sore. She made no protest, but finally she betrayed her discomfort.

"Damn it to hell!" he swore, as he heard her stifled gasp and felt her wince. His passion died abruptly, and he rolled away from her, propping himself on an elbow so that he could see her face. Fear and confusion flickered in her eyes, and his voice gentled. "I'm not a rutting stag whatever you think, and though we have a bargain, I have no taste for hurting women for my own pleasure. You're a woman, not a little girl, and it's up to you to tell me if I hurt you."

Strange shadows moved in her eyes but embarrassment and gratitude were uppermost. "I'm sorry, I thought . . . I haven't . . . it's been a long time, and I thought I'd grow accustomed to . . . thank you for caring." The lashes came down to shield her eyes.

He leaned over and kissed her on the forehead. "Stubborn,

aren't you? You needn't get used to everything all at once. I think a cool cloth would do wonders, at least it did for me." There was more than a hint of laughter in his voice, and when her eyes opened, they were brimming with mischief.

"And what caused the need? Were you held prisoner somewhere by a hungry woman?"

"What a delightful fate! But alas, not mine. No, I was temporarily and deservedly unmanned by a well-aimed boot. The lady in question had no objections, but she did have a previous commitment. Fortunes of war."

"And who tended to you? Though I'm sure I can guess."

"Of course, the lady. I didn't say I lost the war, only that I was wounded in the battle."

Her laughter joined his just as he had hoped, at the silliness of it all.

He did bring her a cool compress of soft linen, and she slept the rest of the night against the comforting strength of his body without realizing how delicate and deep a passage of trust and concern the night had been between them, despite the cloak of bawdy humor.

Jason was far more aware. He had added two more tiny pieces to the puzzle of Mary Smith. The first was a confirmation of what he had suspected from the first—she was used to abusive men, or at least to one who had no care for her well-being. The second was proof by her body's rebellion and her own words that she had not been with her lover for quite a long time.

The weather was still uncertain, but it had cleared enough for Jason to turn his energies back to the shipyard and the multitude of other business ventures which required his attention before he left Seattle again. He worked with a vengeance, deliberately absenting himself from the house for long hours, giving Mary time alone, doing his best not to crowd her. At first, he feared he had done the wrong thing.

When he told her that the couple who cared for the house and the horse in his absence would gladly come in to do the chores and the cooking, she refused, saying it was high time she learned to be useful. He knew that wasn't the real reason, knew she was afraid of having anyone there judging her, which was why he had put off having the help in the first place. When he asked if she wanted to go anywhere in town or even with him to the shipyard, she refused, always politely, but still with a telling note of desperation.

He feared she would continue to be so reclusive, he would have to force her to leave the shelter of the house. He was exceedingly relieved when she proved him wrong.

It began with visits to Angie for advice on cooking and proceeded to brave if brief excursions to the stores where Jason had accounts when supplies ran low and finally to a timid request that she be allowed to go with him to the shipyard after all. There was, despite her fear and mistrust, a need in Mary to be with other people.

Angie had done her work well. Seattle rose to the occasion because belief in a good love story went right back to the town's roots. Louisa Boren and David Denny had been the first courting couple and the first marriage celebrated by the founders, and the "Sweetbriar Bride," known for the flowers she planted wherever she lived, and her husband were still held in great affection. The tale of the Tiger and the Widow wasn't quite as legitimate, but with Angie's careful telling, it was difficult not to succumb to the charm of this current romance. A wild chase all the way from San Francisco and who knew where else before. Poor man, so long without his wife, and everyone knew he hadn't cared a penny for all those other women. And all those strange people out on his island and his little boy, well, who knew what changes would come now that the Tiger had the Widow Smith. Angie knew the power of the tragic widow label and had taken extra pains to keep it intact. Even the men who had courted Mary conceded that the Tiger was a worthy opponent, though they gave themselves credit for having seen Mary's value long before they knew the extent of her beauty. That silvery, golden, shining, shining hair! Who would have guessed it? Who, for that matter, would believe it even now if they hadn't seen it? But it made sense the way Angie Cooper told it. How could you hide with hair like that? And what a brave thing for the Widow to do, cutting it so short to further the disguise under the brown wig. More than a few women felt the weight of their own tresses and thought momentarily of the freedom those short curls would bring, but in the next instant considered the pleasure and power of enticing their men in the private hours with the long, unbound strands, and their sympathy for the Widow increased. She was not, after all, after the men; she belonged to the Tiger. And why had she gone to such extremes and run away from him in the first place? That was easiest of all to explain. Angie had accomplished it with few words and many delicate shrugs and omissions. The Tiger's reputation and the force of the man, well . . . And the Widow's mourning for her dead husband, well . . . See how she had tried to protect her virtue, but remember how strong love is. Almost everyone could remember that, especially the large population of men who wished love was more than a memory.

Wasn't it all delicious, not quite a scandal but very close. A good source of interest, speculation, and indulgence for an extended winter. And the source of the information, well, and well again, everyone knew Angie Cooper wasn't married to Captain Tom, yet she was a good woman and ran an honest boarding-house, and you could believe what she told you.

Angie was frankly enjoying the success of the campaign she was waging for Mary. It was like being involved in a bit of theater. Beyond that, she was genuinely concerned that Mary not be shunned. But she had been as shocked as anyone when Mary had visited her without the brown wig. Only then had she finally understood the excessive privacy Mary had maintained in her room and in the kitchen of the boardinghouse when she bathed, not maidenly modesty at all, but the preservation of the disguise.

"Holy gods, you are a beauty!" she exclaimed. She wondered if Jason knew what an act of trust it was for Mary to reveal her unique coloring, a beacon for her past to follow.

Jason did know. He felt a new awareness of everything, a fine tuning of nerves he had lost when Gaiety had died. Mary touched those nerves in myriad ways. He had not said a word about how she should appear in public. Unwilling to tell him what had gone before, she strived so hard to please him in other ways, it pulled at his heart. For the first days he had expected to come home to find she had changed her mind and fled, but she was always there waiting for him, working to keep the house clean as if it were an intriguing and not quite familiar mechanical toy, cooking meals that sometimes included dishes which hadn't come out quite right. He had always been fastidious in his dress, choosing simple but well-tailored clothes but now he found the smallest rents were exquisitely repaired and buttons so securely anchored, they couldn't be lost. It was another tiny puzzle piece that surprised him until he realized how it fit—fine needlework was every gentlewoman's accomplishment, taught from the time little girls could hold a needle.

Gentlewoman—that she surely was, whatever she had been through since. The full picture was still hazy for him, but parts of it were very clear. Only those who could afford it and wanted the difference made known, raised daughters devoid of most practical skills yet practiced in the "finer" domestic arts. And that intentional ignorance belonged in long-settled and socially structured regions, not in the still-raw West where everyone needed every skill that could be learned.

Jason found himself observing her more closely than he ever had another human being, and he felt more than a little like a hunter stalking elusive prey, more than a little like the beast people called him. He was careful not to ask her where she had learned this or that, hating the fearful and yet defiant withdrawal which was always her answer. Instead, he let her betray herself bit by bit in unconscious ways. Whatever her lack of domestic skills, there were surprising dimensions to her education. She wrote a clear hand, but that could be expected while her cleverness with figures could not. Gaiety had been entirely helpless with numbers, and besides Mary, Jason knew only one other woman, a sea captain's wife, who had more than a basic knowledge of arithmetic. Following the notion that mathematics was unfeminine, most women were taught just enough to be canny in shopping and to make ends meet in a household.

But Mary's knowledge went far beyond that. She knew how to keep account books with swift precision and could usually grasp the problems and percentages of a business deal after one explanation. He shared the task with her without protest when she asked if she could help. It was tedious work he detested but had never delegated for long, being unable to find a clerk whose standards were as high as his own. He had no such reservations about Mary once he saw the order she brought to the ledgers.

At first, the men at the shipyard had been aghast to learn of a woman's hand in Jason's business affairs, but they knew the Tiger would never be so besotted by a female's charms that he would let her damage his commerce, and that led them to new respect for the Widow Smith. The sly looks which had greeted her first visit to the shipyard vanished. Even reserved Rob Mactavish regarded her with some friendliness now. And for Jason, it was another bond with Mary, a way to lure her closer to him while they spent time together working in companionable silence in the dusty cubbyhole at the yard or more often, in the small study at the house.

He discovered one facet after another in her character, as if it were a jeweled surface catching light in a changing multitude of ways, and he longed for the day when the darkness was gone and the light free of shadows. Her dark side baffled, angered, yet touched him most of all. Her terror was so intense, not even in sleep could she face it.

The first time it happened, it had taken him a moment to understand because she had startled him violently out of sleep by the sudden thrashing of her body and her high-pitched scream. He held her by the shoulders and spoke softly, intending either to wake her gently or ease her back into calm sleep. But her voice sounded small and shaky. "Thank you, Jason, I'm awake. I'm sorry I disturbed you."

He drew her against him and stroked her hair in wordless comfort, as shaken as she. He could not imagine a fear so great that when it crept into her sleeping visions, her only defense lay in wrenching herself to wakefulness before it overwhelmed her. He didn't need the confirmation of a next time to know he had seen a pattern clearly.

Her flesh was cold and shivering, and then he felt her moving with frenzied purpose, rubbing against him, her hands stroking and urging. He tried to draw it out, tried to enter and use her gently, but she demanded a harder, faster pace, her slender body writhing and riding him with manic energy. She slept instantly when it was finished.

It was he who lay awake feeling his heartbeat slowing, the film of sweat chilling and drying on his skin, and the thoughts beginning.

He had wanted some sign from her, had waited for it, but he had not considered this. He had not used her; she had used him —fiercely, mindlessly, to exorcise her own demons. He was glad he had not been able to see her eyes in the darkness, but he could not escape the knowledge of what he would have seen— eyes both wild and blind.

He more than half expected that in the morning she would have no memory of the night, but not even that grace was given her. Nor did she claim it. She regarded him solemnly and said, "I'm sorry," very low.

He managed to grin. "That's the most uncalled-for apology I've ever received." But he felt totally inadequate to deal with the situation. The cause was out of his reach. When it happened again a few nights later, he had a sudden yearning for the island, a stronger need to be there than he had felt in a long while. It was time to go in any case. They had stopped there briefly on the way from San Francisco, and the crew of the *Gaiety* had sailed back once since to see their families and friends, but they were anxious to return for a longer stay and tired of dallying in Seattle. So, suddenly, was Jason. It was also time and past to visit the logging camp again. He trusted his crews of sawyers and loggers, but he knew the work was always better after he had made his presence known there.

With the decision made, he moved swiftly, instructing the men to ready the ship for sailing, arranging for the house and horse to be cared for again in his absence, and making sure work would go on steadily at the shipyard. He had expected Mary to balk now that Seattle had proved so kind to her, but she made no protest at all. She merely packed her few possessions, tidied the house carefully, said good-bye to Angie, and was ready to go at the appointed time.

CHAPTER
6

$\mathcal{M}$ary wasn't anxious to leave Seattle; she was frantic to get away from herself, trusting with childish faith that in quitting the little house, she would somehow be able to leave behind the nightmares which had grown so much worse and the equally nightmarish need which had grown in her for Jason. Only he made her feel safe, only his body banished the other from her. She had lost her brief feeling of distance from the dark memories that haunted her, and her dependence on Jason was growing with terrifying speed as she twined herself around his life as tightly as she could, always conscious that Gaiety had been there first, was still. It was not at all what she had bargained for.

She looked at the seabirds wheeling and crying, the water swirling under the *Gaiety*'s prow. She saw the other vessels maneuvering in the Sound. She watched Seattle slipping away. She heard the flap of the canvas, the creak of rigging, and the gruff orders from Captain Hanson to the others. All had treated her with the utmost courtesy when she had come aboard.

Jason came up beside her to lean on the rail and look out over the water. She could feel the difference in him, the sudden calming of his habitual restlessness, but it didn't matter to her at the moment. She had known there was going to be a problem the minute she had left the land.

"Are you having regrets?" he asked softly, puzzled by the look on her face as she turned to him. He cocked his head, waiting for an explanation.

"I should have told you, but short of walking on water, there seemed no other way than this to your island. I reasoned having survived it once, it would not happen again. I am about to disprove my own theory. I am about to be extremely unwell."

He roared with laughter. He couldn't help it; he hadn't realized how much he had suddenly dreaded a change of heart after her calm acceptance of leaving Seattle. Her schoolmarmish explanation amused him mightily. But he sobered instantly as the last color drained from her face, and she leaned over the rail.

He held her to keep her from tipping into the sea, and when he was sure she was steady on her feet, he left her only long enough to dampen his handkerchief in fresh water. He wiped her face gently and then her clammy hands. She bore his ministrations patiently.

"Feel better?"

She nodded.

"I'd take you below to lie down, but I think you're better off staying in the fresh air." He understood now why she had shown no curiosity about the area below deck.

"I certainly am!" She closed her eyes and swallowed hard at the very idea of lying on a swaying bunk in a close room.

"I can remind you of one great comfort. We aren't going all the way to the island today. We're stopping at the sawmill and the logging camp for a few days. You won't be long away from solid ground. It's not far north of here."

She leaned against him gratefully, and he heard her low, heartfelt, "Thank God."

This inner water of the Sound was really quite calm, and she concentrated on the sharp, cool tang of the breeze, breathing it gratefully, feeling her stomach settle down a little after its first violent reaction. The soft mist of the gray day felt good against her face. It was too overcast to see the great mountains, but there were plenty of things to catch the eye. Smoke and steam rose from various sawmills to join the clouds, and they passed a lumber schooner with her decks piled high with timber, obviously bound for the Strait. Little steam tugs were helping the schooner on the first leg of the journey, but the *Gaiety* rode the tide with her sails taut. Mary saw tiny boats with lone fishermen here and there, and a sleek canoe paddled by Indians shot swiftly through the waters along one shore. She saw again how interwoven land and water were in this country, as if a wealth of islands had been flung down randomly on the sea.

Jason pointed out little settlements as they passed, explaining the mixture of names, some the original Indian names, some given by Spanish and English explorers, and some by the more recent arrivals, the Americans. He was telling her how skilled Captain Hanson was in navigating these waters, and then he grinned as he saw her eyelids growing heavier.

"You must find my commentary fascinating since you're falling asleep on your feet!"

"It is surely better than my previous reaction," she pointed out. She spent the rest of the trip curled up in a blanket, out of the way and dozing against a pile of ropes and boxes.

She awakened to shouts as the *Gaiety* was maneuvered into position along the timber loading wharf and made fast amidst a flurry of activity on shore. The sun had broken through and illuminated the scene brightly.

Steam and smoke rose from the shed of the sawmill. The screeching of the saws was eerie and harsh, louder here in this isolated cove than in the bustle of Seattle. There were outbuildings, and all was backed by steep slopes covered with stumps— proof of the logging which had already been done. Great booms of logs rode in the water near the mill.

Seattle had taught Mary what a skid road was, and she saw the carefully laid logs leading in a path of gentle curves upward and out of sight around a fold of land and heavy brush.

It looked an orderly, well-run camp, but she would expect no less from anything owned by the Tiger.

She concentrated on the new sights and sounds as she and Jason disembarked, Jason's arm steadying her as her body continued to roll as if at sea. She was interested in the sights before her, but not as interested as she pretended. Most of all she was fearful, cringing inside at the possibilities of the men's reactions to Jason's arrival with his mistress. She didn't think it would take much—the wrong sort of look, a muttered comment—to make Jason angry. She didn't want that; she didn't want trouble of any sort.

It didn't take her long to realize that she had not only underestimated the men, she had underestimated Jason. Here, a visit from the Tiger was an event, and no man wanted to earn his enmity. He paid too well and dealt too justly for any of them to jeopardize his job by rudeness to his woman. And there was too much suppressed violence just beneath the Tiger's surface. There was no doubt that she was his. He kept her close beside him and introduced her as Mary Smith, offering no other explanation, his attitude of possessiveness saying more than enough. His eyes were as bright and watchful as they were cordial. She began to suspect that Jason's attitude had had as much to do with her acceptance in Seattle as Angie's friendly war on her behalf.

Jason felt the quick pulse of her nervousness, and he began to point out various things and offer explanations, making his voice smooth and matter-of-fact, seeking to put her at ease. "We keep the logs in the water because it makes them easier to handle, cleans them for the saws, and makes for less insect damage and rot. We took some good timber off those slopes," he pointed to the stumps, "but what's coming out of the deeper woods now is much bigger and much better. Even when you've seen it over and over, it's hard to believe the size of western timber. The loggers say it takes three men and a boy standing one on top of the other to see the tops of these trees."

Mary marveled even as she felt a sense of unreality; it was, just as Jason said, nearly impossible to credit that these huge lengths of wood had been part of even taller trees.

Jason's voice went on explaining that the mill produced everything from spars for sailing ships to pilings for wharves and boards and shingles for buildings, depending on the size and type of trees they felled. The lumber went from Puget Sound not only to the States and Europe, but as far away as the Orient.

The figures she had worked on in some of the ledgers began to assume a new reality, and Mary was thinking of them when she was introduced to Mrs. Tomlinson.

"I'm lucky to have her," Jason said. "Her husband is the chief sawyer you met a few moments ago, and Maude does the cooking for the crew down here as well as issuing supplies from the company stores. Nothing makes men quit faster than bad food, and Maude keeps that from happening here."

The woman was standing at the door of the cookhouse. Mary managed to say, "Pleased to meet you," as the introductions were made. The words nearly froze in her throat.

The reaction she had expected but not received from the men was obvious in this short, heavy woman with graying hair. Her words were polite enough, but the faded blue eyes regarded Mary with open contempt and not a little fear.

Mary knew she ought to be amused rather than offended, but she was not. The woman was judging her to be a whore, probably wondering if she intended to offer her services to every man in camp including Mr. Tomlinson, hardly taller than his wife, roped with stringy muscles from years of hard labor and deep-creased from the elements.

The bitter taste of the woman's judgment and her own of herself rose in Mary's throat. Jason had moved away to speak to one of the men. He had watched the men's reactions so carefully, but it had never occurred to him that the venom could come from Maude. He had, in fact, thought that Mary would be comforted by knowing that there was at least one other woman in the area.

Mary spoke very softly, naming herself, but each word was clear. "I am the Tiger's woman, no other's. And you and I will be civil to each other because that is what he wants. Do you understand?" She stared Mrs. Tomlinson down with haughty disdain.

The woman seemed to shrink, and Mary felt her own power expand. It was not the way she would have chosen had there been other choices, but she was learning that the Tiger's protection was indeed worth having. She and Maude Tomlinson were not going to be friends, but the woman would undoubtedly be wary of her now.

She was immensely relieved when Jason told her they would proceed to the logging camp, leaving the *Gaiety*'s crew behind to await their return.

"Horseback is not the way any of them would choose to travel anywhere," Jason said with a grin.

She made no protest when Jason mounted the horse provided for him and reached down to help her swing up with him; she had no intention of being left behind, and there was something comfortingly placid about this massive beast's expression. A small horse would hardly do for a man of Jason's size, but she wished they all looked as docile as this one did.

"All work and no show." Jason laughed, perfectly aware of her close scrutiny.

She rested her head against his broad shoulders and wrapped her arms tightly around his waist, heedless of the audience which included Mrs. Tomlinson. Her task was to stay on the horse, not to impress onlookers. There was no way around it; she was going to have to learn how to ride. Horses were an integral part of Jason's life. He rode like a centaur.

For the first time, she tried to feel the movement of the horse as if she were alone on its back and in control, but perched as she was, the exercise wasn't very successful, and soon, there was so much to see on the trail, she was back to simply holding on.

The first and overwhelming sensation was the absence of sound. It surrounded them, a muffling silence with a force of its own. Here, in the forest, even the scream of the saws was gone. No birds sang, and though they were following the track beside the skid road, the dense brush and the towering trees shut out so much of the sun, Mary felt as if they were moving through dark green shadowed water, brightened here and there by small lost coins of light. Even the thud of the horse's hooves seemed faint and far away, and a shock ran through her at the sudden sound of Jason's voice.

"The skids are never less than twelve feet long, and they're a foot thick. See how regularly they're laid, seven and a half feet apart. That's so that even when the shortest length, a sixteen foot load, is hauled out, it'll rest on at least two skids and not get caught between. The runnels cut in the top of the skids are to help guide the logs, and they're lined with hardwood for added strength."

As he spoke, she viewed the half-buried logs laid crosswise with new interest and saw the absolute precision she had not noted before. It was strangely comforting to see the hand of man in this vast wilderness.

The horse's ears pricked forward. Then the sounds reached the riders.

"What in heaven's name is that?" Mary exclaimed, gripping Jason more tightly, sure the horse was going to bolt.

"Don't worry, he's used to this," he assured her, though he pulled the gelding closer to the edge of the trail. "It's the oxen bringing a load out." His shoulders started to shake with mirth. "I can't wait to see Bull Fletcher's face when he realizes you've heard his performance. You're about to hear the most professional swearing this side of hell."

Mary hadn't long to wait to understand what he meant. The din grew louder, a creaking, clanking, snorting, and rumbling of power, all overlaid by a man's voice bellowing above the animals. "Hump you, Bill! Move you, Sam! You, Brin, Star, you lard-assed, ball-cut sons of bitches, pull!"

Mary's eyes widened as the epithets grew more and more colorful and the procession came into view. The oxen were magnificent, eight yoke of them straining together, muscles bulging, harnessed in wood and leather, brass caps gleaming on the ends of their horns in stray shafts of sunlight.

The animals dwarfed one of the humans with them—a slender young man who darted in and out behind the last of the beasts with swab and bucket, greasing the skids right in front of the huge log being hauled—but the other man was a match for the team. He was a wall of a man, as big as Captain Tom, tall and enormously broad with muscles as thick as those on the beasts he drove, and drive them he did, walking beside them. It was his bellow that was rending the forest's silence, his curses which were growing more fantastic and explicit by the minute, his sharp goad that flicked out with the speed of a striking snake to remind a recalcitrant beast to obey. And it was his voice that strangled in his throat when he caught sight of Mary and Jason in the shadows. His face turned beet red, and he looked as if he were shrinking inside his clothes, head tucked down, huge body trying to look smaller.

At the change in their master, the oxen began to bawl in alarm and pull unevenly. The skid-greaser dabbed his own foot with oil. Bull Fletcher, rooted to the spot and staring, scrabbled ineffectually for his hat, and Jason was in danger of falling off the horse because he was laughing so hard. He fought for breath and yelled, "Don't stop! Go on, we'll see you in camp," before the hysteria of the scene overwhelmed him again. The team kept moving, in step again, to the renewed shouts of Bull Fletcher. Apparently the oxen couldn't tell that "Damn, er . . . darn you, Bill, to hell, er . . . to heck with you Brin!" were phrases different from the normal ones once the man had gotten his volume back.

Mary pounded Jason on the back, warning, "Don't you dare fall off!" but she was laughing too. "What on earth is the matter with that man? Hasn't he ever seen a woman younger than Mrs. Tomlinson before? And what is that dreadful smell?"

"That man is the best bull whacker you're likely to meet, but a lady's man he's not. A rider left the mill to alert the loggers the minute the *Gaiety* was sighted, but you're hardly what Bull or the others are expecting. And the smell is the fish oil the kid was using on the skids. It's a trifle rancid, I admit." He was off again, still seeing the look on Bull's face.

Neither of them was aware of the picture they presented when they rode into camp. Both were flushed and bright-eyed with laughter, and Jason looked nearly as young as Mary. There were only two old-timers who had known Jason Drake when he looked like that most of the time in Seattle, when he had been married to Gaiety, and they hadn't seen him look that way since her death. Fiddler, the cook, said, "Wahl, praise th' Lord an' witness th' Resurrection," under his breath. The other, Jud Carlson, boss of the camp, simply smiled in welcome at the only man who was more powerful than he here and at the Tiger's woman. The rest of the men did their best not to stare. Few succeeded. None of them had ever known the Tiger to bring a woman to the camp.

Two of the faces were familiar to Mary, and she read their

identical expressions of apprehension—they feared that their boss would be furious if he knew they had courted his woman.

"Hello, Red, Bart," she greeted them with a smile. Red's face was nearly the color of his hair and beard, and Bart wasn't faring much better at hiding his embarrassment, but they both looked relieved when Mary's greeting brought no noticeable reaction from Jason.

The men went swiftly back to work. Too much time off was no favor to them. Their wages depended on the amount of timber they got out of the woods, though Jason was a more obliging owner than most and believed in compensation for those days when the weather was so foul as to make any cutting too dangerous.

The camp boasted roughhewn but weathertight buildings: cookhouse, bunkhouse, a shelter for the oxen and horses, a pigsty and chicken coop, a smokehouse, a small cabin Jud Carlson occupied unless Jason was there, and a few outhouses.

The enormous surrounding forest made the buildings look like toys, and Mary had the feeling that she too was growing smaller, her perceptions confused and altered in this singular world.

It was a world different from any she had ever experienced before, and she was at once enchanted and fearful as Jason led her on foot into the area where the men were working. It focused suddenly, the image of these big-muscled men moving in a lusty dance, no less patterned for the vigor of it, each man knowing his job, each man and task necessary to the other.

She watched two fallers working together, cutting notches up a tree, shoving springboards into the notches for a place to stand, removing one, placing another until they were some fifteen feet above the ground, away from the thick, pitch-filled bole of the great Douglas fir and ready to begin the first cut, the undercut. She watched in awe as they swung their axes with absolute timing, one on each side of the emerging cut, one swinging right-handed, one left. It seemed impossible that the two small figures chopping away at the mammoth tree soaring two hundred feet or more could ever bring it down, but the open wedge in its side grew ever wider with the thud of the axes. The fallers worked with steady rhythm, stopping only to lubricate their axes, thinning the pitch that clung to the metal with oil from the bottles they carried.

"Most of them use old whiskey bottles," Jason told her with a chuckle, "because there's some pleasure in emptying them when they're new."

He pointed out the work of the ground crew, equally important but less vivid—the swampers who were clearing the underbrush to make other trees accessible, the hooktenders whose job it was to determine the "ride," the natural resting position of each log, and to prepare the logs to be hauled out ride-side down with front ends axed into round smoothness so that they wouldn't catch on the skids. The buckers each worked alone, pushing and pulling his saw to cut fallen trees into lengths that could be hauled out. Mary could see that this last job must surely be the worst, the underbrush around the logs still thick no matter what the swampers had done previously, the work hard and solitary, the men drenched with sweat. Still, she could not keep her eyes from straying back to the aerial ballet of the fallers.

"That won't come down today, but Jud told me where there's one that will."

Jason steadied her as she nearly fell over a tree root because she was still looking up instead of at the path.

He smiled inwardly when they reached their destination. Jud had obviously told the loggers that Jason and Mary would be coming to watch, and though the men wouldn't do it for him, they were surely going to put on a show for the lady and had even delayed work a bit just for the pleasure of doing so.

The undercut was finished, and as soon as the visitors approached, the men made a great show of deciding where the tree would come down. Jason listened gravely and agreed with their choice, knowing full well it had long been decided. He was actually pleased that they trusted him enough to know he would let them have their fun. Life in the woods offered little enough entertainment. It did worry him a bit that the fallers were Red and Bart; he hoped to God their wish to perform for Mary wouldn't make them careless.

Red made a great show of placing a stake in the ground, measuring the distance carefully to nearly two hundred feet from the trunk of the tree. "We'll drop her right on top of this," he announced.

"Why, that's such a big piece of wood, old tree can't miss it," Bart added, pointing at the slender stake. "We might's well do it eyes shut."

Mary gasped and stared at their next action. It had been hard enough to credit the sight when the other fallers had gone up the tree with a few springboards to aid their progress, but Bart and Red were using only their axes and one board apiece. Making the first cuts as far above as they could, they placed the boards and hauled themselves up from the ground. From that first springboard position, they chopped a higher notch, then drove their axes deep into the trunk, using the handles as their only support while they pulled the boards, wedged them into the higher positions, and swung up on them. It was a display of strength and agility such as Mary had never imagined.

She moved like an obedient sleepwalker as Jason led her to a safe spot, trusting him to keep her from falling because she could not look away from Red and Bart.

At last the two figures were in position opposite the gaping undercut, twenty feet above the ground.

"They'll make the back cut now. It takes the last support from the tree." Even Jason's voice was hushed with expectancy, and Mary saw other men in the area stop to watch, checking their own positions to be sure they were safe.

Suddenly the only sound was the steady rhythm of the fallers' axes. It was as if the forest were one creature holding its breath.

She would have screamed had Jason not seen the beginning and clamped his hand over her mouth before the sound emerged. It happened very swiftly, but to Mary it seemed to take all the years of her life.

The cry, "Timber!" rang out, then was drowned in the voice of the tree, a groaning, cracking whine that rose to an anguished roar as the beast fell and the earth shuddered at the impact.

She saw and heard it all. She saw the axes spinning through the air and Red and Bart falling forever, twenty feet stretching to endless miles.

The air shimmered with floating debris, and an instant of absolute silence beat against the eardrums until it was broken by the last settling noises of the tree and the rising whoops of the men.

When Jason took his hand away, Mary didn't make a sound. She sagged against him, burying her face against his chest. He thought she'd fainted until he felt her trembling against him, heard her trying to say the names, and understood.

He patted her back gently. "I'm sorry. I couldn't let you scream and startle them. Red and Bart are fine, look for yourself. I should have warned you, but they wanted to show off for you. In any case, I just didn't think; I've seen it so many times. That's the only way for them to get clear of the falling tree. They have to jump, and for safety's sake, they throw their axes before they do."

She pushed away from him and caught sight of Red and Bart, perfectly sound, receiving congratulations and jokes from the ground crew but looking anxiously her way. She managed a small wave and a smile which seemed to be enough. Red saluted her and Bart swept a clumsy bow.

She looked at the fallen tree. Its great length had buried the stake; Red and Bart had been very accurate in the skill of their game. The girth of the tree would make her look small, as it did even the big men standing beside it. There was a new tear in the canopy of green reaching to the sky. A shaft of sunlight shifted down the long tunnel, changing with the clouds that were beginning to crowd the sky again. The air still carried the scent of the disturbance, a scent at once of damp earth and of dust, all sharp with pitch, so clean and pure a perfume of death.

It was not only ridiculous; it bordered on madness, but she could not stop the vision. She had witnessed a death, no, a murder. She had heard the victim scream into silence.

She turned back to Jason, her face still pale, her mouth trembling, her eyes shining with tears. A small tremor passed through her, soft echo of the tree swaying and falling. "The wood is needed for so many things, and there are so many trees, so many. But it is like watching something great and grand die. A foolish thought, I know." She bowed her head in embarrassment.

Jason stroked her cheek. His words were as soft as his touch. "It's not foolish. I shared it the first time I saw one of them go down, and I'm still not free of it. They are hundreds of years old, and their like won't be seen again now that we are come."

She glanced up at him in swift surprise. He was so complex, this man, capable of mourning for the ancient forest even as he organized its destruction. He was not the first powerful man she had known, but he was the first who saw clearly what he was doing and who could share power when he thought it useful to do so. Though his presence was obviously an event in the camp, Jason treated Jud with deference, making it clear that Jud did not cease to be the "bull of the woods," the boss of the camp, even though the owner was present. It made perfect sense, for if Jason undermined Jud's authority, it would continue to be less even when Jason was gone. Mary thought of one man in particular who would never have been able to share his authority so, not even for better work and higher profits. She did not want to think of that man or of death; she wanted only to think of being here in this place with Jason and of the life of the camp.

Jason's and Jud's way was, she quickly realized, the only way the camp could work as well as it did. The loggers were not petty, intimidated clerks; each was a law unto himself, strong and skilled enough for the demanding life in the woods and therefore hardly amenable to small tyrannies. They knew as well as anyone that it was still a time when good loggers were far scarcer than the trees which seemed to stretch forever. They weren't paid a fortune for their work, but work they could find when they wanted it. That gave a man strength that went beyond hard muscle.

In the next days she began to see that the loggers had a kingdom, a language, and a code of chivalry all their own and that they were no less class-conscious than other societies.

Mary was both amused and saddened when she realized that Kit, the skid-greaser, and Willie, called the "crumb-chaser" by the men since he worked for the cook, hardly associated with each other even though they were much of an age, not yet men nor yet still boys. She had assumed that they would naturally be friends, being the two youngest, but they were too conscious of the difference in their jobs. Kit had every hope of being a bull whacker some day if he didn't end up wielding an ax, which was nearly as good, while Willie, slightly built and rather timid, was only too aware that he would probably never be strong enough to swing an ax all day long and could hope at best to be a cook like Fiddler. Kit tried to contain his relief that there was at least one other person in the camp who was lower in the ranks than he, but his attitude showed in small snubs, and Willie accepted them.

Mary watched it all with fascination. It was better than most of the plays she'd seen, even the great ones. "Think what Shakespeare would have made of this!" she said, sharing her fancy with Jason.

"He would have made a play of it," Jason agreed. "But once he understood the language and decided on the costumes, it wouldn't be any different from the others. Humans aren't that different one from the other in the essentials, no matter where you find them."

"You're right, of course. *The Taming of the Saw, Log's Labor Lost,* easily done, not to mention *The Merchant of Venison.*" She gestured toward Fiddler, who was carving a side of meat on a red-stained slab of wood.

Jason laughed appreciatively and filed away another piece of the puzzle. It could come from association with other entertainers, people who had toured with theatrical groups, but he doubted that. It was far more likely that her education had been extensive enough to include the works of Shakespeare without the judgment prevailing in many households that most were not suitable for young women.

She missed the sharp speculation in his eyes because she was still watching Fiddler. He wasn't the highest paid, and the men called him "belly-robber" and joked constantly about his cooking, but they didn't nail stacks of flapjacks to the cookhouse door in sign of real disapproval, and they didn't move on; even the short-stake men, chronic wanderers, tended to stay longer than they had planned. Fiddler's pigs were just the right weight, not too fat, which would mean the men threw out more of the food than they ate, and not too skinny, which would mean the cook was so miserly, there was never enough left over. And his chickens were a real drawing card, providing fresh eggs and an occasional chicken stew. He guarded them zealously and set all kinds of traps for the varmints that favored the taste of poultry.

Mary could hardly credit the amount of food the men consumed at each meal. Pots of beans, mounds of potatoes, stacks of biscuits and flapjacks, slabs of meat and bowls of gravy, gallons of coffee and tea, and endless pies disappeared. At supper on the first evening when she and Jason ate with the men in the cookhouse, Mary had supposed it was a special meal, but she had soon discovered that the quantity of food was the same every time and the menu too except for the mornings when Fiddler added his precious eggs to it. And Fiddler's edicts were obeyed. It was his voice that yelled, "Roll out!" to rouse the men at five in the morning after he himself had already been up for an hour, cooking. He allowed no talking during meals; he and Willie had enough to do without having the men delay the washing up and preparations for the next meal. Jud's call of, "All out for the woods!" at 6:00 A.M. came as a relief to Fiddler. It signaled the men to work and cleared the cookhouse of the last stragglers.

Mary was glad they stayed for a Sunday, the one day of rest. Some of the men left to hunt in the woods, some to paddle canoes to an Indian settlement where careful bargaining might provide a few hours with a woman, some even to race to Seattle and hope they'd be back by Monday morning. But some simply stayed in camp, sharpening their axes and doing their laundry after having finished off a few precious bottles the night before. And Fiddler proved the reason for his name, making his lovingly polished fiddle sing through the woods. Two of the men even did an impromptu jig and were surprisingly agile despite their heavy boots. Red and Bart looked as if they would have liked to join them, but since it was hardly as daring as what they'd already done, they contented themselves with tapping their feet.

Bull Fletcher's hammer rang in time as he shoed one of his oxen. He did not see Sunday as an excuse to neglect his beloved beasts. He remained terribly shy of Mary, but she was intrigued by the way he handled the oxen and had found that questions about them were the one way to make him brave enough to talk.

His team was of mixed breeds, but he was proudest of the dark-coated Durhams he used for the lead yoke. They were purebred and had cost three hundred dollars. He had more difficulty discussing another aspect of the team. He told her the name of each animal, names chosen for particular markings, characteristics, or for particular people he admitted he thought of when he yelled. But when he got to two of the animals, his voice faltered.

"Now them's real bulls, er . . . ma'am, that is th' others don't . . . don't have all th' 'quipment they was born with, but, ah, . . . these do." His face was scarlet.

She kept her own straight and asked why bulls were mixed with the team as if she discussed such subjects all the time.

Her attitude did put him more at ease, and he continued, "Well, most bull whackers believe jus' like I do that you need them bulls to put a spark o' spirit into the rest of 'em."

He roared at the animals all day long, so much that by nightfall, his voice was hoarse, but he cared for them as if they were children, doing his own smithing with the double shoes for the cloven hooves, rubbing arnica into any galled spots, keeping the leather oiled and the wood smooth on the harness and yokes, and feeding them the hay, bran, and barley hauled in. Jason paid him as much as he paid Jud—the bull whacker and the bull of the woods each earned one hundred dollars a month, nearly three times what most of the other men received, and Mary could see why; Jud kept the men moving, and Bull kept the logs moving out of the woods.

Despite the privacy the little cabin offered, Jason and Mary had had little time alone except for the night hours when they slept chastely in separate bunks that were all the cabin offered. Jason's days had been busy as he and Jud wandered the woods and discussed what timber they would bring out, what the market was likely to be for the Douglas fir, western hemlock, Sitka spruce, and western red cedar. Mary had trailed along with them part of the time and could now tell the difference between one kind of tree and another and the different uses for them. But these trips, made mostly on foot (Mary had stayed in camp when horses were used), had been hard on Jason though he didn't complain. He didn't have to; his limp was often more pronounced and his face suddenly older and taut, weariness showing in his eyes. For that reason, she nearly declined when he asked her to go for a Sunday walk in the woods, but the protest died unuttered because she feared he would guess the reason.

They followed the stream that ran near the camp and provided sweet, clear water for it. The air was chill and damp with a misty drizzle, but they hardly noticed it; it was so much the rule here, days when any sun at all filtered down were rare in this season. Jason carried a gun just in case they ran into a bear or cougar with a mind to dispute their passage, something Mary devoutly hoped would not happen. The sound of Fiddler's music followed them for a while, then was lost in the shrouding trees and underbrush.

"Good grief! What did that?" Mary stared in wonder at a patch of the woods across the stream. It looked as if a giant in a foul temper had stomped through knocking over some trees, snapping others, snarling branches and brush.

"Fittingly enough, it's called a 'blow-down.' They're caused by sudden violent winds that come out of nowhere and hit randomly."

Mary stared at the wreckage for a moment longer. "I would hate to be in the woods while it was happening."

"I certainly won't argue with you about that. It can be very dangerous. But we don't have to worry about it today. Blow-downs are a rarity. Come on."

He chose a sheltered spot, mossy soft and overhung by tree branches which kept out some of the wet, and sank down with relief, pulling Mary down beside him. He felt no embarrassment and made no protest when her hands began to knead his bad leg though he was still surprised, not so much by the intimacy itself, but by the fact that he allowed and enjoyed it. He was accustomed to people registering that he was crippled, then pointedly ignoring it. He was not used to having anyone notice, let alone acknowledge the problems his lameness brought—the *weakness* it brought, for that was how he thought of it. Suddenly, he saw his own motives for letting Mary get this close to him. She was such a skittery creature, having her know he was far less than perfect seemed to work like a lure to a wild bird, and that was fine with him.

"You're putting me to sleep," he murmured, reaching out to pull her against him.

"I don't want to do that!" she admitted. "Not out here if there really are bears and lions!"

"At least you're honest, it's my protection, not my company you crave." His injured tone was spoiled by his laughter. "There are bears and lions but not right on this spot, as you can see, and they would like to avoid us just as much as we would them. It's the surprise meetings that are unsettling on both sides." He paused for an instant before he added, "Rather like Red and Bart seeing you here. Meet them at Angie's?"

His question took her unaware. He hadn't said a thing about her knowing them and had let them show off for her, but trust him to mark it all down and take his own time before he asked her. Then she realized her defensiveness was foolish in this case, and her sense of humor made her voice quiver though she tried to keep it prim. "When they ran out of shirts that needed mending—and you can imagine how quickly that happened, on the first visit in fact—they took lessons to better themselves. Red studied French, and Bart studied piano."

"Are you serious?" Jason sounded as though he was choking.

"Absolutely. If Red ever gets to Paris he will be able to say thank you, good morning, and several other things, but not very well. And Bart, whose real name is Barton, mind you, knows which keys are which, even if he can't play them in any recognizable order."

He roared, his whole body rocking with mirth, his search for air and control hampered by Mary mimicking Red's accent which made "Bonjour, mademoiselle," sound like "bunny jury, made in my cell." Bart's piano playing, she informed Jason, was a series of completely discordant notes which still somehow sounded like "Yankee Doodle." She collapsed against him, overcome by her own laughter.

"Oh, that was very unkind of me!" she protested finally, hiccoughing as she tried to catch her breath. "They tried so hard!

And now I know how hard they worked for the money they paid me."

Jason sobered too and studied her face, still rosy with laughter. "You've done well here," he said softly. "I'm proud of you."

The sudden change in his voice, the obvious sincerity of the compliment startled her. For a moment, she found herself blushing and groping for speech just like Bull Fletcher. The image made her smile again and gave her the words. "I wouldn't have missed it for the world! I'd never met any people like them before I came to the Territory. They're so different from each other in so many ways. I saw one man reading a tattered copy of *Hamlet* today, but some of them can't read or write at all. Two of the men were figuring out how much they had coming in wages and how much they owed for supplies, and they were doing it with marks on sticks. And the differences in their accents! When a group of them are talking together one can hear as many regions as there are men, everywhere from Finland to Wales, to Canada to New England and other parts of the States. But for all their differences, they are the same."

"Indeed they are," Jason agreed. "They all work to 'let daylight into the swamp,' as they term it. And out here, they've had to learn new ways, just as the sailors and shipbuilders have, and they have to work together more than they ever did in the places they came from. No logger in Maine or Finland ever had to use a springboard and jump all the way down when the tree goes. Trees this big are part of the West, not of other places."

"And you love it. Did Gaiety love it too, did you bring her here?" She was sorry for the words the minute she said them and wished desperately that she could take them back.

She felt Jason stiffen though he answered politely enough. "Gaiety loved just about any place she was, but no, I didn't bring her here. The operation was just beginning then. The camp was a lot more primitive then. And we weren't up here in the big timber at all yet." He struggled to his feet, suddenly feeling the damp in his bones.

"We'd better be getting back before the moss grows over us." He offered her his hand and pulled her upright, stooping back down for the rifle.

She went with him obediently, her throat so tight with misery, she was afraid even to attempt an apology. She was the one who had made the bargain—no questions about the past—and she was the one who had just trespassed and spoiled their afternoon. He was not being rude about it; he was simply withdrawn to some private place of his own, undoubtedly with his memories of Gaiety. That was somehow worse than open anger.

He was indeed thinking about Gaiety, and for the first time there was panic in the memory; for the first time he could not see her clearly no matter how hard he tried. Blue eyes became gray, golden hair silvered, features changed, Mary's image sliding over Gaiety's, making Gaiety's ghostly and indistinct, no matter how hard he tried to focus it.

CHAPTER
7

*T*hey left the camp early the following morning to be in time for the *Gaiety* to sail with the tide.

Mary had hardly seen Jason since they had come back from the woods. He had spent the rest of the afternoon and into the late hours of the night having a final discussion with Jud. Mary had still been wide awake when Jason came in, but she feigned sleep, not wanting to say the wrong thing, still feeling as if he were removed from her, far away with Gaiety. And she was growing more nervous by the minute about going to his island. She had not slept at all.

Jason was more aware of her than she knew, but he was preoccupied, not because he was still dwelling on Gaiety, but because there was simply a great deal to think about regarding business at the camp and at the mill. The anger Mary was sure he harbored for her question had never existed, but he knew he had ended their walk abruptly and had paid her little attention since.

He saw her sad expression in the dim light as she looked around the little cabin. "Surely you won't miss this place?" he teased gently.

She swallowed the lump in her throat. "Yes, I will, because

everyone has been very kind to me here. But I'm sure Jud will be glad to leave the bunkhouse for his own quarters, unless he's like the others, unless all loggers are born without a sense of smell." She made a face and wrinkled her nose. "Wet wool, wet leather, woodsmoke, oily metal, sweat, and Lord knows what else—just the air coming out is bad enough; I'm glad I don't know what it's like inside!"

Her ploy worked, taking Jason's mind off her mood. "I think their noses go numb in self-defense," he laughed.

Word had been sent ahead, and the *Gaiety* was ready to sail when they arrived at the mill. Jason had a few quick words with his head sawyer and accepted a bundle of food from Maude Tomlinson before they boarded. Mary and Maude avoided each other, and Mary resisted a wicked impulse to tell the old bat how much she had enjoyed the loggers: Let her make of that what she would! Instead, she kept her expression politely aloof and her mouth shut.

There was good breeze blowing, filling the *Gaiety*'s sails, and Mary welcomed its cold wetness against her face. She would not, absolutely would not, be sick again. Jason saw her struggle and had the good sense not to offer her any of Maude's food though he himself ate heartily. Mary stayed out of range and kept her head turned away from this activity.

She tried to concentrate on everything except her battle with herself. She could hear the excitement in the crew's voices, especially in the heavily accented banter between Lars and Mogens, two Norwegian giants whose wives and children lived on the island. The crew and Captain Hanson seemed to have no doubts about their ship's course, and for that, she was certainly grateful—all she could see was a blurred world of swirling fog and mist.

Jason found a sheltered place on deck and settled her there with blankets to keep off the chill. He could see her throat working convulsively. Her face was very pale, her eyes shadowed. He took her cold hands in his own and rubbed them, trying to share his warmth. He began to tell her about the people on the island, not only to distract her, but to prepare her for the first meetings.

She tried to give no indication of the shock she felt at his words. A pair of deaf-mutes, an albino child, a hunchback—God above! Her terror of the island grew. What if she reacted badly and hurt them? It didn't matter that there were other people there too; they were Jason's people, strangers to her but all obviously loved by him. She tried to remind herself that she had survived the newness of Seattle and then of the logging camp, tried to convince herself that she could continue to adjust to Jason's wandering world. She tried to concentrate on the warmth flowing from his stroking hands, but she felt colder by the minute, and she clenched her jaw without success against the chattering of her teeth.

Jason left her and came back with a brandy flask. "I'm not sure this is the best idea in the world, but it ought to warm you." He was growing alarmed at her pallor and the tremors of cold. He was finally beginning to realize that it was fear as much as sea-sickness.

He held the flask for her, and she took a few sips, gasping at the fiery taste, but at least she felt a little warmer and faint color returned to her cheeks.

Not caring whether the crew saw or not, Jason drew her against him. "You have as much right on the island as anyone else, and you are answerable only to me."

She drew some comfort from that and knew how much she had changed. She spent the next hours in huddled misery, but at least the brandy stayed down, and since she had eaten little the night before and nothing this morning, the liquor was made even more potent. She dozed and woke and dozed again, sometimes finding Jason beside her, sometimes not—everything had grown very hazy. She hardly noticed when the sea became rougher as they passed into the eastern end of the Strait of Juan de Fuca, but in the late afternoon, Jason awakened her, helped her up and steadied her until he was sure her legs could hold her.

Edges of land were visible ahead, rising out of the sea here and there. Dusk was beginning. They had left behind the drizzle and the clouds; the sea of islands was bathed in a soft golden glow.

"There it is," Jason said softly, pointing ahead, and Mary

gasped at the sight of his island. She would not have cared at this point had it been a large rock as long as it was steady, but she saw an expanse of green woods and cliffs looming larger as they neared, a white house gleaming on the highest point.

"It's so much larger than I expected," she murmured.

"About seven miles long and nearly three miles at the widest point."

She could feel the sudden tension in him, his urgency to be once more in his own domain. As they sailed into the bay at the southern tip of the island, she saw the flurry of activity. A red flag fluttered up a tall pole near the water's edge.

"The red flag says it's the *Gaiety*. If it were any other ship, the signal would be white. It's a game among the children to be the first to spot a ship and correctly identify it, then race to see who gets to raise the flag."

Red for the royal standard, red for the Tiger coming home. Mary kept the thought to herself.

"The bay is fairly deep; we could go in closer, but we'll anchor here. That way, there's less chance that a sudden squall will run the *Gaiety* onto the rocks."

She realized that his explanations were again a kindness because her own tension was flowing back full force, and he was fully aware she was not in the best state to face it all. The combined effects of the trip and the brandy had made her even more unsteady. She could feel her body swaying in exaggerated counterpoint to the gentle roll of the deck, and she didn't need a mirror to know that her face was undoubtedly an unbecoming shade of pale green and the hair under her cloak hood damp and disheveled. She straightened her spine and stiffened her knees, thinking that even the Queen of England would be less than dignified under the circumstances. The result of her efforts would have laid her out flat on the deck had Jason not caught her. He laughed and held her tightly for a moment before he set her on her feet again. "Time enough for dignity when you're on dry land."

She stared at him for an instant, then ducked her head and held onto the rail. His habit of reading her mind was all too disconcerting.

Jason felt the chill again when he took her hand. "There's always curiosity and excitement when a ship arrives. The island is a tightly knit little world, but you'll be able to sort everyone out before long. They might well have news of you already if any vessels have preceded us. Ships in these waters carry news and gossip as well as supplies."

"The Tiger's got his whore with him," a nice little piece of news, she thought bleakly, but she said nothing. Nothing Jason could say was going to make any difference.

The launch was lowered. Mary concentrated on not looking down as she clung to the rope ladder and took it step by step until Jason's hands came around her waist and lifted her easily into the boat. The men rowed strongly and there were hallos back and forth as they neared the shore.

When Jason set her down on the shingly beach, Mary leaned against him, trying to find her balance and seeing the people as a blur until faces and names began to sort themselves out and fit Jason's brief descriptions. It wasn't difficult to identify the two flaxen-haired women as the wives of the *Gaiety*'s sailors, Lars and Mogens, though she wasn't sure which was Ingrid, which Else. They bobbed shy curtseys in unison when Jason introduced them, and they appeared much alike, both large, strong-boned women, well-fleshed and rosy-cheeked, looking as if every single detail of their lives pleased them enormously. They quickly stepped back into the mob of blond children who were greeting their fathers.

Nate and Jon Bradley were undeniably brothers, big shambling men weathered past middle age with gnarled hands that touched their battered felt hats and shy eyes that slid away when Mary was introduced to them. They reminded her of Bull Fletcher.

Mary had dreaded meeting Maggie and Ben Carter, sure after Jason's praise for the way the deaf-mute couple managed their lives that she would be the one to commit some awful breach of manners or insult them without meaning to. But they put her at ease instantly, both of them too gracious to allow any awkwardness. Ben was a ruggedly built man of medium height. Like that of the Bradleys, his skin was weathered and lined from forty-five years of outdoor living. There was a kindness to his features from the wide mouth and prominent nose to the bright blue eyes under dark, bushy eyebrows. The eyes gave proof that he was far from old.

Maggie was short, round, and quick in all her movements, and her coloring was a symphony of browns—dark brown eyes and hair only lightly streaked with gray, pale sun-browned skin which came no doubt from a refusal to be bothered with bonnets or parasols.

Jason spoke to them in his normal voice, but his hands moved too, and they answered with swift motions of their own. Mary watched in fascination and felt a shock of wonder when she realized she understood clearly the sudden rocking motion of Maggie's hands and the look of concern.

"She's not a good sailor," Jason agreed, "the sooner I get her home, the better. We can discuss business later. Where are the twins?"

Maggie motioned swiftly again and smiled ruefully. Jason laughed aloud. "Those little imps. I wonder what the adventure is today? The two of them can think up more to do than twenty other children combined."

The Carter twins weren't the only ones missing from the scene. There were still three people to meet in what Mary now considered something of a royal progress, but none of them was the wood-carver Jason had spoken of, or Jason's mother or his son. Of that she was certain.

Constance Bates and her son Daniel. There was no mistaking the pair. "Daniel is very shy with strangers," Jason murmured, and Mary could see the little boy peeking from behind his mother's skirt. Not even Jason's warning had prepared her for this. The child's skin was white, his hair and eyebrows were white. He was devoid of color except for his pale blue eyes. She had never seen an albino before and instinct made her want to shudder at this difference. But then she saw the anxious fear in the blue eyes, and her heart went out to him. He knew far too well how intolerant people could be.

She smiled at him and said, "Hello, Daniel Bates," as Jason introduced them. Daniel smiled timidly. And then she raised her eyes to the woman's face. The look of the woman was more of a shock than the look of the son.

Constance was fine-boned, fine-featured with pale skin and soft golden brown hair. She was beautiful in a delicately symmetrical way. One would notice the beauty without being arrested by it. There was a pale softness of hues that made her fade from sight even as one looked at her. Except for her eyes. They were extraordinary. Mary could not even tell what color they were. One second blue, the next green, the next brown, none of those colors and all of them, imprisoning the world, seeing through it. A sudden blankness, a shifting of the gaze to infinity. Mary felt as if the woman had stripped her of all pretense, had seen far too much. There was sorrow and fear, but the look of revulsion she more than half expected did not come.

"Constance," Jason said with soft insistence.

The eyes blinked, refocused, and Mary realized the whole incident had lasted only a split second. She shook hands with Constance and found the hand even colder than her own. This was the oddest thing yet.

The last seaside meeting was with Hayes Burke, and Mary felt a wave of pity not unmixed with disdain as the introductions were made. Everything about him announced that he wished it known he was a gentleman, everything from the showy buff clothing with faded ruffles at throat and wrist, so incongruous in comparison to the more practical garb of the other men, to the negligent way he slouched beside his horse as if waiting for the riffraff to clear away.

His hair was thick chestnut, his features regular, his eyes dark brown. He should have been handsome, but he was not. Not even the sideburns and mustache managed to make his face masculine. Weakness and dissipation showed enough to sap whatever strength there might have been, and the look he undoubtedly meant to convey wry amusement and condescension was closer to a leer than anything else.

"Enchanted to meet you, I'm sure. A welcome addition to our fair isle," he said.

She was desperately tired, and the land continued to rock nastily under her feet. "Mr. Burke, you haven't any idea of whether I'll prove a welcome addition or not," she snapped. "Why don't you give yourself a reasonable time to decide." She was sorry the instant she said it, but Jason laughed, and after a frozen instant of sheer surprise, Hayes did too, suddenly much more genuine and likeable than the languorous fop.

"I will indeed," he assured her. "Time is something we have on the island." But his voice was far less lighthearted as he warned Jason, "Beware of the dowager. She's been in high temper since we . . . ah, heard. The news came on Captain Gibson's *Folly.*"

Jason shrugged while Mary tried to puzzle it out. For a moment she feared he had another mistress on the island, but then she realized it must be his mother Hayes was talking about. She sighed inwardly, thinking the last thing she needed now was a meeting with the old harridan.

Hayes touched his hat and mounted his horse, drifting away as the others had done except for Ben and Maggie. Ben had the luggage loaded on a wagon, the patient team hitched to it placidly awaiting the commands of the reins. Maggie had already climbed up on the high seat to wait for him, and when Mary saw Jason's means of transport, she devoutly hoped she'd be allowed to join Maggie.

The horse had been tied well back of the activity, and it wasn't difficult to guess why. He was black as night and looked dangerous. His coat shone with nervous sweat; he stamped and pawed and snorted in a private ecstasy of temper, and when Jason approached him, his ears went back, his eyes rolled, and he showed a convincing set of teeth.

Jason spoke to him softly as he untied him, holding him firmly by the reins close to the wicked mouth. "Come on, Gabriel, get it out of your system. No use arguing." The horse snorted louder and tried to rear, but Jason's tight hold prevented any leverage.

Mary watched in fear and dawning anger. Jason was enjoying the contest, taking the risk just for the hell of it. She caught her breath as he swung into the saddle with a sudden lithe movement that belied his lameness. Gabriel got a firm tap in the mouth with a boot instead of the hunk of flesh he'd been aiming for. He took a few crabbed steps and launched himself into the air, lashing out with his hindquarters. Mary could feel the wrench in her own midsection, but Jason stayed in the saddle. A few crow hops and then suddenly Gabriel surrendered, at least for the moment, slowing to a nervous walk, stopping at Jason's command. Jason put him through a few more paces, then rode over to the others, as Mary watched. Ben was grinning, hands flashing in obvious praise; Maggie was shaking her head and scolding Jason as if he were a small boy.

"Come now, Maggie. He's not so bad. See how well-behaved he is now. He just wants it known it's a privilege to ride him."

"I'll give you a hand up," he told Mary, "or you can ride in the wagon."

She looked at the proffered hand and the challenging gleam in his eyes as he leaned down toward her even while he kept control of Gabriel. She swallowed hard and opened her mouth to tell him she'd go in the wagon, but instead she said, "I'm not sure I can get up this way, but I'll try."

Ben was there instantly to offer his cupped hands, and she catapulted into the saddle behind Jason with her skirts in wild disorder. Shades of the first time, she thought grimly, and held on fiercely, gripping Jason as though he were the last hope of heaven, burying her face against him and hoping he couldn't feel the tremors of terror moving over her flesh.

Gabriel stood stock still for an instant. Mary expected him to go into a frenzy to rid himself of the extra weight, but he didn't. He set off at a smart but not hazardous pace.

It was a fairly steep road they followed up from the shore to the house on the bluff. The light was fading quickly now, the afterglow shot with gold and lavender, the shadows of the trees deep and impenetrable, but Mary saw little, keeping her eyes shut most of the way, hearing the rumble and creak of the wagon growing fainter as Gabriel outdistanced it.

It wasn't a long ride, but it seemed like forever to her. She opened her eyes cautiously when Gabriel stopped, and she drew her breath in wonder. The house was much larger than it had appeared from the sea, and though the hill was not that high, it seemed so with the sea spreading out to the west, south, and east. Surely the wind and weather would be fiercer here on this headland than on a more sheltered spot, and just as surely, it was breathtakingly beautiful.

"I feel as if I'm on the very top of the world," she said, and Jason held her close for a moment as he lifted her down. Even Gabriel respected the moment, standing quietly and then allowing Jason to tie him to a hitching rail.

"Ben will stable him for me," Jason said, and Mary became aware of outbuildings, one of them the barn north of the house and sheltered by trees. She almost laughed aloud. To hell with the people, put them out in the open, but protect the precious horses!

As the dark increased, the lamplight in the house glowed stronger, and Mary could hear the wagon arriving before she could see it. She knew all of it ought to give her a homey feeling, but the day had been too long. She longed for the logging camp, even for Seattle, anywhere but here. Suddenly she was so cold, she could not keep her voice steady. "Jason, ple—please, ca—can I meet your fa—family to—tomorrow?"

She expected him to refuse and be angry besides, but instead he drew her closer. "You are so weary, little one, such a long, long day."

His kindness crushed the last of the energy that had held her upright and gotten her through all the strangeness. The last dusk glow wheeled in circles behind her eyes and went dark as she sagged against him.

He swore softly as he picked her up, angry at himself for demanding so much of her, pushing her even harder with the ride on Gabriel. He had an oddly tender feeling of déjà vu as he carried her into the house and up to his room, ignoring his mother's sudden, strident command of his name.

He blessed Maggie for the lighted lamps and the fire burning in the hearth, glad of the warmth for Mary's sake. He laid her down on the wide bed, took off her shoes, loosened her clothing, watching her pale face anxiously.

Her eyelids fluttered and opened. "I've never fainted before. I disgraced myself, didn't I?" she ventured in a small voice.

Jason stroked her cheek gently. "Not you, I, and I offer my

apologies." He grinned wryly. "I know you didn't plan it, but you couldn't have thwarted my mother's reception more neatly, and I find that both admirable and amusing. I have no doubt that she was waiting in full battle dress with Jamie, not to welcome, but to condemn." He saw the shadows moving in her eyes, and his voice was suddenly harsh. "Remember, you owe nothing to anyone but me."

"All right, Jason, understood," she agreed softly. Her eyes closed again as the warmth began to reach her, her weary body relaxing, no longer fighting the ghost of the ship's motion, letting it carry her into sleep, only dimly aware that Jason had stripped away her clothing before he covered her again.

He stood looking down at her for a moment before he went downstairs. He limped into the parlor, smiling sardonically as he greeted his mother and his son. It was just as he had suspected —his mother dressed in severely formal black, his son in a velvet suit, the empress and her page boy.

"Well, where is the woman?" Ellen Drake demanded, a world of contempt in the final word.

"Your little reception will have to be postponed until tomorrow," Jason replied calmly. "Mary is sound asleep." He enjoyed the flash of rage on his mother's face, and he had no guilt at all for the insult Mary's absence offered the mistress of the house.

"How have you been, Jamie?"

"Fine."

"What have you been doing?"

"Nothing."

"How is school?"

"All right."

The dull little voice and Jamie's refusal to meet his gaze directly reconfirmed Jason's hopeless feeling of alienation from his son, and he was infinitely relieved when Maggie came to tell him that she had a meal prepared for him. He was equally glad that Ellen and Jamie had already eaten. He left their cold presence, following Maggie to the warmth of the kitchen.

Ben was there too, and the three settled at the kitchen table to partake of the ample cold supper. Ellen abhorred Jason's habit of "eating with the servants," particularly because he made no secret of the fact that he preferred their company to hers.

He assured them that Mary was all right, just exhausted. Maggie signed quickly, definitely, saying, "She's different, special. I am going to like her."

"She's different all right," Jason agreed wryly, and he moved on to the subject of island activities, asking about the people, livestock, and crops. "Cade wasn't there this afternoon. Has anyone seen him lately?" Jason asked.

Ben grinned and shrugged, sketching the possibilities with his hands and expressions. Cade could be out fishing, could be having trouble with one of his sheep, could be on a smuggling run. Who knew with Cade. But he was undoubtedly all right and would appear soon.

There was a sudden explosion of sound and the twins burst in, grubby from head to toe, and beaming at the sight of Jason.

"Uncle Jason, we missed the boat comin' in!" Erin shrieked.

"We was clear the other side of the island," Eric offered.

"We were, not we was," Erin corrected.

"Doesn't matter, means the same thing, we wasn't and weren't here," Eric insisted.

Jason laughed as he hugged them. There was none of Daniel Bates's shyness, none of Jamie's aloofness, none of the other children's awe in these two. Brown-haired and blue-eyed, they met everything head-on as a united front and moved with squirrel speed from one thing to the next. They had decided long since to call Jason "Uncle," and since he had no objection, their parents stopped trying to dissuade them. Dissuading Eric and Erin from any course they'd chosen was like trying to turn the tide of the sea. The twins were spoiled; there was no doubt about it. Even Maggie, who as their mother might have been expected to deny it, agreed, fully aware that she and Ben had been overly thankful for the gift of children able to hear from the first moment they had seen the miracle of reaction to sound in the twins. Somehow, Maggie thought, love would bring it all to rights, but she was wise enough to be thankful in addition that the twins had no essential meanness in their natures.

Jason simply enjoyed them, drawing from them the young warmth and liveliness he could not find in his own son. But now as he listened to their excited account of all they had seen until the day fell into dark, all that had kept them from being there to greet the *Gaiety,* he felt the pull of a different warmth.

He heard the children out with patience, but then rather hurriedly, he bade them good night. Maggie made no effort to hide her smile as she asked if he wished a tray to take to Mary.

Jason smiled back but shook his head, "No, she'll sleep the night through I think. If not, I'll come down and raid your pantry."

He knew his mother expected him to join her after his meal, knew she had sent Jamie off to bed so that she could discuss her objections without restraint. It never made any difference, but she never stopped. Something always displeased her. The tension eased as he went up the stairs, disappeared altogether as he opened the door cautiously and heard Mary's soft, even breathing.

He undressed, added more wood to the embers of the fire, extinguished the lamps, and slipped into bed beside her. She sighed a little but did not awaken, nor did she move away when he curled his body along the length of hers.

CHAPTER
8

Mary heard the clink of china and smelled the delicious aroma of coffee. She opened one eye as Jason commanded, "Wake up, sleepyhead, the sun's way ahead of you."

She finally managed to open both eyes, and she stretched widely, until she realized she hadn't a stitch on and Jason was watching her with enjoyment. She pulled the sheet up to her chin. "If you were any sort of gentleman, you'd hand me a robe."

He chuckled. "If I were any sort of gentleman, you wouldn't be here." But obligingly, he handed her his own dressing gown. "Hurry up now, Maggie's cooked you a huge breakfast, don't want it spoiled by maidenly modesty."

Mary wrapped herself in the voluminous robe and slipped behind the screen which shielded a washstand and other necessities. Suddenly she blushed, realizing how accustomed she had grown to living in such close proximity to Jason. But hunger was stronger than thought, and she hurried through her morning's ablutions.

The ham, eggs, and bread were still warm and she sighed with the contentment of having appeased the first pangs. "Lord, this tastes good! Yesterday I thought I'd never be hungry again, and here I am, gorging myself and hoping you've already eaten so I won't have to share."

"I have, hours ago." He welcomed her smile, welcomed everything about the sight of her this morning. Her face was rosy, shining from the scrubbing she'd given it, her gray eyes were wide and clear, and her gilt curls were in charming disarray. His robe, much too big for her, emphasized her slenderness. The doubts he had about bringing her here, about being involved with her at all, retreated.

"This is kind of you," she ventured shyly. "Everyone must think I'm badly spoiled, but I'm thankful for the added breathing space."

"It doesn't matter what anyone else thinks," he reminded her firmly. He had expected questions, but not the first one she asked.

"Why Gabriel? It's a most unfitting name."

"It was a hopeful choice, but he has more than a little of the Devil in him."

"I think it's foolish to have a horse like that when . . ."

"When what?" Jason snapped. His eyes were suddenly cold and watchful.

She realized her mistake too late. The unspoken concern for the added danger from his lameness, indeed the original cause of it, hung in the air between them. "When it surely isn't that difficult to find a well-mannered mount," she said innocently.

His tension eased. "Gabriel isn't so bad. Horses must surely be stupid to let us ride them in the first place, but he's a cut above that since he always lodges at least a token protest. We'll find a gentler mount for you." He saw her dismay. "I promise, you won't be rushed into anything, and you can explore the island all you want on foot, but you really must learn to ride. It's just not practical to be without the skill in the West. You might even find you like it."

"That'll be the day," she said with more spirit than she felt. She had resolved to learn to ride, but she hadn't faced doing it so soon. She quickly changed the subject. "Constance. Tell me about her."

He studied her face for a moment before answering. "Yes, she was my mistress a long time ago. She had lost her husband; I had lost my wife. We made each other a little less lonely for a while. We were friends, nothing more, before her husband died. He worked for me on the *Gaiety* before he shipped out with a higher position on another ship. And Constance and I are good friends now, but that's all. And no, I don't retire my mistresses here."

"It's a good thing you don't; the island would be vastly over-crowded." She made a face at him, and he was so enchanted as before by the brief flare of bold mischief, that he nearly missed her next words.

"I guess I did want to know that, but it isn't really what I was asking about. There's something odd about her. When I met her, her eyes were so strange for an instant, almost blind, yet seeing everything. Oh, I'm not explaining very well. Maybe I just imagined it."

"No, you didn't," Jason replied slowly. "She has the Sight, or whatever you want to call it. And I can't think of a more hellish talent, at least in her case. She never sees the whole image, just bits and flashes, almost always of tragic things. She knew when her husband sailed out on his last trip that it would be the last, but she didn't know until it was too late to stop him, and she knew something was wrong with the child in her womb, but she didn't know until the child was moving within her."

"My God, the poor woman! It's a wonder she hasn't gone completely mad!" Mary's compassion was genuine, but so was her fear—what had Constance seen of her own life? Mary blanked out the images that might have been from her own mind; there was nothing to do until she had a chance to talk to her.

"I can't hide up here forever. I ought to meet your mother and your son."

"You're spared Jamie's presence for a few hours; he's with the other children and Hayes for lessons. We're not raising a totally illiterate brood here. You can face my mother as soon as you're dressed."

Her belongings had been brought into the room, and she marveled anew at how deeply she had slept, hearing nothing, not even the noise Jason must have made when he had arisen, but more of her mind was occupied with thoughts about Jason's attitude toward his family. She searched for a subtle approach and found herself saying instead, "You don't like them much, do you?"

"No, I can't say that I do," he responded coolly. "My mother is not a likeable woman, and Jamie is a sickly, spoiled child. I surely share the blame for the latter, but it doesn't make me like him any better. You'll discover that Jamie gets his way by nearly choking to death when his will is crossed, while my mother gets hers in scarcely less obvious ways."

Mary was so stunned by the icy account, she had half of the buttons on the bodice of her dress done up wrong before she noticed. The island was beginning to seem like a large insane asylum, and she repressed a shiver. Then she remembered what her options were, and her heart steadied. Ready to go, she straightened her spine and followed Jason downstairs.

There was no doubt that Ellen Drake was Jason's mother; the same bone structure, only slightly less prominent, gave shape to her face, and the eyes were the same shape as his, but hers were so golden they had the constant opaque watchfulness of a cat's eyes. The Tiger's mother indeed. She was taller than most women of her generation though not as tall as Mary, and she was lean, her body as stiffly held as if her bones were locked against gravity's pull. Her skin was pale. She was dressed in black, and Mary wondered if that was to mourn her son's moral downfall or her husband's long-ago death or if it was just to set off the tawny hair which was only slightly faded by age. She had no wonder about how they would get along together; she knew they were going to be implacable enemies.

"Ellen Drake, Mary Smith." Jason added no flourishes to the introduction.

"I can't say this is a pleasure," Ellen said, eyes gleaming with yellow malice. "However, as this is my son's property, I have little to say in the matter."

Mary could feel Jason tensing, but she forestalled his temper. "As you say, and as you meant, so I am. What you think of me or what I think of you has very little to do with anything. And if you think I am going to spend my energy and time fighting with an old woman," she saw the description hit its mark and was pleased, "you're very much mistaken. I think we will deal well together by dealing together as little as possible. Good day, Mrs. Drake."

Jason barely refrained from echoing his mother's gasp as Mary turned to him, smiling sweetly and reminding him that she had much to see. Not until they were outside did he find his voice. "That's the damnedest performance I ever saw in my life! It's the first time I've seen her beaten at her own game."

"Unfortunate as it may be, there are a lot of people in the world like your mother. I've met quite a few of them, too many to be dismayed by one more." She remembered them too well, all of those people who were arrogantly self-satisfied and bone-deep cruel because they never saw anyone else's point of view or sorrow or joy. She knew there was an added reason for her instant dislike of Ellen Drake and for the courage to face her—this was the woman who had cared so little for her child that she hadn't known he was badly hurt and in need of treatment, treatment that, had it been good and in time, might have saved him from being lame for the rest of his life.

Jason hadn't any idea Mary's thoughts were traveling on this line because he himself did not judge his mother so harshly. He had paid for his disobedience. It had all happened years ago. The present held far more intrigue for him. He wondered if he would ever be able to predict what Mary's reactions would be. Just when he thought she would be relaxed and happy, the shutter came down and the chill of fear; yet, when he thought she would surely be intimidated or frightened, she stood up and fought like a tiger. The unbidden image, his own image, jolted him, and he thrust it away.

The day was mild, edged with warm sunlight, perfect for exploring the land. Jason was glad of it, wanting Mary to like her first introduction to the island. Ben was working near the barn, and already had the team hitched to the wagon. "I thought you'd see more from the wagon than from the back of Gabriel," Jason told her with a grin. She smiled back, then broke away when she spied Maggie hanging out the laundry.

"Thank you so much for the breakfast," she said. "Food has never tasted so good!" She had already noticed the difference

—Maggie was quite good at reading the shape of spoken words
while Ben did not seem to read them at all. But just to make sure,
she mimed eating.

Maggie smiled shyly, and her hands pictured the wagon moving as she wished Mary a fine day.

Jason helped her up onto the high seat, and they followed the
road that led through the center of the island rather than the
branch that went to the harbor's edge. The land changed by the
minute, here a pasture, there an orchard, there a stand of thick
timber, all with the feeling of the sea close by and sometimes in
sight through a break in the trees, seabirds crying in the calm
air. It was a time of wonder for her. The island was indeed a
small, complete world. Chicken, ducks, and fat cows and pigs
added their own sounds. A mare with a colt that was the image
of Gabriel whinnied shrilly to her energetic child while two other
mares heavy with unborn foals grazed placidly.

"No wonder Gabriel prefers not to be ridden," Mary remarked slyly.

"Yes, he'd rather do the riding," Jason retorted, "and you
can't say that's stupid."

Mary colored under his teasing gaze.

To the east the forest which swept down the slope from
Jason's house ended abruptly in cleared land, and Jason pointed
out a neat structure in the distance, Maggie and Ben Carter's
house. The whitewashed houses she had seen near the harbor
were where Lars and Ingrid Olsen and Mogens and Else Nilsen
lived and where Captain Hanson and David Becam, the other
crew member, had their own small structures. In addition, in the
same area were extra cabins for visiting crewmen and traders.

Further on along the main road, Jason turned the wagon
down a track to the left, and a fringe of trees gave way to more
cleared land and a little house surrounded by neat rows of tilled
earth and fruit trees beginning to bud. Constance Bates was
working the earth, and she waved at their approach. A striped
ginger cat chased playfully at her skirts as she walked to the
wagon.

"Your first real look at the island, Mary. How are you enjoying
the tour?" she asked, looking up. Her smile was warm and

friendly, her eyes clear and focused with none of the strangeness
of the day before.

"I'm overwhelmed! I've never been in a place that feels so
. . . so alive!" It was true. No city had ever given her this sense
of life humming an intricate busy tune all around her, and she
had never before been so close to the country. The summer
retreats of her childhood had not been the same—mannered,
pompous, they had lacked the touch she was feeling now.

Jason and Constance were both beaming with obvious pride
and pleasure as if a beloved child had just been praised, and
Mary was glad she had said the right thing. Jason helped her
down from the wagon, and they followed Constance into the
house.

Everything was shining and warm with color and care and
smelled of beeswax and lavender. Braided rugs lay in rainbow
pools on the wooden floors, and closely woven baskets of various sizes held arrangements of dried foliage.

"It's so peaceful here!" Mary exclaimed.

"Not always," Constance protested with good humor. "I'll
show you Daniel's special room. Jason and the other men built
it for him. He adds just the right amount of confusion to the
day."

The room was an obvious addition, built onto the back of the
house with access through a door from the kitchen. It even had
its own fireplace, and Mary could see why the heat would be
needed during chilly weather. Everywhere there were cages,
boxes, and jars, most with some creature or other inside—a baby
rabbit, a nest of mice, birds, and things not so appealing. Mary's
eyes widened as she took in the extent of the menagerie. There
was nothing depressing about the room; sunlight poured in
through the windows, and the animals were obviously well cared
for and clean, the strongest odor being the sweet bite of the
shavings used for bedding. There were scratchings and little
sounds in acknowledgment of the visitors, but no blind panic,
though Mary gave a start at a sudden loud croak from one
windowsill. A large black bird perched there, staring at them
with bright bead eyes.

Constance explained, "That's Raven. Daniel found him

when he was a helpless fledgling. Daniel wants all of his animals to go free when they're able. Raven is perfectly capable of looking after himself now, and he does, but he visits regularly. Luckily, he doesn't come in, just stops at the sill, though he often follows Daniel around outside. We're not altogether sure he could be trusted with some of the patients here. Tiger surely can't be trusted," she added. There was a sudden chorus of squeaks and squeals of outrage, and the ginger cat who had been sneaking through the half-open door slunk back into the kitchen again. "But as you see, the general alarm keeps him in his place."

They followed the cat back into the kitchen, and Mary said, "What a special little boy you have! And what a marvelous man he will be to have learned so much so early about caring for creatures weaker than he. It must surely bring a better result than comes from the unthinking cruelty children seem to enjoy inflicting too often." She meant the words, but she found she was foolishly thinking about the cat at the same time, watching him roll over on the floor, batting at his own tail. "Tiger"—a fitting name after all, but had Jason given it to her? Was there some special shared joke between them? And if there was, so what? She was shocked by her jealous reaction. She didn't own Jason, it was quite the other way around.

The sudden change in Constance banished the thought from her mind. Constance's eyes were huge and sad. "Yes," she said very softly, "he would have been a marvelous man." Then the smile was back in place, and her voice was normal as she asked them if they had time for coffee.

"No, thank you," Jason answered. "It's time we were going. We're not even halfway, you know, and I want Mary to have a good idea of the island before the day is over."

Jason gave no sign that he had heard what Constance said, but Mary suspected that he had, that it was another bond of secret knowing between them. It was one she did not want to share. Her brief glimpse of Daniel and now this look at his life was already making him precious; the sad foreboding in his mother's words was a terror she didn't wish to contemplate.

They said their good-byes, and Mary tried to make bright comments as they headed back for the main track, but suddenly

Jason reached out and touched her clenched hands. "Whatever she sees, it is a private and unfinished vision, but it's already a known pain in her life. If she can live with it, then so can we. Daniel is her son, and no one could guard him better than she does. If it is possible under heaven for him to live to be a man, she will see that he does."

Constance would guard Daniel as Ellen Drake had not guarded Jason. Mary held his hand in both of hers for an instant, gently trying to reassure the man and the boy.

It was Jason who pulled away, ostensibly because the horses needed both of his hands on the reins, but his voice was husky as he began once again to point out landmarks. He wondered how such a small involuntary gesture of tenderness on her part could have the power to touch him so deeply.

He gestured to a trail meandering off through dense trees. "If you followed that you'd find Nate and Jon's cabin, but if we dropped in on them now, they'd both die of embarrassment. Once they're used to you, it won't be so hard for them. I think they're even more shy than Daniel."

"I noticed that when I met them yesterday. They're like Bull Fletcher. Such big men, yet I think if I'd said, 'Boo!' they would have fallen over. How did they come here?"

"By about the longest way around. They started out as farmers in Illinois. They lived in a tiny community and married sisters who had grown up on a neighboring farm. They were young, they had their own sections of land, and they started their families. Scarlet fever finished it all for them. The young women and the children died. Nate and Jon left and never went back there again, not even when they were entitled to some of the old folks' holdings. They wandered across the country trying a lot of different things: trapping, trading, even had a store somewhere once, gold mining, and logging. I met them when they were hired on in my timber. They just didn't have the knack for it. Good, solid, slow-moving workers, but not the stuff of loggers. A tree to them is something to clear out of a field. They're farmers right down to the bone. Once I knew that, it was easy. I offered them a place here. They came, looked it over, and accepted. Every adult on the island came for some special reason that made him willing to live this way," he added as if closing the subject, and she was sure he was thinking of how Gaiety's death had driven him to seek refuge here.

The road did not run straight the length of the island but curved gently here and there with the land. Mary heard the children singing before the wagon rounded a bend sheltered by trees and the little building which served as the schoolhouse was in sight.

There were waves and shrieks from the window, but Jason shouted, "Keep to your lessons. We haven't time to stop. We'll see you after school," and drove on, pointing out Hayes Burke's house which was beyond and set further back in thick natural brush. It was the only one Mary had seen so far which showed no sign of planting or any kind of agriculture around it, but it didn't surprise her. The idea of Hayes grubbing happily in the dark soil was preposterous.

"I hope you didn't mind not stopping, but school would have been over for the day if we had," Jason explained. "Hayes teaches the children well, but time is often limited because they help with almost everything on the island. At least most of them do," he amended under his breath, and Mary knew he was thinking about his son. She realized she was already torn between pity and dislike of Jamie, before she'd even met him, and she hoped she would be able to ignore both feelings when the meeting finally happened. Now she was glad they hadn't stopped. If Jamie was going to react badly to her, she would just as soon it didn't happen with an appreciative audience of other children.

The foliage was suddenly wilder, more dense around the road, and she drew breath at the beauty of the ferns and tiny first spring flowers beginning bravely in the shadowed light. Jason pulled the team to a halt.

"That little path leads to the pond. It's a pretty spot. Would you like to see it?"

"Oh, yes I would!" she scrambled down from her perch before Jason had time to help her, but then she had to wait while he hitched the horses to a fallen tree. "They're dependable," he insisted with a grin, "but it doesn't do to test their longing for Ben and the barn too hard."

The path wound upward and was slippery with fallen needles

and other vegetation. Mary curbed her impatience to get to the top when she saw how difficult the climb was for Jason.

He felt the joy leave her and knew the reason. "Don't fret," he chided. "I've done this a hundred times, and I enjoy the goal. If you look like that every time you watch me hobbling along, I won't take you any place higher than an anthill."

She nodded and managed to smile before she turned quickly back toward the top, not wanting him to see the sudden tears. He reached her, touched her deeply in the oddest ways, at the oddest times, and she was sure she didn't like it. There was a bargain between them, nothing more. She wiped her eyes angrily and tripped, tried to right herself, slipped backwards, and landed in a heap at Jason's feet.

He reached down immediately to help her up, asking anxiously if she were hurt. She couldn't answer to save her life. The laughter welled up in such an overwhelming wave, she could hardly breathe.

The sound filled the silent space of forest around them, and Jason was frozen for an instant at the strangeness of it. Then, he was laughing with her. He had not heard her laugh before, not this full voicing of joy and amusement. He could not remember hearing so beautiful a sound before. He brushed bits of foliage from her skirt and drew her close against him, still feeling the common tide rippling through them.

"Pride goeth before a fall," she choked and was off again, sagging against him.

"I may go slowly, but I go surely," Jason managed. There were tears of laughter in his own eyes, and he tasted Mary's as he bent to kiss her trembling mouth. Her lips were warm and yielding, but he was wise enough not to spoil the mood by demanding more than the instant of sharing. He drew back with an effort and forced his voice to be easy. "Come on, or we'll never get to the top."

Mary went ahead again obediently, but she felt tightly wound, unfinished. Even her skin prickled, uneasy energy passing under the surface. Just like a damn cat waiting for one more touch to start deep purring, she thought. Treacherous touch, treacherous body. Small cats had no business playing with tigers. Jason, how well he knew how to play with his prey, too much, too little, never predictable. Damn him!

She was so engrossed in her churning thoughts, she blinked in the sudden light at the top of the trail, and it took her an instant to focus.

Her tension eased. It was a lovely, shining place. The surface of the pond lay mirror smooth in a circle of tall trees. The damp scent of the grasses along the water's edge blended with the perfume of evergreens. A pair of ducks glided away from the shore at the humans' approach but did not take flight.

Jason reached Mary's side and whispered, "Look across the pond. We see them all the time at sunrise and sunset, but it's lucky to see one now."

For a moment she saw nothing, and then she gasped in delight. A doe stood not far from the water's edge, the dappled light from the sheltering trees making her fade in and out of the landscape until, with sudden startled movement, the doe bounded out of sight.

Birdsong and the rasp and tinny whistle of insect life filled the air around them.

"It's a wondrous place," Mary breathed, as softly as if the doe were standing there still.

"We're fortunate. Many of the islands have very limited fresh water or none to speak of at all. And it rains less here than in Seattle; the weather can be quite different in the two places. We have this pond fed by underground springs, and we have wells which haven't failed us yet. Of course the rain we do get has much to do with all this greenery and with our water supply, but even during a bad dry spell last summer, we didn't lack. And you mustn't mind the color—a few minerals, a little this and that, but it hasn't hurt anyone."

She had noticed the rusty tinge, but she'd long since learned not to be fussy about such things. "I expect people here just rust away. I'll start worrying when I creak."

"So will I," Jason agreed with a laugh. "In the meantime, enjoy the quiet here while you can. The water's still very cold now, but the summer days will be warm enough so that the children will invade the pond. The sea stays pretty chilly all year round this far north."

They stood in companionable silence for a moment more, viewing the peaceful scene before they made their careful way back to the wagon. At the bottom of the path, Mary froze.

"Should I be afraid?" she asked in a small voice. He followed her pointing finger and saw the slender line slipping across the ground in front of her.

"Not at all. There aren't any poisonous snakes on the island. The warmth has brought this fellow out."

She exhaled on a long sigh. "That's a relief, and now that I know, I can almost admire him. A bright green stripe on black, a little gaudy but effective."

She watched the snake with interest until it had disappeared, and Jason was once more amazed by the unexpectedness of her reaction. "Some have blue markings on black, some gold on brown, and there're other combinations, most of them gaudy, just as you say. I've never seen any quite like them except on the islands, comes from isolation and inbreeding I expect, though I don't really know."

Mary shuddered, the motion so violent, Jason was startled. He studied her suddenly white face in concern, but before he could speak she scrambled to the wagon, leaving him to follow at a slower pace.

Her quicksilver moods were enough to weary any man, and he was suddenly tempted to end the day's excursion and turn back. But then he reminded himself of how strange everything familiar to him was to Mary. He might as well have put her on his ship and sailed her to the moon as to the island. And how strange Mary still was to him. He possessed her body and that was all. The fierce will to know all about her swept over him again. Only then would the possession be complete. And he wanted it complete—to finish or begin, he didn't know.

The northern end of the island was a different world, wilder, more desolate than any of the other sections Mary had seen. There were fewer trees here and fewer signs of man's hands on the earth. Tough clumps of grass grew in rocky meadows, and the sea sound was loud, incessantly rattling pebbles on the shingle below.

"We call this Cade's Cove," Jason explained, breaking the

long silence which had stretched between them. Mary studied the place with interest, glad that the friendly note was restored.

A weathered but tidy cabin stood on the crest of the hill unadorned by trees or plantings around it. A short distance away was a fold from which issued the steady complaints of sheep. Their smell was even stronger than their voices, and Mary wrinkled her nose.

"It's a good thing Cade likes his privacy so well," Jason commented with a laugh. "It takes a while to get used to that particular perfume. Cade pens them when he's gone because there's nothing more stupid than sheep, and they're apt to fall off one of the sea cliffs if they aren't watched."

Mary hardly heard him as she stared with growing interest at the structures on the beach below the hill. The slope swept down gently here, and there was a good-sized spit of land between the bottom of the hill and the high-tide mark. It was littered with a welter of nets, racks, piles of driftwood, and a weathered hut. Rising above all of it was a great carved pole. Mary had at first glance taken it to be an odd, bare tree, and she stared in wonder at the barbaric splendor it really was. Beaks, claws, and gaping faces piled one on top of each other as if great mythical beasts were poised and ready to launch themselves on their enemies, and yet at the same time, the carving had an enduring, timeless stillness.

"I've never asked Cade how he got this, and he's never offered to tell me, but it's as fine a totem as I've seen. We helped him put it up; Cade said it was beneath its dignity to lie on the ground. There are still fierce Indians far to the north, and this is one of theirs. To them, it reads as clearly as the printed word does to us."

"Can you read it?"

"Somewhat, but not as well as Cade can. It's his prize; I'll let him tell you about it someday." The conclusion was closer to the truth than the first statement. Jason knew every bit as much as Cade about totem lore.

"Is it because of this that you call him the wood-carver?" Mary asked curiously.

"No, it's his own work that gives him the name. That too you'll see when you meet him. There are many pieces he's done in his house, but I wouldn't trespass to show you. Cade is a man of many parts. He's a good fisherman." Jason pointed to the beach. "He dries and smokes his catch down there on the racks and in the hut, and sells what we don't use. And he's a good shepherd; wool for spinning and good lamb for the table is never in short supply. He's even adept at one of the oldest professions in the islands, though I don't question him too closely about it."

"What are you talking about?" Mary caught the mischief in his eyes too late and winced at the prim outrage in her voice, but his answer wasn't much better than her suspicion.

"Smuggling, my dear. Dealing in anything which might be more profitable without the tariffs—liquor, wool, fishing nets. We're very close to British territory, and the United States has busy revenue cutters in these waters too. Any place one country borders on another is a good place for smuggling."

"And you condone it!"

"I don't care one way or another as long as excise men aren't killed in the process. Cade's too careful to need to kill them or get himself killed." His eyes were suddenly hard and watchful. "There isn't much law on these islands. How can there be when it's not even settled who owns them." He pointed to the large island lying to the west. "That's San Juan Island, and what authority there is resides there in both the American and English camps. They have enough trouble keeping their own populace sober without worrying about a few peaceful settlers here. We mind our own."

Including smugglers, she thought. She gazed out over the island-dotted water and wondered where the multi-talented Cade was at this moment. She had listened to Jason's account of the Pig War with a good deal of amusement, but now the enormity of what it meant became as real as the earth under her feet.

"What will you do if when the question is settled, you are told to leave Drake's Island?"

The eyes gleamed golden though his voice was low and reasonable. "As I told you, when it is settled, one way or another the United States will be in possession of these islands. But whatever way it ends, and whenever it does, this is mine, and no one is going to take it from me."

CHAPTER
9

*A*n unearthly shriek shattered the air, and Mary turned to see a great eagle, white head gleaming in the sun as his talons stabbed into the soft body of a rabbit. Clenching his prey, he lifted off the ground, sailing away with it.

For an instant she was speechless, and then she said, "Well, Jason, something just took one of yours."

Jason eyed her coolly, knowing full well what the sharp little words meant. "Yes, and I wish he'd take more. The eagles nest here, but they follow the salmon runs inland, so they aren't here all the time. The rabbits are a dreadful mistake. They started with some Else had. The hutches weren't sturdy enough, and now we have a plague of the animals. They have few natural enemies except for the predator birds and us. We hunt them, the birds hunt them, occasionally a mink grabs one, and still there're too many. They destroy crops, just as the deer do."

"And Daniel saves them," she observed softly.

"Yes, and Daniel also eats them when his mother cooks them. It's a separate thing when one is a child. What one saves and what one kills are different. Perhaps it doesn't even change with the years. I can admire the beauty of the doe at the pond even while I know the deer must be hunted periodically to keep their numbers down."

He watched her digesting this perfectly reasonable explanation, then changed the subject entirely. "It's time to go. Jamie will be getting out of school soon. We'll give him a ride back to the house."

He had timed this all very well, Mary knew. And the ordeal of meeting the boy in front of the other children was surely going to happen after all. The pleasure of the day dimmed. She was more apprehensive about meeting Jamie than about anything else here. It was wrong. The boy shouldn't have to be involved in his father's peccadillos.

They headed back the way they had come, and Mary heard herself asking nervous questions, talking about anything except Jamie. "So many creatures, I've just realized, so many for an island. How did they get here? The deer, for instance, and the snakes."

"Deer can swim long distances, as can mink, otters, muskrats, and raccoons, and the snakes, well, they can swim too, but it seems a long distance for them, and as for the shrews and moles, I don't know how they arrived. Daniel thinks they floated in on logs or a few were dropped by birds." Jason smiled at the memory of Daniel's earnest attempt to account for every creature he had ever seen on the island. "Mice and rats go everywhere people go, traveling on ships, in belongings, any way, following the trail of easy pickings. There're legends of wolves, bear, and beaver being here too, but if it was true they must have been hunted out long ago by Indians and white trappers. And as for all the wild foliage, the wind, the birds, even the tides bring seeds. I expect someday dandelions will arrive here from Mrs. Maynard's garden in Seattle," he finished lightly, but she had heard the reverence in his voice as if he were seeing life coming to the island step by step, as if he had made a deep and abiding covenant with this piece of earth surrounded by the sea.

The moment was gone in the sound of children's voices ahead, their shrieks and laughter full of the freedom of release from school for another day.

Even had she not already seen the others, she would not have mistaken Jamie. The twins and the older of the blond children of Lars and Mogens were running around, even Daniel was part of the group though a quieter one. Jamie stood apart, scuffing the dirt with one foot and then the other, his head turned away from the other children. Mary felt a shock once she could see his face. He was slight, and yet at the same time, his flesh had a pallid softness as if it would give like warm wax at the touch. He looked unhealthy, his paleness different from Daniel's. But there was no doubt he was Jason's son.

The bones were there under the slack flesh and vague outlines of childhood. Jason's face was there and surely Gaiety's, slanting the bones more delicately. His son's eyes were as tawny as Jason's, and Jamie's hair grew in the same thick, springy way though it was lighter, no doubt a legacy from his blond mother. If he ever lost the look of sullen discontent so plain on his face now, he might well be a handsome boy, would surely be a man to be reckoned with when the time came.

The differences between him and the other children were all too evident. His clothes were much too good and fussy for his life—the others were barefoot, and their garments were obviously made with an eye to long wear and great activity. Little puffs of dust continued to rise from Jamie's monotonously scuffing shoes.

Mary realized that he was aware of them, had been since they had first come into sight. His eyes slid to them and back to the ground again and again. She realized too, that he was as fearful of confronting her in front of the other children as she was of meeting him. She could see the little movements as he watched the children, could almost feel him praying they would go away, but they were fond of Jason and still curious about the new lady and so crowded around the wagon, asking Jason fanciful questions about his latest time off-island while they eyed Mary curiously. She smiled and asked them what they'd been studying in school.

"Countin'," Eric offered, and Erin chimed in, "We're the best there is in countin', 'rithmetic it is."

Mary could see traces of Ben in the twins, but they looked like Maggie most of all.

"I like reading best," Daniel offered softly, a blush staining his face, his head ducking shyly.

"I like it too," Mary whispered, and she winked at him. Daniel's color deepened even more, but he smiled with pleasure.

Jamie kept his distance all the while.

Hayes Burke appeared at the door and came out to greet them, grinning sardonically, "Nice to have visitors taller than a fence post. Is Cade back yet?"

Jason shook his head, and Hayes turned his attention to Mary. "At least you got to see his domain. It will be interesting for you to meet the man who rules it."

"I'm sure it will," Mary agreed cheerfully, ignoring the slight edge, the subtle challenge to Jason's power, in the words even though she was sure they were deliberate. There was friction between these two men, she felt it now, but she judged that it came from Hayes's jealousy and that Jason had little interest in it. All the while she kept track of Jamie.

Hayes was well aware of what was going on with the boy. Before Jason could say anything, he turned to Jamie and said in his schoolmaster's tone, "James, your father has come to give you a ride home. I would like to introduce you to his friend, Mary Smith."

Jason didn't look in the least perturbed by this usurping of his power, and Jamie had no choice. The schoolmaster's voice was obviously one he responded to with obedience.

He walked to the wagon with his head down.

"Hello, Jamie," Mary offered softly.

He mumbled something, and then his head tilted up, his eyes meeting hers for an instant. She barely prevented herself from recoiling. She would not have believed such malevolence could gleam in the eyes of a child had she not seen it, and she was sure she had Ellen Drake to thank for most of it.

It was a wretched trip back to the house. Jamie refused to respond in more than monosyllables despite Jason's efforts to draw him out. It was painfully obvious that the relationship between father and son was neither close nor kind. Jamie sat between Jason and Mary on the wagon seat and held himself stiffly away from both of them on the bumpy ride.

When they reached the house, Jamie asked, "May I go now, or do I have to stay with you?"

"You may go, but stay away from the cliffs." Jason's voice held defeat where Mary had expected anger, but she also heard the ragged edge beginning in Jamie's breathing. "Charming child, isn't he," Jason said.

"Charming tyrant," Mary corrected grimly. "But Jason, he must care something about you or he wouldn't resent me so much."

"Jamie cares for himself, and that's an end to it." His voice forbade further discussion of his son, and Mary reminded herself that the man, not the child, was her reason for being here. She could feel the tension in him and agreed readily when he asked permission to leave her for a while.

She had the right to be anywhere on the island with or without Jason; he had given her that right, and she wasn't going to let anyone intimidate her. She marched into the house with her head high, but she was glad the door to the parlor was shut and Mrs. Drake nowhere in sight. From the bedroom window, she watched Jason race away on Gabriel. He was right. She was going to have to learn to ride though she doubted she'd ever be able to keep up with him. She tried to think of other details of her changing life, but what filled her mind was a well of tenderness and pity for the man. Pity for the Tiger? But she could not dismiss it. He was so essentially alone. She understood that only too well. Pity for him was pity for herself then, a bond.

She went downstairs again, not wanting to be her own company, and was relieved to find Maggie in the kitchen. There was something wonderfully comforting about the woman despite her lack of words. Mary accepted a cup of tea and fresh scones and honey gratefully and found herself trying to describe what she'd seen on the wagon trip. She used her hands and face in broad pantomime even as she spoke, but she faltered when she came to the meeting with Jamie.

Maggie nodded in sympathy and then grimaced as her hands moved in a pattern Mary didn't understand at first. Patiently the expression and the signs were repeated, and suddenly it was clear. The upright grasping figure was Ellen Drake whom Maggie plainly disliked, and Ellen had too much to do with Jamie. She made him do this and that for her. It wasn't good. Jason and the boy should be closer.

Mary could hardly credit that no words had been spoken aloud. She was hypnotized by the stark eloquence of the gestures. Maggie pitied Jamie and she loved Jason.

There was paper and pencil there, but they had not had to resort to it. "Could you teach me to say things exactly?" Mary asked, pointing from Maggie to herself, moving her hands. She wanted to be friends with the Carters, wanted to be able to communicate easily with them so that they did not have to simplify and repeat everything for her.

She wondered for an instant if the request might be insulting. But Maggie smiled in pleasure and nodded vigorously. They smiled together over Mary's first attempts at the first letters of the alphabet and at simple signs.

"Who would ever have thought fingers could be so clumsy!" Mary said in disgust.

Maggie's laughter was slightly shrill, but the joy and humor in it were unmistakable. Mary doubted she would ever have the fluid grace of movement the woman had; even Ben had it; not just their hands, but their whole bodies spoke for them.

She was glad she felt instinctive trust of the woman, for Maggie was more observant than anyone she had ever met before. Despite vigorous brushing, she could still feel the salt spray in her hair, and she ran her fingers through it absently and wished she could take a full bath. It was as if she'd asked, for suddenly Maggie was in motion. It was just as much of a chore as Mary had feared it would be, but it was accomplished with a minimum of fuss, and though Mary was sure the normal procedure was to bathe in the kitchen where the sink boasted a hand pump and the water was heated on the stove, her bath was set up in the bedroom to give her added privacy in spite of the trips up the stairs that entailed. Maggie helped her wash her hair and then left her with extra buckets of hot water. She sank into the tub with a sigh and closed her eyes, letting the warmth relax every muscle.

Jason opened the door quietly and let himself into the room.

He gazed down at her with pleasure. Her skin was pink from the heat of the water, her hair was a mass of soft, wet curls. She looked as contented as a small child who has just eaten her fill of sweets.

"I'll have to remember how simple it is to please you. Care to have your back scrubbed?"

Her eyes flew open, and she gave a start that threw droplets of water out of the tub. "Why you!" she sputtered, but she was still too relaxed, and his crooked grin was too engaging. She made no further protest, but rather leaned forward to make it easier for him when he took the sponge and began to rub it in slow circles on her back.

"Hmmmm, that feels good," she admitted. She realized that little by little, her impulses to modesty had faded away. And it was only sensible that they had. It hardly made sense to grab for covering when she was Jason's mistress and he had already seen her in every state of undress. Step by step she knew she had resigned herself to it. And was enjoying it? It wasn't a question she wanted to consider. But she knew she didn't want the distance that had yawned between them on the last night at the logging camp.

She sat up abruptly, wrinkling her nose and looking up at him. "You stink of horse!"

He held up a towel and assumed a woebegone expression. "I was wondering when you'd notice and offer to change places. If you stay in there any longer, you'll wrinkle, and besides, the water will be too cold for me."

She stood up and stepped out delicately. Jason wrapped the towel around her and draped another over her wet hair before he began to pat her dry.

"It's not fair. People should be able to purr," she murmured. She rubbed at her hair, then dropped the towel from her slack fingers.

"You're doing a good job of it," he assured her softly as he dried her soft breasts and the satin of her belly.

He ceased his task abruptly, muttering that she could finish drying while he bathed. Not bothering to cover herself, she smiled impudently at his obvious problem. She helped him bail out part of the tub and add the last of the fresh water. "It isn't very hot, but it's better than the smell of Gabriel."

Jason stripped off his clothes, and more than a little bemused, he sank into the water with relief, hearing her giggle because his knees stuck up out of the tub. Though she had never refused him anything since the bargain was made, he knew something had changed. He didn't know why, and he wasn't going to ask.

She scrubbed his back and kneaded the tight cords of his neck. For the first time Jason seemed human and vulnerable. Far more than his lameness, his sad relationship with his son made him so. She couldn't see how she could change that, but she could ease him in other ways. For the first time, what she had to offer seemed to have some value. If only she could forget forever what had been before.

Her hands tensed, and Jason turned his head to look at her. Her eyes darkened and closed for a moment, the planes of her face were tight and hard. He could see her struggle to banish whatever ghosts there were. It was his own battle too because the outcome would touch him.

A shiver ran through her. Her head came up and her eyes opened. They were shining gray flecked with gold.

Jason swallowed hard and got out of the tub, splashing water in his clumsiness.

"Now I'll dry you," Mary whispered. She used the cloth with slow deliberateness, rubbing his flesh in sensuous patterns that burned like fire though her touch was gentle. He shuddered when she knelt before him and ran the towel down his legs and back again to the hard muscles of his thighs around to his buttocks, teasing, enticing. He groaned aloud in shock and pleasure when she leaned forward and took him in her mouth, kissing, nibbling at his flesh, licking off the last drops of water with exquisite care.

"Enough!" he roared suddenly, and she sat back on her heels, smiling up at him lazily, eyes slitted like a cat's. He reached down and pulled her to her feet and to the bed.

He pushed her down roughly and thrust into her, the pulsing ache in his groin making him uncaring of her readiness. But she was ready. Her body drew him in, the passage hot and wet, stroking with the same motions her mouth had mimed.

He couldn't move fast or hard enough, couldn't go deep enough, every nerve screamed for relief, fire erupted in his loins to burn every surface with voluptuous pain, flaring into blinding ecstasy as he surrendered to the convulsions of his body and the dance of Mary's mouth and still coaxing hands.

She gloried in it, gloried in the cries from his throat, in the deep thrusting that stretched and filled her completely and beyond, in the hot pulse of his seed spilling in the depths of her. She held him to her, fingers digging into the hard muscles of his flanks as she took the last of her own pleasure, another ripple of sensation—no great explosion because she had controlled and calculated this too closely, had never ceased to think of what she was doing, but small shocks of warmth ebbing and flowing until she was replete.

Jason rolled away and lay still, surfacing slowly from the mindless well of pleasure. The thought seeped into his brain. It was surely every man's fantasy, but he was no longer sure it was his. He felt as if he had been raped by the beautiful woman now breathing quietly beside him. It was such a peculiar thought, but he could not rid himself of it. There had been nothing of the little girl lost in this passage. The woman who had just taken him had done wonderful things with her hands, her mouth, her body. She had known her power, and she had used it. He felt as if their roles had been completely reversed. But his disquiet was more than that. She had changed forever his hazy imaginings of her past. Perhaps there had been more than one man, perhaps many more than one. If only one, it had not been a short episode of fallen innocence. She had just serviced him like the best of whores; perhaps she had enjoyed it too, surely she had controlled it all. Who had taught her how?

He nearly asked the question, instead he said, "You are just full of surprises, aren't you?"

At the sharp note in his voice, she eyed him warily. "It's what you bargained for, isn't it? Would you rather I bored you?"

"I doubt that will ever be a problem." The words were rueful, the anger gone, what she had given was accepted. He swung out of bed and began to dress. "Much as I would like to dally here, we are expected downstairs for supper, late though we may be."

"How charming to dine *en famille*," she said with mocking cheerfulness, but she took careful pains to arrange her still-damp hair after she had dressed.

It was, as she had known it would be, anything but cheerful. Maggie had gone home to her own family, and Ellen was presiding at the table, serving the dishes Maggie had prepared earlier.

Ellen and Jamie were already eating when Jason and Mary walked in.

"We finally decided not to wait any longer," Ellen said coldly. "Jamie is, after all, very young to wait for what might be a sophisticated hour in other places."

"I didn't ask you to wait," Jason said mildly, not rising to the bait, but Ellen's gaze was on Mary. Their eyes met, and Mary saw the flush on the woman's cheeks, the flash of anger in the yellow eyes, the sure knowledge of what had delayed them. She held herself a little straighter and allowed herself the smallest of smiles, fully aware it was as effective as spitting in the woman's face.

"Is that cropped hair the new style, or did you cut it for reasons of health?" Ellen asked.

Ellen was the only one who had been rude enough to ask, and Mary was tempted to give back a revolting description of an attack of lice, just as the woman was implying. Instead, she sighed daintily. "Yes, it was for my health. I had a dreadful attack of fever, and they cut my hair so it wouldn't sap my strength." A sillier remedy she couldn't imagine, but she knew it was done sometimes.

Jason's eyes were suddenly dancing. "Poor Mary, in a fever. They're very catching, you know." The reference to the earlier heat between them was barely veiled.

Jamie picked at his food, offering no words at all, but Mary caught the angry little glances he threw her way now and then, and she sighed inwardly. It was one thing to do battle with the old bitch, another to war with a child. But the two of them created a solid wall of unpleasantness designed to drive her away, and she had no intention of letting them succeed.

When the meal was finished, Mary offered politely to help with the cleaning up.

"I'm sure that's not what my son hired you for! Maggie can do them in the morning," Ellen snapped.

"Ah, but I'm a woman of many talents, and I'm sure Jason can spare me for a few minutes," Mary replied calmly.

Jason laughed aloud, he couldn't help it. His mother was losing at every turn, and she deserved it. "Tell you what, Mother. Since we delayed the meal, we'll do the dishes as penance."

It started then, as Mary and Jason moved to pick up the dishes, a low wheezing from Jamie, growing louder by the second until it was a horrible, rasping struggle for air. Mary stared in horror at the small heaving chest and at the wide, frightened look in the child's eyes.

"See what you've done!" Ellen said.

"No, Mother, see what you've done," Jason snarled. "Stay here, Mary." He picked his son up and carried him out of the room, Ellen trailing at his heels.

Mary sank down at the table and covered her face with her hands, but she couldn't block out the image of Jamie struggling to breathe. Jason came back for hot water and left again. She was still sitting there shivering when he returned.

He put his arms around her gently, but his voice was raw. "There's nothing you can do, and agonizing over it won't help. Mother knows how to take care of him. She ought to, she's the cause often enough."

"It's awful! Oh, Jason, he was so frightened, no matter what he did to bring on the attack! If you know your mother makes it worse, why don't you take Jamie away from her?"

"And put him where? On an island by himself? He gets these attacks if there's something he doesn't like at school; he gets them if he doesn't get his way; he gets them if it's too hot or too cold. Jamie's reaction to life is to try to choke his way out of it. God! He looks so much like Gaiety, but he hasn't an ounce of her spirit."

She could not accept the utter defeat in Jason's words or the pain his reference to his wife gave her. "Children grow out of the asthma. I know they do, or at least I've heard that. There must be a way to make Jamie happier, and that would surely make him healthier."

"Perhaps, but remember, you are here for me, not for Jamie or for anyone else on the island." He sounded aloof, yet she heard something else. She could not believe it was fear.

"I could scarcely forget that," she whispered.

CHAPTER
10

$\mathcal{M}$ary steeled herself against her fright and began her riding lessons. Jason insisted she ride astride, claiming that side-saddle was not only ridiculous but surely much more difficult. Mary didn't protest as she was quite certain that being wrapped around the horse would give her that much more security. She was in dire need of it.

Dolly was calm and docile, but she had obviously never had such an unbalanced rider on her back. Occasionally she would stop dead, turn her head to regard her rider and blow soft protesting snorts, adding insult to injury. And injury there was. No matter what she did, Mary found herself coming down when the horse was going up and vice versa the minute the pace was more than a slow walk.

Her attitude was not helped by the fact that Jason and Ben were trying unsuccessfully to control their mirth. Ben was much too polite and shy to be grinning so widely had he been able to help it. As it was, he tried to turn away when the sight became too much for him. Jason was worse. "No, Mary, feel what the horse is doing! Once you know the rhythm, you can move with it," he assured her gravely, and then his face creased and he whooped with laughter as she yelped, "Damn!" Her tender posterior had received another swat.

After what seemed a lifetime, she pulled the horse to a stop and scrambled down, landing in a heap because she hadn't quite gotten her feet clear.

"Don't ever get off unless you are clear of the stirrups and everything else!" Jason barked, completely serious now. "Getting hung up in the saddle is a good way to spook the horse and be dragged to death."

"At least it might be faster than being jolted to death inch by inch!" she snapped back, glaring at him as she picked herself up and brushed at her skirt. "That, gentlemen, is the end of today's show. I'm going off on my own two legs for a while."

"Want company?" Jason offered, laughter back in his eyes.

"No, thank you. I'm going in search of my dignity. I won't get lost unless someone connected this island to the mainland during the night."

She hobbled off, and Jason let her go, thinking it was just as well; maybe it would work off some of the stiffness.

Mary walked along, gaining the main track and heading north. Her muscles protested this added effort, but she ignored them and even grinned to herself as she began to picture herself as the men had seen her. Lord, she must have looked funny! Well, she'd show them. It would take a lot of practice, but she wasn't going to bounce helplessly forever.

The day was so beautiful, soft and clear, she hummed as she walked along. She drew deep breaths of the scent, a mixture of sea, damp earth, and sharp-resined foliage, a clean perfume she already associated with the island. She thought of walking to Constance's house and wondered if it would upset her routine to have a visitor again.

She was suddenly conscious of being idle for the first time in a long while. There were no bad plays to learn, no silly dances to do, no mending to finish, no lessons to give, not even the house in Seattle or the cabin at the logging camp to keep tidy. She had no duty beyond pleasing one man.

Her pace slowed as she thought about it. She realized she did

not approve, not at all, nor was there even guilty joy in the
prospect of so many free hours. It wasn't that she wanted to go
back to any of the jobs she had had before or to the constant fear
of being unable to pay for food or shelter; it was just that she
found this complete turnabout equally trying. Her tour of the
island had taught her much. The kingdom might be Jason's, but
the subjects all had their own way to make; they all had services
or products to sell which made them independent. Well, she was
selling something too, but she couldn't see it in the same terms
as vegetables, wool, butter, or fish. It was far too much like the
days she had run away from—then too she had been idle except
for . . .

She suddenly wanted more cover. She wandered off the road
into the thick shelter of the trees, taking a little trail that led to
a shadowed clearing. She sank down on the mossy bank of earth
amidst ferns. A bird voiced protest at the intrusion, but she
didn't hear it. Considering the circumstances, everyone except
Jamie and Ellen had at least been civil, even friendly, on meeting
her. And they had things they could teach her if they were
willing. To spin and weave, to care for livestock and growing
things, to fish, to prepare food with her own hands. The prospects began to seem endless, and she hugged herself in sudden
joy. So many things she had never learned because she had
never been close to the land. They seemed important now for
reasons she didn't fully understand, but one idea occurred to
her with startling clarity. To reach down to the earth and rise up
from it, to coax it to bloom and produce and feed, to have one's
own small acres somewhere—there was so much unclaimed land
on this northwestern edge of the country, it was not so insane
a dream. That land in the wilderness would demand its own
exacting payment she knew, but she also knew the high price of
the long-settled places. For the first time, she could see clearly
why Jason had chosen this place.

She lay back daydreaming on the soft turf. She could picture
the old woman of herself tucked away in some isolated hollow,
wearing raggedy clothes and a battered hat while she defended
her plot from chance travelers. The image made her smile, and
she made note to learn how to use a gun. She laughed aloud at

the idea of asking Jason to teach her and telling him why she wanted to know.

She sprang to her feet suddenly, realizing some part of her mind had been noticing a strange rustling in the underbrush. The sound was louder now, and she listened intently, wondering if it were a deer.

The rustling became crashing, and the beast burst out of the woods with a full-throated roar—big, black, hairy. It took her a moment of frozen terror to realize it was a dog and not something out of hell. Even then, she wasn't sure her first thought hadn't been correct as a horrible, twisted figure followed the dog out of cover.

She closed her eyes and then opened them again, unable to believe that she was truly seeing what her mind pictured. But they were still there. The great black beast, now standing still, staring at her, the hackles on his neck stiff, a low growl issuing from his throat, and the twisted human figure grinning at her malevolently. His hair was as thick and coarse as sea grass, an upstanding brush of black streaked with gray. His forehead was high and bulging, his brows juts of bone and thick hair over protuberant, heavy-lidded dark eyes. His nose was lumped either from birth or battle, and his mouth was thick-lipped, his chin and jawbones as heavy as his brows. His body was bent forward from the shoulders, his back humped. His arms looked long, his whole appearance simian. He looked very strong.

Mary was incapable of moving except for the wild pounding of her heart which was sending shocks along every artery. It was hard to breathe and no matter how often she blinked her eyes, the two figures remained, watching her in the mirror image of her own stillness. There was no way at all for her to escape them. She wanted Jason more than she had ever wanted anyone on earth. She nearly cried his name aloud.

The thought of him steadied her. Jason knew who was on the island. The Tiger allowed no one who was not of his choosing. And now she knew who this man was. She remembered Jason's matter-of-fact description of his deformity, given so that she would not recoil in shock when they were introduced. The hunchback, the wood-carver, Cade.

Fury replaced her fear. "You horrible little man!" she spat. "You did that on purpose! Maybe not coming out of the darkness, maybe that was an accident, maybe you didn't know I was here. But saying nothing, staring at me, you and your damn dog! What did you want me to do, scream in terror, run from you? You've asked for it, haven't you? Jason is very fond of you. I shall have to ask him why."

Cade was clearly taken aback. He stared at her in wonder. Then he grinned. It was not an attractive expression because his face would not allow that, but it held its own warmth and humor. "One makes do with what one has," he said. "I admit the game of troll under the bridge is a tempting one for me. You are Mary. Mary Smith, I believe it is." His eyes met hers in swift challenge.

"Mary Smith it is," she answered firmly.

"Well, well, the Tiger has landed himself a live one this time, high time too." He moved as if to fade into the brush again, and then turned back to her. "By the way, Captain's a lot more harmless than I am. Make his acquaintance, and he'll remember who you are."

For the first time since the awful minutes had begun, Mary smiled. Captain went to her at Cade's command and, with a funny little cry and a wet swipe of his tongue over her hand, proved himself to be more than amenable to friendship now that he had been told it was in order.

"Don't go," Mary pled as the man and the dog turned away. "It is important, you know. It's important to me because it's important to Jason. Could we start all over again. How do you do. I'm Mary Smith, and you must be Cade."

"Pleased to meet you, miss," he replied, executing a jerky little bow, but there was as much friendliness as mockery in his voice.

"You must have been on your way to see Jason. He's been asking about you. He was at the house when I left." She made a face. "I had my first riding lesson today. I failed miserably. The horse and I have widely different ideas about motion and gravity."

Cade laughed uproariously. The sound was so explosive and the sight of his bent body capering in delight so sudden, Mary was alarmed all over again until she caught the sense of his muffled words.

"You'll do, girl, indeed you will! Can sail a boat anywhere, any day, can walk miles and miles . . . can even make sheep think for seconds at a time . . . but, by God, I can't ride a horse worth a damn! If anyone ever builds anything bigger and dumber than a horse, he ought to be hanged on the spot."

Mary's laughter joined his. She decided her visit to Constance could wait until another day. Her muscles had grown even stiffer from the still interval on the damp ground. She limped along with Cade and Captain. Cade laughed when she admitted that the dog's appearance had frightened her most of all.

"He's a Newfoundland. A lot of ships have them on board. Nothing old Captain here likes better than pulling someone out of the water. It's bred right into them. But I've persuaded him to herd sheep too. You met the boy." The swift change of subject wasn't a question. "He's a hard one to know. Don't let him or the old woman make it harder for you than it has to be. Jason's got enough to worry about as it is."

Mary was amazed at how much he had said in so few words. Clearest of all was his loyalty and affection for Jason. Strange how the Tiger bound people to him.

She changed the subject this time, telling him of their trip out to his place, asking if she might be allowed to see his carving some day. He agreed with neutral politeness, displaying neither humility nor arrogance about his work. Mary began to get a clearer picture of him. He did care about Jason, and he was observant about the interactions of people, but there was an aloofness about him, a small but noticeable extra distance between himself and others. Mary could feel it as plainly as she felt Maggie's abiding warmth.

Jason and Cade greeted each other with pleasure, and it pleased Jason further to see that Mary and his friend were on amiable terms. The men went into Jason's study, and Mary slipped away, intending to find Maggie and offer to help with the chores, but she encountered Ellen first.

"I see you've met that horrid man. Surely my son has one of the best collections of grotesques outside of a circus."

Mary stared at her for a long moment. "It depends on how one defines grotesque, doesn't it?" She stepped past the woman.

The next day she insisted on a second lesson on Dolly even though clouds had swept in, and the air was damp and chilly. Jason tried to persuade her to wait a few days, not only because of the weather, but because he had seen the bruises and the raw skin the first episode had caused. But Mary was adamant, and she was very proud of herself when the day finally came when she began to move naturally with the horse. She crowed aloud at the delight of it, and Jason grinned at her. "It's a lot easier when you let the horse do the work, isn't it?"

He still didn't want her going off alone, but when the weather permitted, he had been taking her for leisurely rides away from the house for some days now, despite Gabriel's dislike of a slow pace.

Jason was pleased and more than a little surprised at Mary's reaction to the people on the island. He had not expected she would become so involved. He laughed with her over her efforts to learn finger spelling and signing, assuring her that he knew how stiff one's fingers and body were apt to become when suddenly faced with the new movements, assuring her also that quite suddenly it would all be much easier, but he was deeply touched that she had decided to learn in the first place. He had learned because Maggie and Ben were important to him, but his mother and son still seemed incapable of making any effort in that direction, and even the others on the island who were fond of the Carters in a general way weren't capable of intricate communication with them. It did Maggie little good to be able to read so much of what was said when the speaker could not interpret her answers, and it left Ben very isolated unless someone was there to serve as his interpreter. The twins were good at that, but they were hardly ever still enough to do it for long.

Mary seemed interested in learning everything. Maggie was giving her cooking lessons far more detailed than the time with Angie; Constance was teaching her the fine art of gardening; Ben, in spite of his shyness, found himself showing her how to care for the tack and the horses who responded so well to him even though he had no voice to chide or praise them; Ingrid and Else seemed to be in line to give lessons on making cheese and butter and in spinning and weaving; and Jason had no doubt that Cade would end up teaching her to fish, tend sheep, or carve wood. He wondered what knowledge she would coax out of Nate and Jon, and he laughed aloud at the thought of how distressed they'd be if Mary decided she needed them in her scheme of things.

She regarded him suspiciously. "Don't tell me I still look ridiculous on Dolly! I was feeling so proud of myself."

"No," he assured her. "You look just fine. I was just considering when you might be planning to take over the island. You'll soon know more than all of us put together."

She smiled happily. "That would take some doing! But it's all so new, I'm loving every minute of it. Everyone ought to know how good it feels to dig in the earth or knead bread dough or curry a horse. How good it feels just to be able to do those things. Oh, you must think I'm very foolish!"

"I wouldn't use that word at all." He edged Gabriel closer to Dolly and leaned over to kiss the tip of Mary's nose. "I'm very glad. The isolation here is enough to defeat many." He nearly added, "many used to cities." He had no doubts about that now. Mary had never lived in the country before, that was certain. And he sensed the desperation under this new face of joy the island had given her. She was driven to find some worth in herself even if only by such simple things as the tasks the land offered. He thought of the man whose face he had never seen. One or many? The image of Hayes Burke intruded unpleasantly. What was he teaching Mary or what was she teaching him? Surely she had seen him as well as the others on her island rambles. And she and Hayes, there was much in common there, both possessing a certain sophistication and level of education that showed no matter how displaced they were now. Hayes would have more free time soon when classes were dismissed so the children could help with the work of the growing season.

Jason had never felt any antagonism toward Hayes before Mary—had, in fact, known it was quite the opposite, that Hayes

envied him even while Hayes was grateful—and he resented
feeling it now. He realized even as he tried to deny it that he was
growing so possessive about Mary that he would feel jealous of
any man who might appeal to her. Nate, Jon, and Cade did not
fit that category, nor did Captain Hanson or David Becam, he
was sure. But Hayes did. Hayes with his well-trained mind and
his straight-limbed body. For the first time, Jason saw Hayes as
a woman might see him, saw the finely bred handsomeness. But
Mary's bargain was with him, not with Hayes; Hayes did not have
the power to protect her from whoever it was who haunted her
past.

Scowling, he rubbed his bad leg, refusing to consider the full
implications of his jealousy.

Watching him from the corner of her eye, Mary decided she
wouldn't bring up the subject of his son. She had hoped Jamie
would not interfere in her life nor she in his, but the reality of
the child was more difficult to deal with. When he wasn't in
school, he had taken to following her around. It was a quiet,
unnerving game he was playing. A slight sound, and she would
turn to see him fading away into the heavy underbrush. Or if she
were in the house, a floorboard would creak, a door close softly,
and she would know he had been stalking her again. Several
times, she had called his name, but he never answered, and he
remained as sullen and unresponsive with her when others were
present as he had been in the beginning. She didn't know that
much about children, but she knew there was something more
persistent and strange about this game than normal play or
curiosity. And she didn't know what to do about it. She was
almost relieved Jason had suddenly looked so fierce though she
didn't know the cause for it; matters between the man and his
son were already tense enough without adding her complaint to
make everything worse.

The easy comradeship of the ride had evaporated, but Cade
did much to restore it. They had ridden out to his end of the
island specifically so that Mary could see his carvings. She had
half expected to find twisted monsters in wood and felt guilty for
the thought.

There were indeed some mythical figures, part beast, part

human—otters, bears, ravens, and seals with human limbs or expressions. But Cade explained he could not take full credit for these as the stories belonged to the Indians. It didn't matter; the execution was his own.

There were figures of the children playing and one of Daniel with Raven on his shoulder; there was a woman who even in wood expressed the far-seeing eyes of Constance; there was Jason on Gabriel; Nate and Jon were exactly, solidly themselves; Maggie and Ben stood together, faces serene, hands intertwined, the twins flanking them. And there were animals of all descriptions done exactly as Cade knew them, without the exaggerations of myth, every detail lovingly recorded. None of the figures was large, and the manageable size added to their perfection.

"They are exquisite! Cade, I have never seen such beautiful work." She was whispering, awed by the feelings the little figures evoked.

"They are what I see," Cade replied calmly, and she was aware again of the extra space around the man. He was neither displeased nor gratified by her reaction, immune to the opinions of others. Such a strange man, his hands calloused from work and yet capable of etching the most delicate lines in wood. And there were many well-worn books in the neat little cabin. A man of mind and spirit locked in twisted configurations of flesh. It seemed a horrible injustice, like Jason's lameness.

She saw it then, the gracefully sinuous threat of the stalking tiger's body. The heavy muscles seemed to ripple the wooden skin. But one leg was twisted and the carved eyes were human, Jason's eyes. She nearly exclaimed aloud. Suddenly, she wanted the figure, wanted it desperately, but she knew she couldn't ask. If Jason had noticed it, he had said nothing, and if Cade wanted to give it away, he would. She pulled her eyes from it and patted Captain's massive head as he pushed against her in polite demand for attention.

Cade promised to explain the figures on the great carved pole on her next visit. "You'll have to come by yourself," he told her with a sly grin. "Jason hasn't much patience with fairy tales unless they're of his own crafting."

Jason took no offense. "Cade, if I ever meet a raven or an otter that talks, I'll send it to you, and you can exchange mad secrets."

He set a brisk pace for the ride home. Mary had no trouble keeping up though she had a tense moment when Dolly shied at a rabbit that broke cover right in front of her. "Well done," Jason said, seeing her regain her balance instantly and without panic. "I think you and Dolly can be rid of the leading strings now. Just let someone know how long you're planning to be gone when you ride out."

She made an impish face at him. "I'll tell your mother, and she can hope Dolly'll run off one of the cliffs."

"Be careful she's not there to push you over," he shot back, and they laughed together. He watched her appreciatively. Her hair was burnished to a halo of silver-gold in the sunlight. The gray eyes were untroubled, and the skin over the delicate features was taking on a faint golden tint. She was lovely, she was his, and he savored the pleasure and power of the moment. In a territory where women were as rare as talking otters, he had Mary. He was not and did not know her past, but he had her present and her future for as long as he could hold her.

They unsaddled and cared for the horses in companionable silence and washed their hands and faces in a bucket of water. Jason drew Mary close, nuzzling her neck, nibbling at her ear, and running his hands in long slow strokes down her back. Her skin was warm and damp from the wash, and he could feel her heart quicken.

She settled against his lean strength with a little sigh of contentment, thinking of nothing but the moment, feeling nothing except the pleasurable tremors that rippled through her at his gently insistent play.

"Right now, right here," he murmured thickly.

"Ben?" But it was a weak protest, a vague grasp at propriety already long gone.

"Is very discreet and isn't here anyway." Jason kissed her mouth to silence further argument.

He took her on a soft bed of sweet-smelling hay, and she thought she ought to feel it was indecent with their clothes half on and half off and here in this place, but she didn't feel that way at all. It was strangely erotic to feel flesh against flesh, flesh against cloth, cloth against cloth, and the prickle of hay against her back all at the same time. Dust from the dried grasses danced golden in shafts of light leaking into the barn, and the warm herbal scent enveloped them. Golden light danced in Jason's eyes too, eyes bright and fierce with passion. She closed her own as he bent to kiss her again. His lean hands pushed the cloth of her bodice further open and caressed her breasts, his lips moving to follow his hands, his teeth gently raking her nipples into harder peaks, his mouth sucking at the soft flesh behind. She was making high little mewing sounds by the time his hard flesh entered her, and he heard the pitch change to a deep-throated purr of contentment before his senses whirled to center on his own pleasure.

He had almost said it aloud. As his body had rushed to fiery release, the words had almost burst from his throat. "My God, I love you, Gaiety!" He could feel them singing in his head, caught in his throat. He rolled to his side and took Mary with him, holding her close so that she could not see his face. He was more shaken by what he had nearly said than by the fury of lovemaking; he did not know he had already given voice to the name weeks before in Seattle.

He drew away a little, his eyes veiled, studying Mary's face, suddenly recapturing the image of Gaiety's. The arching brows and curving cheekbones, the straight nose and evenly, temptingly full mouth, these were not Gaiety's features. Her nose had been uptilting over a mouth he had loved to kiss, a mouth which had always looked as if it were pouting a little because of the fuller lower lip though Gaiety had seldom shown real temper. Mary's eyes were closed now, but when they opened, he would see the strange gold-flecked dark-ringed gray, not the deep blue of Gaiety's. And Gaiety's hair had been the color of newly minted gold, not the spun silver silk he touched now. Gaiety had had no qualms about her past, her present, or her future. She had always done as she pleased and had no patience with anyone else's judgment of her. Gaiety had been the most unfettered human being Jason had ever known. Even their marriage had been no necessity to her, only to him because he wanted everything done properly. No, there was no similarity between Gaiety and Mary. He did not know why he had nearly cried aloud to his past, nor why Gaiety was at once so present and so lost.

Floating in the warm aftermath of loving, Mary was unaware of the change in Jason, but something else began to intrude on her consciousness. A cautious rustle, the creak of wood. She roused herself to peer over Jason's shoulder, but she knew, she already knew who it was. The small figure slipped through the doorway and was gone.

Mary shivered violently and began to pull frantically at her clothing even though it was far too late.

"What is it?" Jason was startled, and guilt shot through him as he wondered if she had somehow divined his thoughts.

"I thought I heard someone. Probably not. Oh, nothing!" Her voice was shaking, but she couldn't bring herself to tell him that his brat of a son had been spying on them. Now it was indecent because Jamie had watched them from the darkness. She wanted to weep.

Jason sighed and wearily began to refasten his own clothes. There was no one in the barn. This was her old game of opening like a flower only to shrivel in the instant as if she generated her own killing frost against life and joy. Not like Gaiety at all.

They left the barn in silence. Mary's eyes searched for Jamie, but he was nowhere in sight.

CHAPTER

II

*T*he next few days were the loneliest Mary had spent since coming to the island. Ellen Drake continued to treat her with cold contempt, but that made no difference. The other islanders were as warm and friendly as before, and that made no difference. Jason had not touched her since the episode in the barn. That made the difference. He was moody and distant. Even the bed seemed to have grown wider to accommodate the new distance between them.

The longed-for privilege of being left alone no longer appealed. She tried to convince herself it was because it might mean Jason had already tired of her, but she knew that was not the truth. She missed the easy comradeship they had enjoyed for the first days on the island, and she missed both the casual and purposeful touch of his flesh. It was an incredible, treasonous thought, but it was true. Now she was sure the change in him had not just been caused by her frantic reaction in the barn. Gaiety, his own ghost, was, she suspected, every bit as strong as hers. Two haunted souls were hardly capable of contentment, let alone happiness.

And Jamie made everything worse. He no longer ignored her during the tense meals; he looked at her often, studying her with eyes colder, craftier, and older in his childish face than they had any right to be. Sometimes he smiled, and that was worst of all. He had had no more asthma attacks; he even seemed healthier in his unhealthy preoccupation. He knew she was not going to tell his father what he had seen. He was right. If she told Jason the whole story now, it would sound like the rantings of an idiot, a jealous child-hating one at that. Maggie's fine cooking ceased to appeal at all.

And the child still stalked her, showing only brief glimpses of himself, never confronting her directly. School was over, and he had even more time to play his disturbing game.

It was a nightmare, but it turned bearable dream in comparison to the other, to him of the old nightmare. This new one she could weather. Surely something would change. Surely she could tempt Jason and somehow charm Jamie. Anything, anything at all as long as the bargain with Jason—the protection—continued.

She couldn't talk to anyone about it; she was the interloper on the island. And now she was even avoiding Constance. On her last visit, they had been in the garden together with Daniel. Suddenly Constance had stared at her with the wide, odd look Mary had seen on the first day.

"What is it? What do you see?" Mary demanded, shivers running up and down her spine. She glanced at Daniel to make sure he was out of earshot.

Constance shook her head and blinked, her eyes in focus again, her expression one of weary sorrow. "Rocks, darkness, and the tide. I don't know why, but it is something to do with you. There is danger but something more. I just don't know. You must go carefully."

"And the first day, the first time you met me, what did you see then?" The question she had not been able to make herself ask before was suddenly imperative.

Constance studied her gravely for a long moment before she answered. "It was ugly. There was a man and there was blood, a great deal of blood."

"Is he still alive?" She heard the high-pitched edge of hysteria in her voice.

"I don't know. Honestly I do not. I do know you had much to do with him and perhaps with the blood. But I haven't told anyone this and I will not. There is no threat in you against Jason, and that is all I care about. Why don't you let Jason help you? You're his woman now. Why not tell him the truth?"

"I can't, oh, dear God, I can't!" she moaned, and then there was so much savagery in her voice, Constance took a step back from her. "I hope he's dead! I pray he's dead! I hope the Devil has him!"

Mary left blindly, mounting Dolly and urging the mare to such speed, she snorted in protest.

"Poor Mary, I don't think she's happy," Daniel said softly, coming to stand beside his mother.

"You're right, my love, but maybe the magic of the island will work for her as it has for all of us. Maybe she'll be happier in time." She stroked Daniel's shoulder absently. As horrifying as she found her own fragmented glimpses into other people's lives, she knew Mary's full knowledge of her own life was infinitely worse. The man and the blood. She was glad she had not seen it all, sorry Mary had. She had not expected to like Jason's new mistress, but she found herself not only liking her but feeling a protective tenderness much like she felt for her child. Daniel was so fragile and vulnerable, and so was Mary though Constance didn't know why.

Mary had not been back to visit Constance since that day, and now the sky suited her mood. It was as though spring was not so far and well begun. The temperature had dropped, and the sky was boiling with dark clouds. Jason had pounded away on Gabriel in the murky dawn—it had been the pattern of his days since the episode in the barn. Mary wondered what trails he followed. Though she knew he helped with much of the work on the island, she doubted he was seeking that. And the island, as large as it was, seemed too small for the motion Jason seemed to require now. He must be spending hours riding every path many times over. And he must know her pattern as well as his own, since they seldom met in the course of the day. She found no satisfaction in the knowledge that it was taking as much a toll of him as it was of her. His gait was more uneven. Often she had seen him rubbing the muscles of his bad leg when he was home from a day of hard riding. The gesture was so weary and unconscious, it pulled at her heart even while it angered her. She wanted to ease his pain as she had before but felt the restraint between them too keenly. He and Gabriel were a good match, each bent on surviving just long enough to kill the other. But Gabriel had no choice of riders, while Jason had a choice of mounts. She damned the thought, but her own survival was too old a habit, and she could not help wondering what would happen if Gabriel won.

The breeze grew stronger, whipping at her skirt and pulling at her hair. She watched the clouds rolling heavier overhead. She didn't want to stay inside, and since Jamie didn't seem to ride, she could avoid him by taking Dolly out, but she wondered how the mare would react to the worsening storm. She started toward the barn deciding to test Dolly's temper, and she gave a yelp at the sudden voice behind her.

She whirled around to confront Jamie.

"I have something to show you," he repeated. "Will you come with me?"

She had no reason to trust him, every reason not to. He was trying to make his voice engaging, but there was such a sharp nervous current running through him, she could feel it. And yet, what if he had decided they could be friends despite her relationship with his father? What if he were offering the olive branch and she refused?

"What do you want to show me?" she asked suspiciously.

"It's a secret. It'd spoil it if you knew before."

He put his hand out, and she took it. His flesh was hot and moist. He pulled her along toward the sheer, high southern cliffs beyond the side of the house.

"Wait just a minute. I know you're not to go there," she protested, stopping.

"Have to for the secret," he said breathlessly. He let go of her hand and streaked for the cliff's edge.

She screamed his name in pure terror and ran after him, screaming again when she saw him face her for an instant and disappear over the edge. She dropped flat on the ground and peered over, her heart pounding, expecting to see his body far below. Instead she saw him agilely making his way down the cliff face, using ledges and cracks as if they were a staircase.

He stopped for an instant, looking up at her. "Follow me. It's easy. Secret's down here."

"It's forbidden, Jamie Drake, and you know it. Either go down the rest of the way or come back up, but get off the damn cliff!"

"Are you afraid?"

"Of course I am, you little fool!" The wind carried her words away, but Jamie had heard them. His smile was malicious. "Scaredy-cat," he mocked in his high childish voice. She saw his body sway in the wind, and fear twisted painfully inside her. Had anyone seen them come here? Ben hadn't been in sight, and Maggie was at her own home today.

"Jamie, please get off the cliff before the wind blows you off!" she implored.

"Not unless you come, too."

It was madness to play on the child's level. He was forcing her into a game in which he held all the cards. The sanest thing to do would be to walk away from the cliff, out of sight, refuse to play.

She couldn't do it. What if he did fall? She hated him so much at this moment, she wouldn't put it past him to be careless out of sheer temper and thus kill himself.

She eased herself over the edge and found the first footholds. The wind tangled her skirt and seemed to be trying to tear her from the cliff. "Don't look down, don't look down," she murmured and tried to picture in her mind the course Jamie had taken. She heard stones crunching beneath her and knew the child was finally continuing his downward climb.

Step by step she made the journey, grazing her hands and one cheek on the sharp surface, expecting any minute to plunge to her death. Her heart was pounding in her ears, louder than the wind and the sea. She could scarcely credit it when she reached the rocky base of the cliff. She felt as if the descent had taken hours, though she knew it had only been a matter of minutes. She shook her head and bent over gasping to clear the sudden whirling behind her eyes.

"Well, you made it." There was grudging respect in Jamie's voice. "Now you can see the secret."

She trusted him no more than she had at the top of the cliff, but now she was determined to play the game out, hoping grimly that winning on his terms would give her the victory over him that nothing else could. And surely nothing could be worse than the climb down the cliff. But she eyed the tide nervously, seeing the water dashing ever closer and higher against the boulders.

"Whatever it is, it had better be quick. The tide's coming in." She had no intention of climbing back up the rock wall; she would go around the headland even if it meant swimming partway.

"We're almost there." She heard the nervous excitement in his voice again.

He darted away, and she was suddenly aware of the openings in the cliff, sea caves carved over the centuries by the tide. "Jamie, wait!" she called.

He paused briefly at one of the larger openings. "I have a fort in here with candles and everything." He disappeared into the darkness.

Her shoes clattered on the pebbles as she edged around larger boulders, and she could feel the wet give of the sand beneath. As long as she kept the light in sight, the cave would offer no threat. It was the onrushing sea that held her attention.

She called to Jamie again as she entered the dark space.

"Just a little further," he yelled back.

She could still see the dim glow from the entrance, could still hear the sea, and he was here. If he had drowning in mind, he was going to go under with her.

She followed his voice, winding through the passage. The light behind her faded, and she stopped. "I won't go any further without you or a candle."

Light flickered ahead of her. "Told you I got candles." Jamie's voice bounced eerily.

She followed the twisting progress of the light ahead of her, feeling her way cautiously as the ceiling began to get lower. "Jamie, we really ought to go back soon. I don't think we have much time before the tide will be at the mouth of the cave." Her voice was harsh and unnaturally loud.

"There's more than one cave, lots more, maybe you'll find 'em, but maybe not." The light went out. There was a scuffling sound and then silence except for the vague faraway soughing of the sea.

Even as she shrieked his name, she knew it was useless. Jamie had accomplished exactly what he had set out to do, and she had played the fool to perfection. Her blood pounded with a sudden mad rhythm. Worse than on the cliff, much worse with the weight and silence of the stone seeming to press closer in the absolute darkness. Her ears picked up tiny rustlings now, and she tried not to think of the childish nightmare of huge clawed arms reaching out to tear at her flesh; hardly better to think of thousands of tiny creatures picking away. She would not, could not faint or fall. She would think logically, she would. She didn't know how far in the tide would come, but she was sure Jamie did have a high-ground place within and nearby if she could just find it. She couldn't stay here. She either had to go on or try to find her way back outside.

Jason opened his mouth in a soundless scream of terror when he saw Mary go over the edge of the cliff. Even in the shadowed storm light, the gilt hair was unmistakable. And then he realized that he had not seen her fall; he had seen her deliberately let herself over the edge. The caves, the forbidden caves that held so much fascination for his son. Jamie had to have something to do with this.

He cursed viciously as he yanked Gabriel around and headed toward the beach. If the sea and the rocks hadn't finished them, he might do it with his bare hands. He knew his bad leg would never hold for the climb down the cliff, and the only other way to get to them was scarcely better. He pulled Gabriel to a halt at the end of the beach and flung himself out of the saddle. There was no way the horse could pick his way over the rocky ledge that circled around the base of the cliff.

He swore steadily, violently as he made his own stumbling way over and around smooths and juts of stone, going down hard once as stones rolled beneath his feet, everything made more slick by the rising spray of water and beginning drops of rain.

He stopped dead when he saw Jamie skittering toward him, and Jamie's face went white when he caught sight of his father.

"Where is she?" Jason bellowed.

Jamie tried to edge past him, but Jason's arm snaked out and grabbed the child, shaking him like a rat. "You poisonous little bastard, where is she?"

All the fight went out of him to be replaced by sheer terror as he looked up into his father's blazing eyes. "In the—the ca —cave," he stuttered.

Jason dumped him in a heap at his feet. "You go home, and God help you if Mary's not all right!"

Jamie took off, not looking back. His breath was coming in short gasps but he did not stop. Nothing was going to prevent him from getting out of the reach of his father. Grandmother was at home. She'd make it all right.

Jason knew the caves. He had explored them when he first came to the island. But he would have given his soul now for a lantern. He had a sudden terrible vision of Mary wandering in blind panic from one dark hollow to another without finding the higher places, getting trapped and pulled out against the rocks by the tide. He started calling her name, listening intently in the spaces between the echoes of his own voice.

He stumbled into her in the darkness, and she screamed and went on screaming. He pulled her tight against him, cradling her head against his chest, stroking her damp hair. "Easy, easy, I'm here. I know the way out. Come on now, Mary, we've got to hurry."

Her screaming subsided to little sobs, and she clung to him gasping, "Couldn't make myself move. I felt like a mountain was pressing down on me. Couldn't believe I was hearing your voice, couldn't . . ."

"It's all right now, it's all right." He continued to comfort her even as he led her faltering steps back to the light.

She drew deep grateful breaths of the wet, salty air and felt

the wind, rain, and sea on her face, and she didn't mind slipping
and sliding and getting soaked in the race against the tide. She
was mindless with the joy of being freed from the crushing
darkness.

But once they were out of the reach of the sea, she focused
on Jason again.

"What in the hell were you doing in there?" he demanded, but
there was as much weariness as anger in his voice. His relief at
finding her unhurt had drained his rage. He bent to kiss her,
tasting salt and rain.

Mary was suddenly aware of curious faces watching from the
sailors' quarters and of Lars leading Gabriel toward them. "He
vas going home by hisself. I tink it maybe better he vait for you."

"Much better, thank you, Lars." Jason managed a tired grin.
His leg was knotted with pain now, and he wondered if he would
be able to ride. But anything was better than walking the long
hill up to the house. He gritted his teeth and swung up into the
saddle. Mary climbed up behind him with help from Lars, glad
of the respite from explanations the ride would allow.

The rain pelted them heavily before they reached the barn
and made its own music inside. Mary glanced at the shadowed
corner and away, shivering slightly at the memory of Jamie
watching.

Jason rubbed Gabriel down with hard, steady strokes. "Well,
I'm still waiting. What were you doing, you and Jamie?"

"We were playing a game, quite a deadly one, and I lost."

Jason ceased his labor to stare at her. "Jamie's game, I presume. And you were a fool to play. But I'll make him regret it."

"No, please not! You scarcely touch him or speak to him day
by day, it will just make everything worse if you do so now in
anger. Please, please let me handle it! I can't explain it all, but
your son and I must come to terms with each other, and even
if it was with malice in mind, this is the first time he's dealt
directly with me. Now I want to deal so with him. Please?"

Jason put Gabriel in his stall and leaned against the wood,
trying to take the weight off his leg. He knew what was coming,
he wanted to be alone, and he thought if he had to deal with his
son now, he might kill him. He knew the sight of that sullen,

crafty little face, twisted image of Gaiety, would make his rage boil all over again. "All right," he conceded. "But if anything like this happens again, I'll tan his hide and yours too."

"It won't." She stepped closer to him. "Are you all right? You look ill."

"Just too old to rescue damsels in distress," he assured her, but the white tautness of his face did not ease. "You're soaking wet. Why don't you go along and change."

"You are too. I'll wait."

He was ready to curl up on the straw rather than walk to the house, but he didn't want to draw any more of Mary's attention. There was no way, however, that he could disguise his halting gait, but when Mary inquired again, he told her brusquely, "Don't harp on it! I bumped my knee on the rocks. Being warm and dry is all I need."

She accepted his explanation because she was preoccupied with the coming confrontation with Jamie, but she wished Jason would lean on her and knew in the same breath that she didn't dare make the offer.

She couldn't bear to watch his slow progress up the stairs, looking as though all his normal strength had drained away. She went ahead of him, beginning to strip off her wet, clinging garments as soon as she reached the bedroom.

Jason entered the room and flopped down in a chair just as he was. She looked at him inquiringly.

"Not another word!" he snapped. "I'm not Jamie. I'll change my clothes when I'm goddamned ready, and I won't dissolve in the meantime."

"Yes, sir!" she snapped back. "And it's your chair to ruin too, sir." She closed the door with a bang behind her and went in search of Jamie.

He was in his room with his grandmother. Mary heard their voices and walked in without knocking.

"You are not welcome here," Ellen began, but Mary cut her off. "I'm here to speak to Jamie. Jamie, you have two choices. You may tell your grandmother to leave, and you and I will talk about what happened, or I will let your father deal with you. Which will it be?"

"You have no right!" Ellen hissed. Her cheeks were flushed deep red.

"I do. Jason just gave me the right, and he is very angry." She watched Jamie's face. He didn't like having to make a choice. Somehow his grandmother had lost control of this situation, and he was being called to account. He remembered the look of fury on his father's face, and he didn't want to see it again.

"You go away, Grandmother," he said in a small voice.

Ellen felt power slipping through her fingers, but she also felt fear. Her heart jumped painfully. Jason's whore was watching her, unblinking, and Ellen believed the girl would threaten her physically if she had to.

"You'll pay for this," she murmured as she left, and she heard the trembling lack of conviction in her own words.

"I already have," Mary called after her. Her voice was steady.

"Are you going to hit me?" Jamie's lower lip quivered as he asked.

"Certainly not, unless you think it would do some good. I can't see that it would prove anything except that I'm bigger than you and stronger. You already know that, don't you?"

He looked at her with a puzzled frown and nodded. "What are you going to do then?" The eyes were sly again.

"I'm not sure. Maybe I could just tell everyone on the island what a wicked little boy you really are." She looked around his room at the toys and books; at least his father provided well for him materially if not emotionally. "Or maybe I could take everything you have here and break and burn them so you wouldn't have anything to play with." She saw his eyes flicker to troops of tin soldiers and a stack of well-worn books. "Or maybe beginning right now, you and I could start treating each other differently. Which way will it be?"

Choices again. Her anger rose at Ellen for using the child and at Jason for loving him so little.

"What if you had killed me? What do you think would have happened then? How do you think you'd feel?"

"Wanted to scare you. You didn't die!" His voice rose in a wail as he began to confront her and whatever he knew about death.

"I could have. Your father saved me."

"You didn't have to follow me!"

"No, I didn't."

"You're a silly woman."

"You're a mean little boy."

"You get sick when you go on boats. You were sick when you got here."

"You choke when things don't go your way."

"You're not my mother."

"I don't want to be your mother."

"You don't know anything about anything."

"You know even less than that." It was good, she knew it was. He was venting his anger and confusion, and it was far better out in the open than eating him alive in his stealthy games.

His face was turning blotchy red, and she prayed she hadn't pushed him too far. She had no way of knowing how much control he had over his illness, but she had seen it as a direct response to emotions he couldn't control, and surely that was as unhealthy as the disease itself.

"You're here to take care of my father, aren't you?" His fists were clenched as he stared up at her.

"Yes," she answered coolly, "that's exactly right."

"That's silly." The way he said the word indicated more ugliness than foolishness. This child had been too much alone and too pampered in the wrong ways. And he had seen them in the barn.

"Why?" she asked gently. "Everyone needs someone. You, Master Drake, are not the only person on this earth even if you do think so. And if you ever try to harm me again, you may well cease to be here at all. You put yourself in danger too today on the cliff."

"I didn't," he shrieked in outrage. "I can climb up and down that place easy." He began to wheeze.

"Save your tantrums for someone else. Even if you start to choke, I won't have the slightest idea of what to do." She willed it not to happen. Dear God, if it did, it would confirm his whole sad way of life. But none of her anxiety showed as she watched him.

He drew one cautious breath and then another deeper one.

The rattling lessened. "I saw you and Papa in the barn."

Papa, a child's endearing sound. Her heart pulled, but she answered calmly, "Yes, I know you did."

"At first I thought you were fightin', then not. You were doin' what the cows and horses and the pigs do, weren't you?"

The accusatory question hung between them, and Mary wasn't sure what answer Jamie wanted. He knew what he'd seen, but there was certainly a part of him that wanted denial. She felt inadequate to this task and yet unwilling to make it all worse with a lie. She drew a deep breath.

"Yes, Jamie, your father and I were making love. It is the same and not the same as what the animals do. People bring more heart and mind to it than pigs, I'm sure." How in the hell do I know, she thought. Maybe sows and boars are saying sweet things with their snuffles and squeals. She forbade herself to indulge in the nervous laughter that threatened. "But it isn't something you have to worry about now. When you're a grown man someday, then you'll make love to a woman with your heart, your mind, and your body. But that won't be for years." Don't let him grow up thinking it is ugly and wrong; don't let his life be warped like mine. He needn't know that Jason and I do not use our hearts in what we do.

It was obviously a relief to him that the sentence wasn't going to fall for such a long time, and she swallowed a smile and changed the subject. "I saw how fast you moved on the cliff. You might even be able to keep up with the other children if you tried."

As if that was the problem. It was terribly difficult not to touch him, not to react to the chase of emotions across his pudgy little face, and she was nearly undone when she caught the glitter of a tear before he ducked his head to look at the floor. But she had set a course to meet him on his own belligerent terms, and she wasn't going to shift direction now.

"Even if I keep up, they don't like me," he muttered.

"And whose fault do you think that is?"

There was a long silence, and then he answered, "Mine," in a voice even smaller than before.

"If you know that, then you know everything you need to

change it. It'll take time, but if you treat them well, they'll turn around and be your friends, I know they will."

His head came up and his eyes were very bright. "Are you sure, truly, truly sure?"

"Perfectly sure." It was heart-wrenching to discover just how aware he was of being the outsider, disliked and avoided at every opportunity. "And there's one more thing. I'll speak to your father, and I think he'll agree. You would have to be very, very careful and always tell someone when you go there, but if he says so, perhaps you may go to the caves when the tide's right. Everyone needs a place that is special and private."

"Even you and my father?" Jamie asked curiously.

"Even we." She was glad he didn't ask where that place was. Then she wondered if Jason had some place he went to be alone, away from her. But Jamie's thoughts had run on to something else.

"If I tried very hard, would you be my friend?" It was asked with startling, painful directness.

"It would be my pleasure," she assured him solemnly, and they shook hands to seal the bargain. Very lightly, she touched his soft hair, and he made no move to avoid the contact.

She didn't fool herself. This was a wonderful but small beginning. Jamie had a great deal to think about, and whether or not his behavior would change was up to him. Nor did she try to tell herself that her own motives were lily-white. She had felt her first liking for the child and knew it could grow in the right circumstances. But it was also a war of wills with Ellen Drake.

There were no lamps lighted, and the storm outside had shut down the light of afternoon, making the room murky gray. She could barely see Jason's form on the bed. He had looked so weary; it would be a good thing for him to sleep. She turned to leave again and froze at the sound. A nightmare surely, none of her business if he chose to sleep in the afternoon. The bad dreams, they were one of the reasons she never slept during the day if she could help it; they were always worse then; strange that they should be worse in the light. But the sound came again, and she saw more clearly as her eyes adjusted to the gloom. Jason's wet clothes were strewn in a path to the bed as if he had torn them off. He was normally so neat. And he was not asleep.

She saw it all in a rush as she neared the bed, and all thought of Jamie fled. Some of the bed linen was shredded and the strong hands were now gripping one bedpost so hard, the knuckles gleamed white bone.

Her stomach lurched as the low moan came again, and his body went rigid before it convulsed with the waves of pain. She felt them as if they were attacking her. She saw the muscles of his right leg moving, flinching, knotting with a life of their own. His skin was shining with sweat, and his eyes were half-open, falsely bright with tears of agony, but she saw the sudden focusing, the recognition that she was there.

He had ridden too far, and then the scramble over the rocks and the fall against them had finished him. The first shooting pain had come, the war beginning, totally different from the day-to-day skirmishes. The war between the separate parts of himself was always the same. The muscles and nerves of his lameness in sudden revolt, the pain probing and spreading until it stabbed hot irons into his leg, his groin, his hip joint, and on until the pain was greater than all the parts and the blessed darkness came and released him. He could never make the surrender easier, but the truce was always the same kindness. When the darkness passed, he was whole again, aching and tired, but in control.

But he was not in control now, and she was here, hovering over him, her face pale in his blurred vision.

"Get out of here!" he snarled.

"Not for my life, not even for that!" Her voice invaded his anger with absolute resolve and then was warmer than it had ever been to him. "Please, just tell me what to do to help. Please!"

The pain racked him again, and he turned his head away, biting his lips against sound until he tasted blood. "Nothing, leave me!" he gasped.

She fled then, running downstairs, finding Ellen in her usual spot in the parlor with the endless needlework in her hands. Ellen expected a resumption of the earlier battle, and her eyes gleamed.

"I'll beg on my knees, I'll do anything, but I need your help to help Jason!"

Ellen blinked and the disdainful look faded before it was fully realized. "Jason, not Jamie?"

Ellen had expected Jamie to have one of his attacks and to be summoned to end it. She was off-balance, and Mary pushed her advantage. "Yes, Jason. He's in terrible pain, and it's happened before, I know it has."

Ellen sank back in her chair, all the rigid starch of her normal carriage gone. She turned her head away, and her words were muffled. "There's nothing you can do. He won't let you. He wouldn't even let Gaiety when it was bad. It will pass."

"I'm not Gaiety, and I'm not going to leave him like that when I can help. You won't have to get close to him. Will you do as I ask?" She felt like reaching out and shaking the woman into action, but finally Ellen nodded and followed her to the kitchen. "Just keep bringing basins of hot and cold water and leave them by the door."

She swiftly assembled a bundle of articles and carried the first of the hot water in a bucket up the stairs, praying the treatment she had in mind would help.

Jason had thought her gone at his order, and now she stood over him again. "Please, don't touch me." He was not even ashamed of the pleading because he knew he couldn't bear it, knew he was already nearly mindless with pain.

She ignored him and the knifing pity that threatened to make her useless. She soaked pads of linen in the hot water and wrung them out. She laid them on his leg from hip to ankle and held them there with desperate strength as he groaned and tried to twist away. She knew it was not Jason she was fighting, but this horrible pain that took him from himself and diminished him so savagely. The grim struggle went on, first heat and then cold, and her strength did not fail her, nor did Ellen. The water supply at the door kept pace with her ministrations; until now she would have doubted that Ellen even knew how to keep the stove burning.

Her hair was straggling in damp ringlets and her hands were blotchy red when she saw the first signs of victory. The tight planes of Jason's face had eased, and the twitching knots of muscle in his leg were far less visible. Even the swelling in the bruised knee had gone down.

"Jason, I found laudanum and brandy. Will you take either now?" she asked softly.

She knew instinctively. It fit the Tiger so well. He could have found the medicine in the kitchen more easily than she had. But he would not risk a further loss of control or an easy way which might make him dependent. She was certain he never had, equally certain that these private bouts with agony had begun long ago. It should not have been private, not with the boy and not with the man. Things could be done to make it easier, and they should have been since the first time.

"Don't need anything now," he murmured, trying to smile, his eyes closing sleepily. He smelled the sharp tang but hadn't time to analyze it or brace himself against it before the liniment was on his skin and Mary's hands were kneading his flesh, carefully, strongly massaging the last pain from his sore muscles. He groaned again, but this time it was a low sound of pleasure, and Mary smiled to herself as she continued to work until she could feel the relaxed sinews beneath her hands.

She anticipated his need and tended to him matter-of-factly and yet with infinite gentleness. He was beyond humiliation, drifting in the sweet surcease she had given him.

She sponged him down and the cool water felt blessed. "Turn this way," she said, and he obeyed, finding that strong hands helped him there and helped him back, and he was lying on fresh, cool linen. His head was raised up and supported against her for a moment, and he drank the water obediently, finding it welcome beyond measure on his dry throat. He wanted to thank her, but sleep came in place of words, and the last thing he knew was that the bed coverings were being drawn up and tucked under his chin as tenderly as if he were Jamie's age.

She watched him as he sank into exhausted sleep. His face was still pale, and he looked at once far older than his years and far younger, vulnerable in both guises. She brushed a lock of hair back from his forehead, and her hand lingered for a moment. He sighed, a small acknowledgment of comfort, and his clenched hands uncurled and lay open as the last tension drained away.

It rose from the center of her, a tide so strong and engulfing that for a moment, she could not see the reality of Jason sleeping close by. She saw instead the toll the years would take, would take in spite of his fierce refusal to give in to his lameness until the pain cut away at him and brought him down as surely as the fallers' axes biting into the tall timber; she saw the time that would come too soon, the time when his body would be more twisted, the pain more frequent, his ability to ignore it less, until finally it would make him an old man long before he was old.

The injustice of it choked her with a bitterness far deeper than the child of herself had been capable of feeling when she saw the tall young man from the West, and she hated the childhood neglect which had caused this more than she had ever hated anything or anyone, more even than she hated him, the first and forever lover before Jason.

Her body shuddered as Jason's had, and tears rose to choke her. She jammed her knuckles against her teeth to stifle the sound. Gradually her body quieted, and the tears dried on her cheeks as she imposed the rigid self-control she had learned so well. No past. Mary had no past. But the present was impossible to deny. Jason was the present, and his distress had caught her unaware. Tenderness continued to well through her, a strong, endless freshet. He looked so quiet and weary lying there. She could not afford to feel this; it was far worse than her growing affection for the people on the island.

But she kept her vigil, wanting to be there should he need anything, and when he began to stir restlessly, she left for a quick moment to give instructions to a still obedient Ellen. Ellen who had been so uncaring a mother that she hadn't even known her child was gravely injured. Mary choked back her hatred. At least the woman had helped, and though she was too proud to ask, the anxiety showed in her eyes and her face was chalk-white.

"He's all right. He's been sleeping, and I know he'll be hungry when he awakens. Thank you for your help." The words were stiff, but they were the best she could do.

It was such a soft whisper, she wasn't sure she'd heard it, but it sounded as if Ellen had said, "He's my son." She felt like accusing, "Too bad you didn't think of that years ago"; instead, she asked about Jamie.

"He's asleep. The day's, ah, adventures, seem to have worn him out." Their eyes met for a moment in challenge. No better than two spitting cats, Mary thought in disgust, and she went back to Jason.

He opened his eyes, stretching cautiously, and smiled at her. "Good as new. You must be a witch, even if a disobedient one. Thank you."

"No magic, just common sense. Oh, Jason, how often does this happen? Why wasn't anyone prepared to help you?"

"It doesn't happen very often," he assured her. "I don't make a habit of rock climbing." His grin faded as he studied her set face. "It's no one's fault. I've never asked for help. It always goes away by itself."

He reached out and took one of her hands before she could pull away, turning it this way and that, seeing the raw scrapes from the cliff and the skin reddened and puckered from her afternoon's work. She had lighted lamps as evening dark crept down on the waning edge of the rainstorm, and even in the soft light, he could see how wan she looked, her eyes bruised and heavy-lidded, tear tracks still on her cheeks and a scratch from stone on one.

She snatched her hand away and busied herself dampening a fresh piece of linen, using it to wash away the blood that had dried at the corner of his mouth. "You, all you needed was another injury," she used the chiding words to break the queer silence between them, but her voice was unsteady.

Jason pulled her down beside him, and her attempt to struggle out of his hold was no more than a reflex before she hid her face against his chest. She was so tired, so glad the pain had left him and yet still so filled with the image of it when it was upon him, that she couldn't sort out how she felt.

He stroked the tumbled curls gently. "Poor Mary, it was harder on you than it was on me. I'm sorry you saw it." Her head moved in negation against him. "I'm sorry too that you know so much about pain. You do know, Mary, and I hope I'm not the one who's taught you."

"God, no! Not you!" Her voice was muffled against him, but the vehemence was not lost. She couldn't bear the thought of him taking the blame for what the other had done. There was no similarity. It was a vile sacrilege to suggest it.

There was a sound at the door, and Mary sprang away from him. Jason cursed inwardly but made no move to stop her.

The frustration was familiar now. Every time the door to her past began to swing open, she slammed it tightly shut again. But even the brief glimpses he had stolen made him wary of the full view. She was his mistress, for a price, and he knew nothing else should make any difference. But try as he might to believe that, the fury rose unbidden, and he could not deny the pleasure it would give him to beat the life out of the man who had left his cruel mark on her.

These past days of distance between them had been cold ones. Old images of Gaiety, vague or clear, could not provide the warmth of Mary's presence. A new journey had begun the night he had found the dancing girl dressed in blue. He didn't know where it would take either one of them.

"I asked Ellen to bring supper," Mary said nervously. She saw his protest and forestalled it. "I know you could go downstairs now, but indulge me, please. I would feel so much better if you rested for a while more."

"You have been busy today—my mother fixing supper."

A smile finally illuminated her face. "Perhaps I'll join the army; I've developed a taste for command. But honestly, she did help."

She fetched the tray from outside where Ellen had left it, and the two of them shared the meal.

Only when she was finally curled in exhausted contentment against Jason did she remember Constance's words, "Rocks, darkness, and the tide." And something more indeed, confrontations with all of the Drakes, and a new closeness with Jason. His arm tightened around her, and she fell asleep.

CHAPTER
12

$\mathcal{M}$ary was afraid to say it because the last thing she wanted to do was to jeopardize the new ease between herself and Jason, but she suspected sorrow was far more the cause of his cold attitude toward his son than was dislike. Because she knew Jason and not Gaiety, Jamie looked much like him to her, but there were differences, and she knew he looked very like Gaiety to his father. It was dangerous ground, and she stilled the voice that wanted to demand that Jason see Jamie for what he was—spoiled, yes, but also very lonely, scared most of the time, and in spite of his power to disrupt things, still nothing more than a little boy.

As her involvement with Jason grew deeper and more complex, so did her involvement with everyone and everything on the island. The islanders were like the large family she had never had. They cared about each other and were growing to care about her. She did not know how starved she had been for acceptance and love nor did she know how she had blossomed. But the islanders smiled inwardly at the changes they saw in the face beneath the disreputable hat Cade had given her, laughing when she had told him of the old hermit woman she planned to become. They saw the soft color in her cheeks and her ready smile; they heard her laugh often and saw that the shadows were less around her eyes. They even noticed that the hair which had been cropped for reasons they had never asked was growing longer. They heard her singing little snatches of song as she walked, and often they saw her riding Dolly with confidence and enjoyment now; even Nate and Jon began to look forward to the sight of her and were quick to whip off their hats and wave when their paths crossed. They enjoyed her boundless enthusiasm and determination to learn everything. And the unspoken, shared hope was that the Tiger would not hurt her. It seemed different this time, but he was unpredictable with his women, changeable-like, no woman had lasted long with him since his wife—well, they just hoped Mary didn't wake up some morning to find herself cast off.

Somehow they knew she wouldn't be the same as Constance: Mary wouldn't stay here if she ceased to be the Tiger's woman, even Constance knew that. There was something fierce between Jason and Mary, too fierce to allow placid friendship to take its place. There were changes in the Tiger too, but no one was very clear about what they meant. Yes, he looked happier and younger too, but he was also more watchful, more on edge than he usually was on the island, and mostly he watched Mary.

Love, no, that was a hard word to connect with the Tiger, but possessiveness, surely that.

Mary was aware of the speculation but she didn't concern herself with it; the fact that she was accepted at all in this small world was balm enough. Small, safe world. She felt safer than she ever had before despite the coastal traders that stopped now and then and the steamers and revenue cutters that passed by and could be seen in detail through Jason's spyglass. Safe. That feeling gave her the strength to turn her attention outward from herself.

Jamie was her goal, and it was not even connected with spiting Ellen Drake anymore. He was wrapping himself around her heart like a small insidious vine. She saw herself in him and could not bear the image.

She was glad she had not expected it to be easy to reach him, and she tried to school herself to patience at the truth of it. His first reaction after their confrontation was to spend even more time than usual with his grandmother. A woman more studied in the patterns of laziness, Mary could not imagine. She wondered how she could bear to spend all day doing so little; needlework, knitting, and novels seemed to be her only diversions besides sending Jamie to fetch and carry this and that as if he were her servant. It occurred to Mary that Ellen was like a caricature of a wealthy and idle woman, as if she tried to fit the description from one of the novels she read. The role was totally unfitting for the frontier. For even with the enormous effort and the success achieved on the island to create a civilized place, it was on the edge of nowhere. Even with San Juan Island's troops, there were fewer than a thousand people living on all the islands of the archipelago.

But Ellen was not her concern except in her hold over Jamie. It was not difficult to avoid the woman since she kept almost exclusively to her own quarters or the parlor except for the tense meals the household shared in the evenings. Ellen had learned quickly that Mary had no intention of being her cringing victim.

It continued to be difficult to deal with Jason about his son; she was so conscious of the need not to trespass too far. But she did approach him about allowing Jamie to go to the caves.

"Are you out of your mind?" Jason bellowed. "Not only is it a good way for him to break his neck, it's also a reward for nearly breaking yours!"

"That's not the point," she protested quietly, "not at all. I know there's a risk, but I saw him climb down the cliff; he was very agile, much more so than I." She willed Jason to return her smile, but he did not. "And he'll continue to go there no matter what. I'm sure of it. I don't know all the reasons. I doubt that he does either, but I suspect some of them. It's a place he can go to be alone and play his own games, away from his grandmother, and from the other children who aren't his friends and aren't allowed to go to the caves. I expect it's his own test of courage and defiance too."

"Like my riding the horse when I was about his age," Jason finished for her.

She didn't flinch from his gaze. "Yes, just like that, though pray God without the same result. Every child must surely have some measure of defiance and courage if there's to be any hope of becoming an adult."

He regarded her thoughtfully and the tension in his face eased. "That's an interesting theory, and I suspect it's as valid as any." He paused and then nodded. "All right, permission granted as long as he tells someone where he's going." He wondered what defiance and courage she had practiced in her childhood. He wondered even more at the faint but gnawing pain he felt at her interest in his son.

Jamie took the news of Jason's permission with a careless shrug, but Mary saw the flare of surprise in his eyes which suddenly showed the same golden tints as his father's.

"But you must tell someone when you're going to the caves, you must, Jamie. It's very important. Your father was badly hurt when he was about your age, and if someone had known soon enough what was wrong, he might not have a bad leg now." She glossed over the truth of the incident, but she had caught Jamie's attention.

He regarded her curiously. "Papa, hurt?"

It sounded like a baby sentence. "Of course he was. Surely you know that he was thrown from a horse and broke his leg?"

"Yes, that's not what I mean!" He stamped his foot in frustration. "I mean did it hurt him?"

Realization broke over her, and she fought to keep the tremor out of her voice. "Yes, it did. He was very sick. And he still hurts, Jamie, he still does because the leg didn't heal properly. He doesn't like people to know, so he pretends it's all right. But when he walks too far or rides too hard or gets too tired, his leg hurts him."

She could see Jamie squirming away from the idea that his father was vulnerable, human, but the words came out anyway, curiosity winning. "When he went lookin' for you, his leg was sore then, wasn't it?"

"Yes, it was." Jamie's eyes were suddenly overly bright, and he darted away from her, but she noticed afterwards that he began to look directly at his father when Jason spoke to him and to study him wistfully when he thought he wasn't looking. And he was beginning to spend less time with his grandmother. Small but important beginnings.

Spring had given way to the edge of summer, and the island bloomed. Mary had grown to feel a special peace in Constance and Daniel's presence in spite of the strangeness of the woman and the child. She had grown to trust Constance. No matter what visions and hidden truths were open to her, no matter what she saw, Mary did not believe the woman would harm her. She had told her the truth of her vision of the caves and the safe outcome and had seen the relief in her eyes.

She spoke about Jamie to her as they pulled weeds from the rows of vegetables.

Constance sat back on her heels, glancing to where Daniel was doing his share by picking dead blossoms off the flowers, Raven hopping along beside him gobbling up worms and insects unlucky enough to catch his sharp eye. "Jamie's never been good with the other children," she said. "They're not only aware that he's Jason's son, which gives him some special standing in their eyes, but they're also afraid of his illness."

She looked at Daniel again, and her face was luminous with tenderness. "Daniel's softhearted. Perhaps if I drop a few hints here and there, he'll begin to consider Jamie another of his projects."

Mary was grateful; she had seen how the other children treated Daniel, the younger ones looking up to him for his patience and his knowledge of the wild things. The older ones, the twins, even curbed their boisterous natures to include him in their games and were protective of him. If he took Jamie under his wing, it would be a big help. She laughed suddenly and shared the mental image with Constance.

"Poor Raven, I'm sure he thinks he and Daniel are related," she said, "but he can't understand why Daniel can't fly." No shadow crossed her face as she talked about her son.

Mary spoke to Hayes Burke about Jamie too, discovering that when it suited the child, he was indeed a bright student. "He doesn't like to perform in front of the others," Hayes said. "I seldom call on him to recite. He's apt to have an attack. But I know he knows the answers. His written work is always good."

She appreciated his perception about Jamie. She made no special effort to seek Hayes out, but she enjoyed his company well enough when she saw him because they always found some book or play or idea to discuss. She was so used to the role he assumed of the sly and somewhat mocking gallant, she hardly noticed it anymore. It was an automatic affectation. She had seen him behave much the same way with Maggie, Constance, Ingrid, and Else. At first she had felt rather sorry for him because he did not have the companionship of his own woman, but now she felt pity for the man himself. There was a lack of energy about Hayes which was tangible in itself. He moved and talked with languid indifference; even when he had some point to make in their discussions, he did so without heat. He was the only other person on the island besides Ellen Drake who was not the least involved in the land. Aside from his horse, he cared for no livestock, and no acre was tilled around his cabin. His sole task was to teach the children when school was in session, and that was the one thing he did care about, and he well deserved the produce the parents gave him in exchange and the money Jason paid him. It was as if he were aware of his own lack of fire and determined that the children should flame more brightly than he in spirit and mind. Mary wondered how his spirit had been so quenched. Hayes was like her in this, he never spoke of his past.

Jason and Hayes, the comparison had risen unbidden. Even when they were most peaceful together, there was a tension between her and Jason. He was fiery, uncompromisingly male, and it made her always conscious of being female when she was with him. Even when he was relaxed and vulnerable in sleep and looked so young, he had none of the amorphous quality of a child. Even when he had been helpless and nearly out of his mind with pain, he had been nothing less than a man. He could be gentle or fierce; he could demand or give; he could treat her at one moment like a woman, at another like a child who needed protection, but he never ceased to be a man. It was her image of herself, she realized, that shifted so that sometimes she was the woman and sometimes the frightened child, but always female. She hated the truth of it. And she understood why she pitied Hayes. He was amorphous. He was neither male nor female. With the fire had gone the pulse of sexuality. The pulse never stilled in Jason did not beat at all in Hayes. She had thought she wanted to be like Hayes; she had tried desperately hard to be like him. But when she was with him and knew the reality, she was glad she had not succeeded, no matter that his must surely be an easier way.

The time she spent with the Olsens and Nilsens was far more uncomplicated than visits with Hayes even though it was an exercise in organized chaos, and when she left them, she was usually exhausted and happy in equal measure.

She understood now why homecoming was as good for Captain Hanson and the sailor, David Becam, the quietest of the *Gaiety*'s crew, as it was for Lars and Mogens. Ingrid and Else welcomed them and fed them generously as they did their own families, and there was a steady stream of traffic through the two houses.

Mary spent far more time with Ingrid than with Else, who was shy and unsure of her English around the Tiger's woman while Ingrid was outgoing and uninhibited.

The women had been friends since childhood as had Lars and Mogens. They all came from the same village in Norway. They had shared the same wedding day and had immigrated together to the United States. They were bound into one large family as strongly as if they shared blood relationships. The men shared the life at sea, and the women shared their absence, and all considered their reunions great blessings.

"But ve do not share husbands," Ingrid told Mary one day.

It was strangely and blessedly quiet because the *Gaiety* was sailing off again, and the children had gone with the men, supposedly to help with preparations though all except the children knew it was an indulgence designed to acquaint the little ones with the ways of ships even at the cost of extra trouble and time before sailing.

Ingrid was serene. The *Gaiety* often made short trips to deliver produce from the island to the logging camp, Seattle, and various other settlements, particularly during the lush growing season of summer. And the flour, salt, sugar, tea, coffee, and other things the island did not yield had to be bartered for or purchased outright. Once already the men had gone and come back since the Tiger had returned, and Ingrid had too much confidence in their abilities to worry about them sailing for a few days on the waters of the Strait and the Sound.

She wove strong, even cloth on her loom, the rhythm of the shuttle as smooth as the weave, even as she kept track of Mary's struggles with the spinning wheel.

"Do you miss Norway?" Mary asked softly.

"Some tings, ja, I am sad not to see my family and some old friends any more, but de old must be left behind or der vill be no new joyfulness. Life here is good, good for us women, for de children, for de men. Jason Drake is a good man and because Lars and Mogens are vorking for him, we see dem many more days. No, is better here, even the veather is more kind."

"How right you are, the old must be left behind if there is to be anything new." The spinning wheel stopped.

Ingrid doubted Mary knew she'd spoken the words aloud, and she looked away from the fear she saw in the girl's eyes. She had seen it from the first, but it had been less with the passing days here. So much she would like to know but would never ask. Despite the multitude of practicalities that filled her hours, Ingrid was a romantic. She hoped with all of her heart that the fear would vanish and that Mary and the Tiger would find the contentment in each other that she shared with Lars. She could scarcely recall the unease she and Else had felt at the news that the Tiger had a woman with him. It wasn't their husbands, it was the woman they didn't trust. Together they had conjured a voluptuous wanton capable of taming the Tiger and therefore capable of almost anything else. Their first sight of Mary, white-faced, slender and leaning against Jason, had vanquished the image.

Her reverie was broken by Mary's words, the fear thrust away. "Oh, Ingrid! I have wondered how your and Else's children could be so . . . so much of an age, and now it makes more sense." She blushed as Ingrid hooted with laughter and nodded her head vigorously.

"Ja, ja, it is so. In our village, many born at de same time. Not so much here as in de old country, but for me and Else yust de same. So joyful ven Lars and Mogens first come home after some months avay, babies begin den, good dat dey begin happy, good for babies, good for us. New babies vith de new year, I tink." She was beaming, but it took Mary a moment to understand that she was speaking about the future, not the past. She leapt up to hug Ingrid.

"Ja, is time, Else too. My little Astrid is tree years dis year and her Ulrik. And again, I vill haf a girl, she a boy. It is alvays so, and dis is also good."

She had thought of it before with fear, and before that, with the other with horrified revulsion, but now the thought rose again, and there was strange pleasure in it. To have Jason's child. It was a continual possibility despite the blunt advice Angie had given her, the care she was taking to avoid getting pregnant, and the fact that she had not conceived before. She wondered if Jason thought of it, wondered how he would feel if she were carrying his baby. She thrust the warm speculation away sharply. It was idiocy even to consider it, and she suddenly knew that she had been thinking of a child as a way to bind Jason to her. Given his relationship with his son, that made no sense at all, and for all she knew, he already had bastards up and down the coast.

She bade Ingrid good-bye rather quickly as the children trooped in again, sea-splashed and proud of the help they were sure they'd given. She was glad she had Dolly tethered outside; she was suddenly anxious to be at the other end of the island.

Of all her friendships on the island, she drew the most strength from Cade, and when she was troubled, it was his company she sought. There was an uncompromising reality about Cade as deep and enduring as the sea smoothing the rocks endlessly at the cove. It was as though he had been washed clean of all fear long ago and had become a patient, accepting part of nature. And yet, there was nothing dull about him. He possessed a puckish sense of humor and a mind that considered many streams at once and traveled quickly from one to another. And he loved Jason deeply, as deeply as if he were father to the man.

Despite all his skills and talents, Cade had been an outcast and wanderer for most of his life, revolting to the eye, touching the dark beliefs of many that such deformity was a sign of moral evil. He was strong, and people were willing to hire his strength, but not to offer friendship. Jason had met him in a saloon in San Francisco. Cade had been sitting alone, carving a chain of tiny, intricate figures from a piece of ivory. A big black dog lay beside his chair. Jason had been fascinated by the carving, and Cade had realized that his appearance didn't make a damn bit of difference to the young man. Their friendship had begun. Cade was working at a shipyard at the time. When Jason was ready to sail north again, he had sought Cade out.

"I have an island, and it needs skilled people. Do you want to come?"

"Why the hell not," Cade had said, and he and Captain had sailed aboard the *Gaiety* to a new life.

He had told her the story matter-of-factly with no self-pity, but his affection for Jason was plain.

At first Mary had hesitated to visit Cade without a specific invitation, but he had taken care of that with his usual bluntness. "You creep out here as if you expect to find me doing something ungodly with the sheep." He grinned at her outraged expression. "Come when you will and if I'm here, I'll greet you and put you to work."

She had long since ceased to think about his smuggling as anything more than another task, so much had she been changed by the island. And he was as good as his word. He had given her the old felt hat she cherished; he told her tales of the fierce northern Indians and the legends of the totem pole; and he taught her some odd things. She could never have imagined herself gutting and cleaning fish, but now she could do it without slicing her hands to ribbons or feeling sick. The first time had not been so successful, and Cade had roared with laughter at the distaste that screwed up her face and wrinkled her nose even as he had barked at her to watch the sharp blade she was wielding. She had grown to love the sweet, spicy smell of the alder wood he used to smoke the fish. They discussed the need for good methods to ship fresh fish and shellfish, arguing the pros and cons of various schemes, unworkable so far, as if they were planning to set up a scale-and-shell empire.

"Isn't anything smells worse than bad fish, not even sheep smell worse," Cade asserted, and Mary was in complete accord. "The man that figures out a way to pack fish without brine and smoke so it still tastes sea fresh when it gets there will be a rich man. But so far, most of what's been shipped fresh in barrels or even in tin has ended up just right for a hungry cat."

"Would you like to build an empire?" Mary asked, suddenly serious though she continued to mend the net, another skill Cade was teaching her.

"Nope," he answered promptly. "The first brick a man lays down to build it is himself, and he's never free of the weight of the rest from that day on. Bankers, lawyers, all the men he hires and fires, he's responsible for and to all of them. And the peculiar thing is, he's still alone. That's a heavier weight than I want to carry. I have trouble enough looking after a flock of sheep and a big, mangy dog."

It was Jason they were talking about, and Jason was part of Cade's burden, but she didn't voice her thoughts, particularly because they had veered toward a danger Cade knew nothing of. Instead, she lightened the mood by glancing up the slope at Captain on guard with his flock. "That's not fair! He's not mangy, and he does very well considering he was bred for the sea."

They laughed together as Captain broke into his lumbering run to bring an errant ewe back. Captain's refusal to give up always won over the sheep's inability to know what they wanted to do in the first place.

"Next March I'll expect you to help with the lambing—more sheep, more wool," Cade observed, and then he turned everything around with one of his lightning changes. "If Captain can find his legs on land, you can find yours on the sea. Can you swim?"

"Yes, not very well, but yes, enough not to drown immediately." She answered honestly in spite of her growing alarm.

"Well, then you're better off than I am. I can't swim. Many sailors can't swim. Captain is the only barrier between me and

Neptune's kingdom when I'm out. But I can paddle or sail almost anything that floats. And it's time you learned to leave the land more easily than you do now. It's an important thing to know when you live on an island." The humor in his eyes was suddenly less than the challenge. "And it's more important for you than for most. You are Jason's woman, and he is never landlocked for long. Tigers aren't like other cats; legend says they like the water."

"Legend says too much!" she snapped, but she did not give in to her instinct to run for Dolly and ride away. She faced Cade squarely. "What you can teach, I can learn."

Defiance made truth, and Cade's skill made it possible. He did not want to frighten her; he had but one aim and that was to make her more at ease with the sea. He taught her how to balance in a canoe and how to sail the skiff he used on smuggling runs. He never took her out when the water was rough nor did they go far. Her white-faced misery of the first few times gave way to growing pleasure in the freedom of gliding over the water, and she knew why she persevered—it was one more thing to give Jason, one more way to learn to live in his world. She doubted she would ever experience the shining joy she saw in Cade's eyes when he was on the water, but she was making peace with this other atmosphere and from that came pleasure and sometimes glimpses of exotic creatures.

Cade loved the killer whales with their stark black and white coloration, and he assured her he believed just as the Indians did that they were special and highly intelligent beasts. Mary had been speechless with fright the first time a pair of them passed not too far from the boat. Now she had come to believe they were not particularly interested in eating the craft and its occupants, but she still preferred the porpoises, marked much the same way but a fraction of the size and much friendlier looking with their smiling mouths and bright eyes. Sometimes they would follow the boat, jumping and spinning in the water, clicking and squeaking as if they found endless delight in being alive.

Mary's progress was a secret from Jason though each time she put out with Cade, she expected that that would be the day Jason would come upon the scene and discover all. But it had not happened yet, and she was glad because she wanted to be practiced enough to surprise him by offering to take him out in the skiff.

In fact, she saw far less of Jason during the day than she would have expected when he first brought her to the island, and it was not because of wild pointless rides on Gabriel now. Many of his days began early and ended late. The island covered nearly twenty-one square miles, the inhabitants were few to the acreage, and there was always work to be done—more forest to clear, buildings to be kept in repair, fields to be planted, crops tended, livestock cared for. Jason did not put himself above any of it; he bent his back to whatever task was at hand. It was, Mary knew, another reason that he commanded respect, respect he never would have had had he simply ordered others to do work he never did. And it was surely the reason his body was so strongly muscled; such strength did not come from doing nothing more than adding up figures in account books.

Her body rippled with an involuntary rush of warmth as she continued the ride from the Olsens' house to Cade's Cove. The image flashed into her mind with sudden sharp clarity. She could see every line and sinew of Jason's body, could see the half-smile curving his mouth as it so often did when he played with her hair and ran his hands in lazy patterns over her skin. She could see the tawny lights in his eyes and in his thick hair. She could trace the arch of brows, cheekbones, nose and hard jawline. She could feel the different textures of him, the smoothness of his forehead, the roughness of his shaven cheeks, the soft prickle of the thatch on his chest and groin, the silk of his back, even the ridge of the scar on his leg. She could smell the clean male scent of him and taste the salt of his skin. She wanted him. She wanted him right here and right now. He had been so tired lately, more often than not he fell asleep as soon as they went to bed. She wanted him awake and wanting as much as she.

She moved in the saddle with such sudden violence, Dolly sidled in alarm and nearly unseated her. She reined the mare to a stop.

Sweat stung her eyes. She was at once much too hot and much too cold, flame and ice running parallel lines through blood and nerves.

"What is happening to me?" She whispered the question

aloud and felt as if it were echoing around her a thousand times and a thousand times louder.

She was safe and isolated from the world she had struggled so hard to leave. She had Jason's protection and far less demand from him. It was exactly what she would have thought she wanted, and yet in the space of a short time, she had considered bearing his child and was fiercely hungry now for the sight of him, the touch of him.

She urged Dolly on abruptly, and startled, the good-natured mare scrambled for her best speed.

She was so relieved that Cade was home, she had to restrain herself from tumbling off the horse to sob in his arms. She made herself dismount calmly and tether Dolly.

He took in every detail of her wide eyes and strained face. "Well, Je-sus! What happened to you, fall off your horse?"

"No, I think I've fallen off my mind," she said, but the smile failed.

"Want to talk about it?"

"Can't."

"All right then," he agreed, "you must have come to work, and as it happens, that suits me fine." He did not suggest that they go sailing. The wind was freshening, and white foam already ruffled the surface of the sea.

This time her smile was genuine, and she worked with a will, hammering nails carefully, putting together one of the boxes Cade used for packing the smoked fish destined to be sold off-island. Cade worked nearby on the slats, his soft whistle blending with the grate of the saw, the cry of the seabirds, the rustle of wind and water, and Captain's distant commands to the sheep.

The beat of a horse's hooves joined the sounds, and Dolly whinnied. Mary looked up, expecting to see Jason, wanting to see him and yet at the same time nervous that all she had thought this day would somehow be evident to him.

She sprang to her feet, sure something was wrong when she realized the rider was Ben, obviously looking for her.

Ben smiled, trying to reassure her as he handed her the folded slip of paper.

She was familiar with the handwriting; she had seen it often enough in his business papers, but she couldn't make sense of the words at first.

Decided to sail on the *Gaiety.* Business in Seattle. No time to find you. Back in a week or ten days. Take care. Jason.

That was all. The words danced in front of her eyes, and she could not remember how to move her hands to question Ben nor could she understand his gestures. And Ben was not like Maggie; the silent shape of words on a speaker's mouth meant nothing to him. She wanted to scream aloud in frustration and fear. Ben would understand that even without the sound. But Ben, staring at her in growing distress, had nothing to do with it.

The words were in perfect focus now. Jason had sailed away without her.

CHAPTER

13

She was too late. The ship had sailed. She searched the water to the east desperately and saw a speck of white too far away to identify. It didn't matter. Jason was gone.

All her newly won courage and confidence evaporated. She sat hunched as Dolly finished the journey to the barn.

She slipped from the saddle and stumbled toward the cliffs, staring blindly at the water as she sank to her knees on the hard ground. The harsh sobs rose from the depths of her, tearing at her throat. She rocked back and forth, keening until she was exhausted and gasping for air. Only then did she hear the small voice saying her name over and over.

Ben was standing a little ways away, hands twisting in frustrated pity, and Jamie was kneeling beside her, his face white and worried. "Please, Mary, please don't cry anymore! Papa'll be back. He always comes back. Please, Mary." His lower lip trembled and tears filled his eyes.

"Oh, Jamie," she cried softly. She hid her face against his frail shoulder and felt a small hand patting her head clumsily, a slender arm holding her against him.

Comfort from him was the last thing she would have expected, and the sweetness of it was as piercing as Jason's departure. She knew Jamie was giving her one of his most treasured possessions —the right to his father.

She pulled herself gently out of his hold and sat back on her heels, scrubbing at her face as if she were no older than he. "I'm sorry I've been so foolish, but I'm glad you were here."

Jamie regarded her gravely. "Maybe ladies cry more, but I feel like it sometimes when Papa leaves. It's like . . . like," he screwed up his face in the effort to find the right words, "it's like there's a big, dark hole when he leaves. Not like the caves, I never been scairt of them, but this one is scary. And I'm a little scairt of him too when he's here," he finished in sad confusion.

She reached out and took him in her arms, cradling him, taking back the role of the adult. "Oh, sweetling, he loves you, he loves you dearly!" She forced absolute conviction into her voice. "And I know he doesn't want to scare you. But he scares me too sometimes. He's such a big, fierce man, and he has lots of worries, so much business to keep track of, so many people who work for him and depend on him." And not any of it should be more important than his son, she added to herself. But she knew Jamie would have no such thoughts; he was too accustomed to thinking ill of himself. She knew what a dreadful disease that was; she knew only too well. Whatever the cost, it would be worth it to cure him of that.

Had Jamie not reached out to her, she thought she might have gone mad. It was just as he described it, a big, dark hole, a fearful space in every minute of knowing Jason was not on the island.

What if he meant to cast her off and this was the way to begin? What if he meant to bring another woman back in her place? Why had he left her, made the decision so swiftly to sail without her? She had thought things between them had been well enough.

She tried to tell herself she minded because she could not bear to lose his protection, but the cold, empty space was worst of all at night in bed without his warm flesh pressed against hers, shielding her from even worse night visions than she had. It loomed a larger terror than the enemy she had fled. She could not call it love. Love between a man and a woman was what she saw between Ben and Maggie, Lars and Ingrid, Mogens and Else, bonds of trusting and knowing. Her relationship was not like that with Jason; there was no bond of trust or of knowing between them. She had no name for it, but she was well and truly lost to it. And Jason was equally so—to his lost love, to the ghost of Gaiety.

Mary lay on her side of the bed, one arm outstretched rigidly on the place where Jason should be. Her eyes were wide and dry, staring into the darkness. "Please, Gaiety, please let him go! I will care for him and for your son as you no longer can."

There was no answer from the solitary night.

The islanders treated her with such added kindness, they made everything harder though that was the opposite of their intent. They pretended they saw nothing odd in Jason having departed without her—after all, weren't Else and Ingrid still here too?—but their own behavior was odd as they came to her offering new bits of themselves.

She was staying close to a view of the *Gaiety*'s homecoming path, but that didn't matter. Constance dropped by with fresh flowers from her garden, and for the first time, she talked about her happy years with Mr. Bates. Hayes happened to be passing with a book he thought she might not have read. Even Nate and Jon showed up at the house on the hill with a basket of ripe cherries and faces to match. Ben sought her out each day to suggest that Dolly needed to be ridden, and Maggie signed and spelled at her constantly, urging her to eat more, asking if she'd slept well, and telling her more about her life with Ben than she ever had before.

Maggie explained how she had met Ben at the deaf school where her parents had sent her in hopes that she would be taught to better cope with a hearing world. Ben had been sent by his dutiful, if not loving, guardians, an aunt and uncle who, though they had never been close to his parents due to some rift he didn't understand to this day, had taken over his care when his mother and father had perished of cholera. Maggie had been twelve, Ben fifteen when they first noticed each other, and according to her, she had decided right then that Ben was the one she was going to marry. They ran away together a few years later after discovering that while his aunt and uncle cared little what he did, Maggie's parents had not included marriage in their plans for her. They had sent her to the special school to be better able to cope with their world, but they wanted to protect her from the rest of it. They were more limited than she by her deafness and could not imagine that their little girl could ever mature to be a woman separate from them. When the marriage was an accomplished fact, there had been a reconciliation, but Maggie and Ben had realized they had to go out on their own if they were ever to have their own lives free of the hovering concern of her parents and the cruel indifference of his guardians. That meant that they both gave up the places which were familiar to them, and each became the only thing familiar to the other.

It was not easy. Maggie's gestures became angry as she described the hatefulness of people who judged that those who could not hear or speak could not think either. But the hardest thing of all had been to face parenthood after years of barrenness. They were torn. They wanted to be parents, but they did not want to bring children into the world who would have all their own problems to face. Maggie knew she had been born deaf; Ben did not know. His relatives hadn't even known of his existence until they had been presented with the baby Carter. Whether he had been born deaf or illness had taken his hearing in infancy mattered little to them; either way they had a deaf child to care for, a bitter comfort for their own lack of issue.

Maggie and Ben awaited the birth of their first child. Maggie took the stance of a pregnant woman, the center of balance changed, her arms showing the enormous girth she insisted had been true, her pantomime so exaggerated and grotesque that she drew the smile she wanted from Mary.

The gift had been given. Not one, but two healthy, hearing babies. It was wonderful, but it was also hard to provide for them. Maggie had been working as a cook and Ben as a handyman, but they got only odd jobs and earned little. Most people did not want to associate with the deaf; it was difficult and unsettling. The attitudes they had sought to escape had preceded them to the West. And then Jason Drake came into their lives. He had gone to the kitchen to compliment the cook on a fine dinner at the house of one of the bankers he dealt with in San Francisco. The banker and his wife had smiled nervously and tried to dissuade him, but he had insisted, and he had met the Carters. He did not forget them. After Gaiety's death and the beginning of life on the island, he had sought them out, tracking them down through the network of the people who had hired them for this or that job. He had found them living in a seedy boardinghouse where they were able to work off part of their rent and board, and he had written everything out carefully, asking if they would come to work for him on the island. With the small twins and their few belongings, Maggie and Ben had gone with Jason and had never regretted it. To them, the Tiger was close to God.

Until now, Mary had understood almost everything without repetition, and Maggie had only had to write out a few words, but now, Mary shook her head. Maggie took up the pencil again and wrote carefully before she handed the paper to Mary.

Out of fear, joy and peace. All things under the sun balance.

Mary managed to smile, but she could not imagine anything which would balance the weight of Jason's absence. He was a collector of outcasts, but it seemed certain that he regretted his latest acquisition.

It was another drain of effort and energy to fight with Ellen Drake. There was no doubt about her intentions; they ran counter to everyone else's. That was nothing new to Mary, but without the threat of Jason to curb her, Ellen gained new vigor.

It began with her gloating satisfaction over Mary's obvious distress. "A strange man, my son. I've never understood his taste in women. He picks them up and drops them one after another. Who knows, perhaps your successor will be sailing back with him."

The first arrow hardly found its mark. Mary was too dazed by Jason's departure and Jamie's offer of comfort to do anything more than offer a token riposte. "Perhaps you will dislike her even more than you do me, and perhaps she will dislike you even more than I do, though that is hard to imagine."

The venomous exchanges continued whenever the two women met, as if two queen bees were trying to sting each other to death, but the battle mattered little to Mary; it was just one more thing to bear in Jason's absence. Just one more thing until she found her few belongings picked over and blatantly spread around the room. The blue dancing costume was gone. She didn't care why the woman had taken it, only that she had and that she had invaded the room Mary shared with Jason. Mary didn't question for an instant that Ellen was the culprit.

She found the woman waiting for her in the parlor, but she attacked first, the words sharp and echoing like slaps. "I've wondered what you were with all your useless airs and graces; I've wondered were you born a merchant's, a baker's, or a hostler's daughter? I've wondered if you came from some honest working people you judged not good enough for Lady Ellen. Now I wonder if they were honest at all. Surely you are not. You're nothing better than a petty thief. I want the blue dress back. I want it now."

Some of the blows had landed, Mary knew that. Ellen's face changed from white to red to white again with alarming speed, but there was still something odd in her reaction. She did not deny having taken the blue dress; rather she produced it with a smile of triumph from underneath her pile of handiwork. "You may take it from me, but I will still tell my son, and he can draw his own conclusions."

Mary stared at her uncomprehendingly, and then she started to laugh. She laughed so hard, tears filled her eyes and words spilled out in gasps of mirth. "Oh, do tell him, madam . . . oh, please . . . do! I doubt . . . I do doubt he's forgotten it . . . since," she choked, trying to take in enough air to continue, "since it's what I was wea . . . wearing the night he met me!" She bent over, holding her sides with the hysterical irony of it.

Ellen's mouth was opening and closing like a fish *in extremis,* and her eyes were glazed as she accepted the fact that Mary was telling the truth.

"I'm so glad you're laughin'! What a pretty dress. Grand-mother Ellen, are you sewing it for Mary?"

Jamie's voice stunned them both. He stood in the doorway, beaming because he was sure they were friends now. There was no doubt about his changed attitude toward Mary.

Mary looked at Ellen, all laughter gone. She felt a treacherous wave of pity. The woman looked old and defeated, and the victory lacked any sweetness. She bent to take the scanty garment from the unresisting hands, and her eyes held Ellen's as she spoke to Jamie. "Yes, isn't it nice of your grandmother to fix it for me! I don't wear it anymore, but it has lots of memories attached to it." She understood now why she had kept it.

"He needs love from everyone," she whispered low. The older woman gave one slow nod of acquiescence.

The war was over, the peace treaty signed all through the offices of one small boy. Mary knew it was a measure of how much the old woman did love her grandson that she did not make a last desperate attempt to discredit her in Jamie's eyes. It did not matter that the two women could scarcely be labeled friends; it mattered only that Jamie thought they were and that they were willing to stop trying to tear each other and him to pieces in a contest for his loyalty and love.

Jamie. How much difference he made in the long and lone-some days. She began her campaign in earnest to integrate him with the other children. She took him with her on a visit to Constance, trusting that if it worked with Daniel, it would work with the others.

She knew Jamie both wanted and did not want to go. She didn't demand it, only asked if he would care to. He was ready at the appointed time.

A lump rose in her throat at the sight of him. His hair had been slicked down with water and painstaking care, and his face was pink from scrubbing. His shoes were shined, and he was wearing a dark cloth suit which would have done an old man proud except for the short trousers. He had done it all himself.

"You look quite handsome, Master James," she managed, but she hoped Daniel wouldn't laugh at him.

They walked along together in the summer heat, and she

thought how terribly uncomfortable he must be in his suit, but he didn't complain. As they neared and saw Daniel and his mother outside working the vegetable patch, Jamie stopped and asked, "Could you hold my hand? Just for a minute?" His breathing was uneven.

"Of course, sweetheart." She took his clammy little hand in her own, and the knot of tears was in her throat again. "It's really all right here. I promise. This is a friendly place, for me and for you too."

She saw Constance bend swiftly to her son, and when she saw the welcoming smiles on both faces, she blessed the woman for her understanding and kindness, sure that she had explained to the child that the suit was not cause for humor.

"Hello, you two! Daniel and I had just decided it's time for a glass of milk and some cookies, and now we have an even better excuse."

Under the broad straw hat he wore to shade his delicate skin, Daniel smiled timidly at Jamie, and Mary felt the grip of the hand in hers ease.

They went into the cool shadows of the house, brightened in this season by jugs of cut flowers.

Constance poured milk kept cool in an earthenware crock in the pantry and passed around cookies. Again Mary blessed her silently—it was hard to be formal or uneasy when everyone was munching with obvious enjoyment.

Jamie gathered his courage and ventured a comment to Daniel. "You're lucky to have a mother who can cook like this."

Daniel beamed. He adored his mother and was prepared to like anyone who thought well of her. He was rapidly deciding this Jamie Drake wasn't as bad as he thought. He wasn't ready to show him the special room yet, but when he heard the raspy voice outside, he returned the compliment and made an offer. "I think you're lucky to have Mr. Drake for your father, even though I don't 'spect he can cook. Want to go out and see Raven?"

Jamie looked at Mary for permission.

"That's a grand idea. Constance and I can gossip while you play outside. But I do think you'd be more comfortable if you took off your shoes and your jacket," she suggested gently.

"Would that be all right, Mrs. Bates?" he asked politely.

Constance ignored her son's gasp of surprise and answered Jamie with gravity equal to his. "Perfectly all right. It's a very warm day."

When the boys had gone outside, she drew a long breath. "My God, he can pull your heart right out and tear it to little pieces, can't he? I don't know whether to laugh or cry, but I do know I feel ashamed. None of us have ever given much thought to Jamie. Even when I, well, when Jason and I were, ah, close, I never had to cope with Jamie, who was very young, nor with his grandmother. I had my own home in Seattle, and I didn't come here until this house was built."

"It's not your fault," Mary protested. "He's been kept so much apart and so much on his own, he's more like a little old man than a child. He's been taught too many of the wrong things, too few of the right things. He's going to have to learn to be a child while there's still time."

She told the story of her own weakness on the cliff and Jamie's response as honestly as she could, and she told of the truce with Ellen though not how it had happened, claiming only that they had both seen that the child's good was the only concern. "And as I'm sure you know, Jason can so cook!" she finished with a wavering smile.

Constance's mouth was trembling with laughter even while her eyes were bright with unshed tears. "You, Mary Smith, you and Jamie make a fine pair! You both have the same effect on me."

They moved to a small open window that gave them a view of the boys. Daniel was giving Jamie a tour of the various garden patches. Jamie looked blissfully happy, as if he were suddenly filled with more joy than his small body could hold. He was taking little hopping steps, obviously enjoying the sensation of bare feet even while he listened intently to Daniel.

"Did you know it's his birthday next week?" Constance asked.

"Daniel's?"

"No, Jamie's."

"Surely then Jason will be home! It's already been nearly a week." The words slipped out before she could stop them.

Constance regarded her compassionately. Despite the girl's

enthusiasm over the change in Jamie, the strain of Jason's absence showed; she was thinner, more finely and tensely etched by even so short a time, and her eyes were shadowed as if she hadn't been sleeping much.

"I haven't any knowledge of when he'll come back. Surely it will be soon, but it may not be in time for Jamie's birthday." Her voice was very soft. "It is not a happy reminder for him; it's also the anniversary of Gaiety's death. As far as I know, Jamie's birthday has never been the cause of much celebration except for the cake Maggie always bakes."

"That's hideous!" Mary cried. "It's not Jamie's fault his mother died in childbirth, and it's unforgivable that anyone should make him think it is. A party, that's what he's going to have this year!"

Constance did not point out that this might anger Jason if indeed he were home by then nor that Ellen might interfere regardless of the new truce. Instead, she entered into the plans wholeheartedly, becoming as determined as Mary that Jamie would have his day. They would make it a picnic by the pond. But there was no sense in telling Jamie until it was all but accomplished.

Jamie hopped and skipped beside Mary and chattered about the visit all the way home. "I never knew, at school he's so quiet, but that ol' Daniel, he knows all sorts of stuff an' he's gonna teach me. He even said I could help him weed the vegetables. And Raven liked me, even let me touch him. I think I need a hat like Daniel's."

The irony was inescapable. Jamie had been living on an island a thousand times smaller than the sea-washed boundaries of the land; there was a huge world waiting for him, waiting all around him.

He looked infinitely appealing with his hair tousled and a smear of dirt across one cheek, hands and feet grimy. Mary carried the jacket and the shoes for safekeeping. They were a reminder of another problem to be worked out—the supply of citified clothes must stop. Jamie needed rugged clothes like the other children wore.

He faltered as they neared the house and muttered, "Grandmother won't like me being dirty like this."

"She won't mind," Mary countered firmly. "I'll explain that you were working. Run along and wash up now."

There was no battle with Ellen. She had seen her grandson leave, and she had seen him scamper by on his return. She faced Mary directly. "I am not a loving woman. I have never been. Oh, I loved my husband well enough, perhaps too well, and for it I traveled further than I ever wanted to go and lived in places I never wanted to see. But that was all, and his death was an end to it. I never wanted a child, let alone a grandchild. But I would be blind not to see that the change in the boy is good. And the good of the Drakes is my good. We will not argue any further about it."

Mary's eyes and mouth rounded with surprise. She felt as if she had just been given an edict by royalty. She swallowed the return of laughter and explained the further plans concerning Jamie. Again Ellen agreed without a fight, but her eyes gleamed, and Mary knew she was thinking with some pleasure of Jason's possible anger. It didn't bother her. The change in the woman was so profound as it was, anything more would rank as miraculous.

She was growing tired of staying at the southern end of the island and of searching the sea constantly, seeing every sail and shape as the *Gaiety.* Except for the visit to Constance's place, she had not wandered far from sight of the flagpole and the water since Jason had left. She had not seen Cade since she had ridden away in panic on that day. And she was beginning to feel that as long as she watched, the ship would not sail into view. She took Jamie to visit Cade.

This was a far greater test of the child's courage than the other excursion had been. She had Jamie's own word for it when she explained she was going to ride Dolly out to Cade's Cove and asked if he would like to go.

"I would 'cuz you're going, but," he drew a shallow breath, and his voice was high and shaky, "horses scare me an' Cade scares me worst."

Mary feigned deep hurt. "Why, Jamie, do you think I'd let anything, horses, or Cade, or anything else harm you while I'm with you?"

He shook his head, the color coming back to his cheeks.

"Besides, Dolly is a wonderful animal. She put up with me all the time I didn't know how to ride at all and bounced all over the saddle. And Cade, he knows so much, even more than Daniel does. He can tell you about Indians and fishing and wood carving and much, much more."

"But he's so ugly!" Jamie gasped. "He's just like the monsters in stories."

Mary didn't deny it. "I know. I thought so too when I first saw him. He scared me badly. But now I know what a beautiful human being lives inside of that body. Cade can't help the way he looks; he was born that way just the way I was born to have hair this color and you were born to look like this," she traced his face and ruffled his thick hair, "just the way Daniel was born to look different from other people."

"Why did God do that to Cade?"

She had never wanted to have a good answer to any question as she did to this one, but there was none. "Darling, I don't know. Why should Maggie and Ben not be able to hear or speak? Why should Daniel be so pale and Cade so twisted? I just don't know."

"If I was God, I'd make everything perfect or I wouldn't make it at all."

"But we don't have that power," she reminded him gently. "The best we can do is to try not to hurt other people no matter how different they are from us. Are you coming with me?"

He nodded and walked with determined steps as if he feared his feet would make him run away if he wasn't careful.

Mary mounted Dolly, and Ben, beaming in approval, swung Jamie up in front of her. Dolly made no protest at the added weight, but set off at a slow pace at her rider's command.

Mary kept one arm around Jamie, and gradually she felt him relaxing back against her. But she felt him tense again as Cade's domain came into view. For a moment, she was as tense as he, filled with sharp disappointment because it looked as if Cade wasn't there. The sheep were penned and neither the man nor the dog was in sight.

"Phew!" Jamie snorted. "Somethin' smells awful!"

"It's a combination of sheep and fish; you'll get used to it," she assured him, and then she crowed with delight, "Look, look there, Jamie, Cade's sailing in!"

The skiff came in cleanly through the passage between the rocks. Captain barked when he sighted the figures on the high ground, and Cade raised a hand in greeting.

Mary dismounted and held Dolly while Jamie slipped down from the saddle. He stayed very close to her as she tied the mare and walked to the slope and down toward the water's edge. She took his hand and held it firmly as the skiff was beached and Captain bounded out, followed by Cade.

There was no time to do anything at all. Jamie sucked in air and then screamed shrilly as the huge black body kept coming. Mary didn't even have time to gather the child in her arms before Captain acted. It was as if Jamie's scream had pierced his heart. He dropped to the ground, buried his massive face in his paws and whimpered.

The fear drained out of Jamie as if it had never been. He wrenched his hand from Mary's compulsive grip and ran to Captain, kneeling down beside him to pat the massive head and croon, "I'm sorry, doggie, I'm sorry. Don't cry any more. Guess I scairt you much as you scairt me."

Captain raised his head and gave Jamie the broad, swiping kiss of his tongue. Far from pulling back, Jamie sat down and put his arms around the thick neck. Captain gave a sigh of pure bliss, and eyes half closed, rested his head on Jamie's shoulder.

"It's an unfortunate weakness," Cade whispered as he came to stand beside Mary. "Captain wishes to be loved by every child and lamb in the world. He and the child should have been formally introduced long ago, but I always made the dog stay back even as I did because the child feared me. We have all stayed back, and we have nearly extinguished the child by that, haven't we?"

There was never any compromise with Cade, and she gave him none now. "Yes, and that is why I've brought him to you. His fear of you was no different from mine the first time I saw you—old myths, nothing more. You have things to teach him that he would be better for learning. He needs to learn how to be a child. I think you can teach him much about that."

Cade was still watching Jamie and Captain sealing their bond of friendship, and he continued to pitch his voice so low that the child couldn't hear it. "I can and you can because we were never children, and so we know exactly what a child should be."

They exchanged a long look, and Mary murmured, "Exactly." Denial with Cade seemed a useless exercise.

Jamie laughed a great deal that day. Cade set out to make the time magic for him, and the child responded with wonder and fascinated attention. Cade let him help unload the catch of fish from the skiff and explained how the ones which weren't eaten fresh would be salted and smoked. He showed him the carvings, and when Jamie exclaimed, "Oh, they are . . . so beautiful! Do you think I could ever learn to make things like that?" Mary saw for the first time that Cade was not indifferent. Jamie's judgment touched him, and he took great care in demonstrating how to hold the knife and the wood. "Anything sharp enough to change the shape of wood is sharp enough to change the shape of your fingers," he warned. "It takes a lot of practice, but little by little, you'll be able to see the shapes in the wood and how to free them."

Jamie seemed to understand perfectly what Cade was saying. "I think there's a fish with a curvy tail in here, but I don't know how to let it out yet." He handed the knife and the wood back to Cade. "Maybe you can find it."

Cade agreed. "Perhaps I can."

They went back outside and Cade sat down on the ground, patting the place beside him. "Sit here, and I'll tell you the story of the totem."

Mary sat on the other side of him, as eager for the story as Jamie was though she had already heard it once. But as soon as Cade began, she knew it was not the same. His voice was as deep and rich as the heartbeat of the earth and sea as he spun the enchantment for the Tiger's son.

"Far to the north this totem was carved by a fierce, proud people. Raven is at the top. You can tell it is Raven and not Eagle because Raven's beak is straight; Eagle's would be curved. A totem tells things to the eyes the way words speak to the ears.

This one says that all people who are part of the Raven Clan, or family, are welcome, and the other carvings tell of adventures and legends of the clan. But Raven, he is the best story of all. He's not like the bird little Daniel has, not this Raven of the north. He's so very clever and almost always gets his way by tricks."

Cade's voice became so sonorous, it was as if he were chanting. "In the beginning Raven he made people and living things, but they were in darkness. There was no moon, no stars, no sun. Raven he heard of a chief up the great river, and this chief had not only a beloved daughter but also all kinds of light, and he guarded them all fiercely. Now Raven, he can change his shape, and first he became a speck of dust and tried to get the daughter to drink him, but the water was thrown away by an old woman who was nearly as crafty as he and watched over the girl. So then he became a hemlock needle and hid in the corner of a small wooden box the girl drank from. She swallowed him, and in time she bore a son whom the chief loved as much as he loved his daughter. And the chief could not deny what his grandson asked. First he asked to play with the stars, and he pretended it was an accident when he threw them up through the smoke hole of the lodge. Then he cried for the moon and did the same thing with it when his grandfather gave it to him. The grandfather wasn't happy about what had happened, but he loved his grandson and forgave him. Then Raven as the little boy cried for the box holding the sun until he seemed to be ill, and the grandfather gave him the box. With that, the little boy gave the cry of the Raven, changed into the bird, and flew up through the smoke hole, carrying the box of the sun. Then he flew back to the people and animals he had made, and he broke the box and let daylight out on the world."

Jamie's eyes were wide and round as he glanced at the sky. "Raven sounds a lot like God," he said.

Mary hid a smile, but Cade answered him seriously. "Yes, he does. Different people explain how the world is in different ways. But for you and for me, Raven is just a story, just as the totem is."

It made perfect sense to Jamie. "Are there more stories?" he asked eagerly.

"Indeed there are. Raven did a lot of other tricks, and I think I might remember a few about talking otters and great eagles too. But they will have to wait for another time. Will you come to visit me again, Jamie Drake?"

"Oh, yes, Cade! I would like that very much!" In his enthusiasm, Jamie flung his arms around Cade and hugged him. Cade's face didn't change, but Mary looked away from his eyes; they were suddenly as deep and sad as the world.

Jamie asked if he could go explore the beach, and she watched him fondly as he sped to the water's edge and darted like quicksilver, stopping here and there to turn a stone or shell.

"The young Jason," Cade said.

Mary swung around to face him. "Perhaps, yes, surely partly that, but most of all just Jamie, someone absolutely new and absolutely different from anyone before."

"And you want him to believe that every day is beautiful, that life is beautiful." It sounded like an accusation.

"Yes, yes I do! And you do too or you wouldn't have given him this day and promised him others. It doesn't matter that it is not true. What matters is that every child should believe it for long enough to remember forever. It's your story, Cade. Every child has the right to be your clever Raven, the right to break the box and let the sunlight out for long enough so that darkness can never be the only memory."

She could hardly credit the vehemence of her own voice, and she rushed to erase the sound by making her words calm as she told him about the plans for Jamie's party to be held in two days' time.

"I'll come and Captain with me," he agreed, and he added, "Perhaps Jason will be back in time for it."

"And perhaps not. It is already more than ten days." Her voice was flat, and Cade did not press her further.

But in the long dusk of the next evening, the red flag was raised as the *Gaiety* sailed home.

CHAPTER

14

*T*here had been good reasons for Jason to go to Seattle. The business summonses were legitimate—the possibility that his offer on a piece of Seattle waterfront might be accepted plus Mactavish's wish to make a design change, and even a chance for a share in one of the steamers on the Sound. But his haste to leave the Island had not been necessary; he could have delayed long enough to take Mary with him.

He had run from her, and at first, he enjoyed every minute of his freedom. The crew had said nothing at all, and he met questions in Seattle with the perfectly reasonable explanation that Mary was busy and well on the island, but he avoided going to visit Angie.

He agreed with the change Mactavish wanted to make in the ship despite the added cost and the reworking it would require. The steamer share could be his for full payment in gold. The possibility of purchasing the lot seemed better by the day though the title was somewhat obscure because it had once been part of some of old Doc Maynard's holdings, which always made things confusing. The kindly doctor was more often than not in his cups, had been for years, and had been known to give away, sell, or simply lose the same bits of land several times. Still, Jason wanted the parcel and was willing to be patient.

The feeling did not creep over him subtly; it was more like being clubbed to his knees. He found himself down on the sawdust one night drinking whiskey and winning in a poker game while he contemplated sampling the wares at the Mad House. Suddenly it struck him that he didn't give a damn about the cards anymore, that he didn't want a whore, that the whiskey tasted unutterably foul, and that he was very drunk. No one barred his leaving; the Tiger seemed even more lucky and more dangerous than usual. They were glad to see him go. He scarcely remembered getting on his horse, but he knew where he was going.

He staggered into the house calling her name, his slurring tongue making "Mary" a very long word. His voice echoed in the emptiness. His foggy brain remembered then that Mary was miles and miles away by his own choice. He looked at the stairs and realized he didn't want to climb them, probably couldn't, they were already moving on their own. And he thought of the empty bed and realized he didn't want to sleep in it without her tonight.

"You dumb-assed bastard," he mumbled to himself as he sank into a chair and fell asleep.

He awakened in the morning with a mouth and head as foul as the whiskey that had caused it. His leg was cramped and throbbing. He gritted his teeth as he rubbed the muscles savagely until he could manage to stand, then limped around cursing and holding onto furniture until the leg would hold him. He cleaned himself up so that he looked presentable, and then he went to see Angie.

She took one look at him and pronounced, "Clean and sorry. Do you want something to eat? Do you good."

He winced. "It wouldn't. But I'd be grateful forever for a cup of coffee."

She handed it to him and asked bluntly, "Is it true that Mary's so happy on the island, she didn't even want to come back here?"

"I don't know," Jason admitted. "I didn't give her the choice. I left at the last minute. She was at the other end of the island."

"Are you glad you did?"

"I was but not anymore." He rubbed his face wearily. "I don't know how the hell I feel."

Angie could have felt some satisfaction in seeing the Tiger so confused, but she didn't. She felt sorry for him and for Mary. "So you left her at the mercy of your odd islanders and your mother," she observed slowly.

Anger flashed in his eyes for an instant, but then he grinned ruefully. "Not exactly. She's won every battle so far with my mother, and she has the rest of them eating out of her hands— even my son."

Good Lord above, Gaiety, he's stubborn and blind, isn't he? And I don't really know how Mary Smith feels though I've guessed. Angie nearly sighed aloud in frustration, but she made herself approach the problem reasonably. "It seems to me a simple thing. Go back to your island, go back to Mary. Apologize if you have to, explain if you can."

His laughter held more pain than mirth. "Angie, I've trapped myself better than anyone else could. I can't leave yet. I could have a few days ago, but not now. Not only are matters pending on a piece of property and a steamer share here, but word has come from San Francisco that the *Moon Chaser* has made port. Before too long, she'll be here for a load of lumber. I've got to make sure we've got it ready at the logging camp."

"So send the *Gaiety* back for Mary. It's still very simple." She watched him carefully.

"It would take too much time." He didn't meet her eyes.

"It would take too much of you admitting that you need her," Angie said to herself, but aloud she gave him a noncommittal, "I suppose it would." She knew why he was here; she was the closest connection to Mary he could find in Seattle. And in the days that followed, she knew she was not close enough. He dropped in but never stayed long. She had no impulse to try to seduce him. She admitted with wry humor to herself that it was probably impossible anyway. She had never seen him so restless. It was one of the few generous impulses she had ever had toward another woman, but she sincerely hoped that all of this would work in Mary's favor.

The *Gaiety* finally left Seattle for the logging camp but further delays there had Jason's temper on a raw edge, and the men's obvious disappointment that he hadn't brought Mary with him this time didn't help. When they finally left for the island, Lars and Mogens were highly amused though they were careful to keep the amusement to themselves; it was a new experience to see the Tiger as hungry for his woman as they were for theirs. Even the breeze added to his temper by failing for twenty-four hours, leaving the schooner to wallow and swing with the current before the wind returned to carry her home.

By the time the shore was in sight, Jason was as angry as he was eager—angry at himself for caring so much and angry at her for causing it. His body felt hot and tight in his skin with the surge of conflicting emotions. The *Gaiety* had not been gone long enough to merit a full-scale island welcome, but Ben was there with the wagon and Ingrid and Else with their children. His eyes searched for her and found her standing there, but she was not alone. Jamie was close beside her, her arm around his shoulders.

Jason hated himself for his reaction, but he could not deny the cold hollow that settled over the heat. Mother and child, the image was separate from him and had its own strength. He could not see his place in it.

Mary tried to still her trembling, tried not to lean on Jamie though she thought if she did not have him beside her she might simply sink to the ground. She did not know how to act, did not know what Jason wanted from her now. Had he missed her at all while she had been so lonesome for him? Was this the new pattern he would set for them, coming and going at his will, leaving her behind to wait until he wanted her here no longer?

She saw him clearly as if for the first time, his tall broad-shouldered body and his halting gait, the hard planes of his face, the gold light in his eyes, the sun strands in his brown hair. There was no woman with him; she realized how much she had dreaded that.

She wanted desperately to find some sign of gladness in him, but she found none as he came closer and her eyes searched his face. No smile crooked the hard mouth; his expression was cool and remote. "Hello, Mary, I see you have been busy." He glanced at his son.

"Jamie and I have been busy together. We hope your business went well." She had a crazy impulse to add, "My Lord Jason." This cold formality with the barbs beneath the surface was a mad reunion after the days apart. She didn't care what the others watching this scene must be thinking; this was between Jason and her. Tears threatened, and she swallowed hard. Jamie moved restlessly beside her. Jason had disappointed him too.

"I been out to see Cade, I like him and Captain," he ventured in a small voice. He was offering the information in the hope that his father might like him better for liking Cade, who was, he knew, a special friend of his father's.

A sudden jolt of anger shot through her. She would not let Jamie be hurt again. She tipped her head up briefly, and for an instant Jason could see her eyes clearly under the sheltering brim of the hat. They were narrowed and blazed a warning though she kept her voice even. "Yes, Jamie and I had a lovely time at the cove, and there is much more to tell you. Jamie, would it be all right with you if I rode home with your father and left you to go home with Ben?"

She and the child had come with Ben in the wagon. Tied to the back of it, Gabriel had pranced and danced his way down the hill.

The arrangement was fine with Jamie. He was trying not to let his father scare him, but little shivers were beginning, and he was afraid his breathing was going to go all wrong if he didn't escape. He darted off with relief to Ben, trusting that somehow Mary would fix everything.

Despite the weight of two riders, Gabriel responded to Jason's demand for speed and raced up the hill. For once it didn't frighten Mary; all she could think of was the coming confrontation with Jason. She kept reminding herself that at least he didn't have another woman with him.

Jason ushered her into the neutral ground of the study with elaborate politeness and slammed the door behind her.

She took a deep breath and plunged in before she could lose

her courage. "I don't know why you left so quickly and returned so angry. I don't know whether it had anything to do with me or just with business. You can explain or not, as you like. But I know it's Jamie's birthday tomorrow, and we're going to celebrate it with a picnic at the pond. Everyone is coming. And I won't have you spoil it for him out of jealousy."

He towered over her, eyes glittering golden.

"It's true, isn't it?" Her laughter was jagged. "You're jealous because your whore has taken an interest in your son."

His hand lashed out across her cheek. She cowered away from him, eyes enormous, one hand covering the scarlet mark. A trickle of blood ran from the corner of her mouth where her teeth had pierced her lip.

Jason could hear the blow echoing in the silence, and he flinched suddenly as if he had received rather than dealt it. He opened his arms, and they trembled. "Please?" he asked very low.

She came to him with instant obedience, her body rigid and puppetlike, pulled into small sharp tremors by invisible strings as he settled down in his chair with her in his arms. She hardly knew where she was. She had risked it all and lost. She would not be able to help Jamie further now, let alone herself. The pain of that was far worse than the throbbing of her cheek. She could not stop it; the conviction rose in her that the other was still alive, still stalking her with his terrible, twisted love. Without the Tiger's protection, he would find her. Her fate would allow nothing kinder. Her new friends, her new life on the island, Jason, Jason most of all, all lost.

Jason didn't want her obedience. It made the swelling pain in his chest that much worse. This woman aroused so many emotions in him, most of which he barely understood. Her shot had been too accurate. He had felt a huge surge of jealousy of Jamie, had felt it since his first sight of them standing together, but his temper had snapped at Mary naming herself whore. It was not the way he thought of her, not since the first time he had taken her, and it made no difference that by all standards it was true.

He had never in his life struck a woman before nor loathed himself so much. He knew he ought to offer to set her free and take her anywhere she wanted to go to begin again, but he couldn't bring himself to make the offer. For a long space he could not find any words at all.

Her hat had fallen off when he struck her, and when he tipped her face up against his chest, he saw the toll of his absence he had not seen before—the shadows around her eyes, the new sharpness of her facial bones. She felt frail in his arms. Her eyes were closed, and she was breathing in quick gasps. He could feel the rapid beat of her pulse. Gently he pried away the hand that still covered her cheek, wincing at the bruise beginning and the swelling. Gently he checked to make sure she was not badly hurt, gently he wiped at the blood, gently he cradled her shuddering body against him, stroking her soft hair, and finally he found his voice.

"I'm sorry. God, I am so sorry, sweetheart." He was sorriest of all that he had conjured up her old terror; he knew he had, and it was worse than the bruise on her flesh. "Whatever you want, I'll do." It was as close as he could come to offering her release from the bargain, from him.

The tender touch of his hands, the warmth of him continued to communicate all the concern he could not voice. It filtered through her frozen spirit slowly at first and then burst on her like the sun rising. Jason was not demanding that she leave the island or him. He was giving her more comfort than anyone had ever given her in her life. All of that mattered more than the blow. And he had called her "sweetheart," this man of few endearments; how different it sounded from when she used the word to Jamie.

She looked up at him. "I want to begin this day again," she said softly. "Welcome home, Jason Drake, I missed you."

"I missed you too, Mary Smith." He set her on her feet and got up, and she knew where he was taking her.

She grinned at him and made a halfhearted protest. "Maggie will surely have supper ready soon, and you haven't greeted your mother yet."

"Maggie, supper, my mother, and everything else can wait."

No one impeded their progress upstairs.

Jason soaked a clean linen handkerchief in water from the

pitcher. He sponged away the last dried stain of blood at the corner of her mouth and brushed the soothing coolness over the bruise. "Are you all right?"

"Yes." She could barely say the word. She was mesmerized by his eyes, drugged by his touch, her blood was racing through her veins, her skin and nerves shimmering with so much energy, she felt as if he were touching her everywhere.

With delicate concentration, his lips traced the hurt he had inflicted and still gentle, claimed her mouth, while his hands undressed her. The strength in her knees melted, and he half carried her to the bed. She watched him undress and opened her arms to fold him close when he came to her, sighing aloud at the pleasure of having his lean warm body pressed against the length of hers again. His hands were everywhere, his mouth moving from her throat to her breasts, and lower until he groaned, "Mary, I can't wait!"

"Don't have to," she murmured through waves of undulating heat, and she guided him into her ready flesh.

He arched his back, supporting himself on his arms above her, his hipbones pressed hard against hers, holding himself still, fighting for control as he had not had to fight since the days of his first woman. But Mary would not be still beneath him. Her hands played over his chest, pulling at the hair, teasing his nipples; her head turned back and forth, her mouth biting and kissing his hands; her body rocked under him; and her sheath stroked and rippled around him until he surrendered, drowning in her with a cry of delight and relief.

"Welcome home. I missed you," she repeated, still holding him close within her, not wanting to lose the contact.

He could see her eyes half open, shining as if she were a pleasured cat, and he felt the little current of laughter before he heard it, a purr of pure joy.

"You're a minx." He nuzzled her throat. "You make me feel like I'm eighteen again, and the results are disastrous."

"Not from my point of view. But I'm glad you're not eighteen, indeed I am." Her hands kneaded the strong cords of his back and wandered down to his firm buttocks. "I especially like the gray hairs with the dark here and there on your chest and other places, very distinguished, gives me an idea of how you'll look when they appear at your temples." She giggled again.

"Well, you're eighteen, and you're full of nonsense." He felt himself growing hard inside of her again and wondered with a last grasp of sanity how even laughter could be erotic with her.

"No. I am filled with you."

He rolled to his side, taking her with him, and the first need gone, they enjoyed each other with slow deliberation. Mary wanted to give to and take endlessly from Jason; his first urgency and this renewal told her as no words could have that he had not had another woman while he was gone.

She surfaced from sleep to find that Jason was not only awake and had lighted lamps against the darkness but was munching contentedly from a large tray of food. He winked at her and waved a chunk of bread. "Have to keep my strength up. Can't tell you how it saps a man's strength to grow gray hair. I found this outside. Maggie, wise woman that she is, seemed to guess we might miss supper."

Mary found she was ravenous, and she ate with better appetite than she had had since Jason left though the process was slowed a bit by the sore side of her mouth.

"Tell me about Jamie's picnic." He wished the bruise would vanish; until it did, it would remind him constantly of what he'd done.

The words were said with such soft reasonableness, she wasn't sure she'd heard them. She swallowed convulsively and stared at him.

"Well?"

All his anger was gone, but she still had trouble controlling her voice. "For his bir-birthday—tomorrow. He doesn't even kn-know." Control returned with the image of the small, eager face. "He hasn't even mentioned his birthday! And I was afraid to tell him what we've planned, in case of disappointment. I was going to tell him tonight."

"You're right, birthdays have never meant much in my family." She was sure he was thinking of the anniversary of Gaiety's death, but he didn't mention it. "But nothing will interfere with this one. Do you want to go tell him?"

"Will you come with me?"

To her relief, he nodded, adding, "However, I think we both ought to dress a bit more formally for the occasion." The slanting grin was back, and she touched the corner of his mouth as she passed him to pick up her clothes.

They listened outside Jamie's door for an instant and heard his voice. "He often reads aloud to himself though lately I've been reading to him at night," Mary explained as she knocked and asked permission to come in.

Jamie's voice rang out in welcome, and his eyes got very big and round when he saw his father with her.

"We've got a surprise for you, but maybe I shouldn't tell you until tomorrow," she teased, trying to look thoughtful for a moment, but then she sat on the edge of the bed and put her arms around him. "Tomorrow we are going to have a big, grand picnic to celebrate the eighth birthday of Master James Drake. Almost everyone will be there!" She doubted Ellen would participate, and she didn't know about Jason.

He pulled back and stared at her in wonder. Finally he whispered, "Are you sure it's for me?"

"Absolutely, positively certain sure!"

"Daniel, and Mrs. Bates, and Cade, and Captain, they'll all be there?"

"Every one of them and more people besides."

"Oh, my, my goodness!" He was glowing with joy. He darted a look at his father. "Could you maybe come too?"

"I wouldn't miss it for the world," Jason assured him gravely. "And now you'd better try to get some sleep or you'll be too tired for your own party."

Mary gave him a swift, grateful smile. "I'll be along in a moment. I've just noticed that a certain young man has very dirty hands, and I'll bet his ears are dirty too."

Jamie looked guilty, and then he giggled. "Maybe I forgot 'em."

"And maybe you just skipped them." She got up to dip a towel in water from his washstand. "You know, the point is not to keep the water and the towels clean, it's to keep you clean."

Jason left the room quietly and stood outside. He was utterly

stunned by the change in the child and in himself too. It was the
first time he had ever seen his son as anything more than a
reminder of Gaiety's death, the cause of her death. It was not
only a hideously distorted image, it was equally unjust. He who
prided himself on his sense of justice had condemned his own
son for a crime which was no crime at all but a tragedy of
happenstance. He had condemned himself too. The guilt for her
death had never left him, and the exchange of a squalling brat
for her had galled him endlessly. The memory flared in vivid
colors—Gaiety so white, the blood so red, and the tiny baby red
too, purple-red and screaming as if his lungs were many times
larger than the whole of him. Poor Jamie, his lungs had gone on
screaming, muting the voice to a sinister choking but still
screaming, screaming to be noticed, screaming to be loved.

Jason rested his head against the wall, his throat so tight, he
understood suddenly how Jamie must feel when his breathing
became so difficult.

He heard their voices again, and he listened.

"I thought your face was dirty too, but that's not dirt, is it?
And your mouth's funny."

"No, it's not dirt. I was very clumsy. I bumped into a door
instead of opening it."

"That was silly."

"Wasn't it though."

Jamie, having accepted that, went on to another question. "Is
it true that if I don't wash right an' don't eat what I'm s'posed
to an' don't go to bed on time, I won't grow up to be big like
Papa?"

"I don't know. If I ever meet a very little dirty old person, I'll
ask if that's how it happened."

Jamie mulled that over for a moment and then burst out
laughing, "Oh, you are funny, Mary!"

"So are you and so is my mouth and so is it funny for you to
be awake when there's such a big day coming." She turned the
lamp down and pulled the sheet up to his chin. She rested her
cheek against his for a moment and whispered, "Close your eyes
now, Jamie, sleep will make tomorrow come sooner."

Jason closed his own eyes and shivered as the low, sweet

words flowed over him. He had heard seamen sing "Shenandoah"; he had never heard it as a lullaby. He didn't hear his mother's door open and then close again.

When Mary left Jamie, she found Jason already in bed. Thinking he was asleep, she moved quietly to prepare for bed and blew out the one lamp he had left burning. But when she lay down his voice startled her.

"What is mine I keep, often too harshly. I am a jealous beast. But any help you can give Jamie will be welcome. The change in him is wondrous."

She could hear a tremor in his voice. "Not just any beast, but the Tiger. And the Tiger's woman is not such a bad thing to be," she whispered, knowing somehow that he would not take offense at the name this time. "And Jamie is proud to be your son. He worships you. The change in him is not so great; it is only showing what he has always been underneath the fear and loneliness."

She told him about the comfort Jamie had offered her though she did not confess the depth of her own distress; she told him about the excursions they had enjoyed and that Jamie had hardly been back to the caves at all; and she recounted the incident of the blue dress and his mother.

He laughed at that, but the sound had a strange husky note at the edges, and when he settled her comfortably against him, she reached up to touch his face in the darkness and found his skin was damp. Surely it was from a last wash. She could not believe that Jason wept.

CHAPTER
15

*T*he day dawned with such warm brightness, it was as if even nature had conspired to make Jamie's birthday a success. And when Jason offered him a ride on Gabriel, Jamie looked as if he might explode with the joy of it. He couldn't manage to do more than nod. Ben handed him up while Jason kept a tight rein on Gabriel, but even the stallion seemed to have a sense of the occasion and behaved himself. Mary rode along beside them on Dolly, and Maggie, Ben, and the twins followed in the wagon piled with baskets of food.

Everyone gathered at the pond except for Ellen, and though no one said it, there was a shared relief that the grim old woman wasn't there. Jason shared the feeling though he had done his best to persuade her to come.

Constance and Mary exchanged a long satisfied look. Daniel was doing his work well, behaving as if Jamie had been his good friend forever, easing Jamie's way with the other children. And when Jamie greeted Cade and Captain with obvious delight, he advanced a considerable step in the other children's estimation since even the oldest ones, the twins, were a little afraid of the twisted man and his huge dog.

Eric and Erin initiated most of the games, but they were patient and careful of the smaller children, even of the Olsen girls, Katla, Matilda, and Astrid, and the Nilsen boys, Alf, Jens, and Ulrik, the boys and girls in matching sets of six, five, and three years old. Astrid and Ulrik, the three-year-olds, tended to shriek in disapproval when things went too fast for them, but the twins didn't seem to mind and simply set them sturdily on their feet again after a tumble.

They threw pebbles in the pond, trying to see who could throw the furthest and who could get the most skips from stones, even while they all, except for Astrid, kept an eye on Ulrik who was still as liable to put a pebble in his mouth as throw it. They lay on the bank and tried to catch darting water bugs in their hands. They played hide-and-seek, and Mary was relieved to see that they didn't make Jamie "It" first. Daniel found a toad and showed it carefully around, assuring the other children that toads did not give you warts, before he let it go. Captain galloped along with them, ducking down now and then to assure them he wasn't really so big, and they let him play, even though he spoiled hiding, because he looked so woebegone when they tried to shoo him away. He wasn't above crying pitifully either.

When the food was spread out, the children stopped long enough to stuff themselves, knowing this was a day when no one was going to say, "You've had enough!"

There was ham, chicken, fresh and smoked fish, and smoked venison. There was crusty bread, sweet butter and preserves, hard-boiled eggs, potato salad tart with pickle, fresh fruit, and a seemingly endless supply of pies and cakes.

"What a glorious excuse for gluttony," Mary exclaimed, licking juice off of her fingers. "If we find out when everyone's birthday is, we could do this often."

Jason couldn't resist her rosy mouth. He leaned over and kissed it. "Ummm, you taste like wild berries." He chuckled, "And you'll look like one if you blush any more. Don't worry, everyone's pretending they didn't see that. And when is your birthday? Or are you one of those women who quits having them early on?"

"Well, I haven't stopped yet. I turned nineteen in May, so you see, you've known an older woman all this time."

"That's a comfort. From May to February, I'll only be fourteen years older than you are!" he groaned. "I'll probably go to hell for cradle robbing."

"Rescuing," she corrected quietly, and he kissed her again because he couldn't bear the sudden shadows in her eyes and because he wished he had known the day of her birthday and had celebrated it even though such frivolity had never been part of his life before.

They didn't see the sly nods and smiles of approval the other adults exchanged. Mary's attempts to cover the bruise with powder had not been successful, and the islanders had wondered, but the Tiger was being kind to her now, and that was all that mattered.

They presented Jamie with his gifts after the meal was finished; it was a good way to keep the children quiet until it would be safe for them to wade and swim in the pond, the favorite treat on a hot day and one usually allowed only to the twins and Daniel, all of whom could swim. The little Nilsens and Olsens were allowed in the water only when their parents brought them. Whether Jamie came here on his own or not, no one knew, but at least he could swim; Jason had not entirely neglected his duty but had taught him to survive in the water when the child was very young. Jason remembered those sessions with new pain. Jamie had never cried or protested, nor had one of his attacks; he had liked the water from the first, and more, Jason realized now, he had liked the attention begrudgingly given him by his father.

The islanders had conspired to give Jamie things for his new way of life. From the Carters and Mary were three sets of rugged clothes, garments outgrown by the twins. Mary had altered the clothes in the long nights without Jason. Jamie stroked the faded cloth, grinned, and then jumped up to hug Mary and Maggie and to bob his head at Ben and the twins. Jon and Nate were made more shy than ever by Jamie's exuberant thanks for the fine fishing pole they had created for him. The Nilsens and Olsens added line, a hand net, and various intricate pieces of inventive tackle that Lars and Mogens assured Jamie would coax the fish right out of the water.

Ingrid tittered and told him if that didn't work, "You use cheese, de fishes like it very much!"

Constance gave him a straw hat like the one she always made sure Daniel wore to protect his white skin. Jamie studied the hat carefully, put it on, and beamed at Constance. "Thank you. I bet this took a long time to make!"

Mary realized that Jamie, in spite of his apartness, knew more about the island than she. Of course Constance made the hats and the closely woven baskets which were visible here and there in her home. So much of what the islanders used, they made with their own hands. It continued to be a strange and new phenomenon to Mary even though her own skills were increasing. Until she had come to Seattle and then to the island, she had been surrounded by things made by invisible hands belonging to people one never saw.

Jamie's face glowed when he discovered that Cade had given him a sharp knife in its own leather sheath and a curving, carved wooden fish. "You let him out of the wood!"

"You showed me he was there," Cade pointed out, and the man and the boy exchanged a long look of mutual understanding.

"I'll be very careful with the knife."

Cade jerked his head in assent. " 'Course you will, wouldn't have given it to you if I didn't know that." They smiled at each other.

Mary glanced nervously at Jason, but there was no jealousy, only an approval and a softness she had never seen in his eyes before.

Even Hayes, more relaxed than Mary had ever seen him, had provided a special present for Jamie without losing his image of the schoolmaster. The handmade book was carefully stitched, and the cover was lettered JAMES DRAKE—HIS BOOK. The pages were blank.

Jamie studied it very closely before he asked politely, "Sir, do I have to write in it for school?"

Hayes shook his head. "Read the title again. It says what it means. It is for you. You may write about what you think, what you've done, things that have happened, birds or plants or insects you've seen, anything at all or nothing at all. It is up to you, and it is only for you."

Hayes knew the child well; once Jamie understood what the book was for, he regarded it with as much pleasure and awe as he had the other gifts.

Even Ellen had sent a surprisingly fitting gift—a sturdily sewn drawstring bag big enough for books or collections of a day's adventures.

Mary felt a sudden horrible dread that Jason might have nothing to give his son, or at best, might have chosen something unsuitable. She knew it would not matter to Jamie—his father's notice of him and the ride on Gabriel were gifts enough—but it would matter to Jason. She could hardly bear to watch when Jason presented Jamie with a cloth-wrapped bundle from one of the picnic baskets.

Jamie opened it carefully and gasped. There was a brand-new lantern and a full silver match case. He gazed at his father. "For the caves?" It was hardly more than a whisper.

Jason nodded. "Ben will supply the oil when you need it. Sometimes I expect you will still want to go there. You will take great care, won't you?"

"I will, Papa."

The two pairs of eyes so like each other held in a passage of love and trust so strong, Mary looked away and dug her nails into the palms of her hands to focus the sweet pain into something she could bear. Jason pulled even harder at her heart than the child, Jason who, whatever he thought of birthdays and however little he was accustomed to marking them, had remembered and had chosen the perfect gifts for his son. She thought bleakly that he could not help but think of Gaiety too this day.

There was one more gift for Jamie, something special from Daniel. Daniel explained he had left the box in the woods because it was cooler and quieter there. Mary hid a smile as he

asked permission for them to go look; she wondered what creature from his menagerie Daniel had decided to grace Jamie with.

The children trooped off out of sight, Captain whining in
distress because Cade had forbidden him to follow. "Whatever
Daniel's got in the box, it won't want to see Captain."

Mary had started to settle back beside Jason in the shade,
feeling her eyes grow heavy from the food and the heat, when
suddenly she was swept by unease. She cocked her head, wondering if she'd heard something, but there was nothing but the
murmur of the adults' voices. She got to her feet.

"Where are you off to?" Jason inquired lazily.

"I think I'll just go check on the children."

"And you're the one who believes in children having more
time to themselves. They've only been out of sight for a few
minutes. But if you want to play mother hen, go ahead," he said
indulgently, leaning back and closing his eyes.

She knew he was surely right, but the pull was too strong to
resist. She set off on the path through the underbrush.

Her heart jumped painfully when she saw Daniel. He was
racing toward her, eyes wild, and when he saw her, he screamed,
"Help, please help! Jamie, sick, awful sick!"

She grabbed him and gave him a little shake. "Where is he?"

He gestured back the way he had come. "Not far, right back
there, the others are with him, but they don't know what to do!"
Tears dripped down his cheeks. "We were just pettin' the rabbit,
an' he started chokin'!"

"Daniel, it will be all right! Go get Jason!" She gave him a
push in the right direction, and he started to run again.

She heard the hushed whimpers of the other children and
Jamie's horrible gasping struggle for air at the same time as she
burst upon the scene.

Jamie was lying on the ground, his eyes glazed and his face
nearly purple, and the other children were huddled around him,
frozen in terror, Eric clutching a struggling rabbit to his chest.

"We was just pettin' the rabbit."

Mary suddenly understood. Jamie had been perfectly all right
until now.

She made her voice distinct and calm even as she parted the

group and knelt beside Jamie. "Children, he'll be all right, but you must back away so that he can have more air. Eric, you take the rabbit over there," she pointed to dense underbrush, "and let it go."

There was no need to repeat anything; the children were overwhelmingly glad to have an adult in charge, even Astrid and Ulrik backed away with the others and ceased whining in fear.

She drew Jamie up against her, loosening his clothing. "Jamie, listen to me now. Jamie, it's Mary." His small body writhed in her arms. "Jamie, darling, don't fight it. Just take a deep, slow breath, just think of that, a deep, slow breath, one at a time. It's all right, sweetheart. Don't be afraid. I won't let anything happen to you, come on now, love, just a deep, slow breath." She cradled him, taking care not to hold him too tightly, rubbing his back with slow, repetitive motions, praying her own terror would not communicate itself to him, praying the attack would end. The only sounds in the world were his rasping struggle for air, and her own voice crooning to him.

She wanted to weep when she felt the air going deeper into his lungs, heard the wheezing begin to diminish. "Didn't . . . not . . . purpose."

She hastened to end the choking effort. "Don't talk, don't. Just keep breathing slowly, deeply. I know, I know it wasn't your fault." She stroked his hot forehead. "I know it sounds silly, but I think it was the rabbit. I think you breathed in some of that soft, tickly fur and that caused all the trouble."

He relaxed more and more against her as his breathing continued to ease, and his eyes closed in weariness.

Mary looked up at the bleached death mask of Jason's face and knew the extent of his love for his son. "He's all right, just worn out," she assured him, and Jason swayed for a moment in the force of relief washing over him.

"It was the rabbit," Erin said, her brown eyes huge.

Mary finally realized that Constance was there and Daniel behind her, and her heart ached for their stricken expressions. Tears began to roll down Daniel's cheeks again.

Jason took Jamie from her, and she went to Daniel. "You weren't to know, none of us knew, not even Jamie. He's fine, and now he knows rabbits aren't the best sort of pet for him." She pressed the trembling little body close. "I'm sure you raised the rabbit from a tiny baby, and it was generous of you to give it to Jamie. It's not fair that it turned out so badly, not fair at all, but do stop crying now, please do."

He drew a shaky breath and wiped his face.

"It was a wonderful present. I'm sorry I can't keep him. Maybe you can find 'im again, but maybe he'll be happier in the forest." The small, raspy voice from Jamie startled them all, but Daniel looked at him and smiled with timid gratitude. Mary glanced over at the thicket; much to her relief, the rabbit had disappeared.

Jason was immeasurably proud of his son. "What do you want to do now?" he asked softly. "Do you want to go home?"

Jamie shook his head against his father's shoulder. "I want to go back to the pond."

It was a wise decision. Once the panic had subsided, the children began to play normally again, running up to show Jamie this or that while he rested. When the children were allowed to divest themselves of all but essential clothing and not even that for the very little ones—formal bathing costumes not being the rule here—to frolic in the water, Daniel sat beside Jamie until Jason gave permission to his son to at least wade to cool off. And Ingrid proved the most diplomatic of all. "It is good you are better," she declared as Jamie headed for the water. "This is not party vidout you. And I know, ja, dem rabbits make me sneezes ven I touch de fur."

Jamie was obviously comforted by the notion that he wasn't the only one so strangely afflicted.

Captain tried to save all the children he thought were drowning until he was forcibly restrained by Cade. The mournful howls from the dog and Cade's expression caused a general and forgivable round of boisterous laughter, dispelling the last of the tension.

It was a tired, happy group that straggled out of the woods at sundown, and Mary doubted anyone could be happier than she. Jamie had not only come a long way toward becoming part of the island children, he had exerted some control over his affliction. She found that infinitely hopeful.

Though there was room for him in the wagon, Jason was

reluctant to relinquish the contact with his son and so held him against him as he guided Gabriel home. Jamie fell sound asleep, rousing only briefly when they put him to bed, murmuring, "It was the very best day."

" 'It was the very best day,' to quote my son," Jason said when he and Mary were alone. He held her in his arms as they drifted into sleep.

On the edge of sleep, she carried the knowledge beyond. For as long as he would keep her, this was home, he was home, just this small singular space of one person in the vast world, independent of any particular plot of land or arch of roof. She had never felt this sensation before; it was as strange as if she had suddenly found that she could fly. And Jamie was part of Jason; it did not seem odd that she had known the child was in trouble.

CHAPTER
16

$\mathcal{J}$amie's new life began in earnest with the picnic. The twins and Daniel showed up the next day to ask if he could come with them, Daniel fervently promising, "No rabbits."

It was at once difficult and joyful to let him go, but both Jason and Mary knew the risk was necessary, else nothing had been changed or gained. And with a broad smile and swift signs to the twins, Maggie provided Jamie with a packet of food like the others had—who knew how hungry one might grow during an adventure? Mary read Maggie's warnings—the twins were to be careful of the younger ones, but they were also to enjoy themselves.

"I won't take them to the caves, Papa, their folks don't like them to go there," Jamie advised his father out of hearing of the others.

Jason smiled, relieved of having to issue a warning. "That's a wise decision, Son." The word came with sudden ease which continued in the following days.

Strangely, Jason found his attitude toward his mother had changed too, or perhaps both of them had changed. He could see her more clearly than he ever had. The arrogance was still there, but beneath it he saw that she was aging. There was a new frailty about her, the shadows of fatigue around her eyes and mouth though she did very little.

"Are you feeling all right, Mother?"

Ellen was startled by the genuine concern in his voice. "I'm feeling like the old woman I am."

Jason grinned at her. "Fifty-two isn't exactly ancient."

"Old enough." She changed the subject abruptly, and Jason stiffened and then stared in shock. "That girl, that Mary. I'm never going to like her and she's not going to like me, but she's almost good enough to be a Drake. She's good for you, and she's good for Jamie. Hang onto her, if you can. And if you tell her what I've said, I'll deny it. Close your mouth, you look like a frog," she added unkindly.

He wished he could touch her in some gesture of affection, but he could not. He could not remember a time, not even when he was very small, that included physical comfort between them. He could remember his father tousling his hair and hugging him in a quick, rough man gesture, but he could not recall any contact with his mother other than the impatient straightening of his clothes and a slap now then for some offense against her idea of proper behavior. He had never realized the lack before or mourned it, and he knew why he did now—Mary and the way she was with his son.

Ellen eyed him sharply. "You needn't worry about Jamie when you leave again; I won't keep him from his friends."

He hadn't been thinking of that at all, but she was right, he would be leaving soon.

He didn't relish telling Mary because in fairness he felt he had to give her a choice this time. He was sure that given that choice, she would remain on the island where she had made her own place with Jamie and the others. Things were not the same as when he had left, and much had happened since his return. He had also deliberately avoided discussing the business he had transacted; it was a reminder of the whole miserable episode. But as he ignored the bright day outside and worked on the ledgers, he suddenly wanted to share the new ventures with Mary as much as he knew he *had* to tell her of his plans.

"Jason, oh, Jason!"

When she burst into his study sometime later, he was sure something terrible had happened until he realized her face was flushed and shining under the hat cocked over one eye.

"I did it, and it worked, it really did! They told me how, but I did it by myself. It felt so funny, hard and very soft at the same time, stretchy and warm. Wonderful! She looked at me once, but she didn't mind, she really didn't! If she had, none of it would have happened, would it?" The race of words stopped with the question, but he didn't have the slightest idea what the subject was, let alone the answer.

Her excitement over the mysterious event was contagious, and he could feel the tide of hilarity rising as he spoke. "Hard and very soft, stretchy and warm. I can think of a couple of things, but I don't think they're what you're talking about. Who is she who didn't mind and what happened? What have you done?"

She spun around, checking so suddenly that the hat tipped even further. Hands on hips she glared at him in mock outrage. "It undoubtedly seems commonplace to you, but it's the first time for me."

"Have mercy! First time for what?" Jason demanded, voice cracking with laughter.

"I milked a cow, all by myself I did! Jamie learned too! He's still there. And it was wonderful. You've probably done it hundreds of times, but I haven't. And they said she gave just as much milk as she ever does. She's Patches, you know, the cow with the big splotches of white that look like someone sewed them on."

He howled with amusement, then gave a grunt of surprise as she dropped into his lap. "Serves you right for mocking my new and useful talent," she scolded, leaning back against him, feeling the sweetness of the laughter rippling through both of them. Her eyes fell on the open ledgers, and she sobered. "I'll do that for you if you'll just give me the figures. I know you hate doing it."

"I didn't just run away when I went to Seattle." She stiffened in his arms, but he knew she was listening intently. He sketched the basics of the changes in the ship and the purchase of the lot and felt her relax. "I've even got a chance for a share in one of the Sound steamers, despite my preference for sail, because it's in need of many repairs, including a new boiler, but once it's spruced up it'll take its share of the passenger and cargo fares, and they're high, and likely to remain so for some time to come." He hesitated, and now feeling his tension, she twisted around to be able to see his face.

"What's wrong? Don't you think the boat can be fixed?"

"It isn't that." He took a deep breath. "The *Moon Chaser* made port in San Francisco some time ago. The crew had leave while the ship was outfitted for her next voyage. She's on her way to Seattle now. She'll take on last supplies there and a load of lumber from the logging camp before she sails west again. Captain Pollard and his wife will come here for a couple of days, but when they and the *Moon Chaser* sail, the *Gaiety* will too. I have to go back to San Francisco."

She froze, choking back the urge to wail, "Don't leave me again, don't leave me alone!" She could hear the pleas ringing in her head so loudly, she almost missed his next words.

"It's your choice, and I'll accept whatever you decide."

"Choice?" In her misery she still didn't understand anything except that Jason sounded miserable too.

"Whether to go with me or not!" he snapped, sure of her answer, impatient to get it over with.

She was shaking in his arms. "Yes, my God, yes! Oh, Jason, I thought you meant to leave me behind again."

It was Jason who took a moment now to sort the words and put them back together again and realize what she was saying.

She studied his face and saw what he was thinking with such clarity, it terrified her. He wanted two entirely different things from her, and unless she was very careful, either one would disappoint and anger him.

"You cannot have it both ways. If you can leave Jamie, then I must," she said with slow deliberation and felt him wince as the thrust found its mark. "But I think there is a way around this, and I think the way is Jamie himself. He doesn't need San Francisco or any of the world beyond this island right now. He is just beginning to know how wide a world this small place is; there is time enough for him to learn later how much further it goes. But there is a risk that he will choose to go with us rather than to remain here. Would you allow that?"

Jason scowled, thinking of the complications of having Jamie with them in San Francisco, admitting to himself that he wanted time alone with Mary. Finally, he agreed. "It would have to work somehow."

"Do you know how to fish?"

"Yes, but what does that have to do with anything?"

"Everything. Let's take Jamie out fishing. If he's having a good time when we ask him, I think he'll be even more inclined to want to stay here."

"Devious, that's what you are," he teased, but he could see the merit of the plan. Then he blinked in surprise. "Take him out fishing, I think you said. Do you, of all people, mean in a boat?"

"Lars and Mogens both have small boats; I'm sure they'd let us use one, or we could borrow Cade's if he's not using it," she suggested innocently. She smiled at him. "Cade's been teaching me. I've never sailed very far or in a high wind, but I'm a fair sailor now on calm days in a small boat."

Jason hugged her close. "You never cease to amaze me!" It struck him again that the pattern of her fear and her courage remained a mystery to him. That she would go out on the water when she did not have to was the last thing he would have expected.

Jamie was beside himself with the excitement of the adventure, and the fact that he was with his father and Mary mattered far more to him than the possibility of catching fish—until he got his first bite.

He was so surprised, he nearly dropped the pole. "Oh, my, oh my goodness!" he chirped. "Something's there!"

Jason steadied him, testing the pull on the line. "Feels like it might be fair size. Let him play with it now to make sure he's taken the hook."

The line pulled and a flash of light leapt and fell back into the water.

Mary watched the man and the boy working together to land

the fish, and she felt joy so profound it was pain. Jason looked
so young, so carefree, and so tender, again she felt more protectiveness for him than she did for his son. She thought if she had
one wish in all the world at this moment it would be that Jason
would never be hurt again in any way. So short a time ago all
her wishes had been for revenge or for oblivion.

Jason was so aware of everything, it was as if he were seeing
new dimensions and colors, earth, sky and sea newly defined,
newly born. An eagle soared in the distance, seabirds etched
their patterns in the sky, a shoal of herring rippled light and dark
near the surface of the water and spilled upwards in brief show-
ers of silver. He was proud of how well Mary handled the boat.
He was proud of his son's close attention to his instructions.
There were no two people on earth he would rather be with than
these two.

For the first time he imagined Mary in the years ahead, still
with him. But the old frustration rose to haunt him at the
thought. He knew only what he had learned of her day by day.
It was not enough because she did not trust him enough to tell
what had been before. Love could not flourish where there was
no trust. "Love": it was a word not spoken between them, not
part of the bargain. Surely it could not be true that he loved her;
that kind of love belonged to Gaiety and had died with her. The
image of Hayes, of other men rose unpleasantly in his mind. He
reminded himself sharply that Mary never betrayed any special
interest in Hayes, seemed, in fact, closer to Cade than to the
younger man. And whatever man or men had been in her past
had, by all he knew of her, given her only fear and pain. The
bargain she had made with him had been out of need, not out
of lust or love. Whatever she felt for him, it was doubtful she
would seek another lover outside of their bargain. Admitting
that the sudden shafts of jealousy were unfounded made them
frightening. If there was not love, how could there be this madness? He felt naked, vulnerable, unmanned, and he loathed
himself for the weakness.

The landing of the fish saved him from himself. It was a
good-sized cutthroat trout, greenish blue and silver, dotted with
black and boasting the red streak below the jaw that gave the

species its name. The excitement of Jamie's first catch obliterated all else as Jason concentrated on helping his son haul the fish into the boat without falling out of it himself.

"Well done! We'll fry it for supper," he promised as he removed the hook and plopped the fish into the bucket with a little water.

The light dimmed in Jamie's eyes as he stared at the bucket. "He's hurt."

"Jamie, that's food now. You caught it fairly. And it's a hot day. Fish spoil very quickly and can make you sick if you eat them after they've gone bad. To leave it alive in the water will help keep it fresh enough to eat when we get home. But I would hope that you will never hunt or kill anything unless it is good for food or threatens your life. Do you understand?"

Jamie nodded gravely. "I think so. It'd be wrong to kill an eagle or a sea gull or to step on a snake 'cuz they aren't after me an' nobody needs to eat 'em. Is that right?"

Jason smiled at him. "That's exactly right."

Mary blessed Jason for the gentleness of his voice as he spoke the hard reality. She could see that it made sense to Jamie. He was part of a world where surviving meant giving and taking from the land and the sea; her own childhood of smiling merchants who sold the catch of others was not Jamie's life.

But she sensed a change in Jason's mood, a lessening of the easy enjoyment he had seemed to feel until now, and her belief that it had to do with telling his son of their planned departure was confirmed when he broached the subject.

The fishing line was out again, and Jason watched the cork float bobbing as he spoke. "I have to leave again, Jamie, and this time, Mary will go with me. I have a lot to do in San Francisco." He could feel Jamie tensing as if for a blow, and with an effort, he kept his voice calm as he continued. "We don't want you to be sad. If you choose to leave Daniel and your other friends to go with us, you may. But you must understand that the trip is for business. There will be day after day on the boat with no place to play but the deck and no other children will be with you, and then there will be many meetings with bankers, merchants, and investors, long dull times doing nothing but sitting in stuffy rooms listening to people talk. That's how it will be if you go."

Jamie still had trouble making choices, and he wanted to know all the facts before he decided. "What are bankers, merchants, and investors?" It was as if he were asking about rare birds. Jason stifled the laughter that threatened. He missed the tightening of Mary's mouth and the sudden bleakness in her eyes as he explained in the simplest possible terms.

"They don't sound like much fun," Jamie said.

"They aren't."

"And I'd have to dress right again, wouldn't I?"

"Yes, you would."

"Would I be back in time for school startin' again?"

"No, but we could ask Hayes to send your lessons with us so you wouldn't be behind when you returned," Jason proposed, knowing perfectly well that school was far more attractive to the boy now that he was included in the activities of the other children.

"If I don't go this time, will it mean I never get to go at all?"

Jason recognized the seriousness of the question and answered it in the same spirit. "It doesn't mean that at all. What I have will someday be yours, and all too soon you will have to learn all about it. To do that, you will have to leave the island for days and months at a time."

Jamie swallowed hard. "How soon is 'all too soon'?"

"I'll give you a few years yet," Jason assured him with a smile.

"Papa, I think I'll stay here this time," Jamie announced slowly. "I'll miss you an' Mary, but I got things to do here now, an' Grandmother will be sad if we all go away together."

"I think you've made a wise decision. And I think you have another bite on your line," Jason said as he saw the cork jerk. When he looked at Mary, he saw only smiling approval.

There was a flurry of excitement late the next afternoon. Gibson's trader, the *Folly,* was coming in, and Captain Pollard and his wife were on board, spotted clearly through Jason's spyglass.

Mary put on her pale purple dress, smoothed her hair, and rushed downstairs. Jason was just coming into the house, his eyes bright with excitement. "There you are!" he exclaimed, as if she'd been missing. He planted an abstracted kiss on her forehead and gave her a pat on the rump as he turned her back toward the stairs. "Hurry up and change into something pretty and bright for supper. The Pollards are great friends of mine, and this will be a festive evening. They'll be here shortly. Ben's already heading down with the wagon, so don't dally!"

"But I . . . I've got to tell Maggie something first," she said, changing her protest and swallowing tears of embarrassment.

"All right, but be quick!"

She ignored Maggie's protesting signs. "I don't want to disgrace him, so please, do as I ask, but wait for a while before you do it so he'll be too busy to do anything about it." She wrote it out after she'd said it, and she didn't feel guilty because Maggie looked angry rather than hurt, plainly having planned to pretend she hadn't understood. Maggie conceded defeat, but she not only signed to Mary that Mary was wrong, she wrote it down.

They looked at each other and smiled ruefully.

Keeping out of sight at the window, she watched the couple arrive to Jason's hearty greeting. Jamie stood shyly by his side. Time enough to meet them tomorrow. She settled down to read, willing herself not to mind missing the activity below. She was concentrating well enough not to hear the careful opening of the door. She gave a startled cry when Jason suddenly loomed over her.

"A headache! An obliging one to allow you to read in such comfort. I came to see if you were all right, and indeed you are. You're as bad as my mother. She too finds it distasteful to associate with sea captains though at least she usually puts in an appearance. The Pollards are worth both of you and many more besides!"

She bent her head, hiding her face from him. "I'm sure they are. But it isn't fair to compare me with your mother. I'd like very much to meet your guests, and I will tomorrow. I made up the headache because it shouldn't offend anyone—many women have them all the time, or so I've heard." The attempted humor failed utterly in the low, shaky notes of her voice. "It's my fault, but I didn't know they were arriving tonight. The rose dress, I washed it this afternoon. It's hanging outside, much too wet to wear." Her hands played nervously with the fabric of the dress she was wearing. "This will do for tomorrow, but it isn't suitable for tonight. I didn't want to shame you. I'm truly sorry," she finished miserably.

He didn't understand at all even as he watched dark splotches appearing on the bodice of the soft purple dress and knew them for tears. And then comprehension dawned, and he wanted to weep too. "Change into something pretty and bright for supper," he'd told her, not really thinking, just wanting her to be wearing some special dress for a special occasion. Such a little thing, yet not little at all. The neatly dressed hair and the crisp fabric of the dress; the flush on her cheeks and the sparkle in her eyes; he should have known she was looking forward to meeting the Pollards as much as he'd been looking forward to welcoming them. And with careless words, he'd spoiled it for her, taken more than she had to spare from her small store of self-confidence. She had sought to spare him shame and had received his bad-tempered insults for her pains.

Mary was so different from his other mistresses, and different in the way he himself regarded her. He had never noticed much about what she wore beyond his dislike of the false widow's weeds. Only with Gaiety had it been like this, a constant perception of the essentials and little notice of anything else. But even Gaiety had asked for things, for clothes and baubles that caught her fancy. All of them had asked or hinted, and he had always been generous as a matter of course, had often seen things he had casually thought would please this or that one, had showered careless gifts in great abundance.

Mary had asked for one thing, for his protection; she had paid dearly for it and continued to pay. She had never asked for anything else. And he had been blind to her most obvious practical needs. His accounts in Seattle had been open to her, but now he recalled that the only items she had bought were foodstuffs.

"Goddamn it to hell!" he swore, and her head came up, eyes big and scared.

He reached out and brushed the tears away, feeling new pain when she started to flinch away involuntarily before she checked the movement. "My dear, I'm a clumsy fool. You look lovely in that dress, and it doesn't matter what you wear anyway. The Pollards would love you if you were wearing a flour sack." He pulled her to her feet. "Ummm, come to think of it, so would I—a very small sack." He was relieved to see her smile. "Come on, time to go downstairs. They don't know about the headache, so there are no explanations to be made except that you take a long time to dress . . . I've heard that many women do."

The liking between Mary and the Pollards was instantaneous. Clem reminded her of Angie's Captain Tom. Though he was not so overwhelmingly large, he had the same far-seeing eyes set in a weather-crinkled face bedecked with a full beard, and he radiated the same kind of enormous vitality. It was as if the brotherhood of the sea molded men in a particular way. And it was soon apparent that Henrietta, "Etta" as she insisted, was a fit mate for him. Gray-haired like her husband, she was tiny and quick, with a bright gleam of humor and interest lighting her blue eyes.

"Don't let her fool ya," Clem warned, "th' crew'd ratha face pirates than cross Etta's tempa. Matta o' fact, pirates feel th' same. We was boarded once an' old Etta cracked a skull with a belayin' pin."

"T'weren't tempa oah courage, Clem, t'were pure feah," Etta protested.

Though they'd been sailing the world for decades, the Maine of their childhoods had stayed in their voices, and Mary loved the sound of it. The couple fascinated her, and she begged for more stories and listened as wide-eyed as Jamie.

They were both close to sixty now, and most of their years had been spent at sea. As soon as Clem had gotten his first captaincy at only twenty-three, he had gone home, married Henrietta, and their true home had been aboard one ship or another ever since. They had shared the glory of the clipper ships and the China trade, and they had been among the first to venture to the ports opened in Japan in 1854.

"Fust time Etta an' me went to China, back in thirty-eight it were, I had to leave 'er in Macao. Chinese had mighty peculya rules then an' ya couldn't bring yoah family with ya. Couldn't travel much noah do a thing without pamission. We were restricted to a trade district, near Canton it were, an' men called Cohongs did th' durty work o' makin' money foah th' empera. Th' Cohongs were really high-up mandarins who took false names so they wouldn't be dishonored eitha. Mah, some of theah houses were past believin', full o' marble floahs an' silk an' velvet, fancied up with inlaid furniture, paintin's, porcelains, an' all sorts of otha treasures. Could hardly keep mah eyes in mah head fust time I was invited to one. 'Course, th' Opium Woah changed all that not only foah th' British, but foah us too. Poats opened up, an' Etta was allowed to come with me. We traded tools, iun, coppa, furs, all sorts o' things foah cloves, nutmegs, silk, tea, jade, an' all soats of otha things.''

Etta told stories of kings with many wives, of exotic birds and beasts, and she insisted that the strangest feeling of all for her was to be on dry land. "Takes a mite o' time foah me to get mah land legs, don't seem right to be standin' on anything so still.''

Mary crowed aloud at that and confessed how opposite her own problem was.

"Do you have children?'' she asked, still pondering the oddness of living one's life at sea. She was sorry for the question as soon as she saw the shared sadness, but Etta answered calmly.

"We had a son, Samuel, a fine boy. He was boarn in Macao. He died in th' woah, fightin' on a Union ship. Didn't want him to go, but he were a man an' had to choose his own way. He left no wife, no children.''

"I'm sorry," Mary said.

"It's an old sorra, deah," Etta assured her with a kind smile and went on to describe Japan vividly because Jamie had expressed particular interest in that place. Mary suspected it sounded like a fairy tale to him, and she and Jason exchanged a smile at the look of radiant wonder on his face.

Even Ellen, whatever her feelings about sea captains, was on her best behavior and listened politely.

"They're wonderful!" Mary exclaimed when she and Jason were alone. "They're truly citizens of the world. They've seen so many places, so many people, and there's a kind of gentle tolerance about them. Wouldn't it be grand if everyone was like that?"

"Indeed it would," Jason agreed as he drew her against him, his fingers playing with her silky hair. "You're wonderful too. You were very kind to them."

"They were kind to me," she countered, but she did not explain that she had wondered if they would scorn her because she was Jason's mistress.

"One thing I don't understand is why they don't own the *Moon Chaser* outright. Surely after so many years of work, they could afford to."

"Yes, they could, but it's a 'don't-put-all-your-eggs-in-the-same-basket' theory. They own shares in other ships and cargoes, just as they do in the *Moon Chaser,* though in that case they and I are the only shareholders. It's a way to give at least some protection to everyone concerned. If the ship is lost, the loss is shared, just as profits are."

Mary shivered against him. "What a dreadful thought! They could be lost too in that case."

"Yes, they could. That's a risk they've lived with every day they've been at sea, but it's the life they love, and Clem's a fine captain. And believe it or not, that little Etta is one of the best navigators anywhere. She can hardly hold the instruments—they're so heavy and she's so small—but her mathematics are always accurate, like yours."

"I wouldn't trust myself to guide a ship anywhere out of sight of land even if the way was painted on the sea, but you seem to be navigating pretty welllll!" She ended on a throaty gasp as Jason's hands strayed in teasing, feather-light touches across her skin.

"Ah, but this is a familiar journey." His voice vibrated against her throat.

Mary wore the rose dress as the next evening saw Jason's house full of people for the first time since she had come to the island. The islanders, bringing food so that Maggie wouldn't have to do all the cooking, had come to visit with the Pollards. The party was as successful as the picnic had been, without any crisis worse than Astrid and Ulrik smearing each other with jam just for the fun of it.

Even Cade was there.

"Still have them miracle sheep givin' one hundred an' fifty pounds o' wool each?" Clem asked Cade.

"Yep. I expect I'll have them until someone decides which country owns these islands," Cade answered, and the two men laughed together.

When Mary asked Jason what it meant and wasn't that an awful lot of wool from one small sheep, he laughed too, and his eyes gleamed. "It's a special breed all right, and depends a lot on not having customs officials about. If it could speak, a good part of the wool would have a British accent."

Mary finally understood. Cade's smuggling runs included bringing in cheaper foreign wool without paying duty on it and selling it at a higher price along with his own in American territory. It no longer shocked her, and she laughed with Jason.

There was only one disquieting incident, and she was not even sure it had happened. But for a brief instant, she thought she had seen the strange look in Constance's eyes as she gazed at the Pollards. Somehow, the gaze touched her too. And then Constance was behaving quite normally again, and Mary knew there was no use in asking. If Constance had seen something she thought Mary ought to know, she would tell her; otherwise she would admit nothing at all.

The party flowed on with laughter and more stories as the children fell asleep one by one until the adults ended the festivities with the reluctant knowledge of chores to be done on the morrow.

CHAPTER
17

When the *Gaiety* sailed, Mary was particularly grateful to Cade. He had made a special point to be there, giving Jamie his own kind of support, an invitation to visit the cove. Daniel was there too with his mother and with the twins, and Mary was sure the children already had adventures planned clear up to the day school would begin again.

The only bad moment came when she hugged Jamie tightly in a last good-bye. He returned the pressure fiercely for an instant, but managed to whisper, "You take care of Papa so his leg doesn't hurt him." She was in more danger of tears than he, when she promised she would. She envied the cheerful faces Ingrid and Else showed to their husbands; these separations were part of their lives, and they judged it part of their duty to let their husbands depart with light hearts.

Gradually the waving figures on the shore grew smaller until they faded away. Mary blew one last kiss to Jamie even though she knew he couldn't see her. When she turned, she found Etta regarding her compassionately.

"I was lucky. I neva had to leave Samuel when he was small."

Jason looked over and smiled at both of them. It was harder for him than it had ever been before to leave his son even though, paradoxically, Jamie was better off now than he had ever been before and better off on the island than he would be traveling with them. He knew how difficult it was for Mary and was glad she had Etta beside her now. Etta had not been subtle about how she felt. "You lose that gal, Jason Drake, an' yo'ah a darn fool," she'd told him.

As Cade had warned, so Mary found that being back on the *Gaiety* was not like the excursions in the skiff. The lurch and roll of the deck high above the water made her queasy, but it was far better than it had been, and for the first time, she thought she might be able to get used to it. Yet, she was grateful that they reached the lumber mill by nightfall by grace of the wind and tide. She and Jason were to stay there so that Jason could make sure all was in order with the cargo of lumber while the *Gaiety* would sail on to Seattle the next day where the Pollards would collect their ship and crew.

They spent the night at the mill, and Maude Tomlinson, the head sawyer's wife, even curbed her disapproval of Mary when she saw that the Pollards treated the girl with affection and respect.

But the parting in the morning came as a shock to Mary. Etta hugged her tightly for a moment. "Take ca-uh o' yoahself an' take ca-uh o' th' Tiger. Th' two of you fit; given th' yeahs, you might fit just as well as Clem an' I do."

Mary hardly heard the compliment. "But you'll be back on the *Moon Chaser*! Surely we don't have to say good-bye now!"

"Ayuh we do." Etta's eyes began to sparkle. "Theah's a race on now. Th' *Gaiety*'ll sail back as quick as can be, an' you an' Jason will head out on 'er. Clem an' me, we've got to haul th' crew out o' th' sawdust 'foah we can leave Seattle, but then we'll be towed by steam tugs right to heah an' right on out to th' Pacific once th' lumba's loaded. Might not be so fast, but t'will be steady, while th' *Gaiety*'ll have to search foah th' wind an' ride th' tide clear out th' Strait. Got to give th' boys theah fun," she insisted with an indulgent smile. "An' anytime sail an' steam are matched, that's fun! But you watch us, if yo'ah theah, you watch when th' *Moon Chaser* catches th' wind, that's a sight indeed."

Etta's excitement was contagious and eased the sadness of parting. "It's not something to worry you, but if you have time, I'd be so grateful if you'd give my regards to Angie Cooper. She has a boardinghouse in Seattle, and she was kind to me. I'd like her to know that everything is all right."

"Why, t'won't be any botha! I'm already carryin' a letta from 'er Captain Tom. Th' *Moon Chaser* an' th' *Angie Cooper* met up some time back."

A warm wave of joy swept over Mary, and she kissed the smaller woman on both cheeks. "So the world's not so vast after all! I'm so glad to know that Tom's all right and still thinking of Angie, and now I know I'll see you and Clem again." It seemed only just that if the world should hold the chance of bad meetings, it should also contain the good.

"O' course you will, child," Etta scolded, but her eyes were soft.

"We'll see you beyond the Strait!" Mary called as the schooner slipped away.

"If yo'ah lucky," Etta called back.

Jason put his arm around Mary and held her close for a moment, proud of her laughing involvement. "Everything's going well here. What do you say we ride up to the logging camp? Even if the *Gaiety* makes it back tonight, we won't be able to leave until tomorrow."

It was not totally for her that he wanted to go; he wanted to praise the men for a job well done. Mary realized that, but it made no difference. It was wonderful to see Jud, Bull Fletcher, Bart, Red, and the others again. This time they welcomed her as if the Tiger had never come here without her. Fiddler even found time after supper to play a few tunes, though it wasn't Saturday night or Sunday either.

They left in a murky predawn darkness made darker by the enshrouding forest. Yet, when they were in sight of the water again, they saw that the schooner was there before them.

Jason's face tightened in anger. "Damn, they risked running in the dark!" Then he shrugged. "Ah, well, they made it, and I know how important it is to them to prove their worth to Clem. Come on, before they sail without us!"

They entered Admiralty Inlet and sailed as close to the wind as they could, watching for luffing of the sails that would mean they were too close and would risk having the wind back the canvas and stop the boat in the water. They watched every ship within sight behind them, knowing that sooner or later, the *Moon Chaser* would begin to make up their head start with the help of the tugs.

Mary could no more resist the excitement of the game than the rest of them, and she felt a rush of anxiety every time a new ship was sighted. The *Eliza Anderson* steamed past them on her Victoria to Olympia run, and they waved at the steamship, which blew a few notes on its famous calliope in a return salute.

Jason smiled as he watched Mary. She was flushed with excitement, exclaiming at the beauty of the distant snow peaks on this clear day and borrowing Jason's glass often for a closer look at settlements and mill towns. It was a happy change from her previous discomfort on board.

They passed to the north of Port Townsend with its wharf fronting a cluster of frame houses and stores. The town boasted nearly six hundred people now and was proudest of all of having won the customs house back from Port Angeles.

Across the water to the north lay Drake's Island. Mary thought of Jamie and the others and wished them all well.

Their luck held in the Strait of Juan de Fuca until they had passed Port Angeles. Then the wind and the tide failed them. Captain Hanson and the crew looked longingly at a passing tug, and Jason snorted with laughter. "Thinking of cheating?"

Captain Hanson had the grace to look abashed. "It did tempt me for a moment. I don't think we're going to go much further until tomorrow, if then. We'll be lucky not to drift backwards."

"Well, we still don't know when the *Moon Chaser* will be under way. Remember, Clem has to find his crew in Seattle and then there's the lumber to load."

"You didn't happen to ask that the loading be a bit slow?" the Captain asked hopefully.

"I thought of it, but no, we'll win fair and square." Jason was suddenly serious. "And we won't run at night."

They anchored near a sheltering cove out of the main traffic lanes to wait out the calm and the night. Most of the sail was furled, lanterns illuminated the ship, and Jason was thankful there was no fog to increase the hazard of another ship plowing into them.

It was Mary's first night below in the *Gaiety*'s master cabin, a luxurious room of polished wood and crimson plush with a big built-in bunk. "I know what you're thinking," Jason accused when he saw Mary's expression at her first sight of it. "It looks like a floating bordello, but it's a cheerful place when the weather's foul."

"How would I know what a bordello looks like?" Mary pretended outraged innocence, but in fact, she was so grateful to be going with him, she only cared that she and not some other woman was to occupy the cabin with him.

It was going to take her a while to grow accustomed to being enclosed in the rocking world. She lay down abruptly as a wave of nausea swept over her. "I will get used to it," she promised when she opened her eyes to Jason's worried frown. She closed her eyes again. The lantern overhead was swinging slowly in its brackets. It had been a very long day, and suddenly she was very tired, the need to sleep greater than any discomfort.

Jason undressed her and washed her hands and face with cool water.

"Sometimes you're very nice," she murmured.

"Just sometimes?" he teased and his eyes were tender, but she was asleep.

They all cheered in the morning when they set the *Gaiety* on her course again and felt her gathering speed as the canvas filled. They saw no sign of the *Moon Chaser* until they had left the Strait bounded by the long line of Vancouver Island to the north and the Olympic Peninsula to the south. They were standing off Cape Flattery in the waters of the Pacific when Jason cried, "There she is!" and handed the spyglass to Mary.

The tugs looked ridiculously small and toylike as three of them towed the huge ship, but they puffed along gallantly.

"She's beautiful!" Mary exclaimed. Even with her decks piled high with lumber, the *Moon Chaser*'s two-hundred-foot length was a graceful expanse of shining brass, highly varnished wood, and complex rigging. Soon, even without the glass, Mary could make out the figures of Etta and Clem on deck among the crew.

The lines were slipped, the tugs dropped away, turning back

to the Strait, and the sails were set on the big ship in a swift, precise dance of skill accompanied by booming male voices singing:

> A Yankee sloop came down the river
> Ha, ha, Rolling John!
> And what do you think that sloop had in her?
> Ha, ha, Rolling John!

"Clem always makes sure one of his crew is a good chantey-man though he himself can lead as well as the best," Jason explained.

The verses went on until the white sails were taut in the wind, and the *Moon Chaser* found her own heart and began to gather speed. When the ships were within hailing distance of each other, Mary felt the cry rise in her throat. "Fair winds, fair winds to China and back again. God keep you safe," she called over the water.

Even over the sea sounds, the creak of rigging, and crackling of sail, her words were clear, and Etta, standing beside Clem at the helm, called back, "Smooth sailin' in all watas, Mary."

Clem saluted them. "Well done, *Gaiety,* we'll beat you next time!"

As the two ships drew away from each other, the chanteyman began another song. Other voices joined in, sending the sound across the sea.

> Oh, Shenandoah's my native valley,
>   Away, you rolling river!
> Oh, Shenandoah's my native valley,
>   Away, we're bound to go
>   'Cross the wide Missouri!
>
> Oh, Shenandoah, it's far I wander,
>   Away, you rolling river!
> Oh, Shenandoah, it's far I wander,
>   Away, we're bound to go
>   'Cross the wide Missouri!

The verses grew fainter. Mary's eyes were filled with tears, and Jason's voice was husky, not only at the sound, but at his memory of Mary singing the song to his son. "That was a tribute to you. It's surely the most beautiful of all the sea chanteys, but it's usually sung only as the men hoist the anchor."

Jason's arm was around her waist. She could feel his body riding easily with the roll of the sea, and she too felt the rhythm naturally, a slow sweet motion her flesh and spirit had always known though she had fought against it. She blessed Cade for the hours in the canoe and the skiff, but she knew it went beyond that to seeing, really seeing, the beauty of the *Moon Chaser* heading out to sea, bound thousands of miles away. She was sure Clem and Etta were smiling in pure joy to be free of land again.

It took them more than three weeks to make the trip to San Francisco, and in those days, Mary came to feel as if the *Gaiety* were another home, even safer and more isolated than the island. She grew to love the precision of life aboard. Far enough out to avoid the pull of the tides, the ship glided along when the wind held and sulked in stillness when it failed, but the men were pleased with her overall progress. In the vastness of this water, they sailed through the night when the sky was clear and the winds held.

They exchanged friendly waves with other sailing vessels and with steamers. They fished, and Mary was as excited by her first catch as Jamie had been by his. They watched the land, Jason giving the glass to Mary and telling her what to look for when he thought there was something on the rough coastline she ought to see. The boiling mouth of the great Columbia River appeared, with its shifting sandbars that could keep a ship from entering for weeks or treacherously wreck her when she finally did make the run for the river. Mary was not the only one who was relieved they did not have to make the attempt.

They were well supplied with food and barrels of fresh water, replenished by two rainfalls in the first ten days. The men bathed mostly in salt water though, and left the privilege of the fresh to Mary. On one of the rainy days, she simply let herself and her clothing get soaked while she scrubbed her hair under a heavy spout of water that ran off one of the booms. Jason accused her of being mad.

"No, just clean," she laughed, looking up at him through spiky wet lashes.

He kissed the tip of her nose and teased, "Haven't you noticed there's no dust on board?"

"Invisible sea dust—takes a woman to see it," she insisted, tugging his head down so that she could kiss him properly. She had no shyness in front of the crew. There didn't seem any point in pretense. Captain Hanson and the others knew what she was to Jason.

Even when the sea grew rough now and then and threatened her newly discovered sea legs, the wish held—the impossible wish that she and Jason could sail on forever in the small close world of the ship. They were more at ease and happy together here than they had ever been, and she did not fool herself into believing that it was more than the condition of the voyage. Jason was supremely happy, relaxed, and skilled at sea. He even seemed less lame despite the movement of the ship. He never impinged on Captain Hanson's authority, but often it was he who guided the craft, and he took his turn at watches.

Mary regarded the joy Jason gave her as the overflow of the joy the sea gave him. She stored up memories of the nights of his lovemaking and the days of his laughter and kept the fear at bay. She wanted to be with him; she did not want to be back in San Francisco. The city was too cosmopolitan, too heavily populated, too closely connected with the eastern states. And it had too many temptations for Jason, too many women more beautiful, more skilled, and more desirable than she. It was a fear in itself to admit that this was an even greater terror now than the risk of being recognized in her undisguised state.

She stared at the figures in the ledger without seeing them at all.

Jason's voice came again, "Where have you gone?"

She blinked at him, pushing away thoughts of San Francisco and focusing on business. They were spending time on the ledgers and concise reports, making sure everything was in order for the sharp eyes of the men who would check them for Jason's worth.

She studied him thoughtfully and asked a question of her own. "Do you ever get nervous about how all of this must balance so closely?"

"I lie awake nights wondering if two bits missing will bring me down."

She resisted the appeal of his crooked grin. "I'm serious," she said. "As long as the lumber sells well, the rents come in from San Francisco, the *Moon Chaser* continues to make a profit, the hope of a silver strike remains high and the price for silver good, as long as you build good ships and can sell or sail them, as long as everything works perfectly, it all keeps going. But the loans and the notes you pay on, they all carry high interest rates, and if you couldn't meet your payments it would take very little time before you owed an enormous amount. And I suspect you plan to borrow yet more for your new schemes in Seattle; otherwise, we wouldn't be doing all this work." She stopped, suddenly aware that she had surely gone too far, but there was no anger in his voice.

"Are you afraid I won't be able to feed you?"

Her courage returned with his reasonableness and her concern for him, and she protested vehemently. "Of course not, this hasn't anything to do with me, but it has everything to do with you! You've worked so hard, I know you have, and I hate the idea of your losing everything because you're overextended! It's a bad time. It's been getting worse since the war. So few know what's happening. You can't know one day to the next whether greenbacks can be used to pay a debt or not, and gold and silver coins are in short supply compared to the need. And President Grant is an idiot who loves the successful too much because he was never a success until he was a general. Think of it, a general who couldn't keep a store well enough to keep it at all! So he worships them, he worships the manipulators, speculators, and bloated bankers who are running this country now and will keep running it until someone stops them. And it won't be Grant who does that. He wants so much to believe in them, he'll never know what's happening until the damage is done. Black Friday, only a year ago, surely you remember! Fisk and Gould nearly cornered the gold market, and they used privileged information to do it, before President Grant understood what was happening.

And yes, he ordered the Treasury to sell gold so that business could go on, but think how many thousands were ruined before the President understood and stopped it. And last year was only the beginning of his term; God knows what else he'll bungle before he's through."

"Sounds to me like a perfect time for enterprising business-men to me," Jason remarked with careful humor. He was not angered by what she was saying; he was stunned. The door to her past was swinging open again, and he didn't know what to make of the new information. How in the hell could she know so much about what was going on—why would she care enough to know? She mentioned Fisk and Gould as if they were people she knew personally and despised.

"You know what I mean," she snapped in exasperation. "The loans and interest payments become more dear as money becomes more scarce because every time you have to borrow more, the rate is higher."

"Yes, I do know." He still felt no anger for her interference; it was his hide, not hers, she was trying to save, trying so hard she was betraying herself. "I told you, I like to gamble, and I have a habit of winning. But I'm not completely foolish about it. Greenbacks have never been the problem in the West that they have in the East. And you'll notice I'm not betting on the railroad coming to Seattle soon even though almost everyone else is. I like some certainty in my bets when there are no cards or dice on the table."

Mary looked at him curiously, thinking of all the people in Seattle who were so certain of the railroad. She had noted the lack of railroad shares in Jason's dealings. "I've wondered," she admitted. "And I hope you're wrong. Why do you doubt that the Northern Pacific will come to Seattle? It's the perfect terminus."

"Not from the railroad's point of view. People already own the land in Seattle, and this railroad is in the business of selling land, not buying it. Congress gave it almost no money but nearly endless land, and it's been building its own towns all along the route. The men who are financing it and ferreting out their profits are the same kind as those who engineered the gold conspiracy. I have a distaste for being involved with their kind. It's not only an offended moral sense; greed like that almost always ends in a crash, and one must be very powerful indeed not to be buried in the rubble.''

He was not like the other man, not at all, Mary thought. Suddenly not even her fear of the other was as strong as her joy in Jason.

Jason watched the shadows shifting and pooling and then lifting from her eyes. When she looked at him directly again, they were soft gray, the outer rings very dark, the gold flecks dancing. He swallowed the last impulse to ask her how she had learned what she knew.

"Enough work for today, let's go topside."

"We don't have to work any more. We don't have to go up there yet either." Her voice was husky and the tip of her tongue played over her lips invitingly.

He recognized a variation on the same pattern—when her past rippled through her dreams or her days, she turned to him and found oblivion in the deliberate seduction of his body. Part of him still rebelled at the use, but a greater part would have her close any way she would come to him. He knew her body better now than he had when the first nightmares had driven her screaming to wakefulness, and he kept his own control and played his mouth and hands over her flesh until he knew the match was equal between them.

"Now shall we go on deck?" he asked a good while later.

She smiled and kissed his shoulder. "Trying to protect your virtue?"

"No, I'm trying to save my strength." He patted her bottom. "Come on, get dressed. I'm feeling old and weak."

Her need for him grew the closer they got to San Francisco, and she had to fight hard not to cling to him constantly. She wanted his closeness even more than she wanted his lovemaking. She wanted his smile and the sound of his laughter. She wanted to know what he was thinking and what he dreamed of. She had never wanted to know another human being as much as she wanted to know this hard man with so much tenderness beneath the surface.

They stopped at the redwood logging camp on the Mendocino coast of California, and Mary kept her eyes shut most of the time it took to sail the *Gaiety* through the narrow opening between rocks into the doghole. Her eyes were still shut when she felt Jason coming to stand beside her.

"Did we make it?"

"In fine style." He didn't see any reason to mention to her that storms were often sudden and violent here, or that ten lumber schooners had been lost in one year a while back. But they would not have put in at all had there been any sign of trouble brewing in the sky.

She ventured a peek and then opened her eyes fully.

The camp was different, far different from the one on Puget Sound. They had to climb a steep wandering ramp of wooden steps to get to the top of the cliff scarred by a tangle of chutes and wires that were used to get the lumber down to the ships once it had been brought out of the woods in manageable size. Here, the giant redwoods were felled into a cradle of cushioning boughs because despite the wood's resistance to weather and rot and its superior durability for railroad ties, shingles, and house siding, the trees were brittle and could shatter at the impact of their own enormity on hard earth. But the difference went far deeper.

Mary had expected the camp to be much like the one in the Washington Territory. But when she saw the steep climb involved, she knew it was going to be difficult for Jason. At first, she noticed nothing beyond her concern for him. She was ahead of him as they mounted the steps, and she heard him catch his breath sharply too many times as his bad leg protested the strain of the effort. When they were finally at the top and men were coming to greet them, she moved a little in front of Jason and risked slipping her hand back beneath the cover of her skirts to touch his bad leg. The thigh muscles were knotted and twitching against her hand, but he hissed in her ear, "I'm all right. It'll be all downhill when we leave."

All she really wanted was to make Jason lie down and rest while she kneaded the soreness out of his leg, but she fixed a smile on her face and tried to pay attention. She wished she hadn't.

There was fear of the Tiger here, but no liking. Jason was just another of the mostly absent owners in this camp, and there was a current of badly concealed hostility that he should interrupt their work to look at his investment. And here the men made little attempt to hide the intensity and direction of their interest in the Tiger's woman.

Jason's eyes narrowed to slits, and a muscle pulsed in his jaw. Lars and Mogens, who had come with them, were suddenly standing very close, and she could feel the menace from them as strongly as from Jason.

"No trouble, Jason, please, for my sake," she whispered desperately. He looked so grim, she nearly backed away from him, but then he gave a small nod of acquiescence.

It was hardly necessary. The smoldering rage emanating from the Tiger flanked by two equally murderous looking blond giants had reminded the loggers that whether they liked it or not, the man did have a great deal to do with their livelihood, at least while they worked here. And they were mollified when he listened to them carefully and showed his own knowledge by his questions. The men had not met him before—the crew in this camp had changed often since the last good cook had left —but they'd heard the legend, and now they had their own experience to add to it. It made the disruption worthwhile.

Not even the soaring majesty of the coast redwoods made much impression on Mary. She hated every minute of her visit to the camp. It was a wild place, and the men were big and hungry. If they decided to, they could easily overpower Jason, Mogens, and Lars, and she would be theirs. Here she was the Tiger's whore, and she felt it. She retreated into all the dignity she could muster, but when they went back down the cliff, her knees were shaking so hard, she feared falling with each step. She was shaking all over by the time the launch was rowed out to the *Gaiety*. She wanted more than anything to be back aboard. Even the passage out of the tight cove lost its terror compared to what she had just faced, but she could not find the strength to climb the rope ladder. She reached for it and then sank back, trembling uncontrollably.

Jason went ahead while Mogens lifted Mary as if she were one of his children and handed her up to him. Jason gathered her in his arms and carried her to the cabin, gritting his teeth as he managed the gangway with painstaking care, unwilling to relinquish his burden until he had her safely inside.

He put her down on the bed, wrapped her in the coverlet, and stared into her eyes. Her hands were icy cold in his. "I wanted you to see the redwoods, but I should not have taken you there. The spirit of this camp is not like the one up north, and it's worse than the last time I was here. If a new boss and a new cook, especially a new cook, aren't found soon, there won't be a crew here at all."

That drew a wavering smile from her. "It's hard to believe a cook can make so much difference, but then I remember how much Fiddler has to do with everything at his camp."

"The men are isolated, they work hard, and there's little pleasure. Food becomes very important." That hunger for women became important too, was the unspoken thought between them.

Jason's grim self-blame still showed on his face, and Mary read the strain of the climb there, even before he began to rub at the cramping muscles in his habitual, unconscious way.

The memory of the terrible siege after he had rescued her from the caves obliterated all else. "Lie down, let me do that."

He protested that it wasn't necessary even as he surrendered to her ministrations because she looked so anxious. And she did ease him, her hands moving as if they knew exactly where the pain was and how to draw it out.

On the edge of sleep, he forced his heavy lids open. "Feel the difference? We're out of the doghole." His eyes closed again.

She watched the last of the sun drowning in the sea, and she watched Jason sleeping. She wished more than ever that the *Gaiety* would turn around and sail back to the island or sail on forever. The leering acknowledgment of her position as Jason's whore, and the avid judgment that she must be extremely talented in bed—she feared she would read the same expression countless times in San Francisco.

CHAPTER
18

*O*n the day they made port, San Francisco gleamed in the sun on the hills above the water.

Mary saw none of the beauty. She remembered how exhausted she'd been when the troop of players, herself among them, had finally arrived in the promised Paris of the West and how threadbare they had looked compared to what San Franciscans then expected from their major entertainers.

Five of the nine who had made it all the way west went off to play what they hoped would be a more appreciative audience of farmers, miners, and loggers, in any small, culturally starved settlements they might come across. The four who were left simply dispersed like fog under hot sun. Frederick and Felicia Fanton, their stage names intact, their marriage punctuated by violent arguments after every performance, talked vaguely of taking ship for Hawaii or South America, then were gone. Mary and a woman who called herself Stella were left. They had studied each other with wordless honestly, sharing the memories of bad food, bad lodgings, and the fact that they had never become friends and never would.

"Take care, kid, and good luck. I'm off to find some generous dude before everything sags any more than it has."

Mary had not seen Stella or any of the others again. She remembered with equal clarity her struggle to find a job and stay alive without a man to protect her. And then she had fled. And now she was back, having lost everything she had fought for. Her only job was to please her protector.

Jason took a suite at the new Grand Hotel at Market and Montgomery. His name was registered, hers was not. She tried to assure herself that it was doubtful that everyone staying in the four-hundred-room hotel was more virtuous than she. Still, she was overawed by the luxuriousness of their quarters and felt very shabby.

Then her mood shifted completely, and suddenly she saw her lack of finery as a blessing. Surely Jason wouldn't expect her to accompany him in her plain wardrobe. She didn't even mind the idea of being a virtual prisoner in the hotel until they sailed again; she would be safe. She relaxed a little when that seemed to be Jason's plan. He left her at the hotel, telling her to rest, while he went out to set up the first of many business meetings. That night, they had supper in the room.

But the respite was brief. The next day he told her he had a surprise for her. A carriage was waiting.

"Couldn't you go without me?" she ventured timidly.

He hooted with laughter at the thought. "Absolutely not." But he didn't tell her where they were going.

When the driver pulled the horses to a stop at their destination, Jason expected Mary to see the humor of her suggestion that he should have come alone, but she didn't. She stared at the blue and gilt façade of the shop belonging to Madame Antoine, Modiste. "It looks terribly expensive," she whispered. And she remembered. Frenchie had once received some delicate lingerie and a pair of gloves purchased here by an admirer and had decided he must be wealthier than she had thought.

"That's between me and Madame Antoine," Jason chided. "You aren't to bother about it."

She knew the moment she entered the plush, well-appointed shop that anything purchased here was going to be every bit as dear as she feared. The sample dresses and the swatches of material were exquisite. She made one last attempt, murmuring, "I'm a very good seamstress, truly I am. If I had some lengths of material, I could do the work myself."

"I didn't bring you to San Francisco to sew the hours away." A sharp note had entered his voice, and Mary subsided.

Madame Antoine—middle-aged and sleekly French in severely cut and beautifully tailored black with white lace at collar and cuffs—greeted Jason effusively. Beyond the fact that he was a good, if not frequent, customer, she liked the Tiger. She liked the stories about him, and most of all she liked the maleness of him. It was an aura few men had, and it made her feel very female. Behind a façade of practiced politeness, she studied the Tiger's new woman, and her dressmaker's eye was instantly intrigued. Lovely lines, spectacular coloring, but different, very different from his other women. The dress the girl was wearing was made of poor stuff, but it was well made and of simple design. Good, she and Jason would not have to charm her out of extra ruffles and the other gaudy extras some of Jason's women had favored.

Madame settled them in comfortable chairs next to a table and began to lay out sketches and bits of material as her assistants supplied them. A piece of deep apricot silk caught Mary's eye, and suddenly she wanted it. The tip of her tongue touched her top lip nervously. She was accustomed to not having what she wanted—"the brown will do. So suitable, so durable. It doesn't do to be ostentatious"—but it didn't help. Jason was determined to buy her something anyway, and she wanted the silk desperately. She knew it would become her and make Jason proud of her when she wore it. "Please, may I have this?" she asked softly.

"Of course," he agreed vaguely, eyeing the other colors and fabrics. "This blue would suit you too. I like you in this color." He smiled, remembering the dancing costume.

She swallowed her disappointment, putting down the silk, taking up the fine wool he favored. It was lovely and much more delicate than anything she had had before. "It's settled then. If Madame will take my measurements and make it up as she thinks best, we can go."

She stood, offering the piece of material to the woman with a smile, but Madame Antoine was obviously distressed and having difficulty returning the smile. "I have displeased in some way?" she asked anxiously, her eyes on Jason.

Jason was totally baffled, and then the reason for Mary's actions dawned on him—the wide-eyed wonder with which she had regarded the apricot material, the quick relinquishing of it when he mentioned the blue, were the response of a small child who has been told that a prayer book is healthier than a box of chocolates and who knows there's no point in arguing. He swallowed the lump in his throat and spoke gently. "My dear, I said the blue would suit you too, not instead of. I won't have you suffering from headaches because your best dress is wet."

She was torn between laughter and tears. She threw her arms around him and buried her face against his chest. "It is too generous!"

He stroked the soft, silvery hair. "It's only the beginning."

He meant what he said. It took hours. Materials and styles were discussed at length, and when he discovered that Mary's choice had ended with the silk, he made the decisions. He chose deep, glowing colors, avoiding all that were too bright or too dull. There were many shades Mary had never worn before, and they were perfect for her coloring, as if Jason knew her far better than she herself did. The same unerring instinct showed in his selection of styles and his insistence that ribbons, ruffles, and trims be kept to a minimum. "I don't want her disappearing in fuss and feathers," he told the modiste, who knew his taste and agreed in any case. The threat of a single dress order had long since vanished, and she clucked her approval of Jason's selections.

He forgot nothing. Undergarments and night rails were ordered, day and evening dresses, even light smocks and skirts for casual days on the island, heavier clothing for the coming winter there, and two special split skirts of durable material to make walking in the woods and riding astride easier. Bonnets, shawls, cloaks, gloves, and all the little accessories were added to the list.

Though it was all for her, Mary felt as if she were watching it from a great distance while her body was measured, draped, and adorned. Jason did everything so capably from planning a ship to sailing it, from wielding an ax to building a sawmill, why should he not also be capable in this? But her earlier flash of joy was gone in a tangle of confusion and a knot of jealousy. He had so obviously done this many times before. Where were they now, those other women he had dressed with lavish generosity? They could not all be like Angie, gone on to fair contentment with another man in another life. And had he done this early in the relationships or when he was growing tired of them and sought first a diversion and then a paid dismissal? Was it truly business or was it more restlessness for the city and what it could offer him that had brought him to San Francisco? She had never owned such things before, and now she doubted that she wanted them. The vanity of looking pretty was a simple thing compared to the knowledge that much of what Jason was buying for her was for public appearances, for going places where she would be seen. She had known that when they came to San Francisco, but not how openly and extensively she would be displayed. She remembered the looks on the faces of the loggers and the carefully controlled blandness in the expressions of the hotel clerks. Her courage vanished. *Easily seen, easily traced.* And what would she do if he left her here when the chase had grown easier for the other?

Jason had indeed been in the shop before but never had he so concerned himself with the outfitting of one of his women. The others had known exactly what they wanted and had only desired to add to already extensive wardrobes. Jason's interest had been limited to the pleasure of watching the happiness the gifts gave the women and to making sure none of them indulged in too garish fancies. He was fully aware of Madame Antoine's carefully hidden surprise and elation at the extent of his purchases. He was equally aware but less able to deal with Mary's changing response.

He knew her joy and gratitude for the apricot silk had been genuine, and he knew that joy was totally eclipsed now. Her face had grown very pale, her eyes deep and sad even while she tried to make all the appropriate, enthusiastic comments.

This was neither the time nor the place to discuss it, that much he knew. The rest was a mystery as Mary so often was. He would have sworn she had never had pretty clothes before, but that made little sense if her background was as rich as he surmised. Had she then once possessed beautiful things and lost them with the choice of that first lover? He assured himself that her reactions did not indicate rediscovery. She remained an enigma.

The small spark of anger found tinder and grew into ever brighter flame. He had done his utmost today to please her, and his reward was the growing wariness and withdrawal in her great gray eyes. He could feel her slipping away. It was as if the sweet days on the *Gaiety* had never been. He asked himself for the countless time why he kept her. No matter how hard he tried, there seemed to be no way to build shared memories and trust with her. She not only denied the past before him, she denied the past months they had shared. Not even good memories seemed to reassure her that good days were yet to come. His need to be quit of the problem she always was, burned suddenly hotter than anger or desire.

The clothes would be delivered to their hotel, a few articles no later than the next morning so that mademoiselle would have something suitable to wear in this fair city. Jason paid the bill and escorted Mary to the carriage. He was stepping up to join her when Madame Antoine called to him.

"Un moment, if you please, Monsieur Drake. I am certain I 'ave made *une erreur."*

Jason turned from the carriage and followed her back into the shop, grimly sure she had decided to charge even more than the high prices he had paid. He was spoiling for a fight, and she would do for a start.

"Ja'son, I 'ave seen the others an' now theze one. She ize not the same. It was not a trick. She deed not wan' so grand a gift. It might be bad for my business," she admitted with a little smile, "but *peut-être* you keep theze one, my fren.'"

When she saw the look in Jason's eyes, she wished she had minded her own business as she usually did, especially with a customer who paid in advance. His "good day" was a curt dismissal.

Mary could feel Jason's anger in the close confines of the carriage, and she was appalled at the ruin she had brought on the day.

"I'm so sorry, Jason. I'm just overwhelmed. I've never had such beautiful clothes before. I'm truly grateful." Her voice faltered and died away at his lack of response.

So, his first guess had been correct, but he still didn't know why—an aristocratic family fallen on hard times? She wouldn't tell him, this scheming infant who was even capable of arousing the protective instincts of a hard-bitten French modiste. No doubt too many others felt sorry for Mary and judged him the aggressor. They never saw the claws sheathed in young velvet, but he could feel them digging ever deeper into his flesh and spirit.

He heard a little sniffle and rasped, "If you cry, I think I'll throw you out on the street," without looking at her.

When they arrived at the hotel, he escorted her to the room. "I'm going out. You may order food brought to you here. Summon the maid if you want anything."

She nodded miserably, but as he left, he heard her bid him softly to take care of himself. He turned back long enough to snap, "I'm not the one who is a mewling infant!"

He walked for a time, and when his leg protested, he hailed a hansom cab and had it drive aimlessly about the city while he stared and saw nothing. Finally it was late enough and he went to the Bank Exchange Bar. His hopes were rewarded when he spotted Owen Trenglyth in his usual place. Owen's dark eyes lighted with pleasure when Jason greeted him.

"Heard you were in town, hoped I'd see you sooner or later, but gossip has it that you didn't come alone. Where're you hiding her?"

"Word travels goddamn fast, doesn't it?" Jason snarled, and Owen cowered in mock terror.

"Whoa! So the Tiger wants to fight, does he? Little lady won't put up her fists, or has she slipped away in the city of sins? Well, not even for friendship's sake am I going to let you punch me."

Jason felt himself relaxing. He grinned at Owen. "I'll wait until you're less steady on your feet."

"I'm steady most of the time now, growing more respectable by the day," he claimed piously, and Jason laughed aloud at that.

Owen could outdrink and outbrawl anyone he knew. Of only medium height, slim and wiry, his fists carried terrific power for his size. Jason knew that from personal experience. He'd gotten in the way of Owen's right at the start of a barroom brawl years before. Caught off-balance, he'd crashed down, taking Owen's intended target with him. Owen had helped him to his feet with fulsome apologies. "Damn, fella, sorry about that, want to hit me back?" Jason had declined the privilege and fought at Owen's side as the brawl developed into a full-scale war of fists, furniture, and glass. When it was over, no one was quite sure what it had been about or who had won, except for the obvious casualties still unconscious on the floor. Most of the men contributed good-naturedly when Owen passed the hat, and the saloon made a profit on damage that night.

Their friendship had begun as Owen and Jason nursed cuts and bruises in Owen's rooms after the fight, and it had never faltered. A year older than Jason, Owen had dark hair and eyes and swarthy skin that testified as much as his name did to his Welsh heritage. In repose, his eyes were wary, his face sardonic, hard planes and angles with small scars here and there from his fighting. He was quick to anger and as quick to forgive. And when he was amused, his face changed completely, becoming so open and full of laughter, one had to laugh with him. A complex man. For all his street knowledge, he was highly educated and a very good lawyer. He defended his clients with the same fervor he devoted to his pleasures, which usually included a beautiful mistress. He had been Jason's attorney for most of the years of their friendship. And he could call him the "Tiger" and get away with it.

He regarded his friend carefully now, seeing the anger and distress still there despite the easing of tension. "You want to talk about it or drown it?"

"Drown it." He was making some headway with that decision when he decided there was something else he wanted. "Jardene's girls still the best in town?"

Owen nodded. "Far as I know. I've been out of circulation for a few months now. I might even marry this one." It was the woman, Owen knew, and he was giving Jason an opening to talk about her. But Jason wasn't dull-witted even with a haze of alcohol shrouding his brain.

His eyes met Owen's. "I can't, not now anyway, just can't talk about her. It's enough to say I was a fool to get involved with her, and I wish I hadn't. I'm heading for Jardene's, want to come along?"

"Nope, I'm practicing fidelity, mostly because Carrie keeps me too tired for anything else." He didn't ask how the Tiger had fallen into the trap, but he hoped he'd find out soon, hoped he'd meet the woman. This was a new twist; he'd never known Jason to have any trouble getting—or getting rid of—a woman.

"There'll be some meetings I'd like you to sit in on. I'll see you tomorrow or the next day," Jason said in parting.

Owen watched his purposeful progress out of the saloon and thought he'd be even happier than usual to go home to Carrie tonight. But he'd have to stay a while yet to hear the end of a nearby conversation. He hadn't lost track of it even while talking to Jason. It would help his client a good deal if the secrets kept pouring forth so freely.

Jardene, born Jane Dibley, welcomed Jason like the Prodigal Son, and when he specified any but a blonde, he was introduced to Ruby, full of breast, curving in all the other right places, and graced with a thick length of shining red hair. Her skin was creamy white with golden freckles, her mouth was full, her nose pertly uptilted, her eyes slanting cat-green. In her early twenties, she was full-fledged, quick-witted and capable of pleasing a man in a multitude of ways. She eyed Jason appreciatively, liking what she saw, and she led him to her room, hoping he hadn't drunk so much as to be incapacitated.

Her hopes were more than rewarded. Jardene had promised this one was a tiger—she had happily retired her body from service behind rolls of fat and an equally plump bank account but there was nothing wrong with her memory—and Ruby found that he was. He knew how to please a woman and how to take his own pleasure. She felt as if he possessed every inch of her body, including some even she hadn't known about before. She was glad he was her exclusive property for the night, and she fell asleep with a small, satisfied smile.

Jason slept too because he was tired of thinking and sexually satiated. But when he awakened at dawn, there was no satisfaction at all, only disoriented panic. No slender body nestled against him; the voluptuous form beside him slept quite independently, curled in on itself for warmth. And the curls trailing across the rumpled linen were bright red. He dressed so swiftly and silently, Ruby was still sleeping when he left.

It took too long to get back to the hotel. He was sure she wouldn't be there anyway, and he had composed a long mental list of places to look by the time he opened the door to their room. It took him a minute to believe that she was still there, still in yesterday's dress, curled up asleep in the chair by the window. Every hour he had been gone showed on her face.

She had wept the forbidden tears, and then she had begun the wait for Jason. She had packed her belongings because whatever happened, it was doubtful she'd be staying. Whether he planned to rid himself of her now or later no longer mattered; she had precipitated it. Jason was truly angry, and when he returned, he would surely tell her to go. It was almost a relief; she had dreaded it for so long. If he did not return, it was absolutely certain that she would have to leave. The ways of survival were too familiar to her now to ignore that, but she didn't want to consider it no matter what the dictates of self-preservation. She found herself saying it aloud, "Just let him be safe, just let him be all right. I'll go anywhere, do anything." The incantation had a thousand variations that were all the same. And she couldn't stop seeing the image of Jason felled by the ruffians on the night she had rescued him. She prayed his temper would not lead him to worse tonight. Finally at dawn, exhaustion overcame her.

Now, Jason studied her as she slept, enduring the wave of tenderness and remorse that swept over him, wondering why she was capable of making his life so complicated, wondering why he allowed her to do so. He was too weary to puzzle it out. He awakened her gently, not wanting to startle her, calling to her softly.

His name was a glad cry, and she threw herself into his arms, risking his rage. "You're all right! Oh, Jason, I feared you'd do something foolish because I made you so angry!"

"I did do something foolish, but it's past now. Would you like to unpack?"

She knew he had been with another woman; she could smell the scent of her. It didn't matter; he had come back this time. And he had asked her to stay. She put her clothing back in the wardrobe.

Jason came up behind her, drawing her into his arms until she was pressed back against him, needing the contact with her. She rested against him with a little sigh, and then she made a quick turn and kissed the hard edge of his jaw.

"I'm starving! I want breakfast, a bath, and some more sleep, and I think you need all three too." Her nose crinkled slightly, and he was suddenly aware of Ruby's heavy musk. He kissed her deeply for the words she hadn't said.

He ordered champagne with breakfast, and afterwards, Mary nearly fell asleep in the tub as he scrubbed her back and let his hands wander. She was blissfully happy because he had already bathed, and the ghost scent of the other woman was gone.

The first of her new clothes were delivered as she and Jason were preparing to go to bed, and she sighed inwardly, thinking surely she would have to try them on to avoid the trouble of the previous day. All she really wanted to do was sink down and sleep.

Jason smiled ruefully. "They're not going to come between us again. Get into bed. You can try them on later."

He got into bed beside her and cradled her close. "But I must ask what I should have asked yesterday. Why did it upset you so?"

She was so relaxed and sleepy, her words were slurred. "Foolish, see now, so foolish. Never had things like those before. And so many. Thought maybe you were getting tired of just me. Men do that sometimes, don't they? Give nice things for good-bye."

It was true, though he hadn't meant the clothes for that purpose. And there was something more, something she wasn't saying. But then, she never did open the door very far.

Soon, she was fast asleep. He drank in the scent and feel of her, infinitely glad the silky hair was gilt, the skin honey, the curves gentle and firm. Faint spice and roses. The scent was so familiar. He felt as if he'd come home.

It was late afternoon when he awakened. Mary was curled toward him, one hand on his rib cage, one leg resting lightly against his. The shadows beneath her eyes were less, and faint color touched her cheekbones. Her mouth was full and rosy, relaxed in sleep. He nibbled at her lower lip. Her mouth trembled and turned up in a smile as her eyes opened. Dark-ringed deep sultry gray alive with golden light staring into his.

His hands caressed her carefully, tracing the tender hollow of her throat, smoothing the satin of her small, firm breasts. The nipples tautened and rose beneath his palms and his hands moved lower, touching her ribs and the sharp curve of waist, gentle curve of belly, one hand slowly wandering to the soft down, soft rise, soft warm valley.

The gray eyes closed then. She moved against his fingers and murmured in inarticulate delight when his mouth followed where his hand had been, tracing the secret contours with delicate skill.

The wave of exultation and passion broke over him, making him tremble with its force.

His mouth found hers as he thrust home. That thought again, *home.* Warm, pulsing flesh taking him in, welcoming him endlessly.

She tasted herself for an instant, alien female essence on Jason's mouth and then nothing but Jason, Jason filling her with the hard male gift of himself, Jason blocking out the light of afternoon and filling the universe. There was no thought of the other man in this achieving of the essential purpose without pain or guilt. Nor had the woman Jason had bedded last night anything to do with it. In the hours alone when she had doubted she would see him again, Mary had faced the fact she would mourn for the loss of Jason more than she had or ever would sorrow for anything else in her life.

She still didn't know if it was love; she still doubted she was capable of loving, doubted love should need so much as she needed from this man. But she wanted to give to him too, whatever he needed. This too was somehow changed from the tawdry calculation it had often been, now a joyful gift fully realized.

She matched him perfectly, her bones and joints strangely pliable so that her body undulated in sinuous patterns and her flesh took his flesh inside again and again, deeper and deeper, caressing it with rippling waves until he was groaning aloud, and she could hear, "Mary, oh, that's good, so good!" over her own cries.

"Now, Jason, now."

He touched the depths of her, and they rose up together in bright flame.

Her breathing slowed, and she opened her eyes. She had no idea how long it had been since release had come and soft oblivion. Little flickers of pleasure still warmed her. She could hear the slow evenness of Jason's breathing too, and she turned her head with sudden reluctance. He was propped on one elbow, watching her lazily through half-closed lids. His tawny eyes told her everything she needed to know. They didn't have to talk about what had happened, not now. Perhaps later there would be words, but now their bodies had said everything there was to say about needing and giving and taking.

She nestled against his broad chest with a little sigh of relief, and they slept again, waking to gentleness satisfying but so devoid of urgency, it was like a faint echo of the fierceness that had been before. This is its own sweet memory, she thought, even as her hands stroked the flexing muscles of his back. Memory, a sad pressed-flower word for this. She forced it from her mind.

Jason took her to Delmonico's for a late supper, and Mary didn't need the mirror to tell her that the apricot silk suited her. The look in Jason's eyes was reflection enough. Madame Antoine was too good at her craft to have missed the look of longing in the girl's eyes, and the first pieces she and her helpers had completed had been a day dress, a cloak, and the silk. The neckline was cut in a low but not scandalous **V**, trimmed with delicate lace. The waist was fitted, the overskirt smooth in front, sweeping to soft fullness in the back. The underskirt was of a deeper shade, straight in front but showing three gracefully tiered flounces down the back from beneath the shorter overskirt. The cloak was gray, but of so lustrous a hue and of such fine wool trimmed in dark fur, that it bore no resemblance to the dull colors of her old wardrobe.

"I feel like an empress," she said as they set out, and she kept the tremor out of her voice. She was the Tiger's woman and the Tiger was beside her. It was his wish that she appear publicly with him, and so she would. To refuse was to lose him. And if he could not defend her from the other one, no one could.

"You look like an empress, at the very least," Jason responded.

Owen Trenglyth's normally disciplined face froze in stunned surprise when he saw Jason and the woman at his side. Owen had brought Carrie to Delmonico's as a reward for being patient with his lateness the night before, and they were just beginning their meal when the other couple appeared.

"Do you mind some company?" Owen asked Carrie.

"'Course not, long as it's not all law talk," she replied good-naturedly.

Jason caught sight of Owen as the man stood up, and he was amused by the still-startled look his friend was unable to hide. He accepted the invitation to join the other couple without hesitation. He thought it would be pleasant for Mary to have another woman to talk to, and he wanted her to meet Owen.

She acknowledged the introductions shyly and joined Jason in urging the other two to continue with their meal. She asked Jason to order whatever he thought would be good, and she chatted amicably with Carrie.

Owen knew he was staring, and he tried not to, but he kept missing what Jason was saying, an unusual circumstance since he was usually able to follow several conversations at once. His eyes kept straying back to Mary. She was beautiful, no doubt about it. He had never seen coloring like hers before. The shining gilt hair, deep gray eyes, and pale honey skin were a startling combination enhanced by the apricot dress. And he knew that whatever the unmentioned problems of the night before, this woman and Jason were sexually close now. It surrounded them in an aura he couldn't mistake. There were outward signs for a careful observer in the fullness of Mary's much kissed mouth, in the sudden light in Jason's eyes when he looked at her, but most of it was invisible, a current running so strongly between the two that Owen felt that if he put his hand between them, he would feel its charge running through his flesh.

She was beautiful, but she was unlike any woman he had ever known Jason to have. Woman and not a woman. Too wide-eyed and vulnerable for a woman, too old and knowledgeable for a child. Well-educated—he could hear it in the way she shaped her words, could see it in her unconscious ease with the crystal and silverware. And she was terrified. He knew it was true. Though she kept up her end of the conversation and smiled at the right times, her eyes searched the new arrivals again and again. Fear would flicker, then relief, then fear again in a constant cycle. Owen wondered who in the hell she was so afraid of. He nearly snapped the stem of his wineglass he tensed so with the urge to beat the life out of whoever it was.

No wonder Jason had his hands full; this complex creature aroused protective urges without even trying. Owen knew suddenly that he had seen Mary before. No wonder he hadn't recognized her right away; she'd had brown hair then, when she'd been dancing at that saloon. He'd seen her there a couple of times before Carrie had begun to occupy his nights and his roving eye so fully, but he hadn't been with Jason on the night Jason had discovered her and had gone after her though he'd sure heard about it. And they were together now. It struck him that they even looked alike, in the eyes, in the strange golden light they both possessed. The more he thought, the more complicated it seemed. "Extraordinary!" he said aloud, adding weakly, "The wine, I mean."

"Of course," Jason agreed with a wicked grin, fully aware of his friend's discomfiture. He had never seen Owen so distracted. He wasn't jealous; Carrie was a beautiful brunette, and she and Owen were obviously very fond of each other. It was just rather comforting to have his friend thrown into the same confusion he himself had endured since the first time he met Mary. He had a further motive too; it gnawed at him constantly, Mary's denial of any past. If there was anything in San Francisco that would help him to know more, Owen would be able to find it. The thought was not without guilt; the burden of his promise to Mary not to pry into what had been before was heavy.

It was very late when the foursome left the restaurant, but Owen and Carrie were already thinking of the next night. After a whispered conversation, they invited Jason and Mary to supper. Jason could see Mary's eagerness, and he accepted.

"Oh, it is kind of them to invite us!" Mary exclaimed happily, giving a little skip beside Jason as they walked back to the hotel. The damp night air smelled of the sea, and it was a relief to be moving after the large meal.

"Your friend Owen has the liveliest eyes I've ever seen, and Carrie is so warm and friendly," she went on, and Jason understood the cause of the bubbling joy perhaps more clearly than she did. Carrie was openly and contentedly Owen's mistress, the last person in the world to judge Mary's relationship to Jason. In an obscure way he didn't want to examine, it bothered Jason that Mary was still sensitive and uncertain in her position as his woman. There was a vein of arrogance in him that made him think she ought to be damn grateful; Lord knew the others had been.

Owen had provided Carrie with the means and she had supplied the taste in furnishing their little house. It was a far cry from Owen's old bleak rooms in his law office. Carrie's taste in furnishings was surprisingly different from the flamboyant style she affected in dress. The emerald green gown of the night before had been replaced by ruby-red satin and a quantity of lace, but she welcomed Mary and Jason into a house decorated for quiet contentment. Wooden surfaces gleamed by lamp and candlelight, Carrie explaining that she had no use for the hiss and pop and less flattering light of gas. Everything was clean and neat, but nothing was forbidding. Owen's books on law, economics, and philosophy were intermingled with the novels Carrie favored. The worn and varied bindings gave proof that books were read in this house rather than being chosen for a matched display. Furniture had been chosen for comfort rather than for style. Subtle touches of deep jewel colors glowed richly in the carpets and upholstery.

Mary felt the tension leaving her as soon as she entered the house. Here was a safe place among friends, almost as safe as the island. No evil would find her here; *he* would not find her here.

Owen poured sherry for the ladies and whiskey for himself while Jason added wood to the glowing fire that had banished the night chill from the room, and the foursome settled down comfortably.

"This is a wonderful room!" Mary complimented Carrie. "It invites one to come in and be happy."

"You can call it anything but a parlor," Owen warned with a laugh. "Carrie told me from the beginning that we wouldn't have such a thing in our house."

Carrie wrinkled her pert nose in disgust. "Aye, an' it's sure I am there's no cause for sech a place in a kind house. A room that's niver touched save fer them you'd just as well not see or fer thet old divil death himself."

After an instant of stunned silence, Mary and Jason burst out laughing at the theatrical brogue. Carrie's eyes sparkled with mischief.

"You see, I've gotten rid of it unless it comes to the subject of parlors," she said. "My family worshipped a fancy parlor next to God Himself."

Now, the musical lilt of her voice was explained, an audible song even without the brogue. Her coloring too showed her origins in the clear white skin, the deep blue eyes, the fine features and full mouth, the wealth of red highlights in the heavy, dark hair. Mary listened in fascination to Carrie's brief, laughing history of her past.

She had been born in Ireland but remembered little of it except trouble, hunger, and a perpetual hate for the English. Her father she described as a brave, brawny man, who had managed to bring her and her two brothers to America. Her mother, always frail, died during the passage. Mr. Maguire's mourning was over by the time they reached Boston, and nothing on earth could shake his conviction that here was a land made for the likes of himself. He worked hard and proved his point. Within a year he had married a well-to-do widow, a second generation American, but still of good Irish stock.

"He loved her, right enough, but he wasn't sorry she had money behind her," Carrie said. "And he loved her three children too, a boy and two girls. Then he and my stepmother started on a new brood. I'm not saying it was a bad life because it wasn't. My stepmother was good to me, and all of us seemed to get on fine. There was plenty to eat, there was plenty of money—everything my father touched turned to gold. The fact that a lot of people don't care much for the Irish never seemed to get in his way. When I left, he owned several fish markets, a bricklaying company, and other businesses. But it was the parlor that finally sent me on my way.

"You see," she went on, "Once it was fairly certain God hadn't called me to take the veil, proper young men were allowed to call, and we'd sit in that proper parlor, making properly boring conversation and never being alone. It's as if those who've been very poor need to be very proper once there's money about. And I began to see that I hated that proper parlor and the proper young men and that if I didn't leave soon, I was going to be caught with one of each. So away I went, and I've never been back. Oh, I've let them know time and again that I'm just fine, but not exactly where I am. They've got their lives, and I've got mine. I've dealt cards, kicked up my heels, sung a few songs, sold a few things which shouldn't be for sale, and now I'm being spoilt silly by Owen." She smiled fondly at him and he smiled back, not in the least bothered by her bawdy past.

Mary felt a sudden overwhelming desolation. Here was the perfect time to say, "I hate parlors too," to reminisce, to be as open as Carrie was. And there was no way she could do it, no way at all.

Owen was teasing Carrie about starving her guests while filling them with Irish fairy tales, and Mary was sure her lack of comment had gone unnoticed, sure until she felt Jason's gaze and turned to look into his eyes. She had never seen such a look of gentle pleading there before. She could almost hear him saying, "Trust me, tell me."

She looked away, smiling with false joy and rising to join Owen and Carrie as they led the way into the little dining room where dishes on the sideboard were uncovered to reveal fish, fowl, salads, and sweets with exotic fruit.

"My God, Miss Maguire, what do you serve when you give a proper, formal dinner?" Jason teased behind her, seeming as at ease as he had been before, but Mary doubted the goodwill still extended to herself. She refused to let it spoil this evening. He had promised from the beginning to leave her past alone, and she would hold him to it. Defiantly she pushed the vision of silent pleading from her mind and enjoyed the company of her host and hostess.

But Owen was too sensitive to have missed the sudden cooling between the couple. After supper, he played the genial host by suggesting that he and Jason retire to his study to smoke foul cigars and talk business.

Carrie made a face at him but admitted it was her fault. "I can't abide the smell, it hangs around as if something died in the walls, and I can't persuade him to smoke a pipe. Ah, well, off with you, Mary and I will amuse ourselves quite nicely, thank you."

Owen's study was small, like all the rooms in the house, and like them, it was furnished for perfect comfort, in this case with heavy masculine chairs, a desk, and bookshelves. Owen poured brandy, and he and Jason puffed away on the notorious cigars and talked lazily of business because Owen couldn't think of the right way to approach anything else.

The voices rising in harmony solved the problem for him. He had left the door ajar just in case Carrie sang, because he never tired of hearing her, but this was a treat he hadn't expected. Carrie's voice was rich, full, and deep, and the pure high notes weaving sweetly around it were perfect counterpoint. They were playing the piano together too, he could hear the complexity of more than two hands. He almost laughed aloud with them when the music suddenly broke off to be replaced by giggles at the sudden discord before the notes flowed smoothly again into "Black Is the Color."

"I would to hell I knew who he was!" Jason snarled, and Owen froze, already half comprehending where this was leading, wanting to hear more.

"Do you think I've run mad? I haven't, but damn, I will if I don't find out soon! Sing, I knew she could. I've heard her with my son Jamie and other times, when she's been happy on the island. And play the piano, yes, I knew she could do that too. Little by little the betrayals come. I find she knows this or that, is ignorant of the other. But it is so little, it would take more years than my life to discover all. Where does she come from? Why did she leave? Who was her lover before? Why did she desert him? Or did he cast her off? I want to know, and I want you to help me find out. You can do it. I know you discover things your clients need to know. There's the telegraph and now the railroad. I don't care how far away the traces lead; I don't care what it costs, do anything you have to do, hire help, anything, but find out!"

Owen's cigar suddenly tasted as foul as Carrie claimed it was. He stubbed it out with great precision, buying time. Finally he found his voice. "I believe what Carrie's told me, but that's all I know of her, and a lot of the details are missing. I don't care. Maybe someday I'll know everything, maybe not. I don't care," he repeated. "I love her. Before doesn't matter. What matters is what we've been to each other from the day we met. I expect this'll come as a surprise, but I really do plan to marry her whenever I can convince her that being married doesn't mean sitting in a stiff parlor." He was gratified by a brief flash of humor in Jason's eyes. "And if she never is convinced, that's still all right. I don't want to lose her for lack of a license. Apparently though, I know a great deal more about my woman than you do about yours."

His manner had altered subtly. Now his questions came rapid-fire as if he were in the courtroom, his authoritative voice causing Jason to respond without hesitation.

"Do you fear her? Fear she might harm you?"

"Of course not!"

"You're sure? No gun or knife in the dark. No harm to your son?"

"Jesus, Owen! She saved my life the first night I saw her. And she's working wonders with Jamie."

"All right, then that's out of the way. You don't believe she's a born murderess. And even I can tell she came from a background of some culture. Do you want to marry her?"

"No! I don't want to marry anyone. I had a wife and she's dead. That's enough."

"So you don't need to know anything for legal reasons. Does she please you as your mistress?" Owen wondered if he'd gone too far with that one, but Jason answered.

"Damned if I know. She's not like any woman I've ever had before. Sometimes, yes, she pleases me and I'm glad she's mine, other times, no, and I wonder why I ever took her on."

"And you doubt she's yours?" Owen's voice was suddenly very soft.

"Yes. I doubt that all the time. I can almost see the other man. I don't know why she left him or if he left her, but I know he's somewhere, and I know he knows all the things about her that I don't. Mary Smith. I don't believe it, and I doubt she was raised by an old aunt. And I'm sure the other man knows what her name really is, who she really is. Owen, why can't I make you see? Shades of what and who she really is slip out and disappear again. It's impossible to trust someone who claims no past. We all have one, and it has so much to do with what we are right now. I don't know what Mary is today, and I won't know tomorrow either because I can't find yesterday in her life. But *someone* knows. And I want you to find out, find him."

Owen drew a deep breath, shaken by the depth of desperation in his friend's voice. "You don't want to marry her and you haven't said you love her," he offered gently. "From what you've said, I gather you find it impossible to love someone who is so elusive. And yet, you keep her as your mistress and take pleasure in her. This other man haunts you yet you don't even know whether or not he exists or whether he is still important to her. You've conjured up a demon rival and are tormenting yourself with it. There might have been one man or more than one;

you've certainly had your share of women, and Mary, whatever she feels for you, surely knows you had a wife and loved her. Sometimes the past should stay buried; certainly it should when it brings only pain to remember." He said the words very firmly.

"You've got to look at it sensibly, old friend," he continued. "If Mary's past had been joyful, she wouldn't hide it, I'm sure she wouldn't. But there's something bitter there. Probably she would have been better off to make up a bigger pack of lies, a more elaborate scheme to tell you, but she didn't. There's something honest and shining about her, and you possess it at least for the present. Carrie's a blithe spirit and doesn't care what people think, she had too much of their proper thinking before, but I expect Mary does care. I expect it's difficult for her to be publicly labeled your whore. But she's still with you, in spite of that, for whatever reasons. And Jason, I won't help you destroy that or her. I just won't. You'll have to find someone else to do it. It won't last forever, but it's still the essential spirit of the West—a man or a woman has the right to start over and make a new life here. I won't violate that spirit in Mary, and I think you're damn lucky to have her, whatever the terms."

For a moment there was tense silence between them, the music of the women stirring in the background, and Owen wondered if his friend was going to take that swing at him after all. Then Jason smiled bleakly. "Gaiety didn't have it, Carrie doesn't, but Mary surely does. I can't blame you for your refusal; she arouses the same protective instinct in me even when I'm furious with her. Even Jamie's come to the point where he tells her to be careful doing this or that."

"She's vulnerable," Owen said. "And that is a very special kind of trust. And a burden."

When the men joined them, Mary looked up, sudden panic in her eyes, but there was no coldness now in Jason's, just a soft sadness. She felt tears prick her eyelids, and she was glad to concentrate on the music when Owen asked for another song.

She and Carrie sang "Shenandoah," and Mary let the swell of emotion rise and sweep away in her voice.

Jason shivered slightly, feeling the notes physically, an exquisite touch along his spine. The sad longing of the song, it was Mary's. For the first time, he saw clearly her tragedy rather than his frustration. If he found it so hard to live without her past, how much more difficult it must be for her. Never to say, "I remember when I once did this or that, I was there two years ago or three, my hair is the same color as my mother's, I have my father's eyes," never to say any of them or the myriad other references to things past that gave direction and continuity to the present. To regard even the smallest slip as a terrifying self-betrayal.

Did he love her after all, this woman who was so unlike Gaiety? He flinched from the question, but acknowledged that the urge to protect her had risen to fierce white heat.

CHAPTER
19

Owen and Carrie made the days in San Francisco much easier for Mary. There was no choice about being seen, but with them, she felt protected, part of a small, safe set. The two couples spent much time together, dining out, seeing plays and dance programs, listening to concerts, sampling the varied offerings of the city. The men even took their ladies to a horse race one afternoon, and Carrie and Mary made a mock serious business of using their woman's intuition to decide which horses would win.

Owen looked at Jason and shrugged. "It's as good as any system I know, even if some of the nags they've chosen do have only three legs and are stone blind."

But when they started discussing how much they'd bet and what odds they'd look for on the horses, Mary blushed and stammered, "I didn't . . . I mean it was just for fun. I . . . wasn't thinking of betting money."

Jason understood her embarrassment immediately. If she had any money at all, it would be very little and not to be risked on this. The jump of pain in his heart was familiar to him now. He

had attended to the needs of her wardrobe; he had not thought
of giving her pocket money and the freedom it brought, and she
had not asked. He suspected she would not have accepted it
directly from him in any case; he was quite certain when he
thought of it, that even the money she had needed to escape him
after their first meeting had been stolen by her doubtfully
French friend. But now the horse racing gave him a chance to
ease her situation. One way or another, Mary was going to win
some money.

"I'll bet for you for luck," he told her and strode away with
Owen before she could protest.

"Don't worry about it," Carrie admonished. "The money I
gave Owen to bet for me is his anyway. Why shouldn't Jason bet
for you? Who knows where luck comes from?"

There wasn't anything Mary could do about it anyway, so she
turned her attention back to the bustle of preparation for the
first race.

By the time the last race was over, Owen and Jason couldn't
look at each other without going off in whoops. They'd only
been betting for fun, but they'd sought out the gamblers offering the best odds, and just for the hell of it, they'd followed the
women's choices. Carrie and Mary hadn't been correct in every
case, but the odds had been so good on two of their long shots,
it had proved a very profitable outing.

"Carrie, me darlin', I can't let you out of my sight now and
lose a sure system like yours," Owen told her as he stuffed bills
and coins into her reticule and a few into the bodice of her dress
despite her giggling attempt at outrage.

"Considering our discussion of worthless paper, I thought
you'd prefer this," Jason said, and he poured a stream of gold
and silver into Mary's lap. He shook his head and put a finger
to her mouth when she started to protest. "None of that. These
are your just winnings, and I've won a good deal more, all by
your and Carrie's hunches. Moon Runner, what a ridiculous
name for a horse. I just can't imagine why you picked him."

Her surrender was guaranteed by his tender smile. The coins
were worth nearly a hundred dollars. It was not, she assured
herself, the same as being paid for going to bed with a man. She

glanced at Owen and Carrie still teasing each other, and her face was bright, her voice serene when she asked, "When will you take me shopping?"

"Tomorrow," Jason answered promptly even though he thought it might be better if she went with Carrie. He thought she probably had mysterious feminine necessities to buy that even his expertise didn't cover, and he was still thinking that when they set out on the expedition. Her first purchases totally dispelled the notion.

The clerk assured her that these were the finest knives made, but she wanted Jason's confirmation. "Well, what do you think?"

He looked at her blankly, still not understanding why she was interested in this particular display.

She stamped her foot. "Jason, please don't gawk! I don't know anything at all about knives unless I've cut myself with one, and then all I know is that it's sharp. I want to buy truly fine ones for Nate and Jon, for the crew, and for Ben for Christmas, and I don't know the difference in the ones used for different tasks. I want a special set for Jamie's wood carving too. There are differences in knives, aren't there?"

"There are." He started to laugh. "Oh, Mary, I thought you needed to buy ah . . . well, secret female things, and instead, I find you buying knives!"

"Secret female things? Do you know something I ought to know?"

The clerk hid his grin as he watched them. It was nice to see a young couple who could laugh together, who were so obviously in love.

Mary enjoyed every minute of her shopping trip, including a few secret purchases she did keep from Jason, but she kept a specific figure in her head and the coins to match it in her possession, enough to pay passage for quite a distance if she ever had to board a ship other than the *Gaiety* again. It was the only concession she made to thoughts of the future. She had set herself to enjoy every minute with Jason and to please him; the musky scent of the other woman was a strong memory. She was even growing accustomed to the use he made of her in his business dealings, and once she saw that each meeting was clear of anyone she recognized, she had even begun to share Jason's amusement at the effect she had on the men.

He did not require that she be with him every time. He produced her only at strategic junctures as if he were whisking a rabbit out of a hat in order to lure eyes away from the real trick. He always had a good excuse for having her with him—they had this or that to do right after the meeting, and he was sure the gentlemen would excuse the presence of his lady. What he was sure of was that the men were so discomfited by her presence and so distracted by her beauty and their own fantasies, they were apt to ask fewer questions of him and agree more rapidly to what he proposed. He had no guilt about it; had he a wife of equal intelligence and beauty, he would have done the same thing. It was a new experience, and one he found he enjoyed a great deal, to have a woman who was not only interested in what he was doing, but understood most of it.

He took her with him to the meeting with the other men who had shares in the redwood camp. Few of them possessed even half the knowledge he did of logging camps, and he knew it was going to be difficult to convince them that there were serious problems there which could be solved in fairly simple ways. He and Mary went to the meeting as fellow conspirators.

He could gauge by the surprised looks that half of the men hadn't heard about her. The other half had, and they were all stunned to see her here with him in Owen Trenglyth's law offices. Owen himself kept his face bland though he was filled with mirth as he watched the Tiger and his woman manipulating these powerful men.

Mary responded demurely to the introductions and took a seat out of the way of the proceedings, keeping silent and listening intently to the conversation. The quick glances darting to her and away told her just how aware the men were of her presence.

The falling production—and this in a time when lumber prices were teetering up and down—and the seemingly impossible task of keeping a steady crew at the place were quickly established because they were undeniable facts.

"Pardon me, Jason," one of the men apologized, "but I don't think I heard correctly."

"Yes, you did, Frank. I said that what the camp needs is a good cook. That will solve even more problems than getting a new bull of the woods which is also needed."

The men stared nonplussed at the Tiger—maybe the woman really had turned his head. Cooks in lumber camps or elsewhere were certainly a domestic matter.

Jason's voice was smooth. "I know it sounds like a very minor detail though it isn't. But since you obviously consider it a woman's territory, perhaps Miss Smith can convince you where I cannot. We didn't eat at the camp, but we had a cup of coffee. That was enough for me, as I'm sure it was for her. Perhaps she can explain better than I."

Jason had warned her what he was going to do if he got the chance, but it was still disconcerting to have all the attention focused on her. She wasn't aware of it, but her downcast eyes and the color in her cheeks added immeasurably to her appeal. Jason and Owen looked at each other once and then away for fear of ruining the effect with laughter.

Jason had given her the clue in the first name—Frank Shelton, a powerfully built middle-aged man and a major stockholder. Her voice was soft and a trifle hesitant. "Mr. Shelton, I really have no business speaking here, and I know that, but since Mr. Drake has asked me to, I'll try to explain."

Jason barely smothered the sound that rose when she called him "Mr. Drake" in exchange for his "Miss Smith." He felt as if he were locking his jaw beyond repair as he tried to keep his face straight.

"The coffee was horrid. I don't suppose you've ever done it and neither have I, but I imagine if one were to boil dirty blankets for a very long time and then drink the fluid from the pot, one would have a good idea of what that coffee tasted like."

There was an appreciative rumble of laughter, and one voice muttered, "I've always wondered how my wife makes coffee, now I know."

Mary smiled at them and waited until she could be heard again. "Here, if the coffee is bad at one place, you can go somewhere else. Well, most of you can," she amended, causing another stir of laughter. "But at the logging camp, you haven't any choice at all and nowhere else to go. Gentlemen, I can assure you that the food cooking smelled even worse than the coffee tasted, though that hardly seems possible." She paused, and when she spoke again, her voice was pitched so low, they had to strain to hear. "It's amusing here where there are so many places offering so many things, including more good food than one could eat in several lifetimes. It's not amusing there. Not at all. There, there is absolutely nothing except work, sleep, and food. The hours are long, the work is hard and dangerous, and it seems the least a man has the right to expect is decent meals. Surely you have all been angry at one time or another over a bad meal. Imagine, please, how you would feel if you received nothing but bad food and it was considered part of your wages. You'd move on as soon as you could, just as the loggers there are doing."

"Have you ever been in a camp where the food was good?" Frank Shelton asked with polite determination to break the lady's spell. She had no business speaking here; it was quite out of order. But his eyes widened at her answer.

"Yes, I have. I've been in a camp where even the short-stake men stay longer than usual, and everyone knows the food will be ample and good at every meal. I haven't done the work or stayed there long, but I've seen what it's like to work in the dark woods where if something goes wrong, you've every chance of being crushed to death by falling timber. Even one wayward branch—I'm sure you gentlemen know they are called 'widow-makers' by the loggers—even one of them, falling from so far above and being so large to begin with, can crush a man's skull or cripple him for life. And the brush is so thick even with the swampers working to clear it, it is not always possible to get out of the way. And then there's the sweat and the rain that wet the ax handles and make them slippery. The blades are very sharp; I'm sure they cut into flesh and bone even more easily than into wood. I did not see it happen, but I saw what the wind had done in the woods, and I wonder, what would it be like to be there when it was blowing? Quite horrible I suspect, with no safe place and the world falling down around you.

"Hours, days, months on to years are spent in constant danger by those men, and out of their labor you reap a profit, and ships, railroads, wharves, houses, endless things are built. It does seem that at the very least, the loggers deserve a well-run camp and good food for their labors." A hint of steel appeared in the gray eyes though her voice was still soft. "And until you have more loggers than you have timber, the men will not stay long nor work for less than that."

There was utter silence in the room after she finished. Then Frank Shelton cleared his throat. "Gentlemen, I think we can agree that a new boss and a new cook must be found immediately and paid suitably. Are there any objections?"

There were none. When the meeting broke up, the men still looked dazed. They bade good-bye to the Tiger's woman with far more respect than their greetings had held.

Jason was as awed as the rest of them. He had expected her to plead the case, he had not expected the stark eloquence nor the depth of her knowledge and commitment. "That was well done," he managed.

"I thought of Fiddler and of Jud, Bart, Red, and Bull Fletcher. They made it easy." She did not add that the thought of them also made her homesick for the land far to the north.

"I'd hate to argue a case against you in court." Owen sketched a bow in tribute. He had become used to Mary's knowledge of Jason's business affairs though at first he had found it disconcerting. Now he felt something close to envy. He didn't want to change anything about Carrie, not really, but still, it would be nice if he could share his professional concerns with her as he had the private aspects of his life.

He turned his attention back to Jason. "Well, you got your way, and you'll probably get the new loans too. But are you sure you want them? I expect they'll change it back again, but right now greenbacks are illegal to repay any debts incurred before 1862, and that's going to make the money situation even tighter. And lumber prices look to be going down some more."

Jason grinned good-naturedly. "My financial advisor, a Miss Mary Smith, has already suggested that I'm overextended, but it wouldn't be any fun without the risk, would it?"

"Not for you, I guess," Owen conceded. He and Mary exchanged a look of fond understanding. It was true, the gamble and the game of acquisition mattered as much to Jason as the actual ownership.

They went on to discuss Jason's silver shares in Nevada. They were surely a gamble and an expensive one at that, the cost of the mining having continually risen though no high grade silver had yet been found on the claim. And the silver market itself had had its fluctuations, including a severe crash not long ago.

"I want to stay in, at least for the time being," Jason said firmly. "I don't suppose it will be another Comstock Lode, but I still think something will come of it. The land is near some rich strikes."

Owen gave up trying to dissuade him and asked them if they would care to come to supper. "Carrie's got it all planned, so you can't refuse."

Mary thought the evenings with the couple at their home were the best of all. She had quickly understood that the men Jason did business with might take them to a restaurant or accept their invitation for the same, but the ones who had wives and children were not going to take the Tiger and his mistress home with them; Jason alone would have been acceptable but not Jason with his woman. It was fine with Mary; she did not want to meet endless women like Maude Tomlinson who would hate her on sight.

She would have liked to visit Frenchie, but she did not. Even Jason had thought of it, and he had been taken aback by her curt refusal though he had accepted it.

"She is part of my old life; I don't want to go back. It was not a very happy time," she had said, saying more than she ever had about anything in her past. But it was less than the truth. Perhaps Angie had written to Frenchie; perhaps Frenchie did know much of what had happened to her after she had arrived in Seattle, but perhaps not. The less clear the trail she left, the harder it would be to track her down. What Frenchie did not know she could not tell anyone else, even inadvertently.

One of the last important meetings Jason had was with a group of bankers. From them, he planned to get the money to buy the share in the steamer and to finance the purchase of the

Seattle lot. Again Mary stayed in the background, providing a quiet distraction while the men argued over percentage points and other terms of the loans.

One of the bankers, a short, round-faced man whose eyes were mild behind wire-rimmed spectacles, glanced at her more than once. She was used to that now, but when the meeting was adjourned, she felt a prickle of unease as he made his way purposefully toward her. She glanced at Jason, but he was across the room, deep in conversation with Owen and another man.

She looked up into the eyes glinting behind the lenses. He looked kind enough, but he also looked curious. She could not remember his name and was sure today was the first time she'd ever seen him. "I beg pardon, miss, but are you from New York?"

She felt her heart jump out of rhythm, felt her blood pound and drain away, and she steeled herself into more control than she had ever exerted in her life. "Oh, have you been there?" she exclaimed softly. "I never have, but I would so much like to see it someday. I've heard it's a marvelous city. I did visit Boston once, but I don't suppose it's the same," she added, risking it to cover any sound of eastern schooling he might detect in her voice.

He smiled at her ignorance. "No, it's not the same at all. The English and Dutch beginnings are quite dissimilar and so are the cities." But he was not to be deterred from his original subject. "It's extraordinary, if you'll permit my saying so. Years ago I met a little girl who had the same color hair and eyes you do, and she would be about your age now. I don't even remember her name, but the look of her comes back with you."

Mary shrugged and hoped she was smiling. She couldn't tell, her mouth felt so stiff. "They say everyone has a double, perhaps you saw mine. Now I have yet another reason for visiting the city some day. I think it would be quite interesting to meet one's own image."

"My, no, you mustn't say that! The rest of the legend says to look on one's double is to risk death."

"Then perhaps I shan't ever visit New York at all." She made her eyes very wide. The man was obviously a bit of a pedant, and perhaps there was no hidden warning in his words. She still could not remember ever seeing him before, but there were many faces from the past which she had surely forgotten along with those she wished she could forget. She wished he'd forgotten hers, and she wished he'd go away now. He could not know how little Jason knew of her past, but he certainly would know if Jason overheard them. Jason would ask questions, she knew he would. She looked over at him, fear and longing mingled in her expression.

The man completely misread her due to his own vanity. "I expect the Tiger, er . . . Mr. Drake is rather a jealous sort," he said, nervous and preening at once. "And I have monopolized enough of your time. Good afternoon, Miss Smith."

He hurried away, leaving Mary to struggle against a rising tide of hysterical relief. She clenched her gloved hands together until they hurt, knowing she would be lost once the laughter began. My God, she thought, we all do have our weaknesses.

When Jason came to escort her out, he studied her face carefully but said nothing until they were safely in a cab heading back to the hotel where he was due to meet the chief agent who handled the cargo brought in by the *Moon Chaser*.

"You look very odd, and little Mr. Babcock looked frightened to death when he scurried away, hardly the picture of the successful banker he is. What did you say to him?"

"Babcock, is that his name?" Her voice was strangled at this added jest, and she couldn't hold back the hysteria any more. "I didn't say . . . anything. That . . . little dumpling of a man saw . . . saw me looking at you, and Jason, he actually . . . thought," she paused for breath and got the rest out in a rush before laughter overcame her again, "he thought you'd look at him and see him as a threat because he's so charming and handsome with his balding head and his little belly."

Jason was laughing too as he drew her into his arms, but the intensity of her emotion worried him. She was shaking with the force of it and then suddenly clinging to him and hiccoughing in her effort to regain control. He realized then what a strain it had been on her, the role she had had to play, all the new people she had had to meet.

"After this meeting with the agent—and it's not really that important since most of the cargo has already been sold—I will have done all the business I can do this trip. We've been here nearly a month. What do you say we sail for home?" The island was suddenly clear and beckoning in his mind, and he missed Jamie as he never had before.

He felt the frenetic energy leaving her as she relaxed against him. "I should like that above all things."

Carrie and Owen saw them off, Carrie whispering to Mary at the last moment, "Any time you're in the city, you come see us, no matter what." Mary accepted it for the kindness it was— Carrie knew all about the precarious business of being a mistress, and she wanted Mary to know the welcome remained whether or not she was with Jason. Mary hugged her tightly and thanked her for all the good times they'd had.

The trip home seemed to last forever. They were on the edge of winter, and rainstorms swept over them again and again. Wind and angry seas gave them some rough sailing, effectively destroying Mary's newfound ease with the sea for several days.

Jason came down to check on Mary, fighting his way to the cabin, sure she must be terrified. He brushed her hair back from her damp cheek. "We're riding the storm beautifully. I just wanted you to know we're not in any danger."

"That's too bad," she groaned. "I was hoping for a quick drowning."

"That's my valiant sailor," Jason chuckled and bathed her face, despite the water sloshing everywhere, before he went back to his duties on deck.

Mary drifted to sleep thinking that maybe she would live after all and that Jason was very sweet to take such tender care of her despite her quite repulsive seasickness. She was not in the least bit frightened of the schooner's, going down; she felt far too ill to worry about it.

The next time the sea rebelled, Mary's stomach didn't, and she was proud of herself though not foolhardy enough to push her luck by eating before all was calm again.

Ironically, their worst time came when they were on the last leg of their journey, and this time Mary was afraid not only because she could feel the tension in the men without even looking at their grim faces but because even before the storm was fully begun, she could feel the ominous, rising fury of the sea gathering itself to destroy anything it could reach.

They were in the Strait of Juan de Fuca, the wind mounting in force by the second. Jason caught sight of her still standing on deck and bellowed, "Get below, and stay there!"

She opened her mouth to scream back at him and then closed it again. If she stayed above deck, she would be just one more thing for him to worry about.

It was funny. Before, she had been too sick to be frightened and now she was too terrified to be sick. She heard her own shrieks of laughter filling the cabin, louder than the roar of the sea and wind, and she clapped her hands over her mouth, biting at her fingers until the pain steadied her.

She held onto the bunk as the ship bucked and rolled, and she heard the low moaning of the *Gaiety*'s timbers. The single lamp she had lighted was swaying in its brackets. Grimly she remembered that fire at sea was one of the worst hazards. She wondered if the oil could spill from the lamp, and if it did, would it fall in flame. Slipping and falling, she crossed to the lamp and doused the light. Little light filtered into the cabin, but she preferred the murky darkness and even drowning to being burned alive.

She lost track of time, and she ceased to peer out the porthole at the mountains of water. She simply kept repeating to herself that the sea would not have them, could not; they would not, could not die because they were too close to home and too many people needed them.

When he entered the cabin and before the glow of the lantern he carried illuminated her, Jason heard the eerie chant.

"It's all right, sweetheart," he crooned, putting his arm around her. "We've made it. It's still rough, I know, but the wind's decreasing, and we're safely anchored near Port Townsend. I'm sorry the lantern went out and left you in the dark."

"It didn't. I put it out. Didn't want a fire at sea on top of everything else." Her voice was harsh from her raw throat, and he wrapped her closer in his arms.

Twenty-four hours later they were in Seattle even though the only thing all of them wanted was to be home on the island. But this diversion was the only sensible course since Jason now had the money to finalize the new deals. There was no sense in going to the island only to have to sail again immediately.

While Jason was working, Mary spent most of the time with Angie, who was in high spirits because she had had a message from Tom even more recent than the one brought by the Pollards. She expected her captain home by early spring.

She looked Mary over shrewdly and pronounced, "A little peaky from the boat, a lot happy from Jason."

Mary nodded, knowing she was smiling like an idiot but unable to prevent it. It didn't matter that Angie knew more because Angie knew much anyway and lived in this far north country, not in San Francisco.

They chatted and laughed together, and Angie's wonder grew as she realized how thoroughly Mary loved the people and the life on Jason's island. She even noticed how Mary's hands gestured as she spoke. Mary explained about Maggie and Ben, realizing she was unconsciously readying herself to be with them again.

Angie did not point out that she too had met the Carters though she certainly hadn't made any attempt to communicate with them, but she gasped in disbelief at Mary's glowing descriptions of other islanders. "You like Jason's little boy? And his mother? Good Lord!"

"Jamie's wonderful, he really is. We had our problems at first, but not now. And I didn't say I like Ellen Drake," she smiled ruefully, "just that we seem to have signed a treaty." She didn't think it quite fair to the people involved to give Angie all the details of her relationships with the islanders.

"Jason wasn't happy when he was here without you." Angie finally worked it into the conversation. Despite the feeling of ease and closeness between them, she realized Mary still had many hidden corners, and she accepted that.

"I wasn't happy when he was gone," Mary admitted, but that was as much as she was willing to say about it.

It was blustery again when they sailed for the island, but that was better than being becalmed for days, and it wasn't anywhere near as violent as the big storm on the Strait had been. They didn't stop at the lumber camp this time; another delay would have been intolerable. Mary felt tears of sheer joy prickling her eyelids when the island grew larger and larger until the people were visible on the shore. The rose bark of the madrona trees near the water's edge and the red flag welcomed them in the last glow of sun.

As soon as she was ashore, Mary opened her arms, and Jamie hurtled into them for a babbling reunion.

"Miss you, missed you so much!"

"Me too, I missed you, Jamie! I swear you've grown a foot! Oh, you look so handsome!"

"You do too. I mean you look pretty and that's a pretty dress."

When they'd assured each other that they really were together again, Jamie pulled away a little and looked shyly at his father. They started to shake hands, but then, Jamie lurched forward. At the same moment, Jason's arms went around him. Their faces were identical in joy close to pain, and their voices murmured low to each other. Mary looked away and concentrated on greeting everyone else before she broke down completely.

It was so good to be home again, even Ellen looked benign when they arrived at the house and greeted her, and she offered quite a cordial thank-you for the new novels they brought her. But best of all was to be home with Jason in the private world of the room with its view of the sea.

They had bidden Jamie good night together, and in spite of the excitement of their return, he had gone quickly to sleep. His days were long and full now with friends and school and never enough time to do everything he wished. However much he had missed them, the fullness and health of his days showed on his rosy face. It was at once reassuring and sad, a heralding in even so young a child of the independence that would be part of the man.

The cold November wind pushed against the windows, whining to come in. Mary burrowed against the warmth of Jason, and he shifted in his sleep to accommodate her. This was what mattered. He was her reason for being here.

CHAPTER
20

*T*he weather was raw and wet interspersed by days of sudden softness and sunshine. It didn't matter to Mary; she was wrapped in her own warm contentment. Everyone on the island, even Ellen, seemed to be in a holiday mood. The constant work of the planting and harvesting seasons was over though no day ever passed without chores to be done in the care of livestock and the land.

They celebrated Thanksgiving together at Jason's house, and everyone brought something to the meal, as they had to the picnic. Even Hayes provided a brace of wild ducks, proving himself to be a good hunter if not a farmer.

To Mary, it seemed the perfect celebration of the feast, a gathering of friends and a sharing. She had never known anything like it before the island, and there was a chill of particular loneliness when she recalled how last year had held no celebrations of any kind. She doubted that it had for Jason either unless Owen had taken him in; she remembered he had been in San Francisco for Christmas.

But here, Thanksgiving was hardly over before the island

buzzed with Christmas plans and secrets. Jamie was in a constant state of high glee, often smuggling odd lumps under his coat into the house and up to his room after he had been to visit Cade. When she gave him a ride to and from the cove, Mary pretended she didn't notice anything strange in his whispered conversations with Cade nor that he was carrying anything. Even Hayes admitted that he seemed to be spending half the day on Christmas projects with the children. Mary helped there when she could.

The air was sweet with the smoke from fireplaces, and on clear days they could see wisps of smoke from other islands. Inside, the smell of evergreen pervaded, and where there were children, trees were decorated with handmade ornaments well before the big day so that they could be admired for a suitable length of time. The one thing the adults had long agreed not to have were the candles; while beautiful, they were so dangerous. The children didn't seem to mind the lack.

Mary was utterly charmed by Daniel's tree which was decorated with funny-looking animals made of everything from paper to pinecones, but she made sure she praised all the children's efforts equally. She and Jamie did their tree together and giggled at its lopsided brightness of painted paper chains, cloth cutouts, and strings of dried berries.

"Next year we'll do it straighter," Jamie promised. "I'll be older then."

"So will I, but I bet I won't be any better at decorating trees," Mary said, still laughing, refusing to consider whether or not she would be here next year at all.

Jason hardly recognized himself. The only joyful Christmases he could remember were the few he had had with Gaiety, but now he found himself in a constant state of delight. Everything amused him from Jamie's ill-concealed packages to the twins' suddenly exemplary behavior, but Mary delighted him most of all. He felt as if he could put out his hands and warm them on the joy radiating from her. She whirled through the days with laughter, endless plans, and bits of songs sung unconsciously in her high clear voice, and she turned to him at night with a glad and giving heart. He had never felt he had possessed so much of her before, so much that went beyond their physical joining. For once, the specter of her past seemed to have ceased to haunt both of them. For now, he realized, he was living life as she tried to live it, as if each day were separate from the one before and the one to follow.

At last Christmas Eve arrived, fittingly christened by a flurry of snow that did not settle but added a last brief flourish to the night. The islanders gathered again in Jason's house to exchange gifts which would be opened at their own homes the next morning, and to sing and feast together. The children, including Jamie, were allowed to open the identical packages from Jason and Mary, and there were shrieks of appreciation when each of the oddly shaped packets revealed rainbow-colored hard candies and a bright orange, exotic treats the island children rarely enjoyed. Mary smiled to herself when she thought of what two rather larger children would find when they opened their gifts from Jason in the morning. He was giving Nate and Jon a large jar of candy and three oranges apiece; he knew there wasn't anything that would please them more.

When the singing began, the two brothers offered their own special gifts. Mary was so full of love for these people who continually surprised her with yet another talent or skill, at first she didn't dare sing at all for fear of her quivering voice.

Nate and Jon, so shy they hardly ever spoke at all, made the sweetest music she had ever heard on a flute and a fiddle, their big, work-roughened hands delicate on the instruments, and David Becam, normally as shy as they, proved to have a rich bass voice, true on every note.

When she was sure of her own voice, Mary joined in. They sang religious and secular songs, and when some didn't know the words, others did. The children proudly offered "O Sanctissima," their piping voices singing the song in Latin as Mr. Burke had taught them. Ingrid and Else, large and glowing in the last days of their pregnancies, persuaded their husbands to join them in two songs from Norway.

Cade winked at Mary and whispered, "Quite an international gathering we have here." Even his distorted features looked soft tonight.

Mary glanced over at Maggie and Ben. Though they could neither hear the music nor sing, their faces were alive with joy and she saw that Maggie's foot tapped in time to the music whenever the vibrations were strong and rhythmical enough for her to feel them.

The "Coventry Carol" was Mary's favorite of all the songs, and the group did it justice, the deep voices of the men blending perfectly with the higher notes from the women. She could hear Jason and Cade beside her, and it touched her that these hard men would sing the lullaby carol.

> Lul-ly, lul-lay, thou little tiny child,
> By, by, lul-ly, lul-lay.
> Lul-lay, thou little tiny child,
> By, by, lul-ly, lul-lay.

Even Ellen was singing.

When it was time for the evening to end, Jason, Mary, and Jamie stood at the door bidding good-bye and happy Christmas to everyone. Moving light and snatches of song marked the various progresses home through another light drift of snowflakes. Hayes offered to take Cade up on his horse with him, but Cade as usual preferred to walk with Captain who had waited outside for him with only an occasional howl of protest when Jamie or Daniel had seemed too slow in coming with the next handful of food.

Jason saw the sadness in Mary's expression as she watched the two men leave. "Don't worry about them, they're going to be with Nate and Jon tomorrow for a bachelor Christmas, and I know it will include some very good smuggled rum and brandy. There will be three of them to take care of Hayes, so he ought to be safe enough."

She heard the note of disgust and looked up at him questioningly.

Jamie had scampered back into the warmth so Jason could answer freely. He didn't try to deny to himself the pleasure it gave him to tell the truth in the baldest terms. Hayes had had enough of Mary's time and attention during preparations for the holiday. Jason didn't want her feeling sorry for the man tonight.

"If there's a worse drinker in the world than Hayes, I've never met him. It doesn't take much to make him a sodden, loud, and self-destructive idiot. It's the main reason the island is good for him. He doesn't get hold of liquor very often. Cade won't sell it to him, and he's the major supplier. But if Hayes wants to make an ass of himself on Christmas Day, the men will let him do it."

"I'm glad that's not what you're going to do," she said, standing on tiptoe to kiss him. She sensed without knowing why that it would be dangerous to pursue the subject, but she wondered if he knew what had made Hayes such a sad waste of a man.

Jamie was up at dawn making "accidental" noises until the rest of the household was awake too, and he was as excited about what he had given them as he was about the gifts he received. For his father, there was a heavy piece of polished wood with JASON DRAKE carefully carved across the top. "To hold your papers down," Jamie explained, and his father nodded gravely. "Just exactly what I need, and I'll think of you every time I see it on my desk."

For Ellen there was a box covered in seashells. "I didn't make the box," Jamie admitted, "but I put all the shells on. It's to keep your sewing things in."

"Thank you, child. It's perfect for that." Ellen was obviously pleased by the time her grandson had spent on the box.

For Mary there was a charming, chunkily carved horse intended to be Dolly. She thanked Jamie with a hug and a kiss, and honest to the last, he told her, "Cade helped me with the hard parts, like the ears and some of the legs. Next year I 'spect I'll be able to do it better."

"When you're older," Mary agreed solemnly, and they both looked at the tree and burst out laughing.

Jamie was entranced by everything given to him. He did not compare things in value; the only thing that mattered to him was that one friend had chosen to give him this, another had chosen to give him that. He was even genuinely pleased by the practical woolen vest his grandmother had knitted for him for added protection against the cold. But he was struck dumb when he first saw the gift from Jason and Mary. They had decided to make it a joint gift when they had purchased it in San Francisco because the fact that it was from both of them wouldn't seem so much like spoiling him.

It was a gleaming wooden box which when opened revealed rows of the finest carving tools available fitted into their own places. There were blades in various shapes, sizes, and angles designed for making everything from the roughest cuts to the most delicate details. The hardwood handles gleamed nearly as brightly as the blades.

"Mary and I can't teach you how to use them, I'm afraid, but Cade can," Jason said gently, his throat tight with the look of utter wonder on his son's face.

Jamie reached out and touched each piece with great care, and then he got up and kissed first Mary and then Jason. "It is the most wonderfullest thing I ever did see," he said. His eyes crinkled with mischief, "and next year I 'spect I'll be able to use 'em better . . ."

"When you're older," Mary chorused with him and explained the joke to his father and grandmother.

Mary was surprised to find a gift from Ellen to her, and she smiled in pleasure when she discovered a warm vest like Jamie's, knitted in soft gray. She looked up to thank the old woman and found Ellen regarding her with a strange expression, the shawl from Mary flowing through her fingers.

Though Ellen wore black most of the time, Mary had not chosen a drab shawl for her. It was rich silk with fine fringe, brightly patterned with oriental birds and flowers. A deep burnished gold was the predominant color and set off the lights in Ellen's eyes.

Mary and Ellen voiced their thanks at the same time, and that drew a smile even from Ellen. It was the softest moment there had been between them, and Mary found herself seeing the woman more clearly than she ever had before. Suddenly she wondered if Ellen was well. There was a blue-tinged pallor to her skin, and lines she had not noticed before. The thought bothered her more than she would ever have thought possible, but she knew how any inquiry would be met.

Ignoring propriety, she sat on the floor beside Jason's chair

and turned her attention to the gifts from the islanders, exclaiming over the care and love that had gone into all of them:
the smoothly woven cloth from Ingrid, the delicate lace from
Else, the basket from Constance and Daniel, carefully written
recipes from Maggie, sweet-smelling dried herbs and flowers
from Ben and the twins, a deerskin pouch from Nate and Jon,
an old and valuable copy of Blake's poems from Hayes—the
words leapt into her mind, "Tyger, tyger burning bright"—
and from Cade had come the Tiger himself, the beautifully
carved crippled tiger with the tortured human eyes. She hoped
Cade would treasure the books she had given him as much as
she would treasure this.

She looked up to find Jason watching her, but he said nothing
about the carving. He was stroking the fine fabric of the shirts
she had made for him. "So these are what you have been working on so diligently even back to the calm days, such as they
were, on the trip back from San Francisco."

Ignoring the others, he leaned over and kissed her. "Thank
you, my dear." His eyes told her that he was truly pleased. His
wealth and her lack of it had precluded her buying anything truly
valuable for him, so she had offered her time and skill instead,
as the islanders did. He understood and found the gift precious.
She also had the private satisfaction of knowing that the shirts
would fit his big, broad-shouldered torso better than any others
he had. That led to other thoughts which were going to make
her blush if she wasn't careful, and Jason was sure to know what
she was thinking. But when she met his eyes again, there was a
strange plea in them as he handed her a flat box.

She opened it and gasped. On a bed of dark velvet lay a
filigree necklace of pale yellow gold and moonstones with an
equally delicate bracelet. The gold of the metal and the shimmering bluish gray of the stones—she knew he had chosen them
for the colors in her eyes, and she knew that he'd had the jewelry
made especially for her while they were in San Francisco. Suddenly she also knew why he looked so uncertain.

She had no jewelry at all, and Jason could not know that what
little she'd had had been sold long since. He must be doubting
that she cared for it. She knew why the doubt had risen now. All
the simple gifts made with hours, patience, love, and little else

by familiar hands had conjured it. And now this magnificent gift Jason had planned must seem like nothing more to him than the sort of expensive, obvious baubles men gave to their mistresses. Remembering her first reaction to her new clothes, he must fear as much for this gift to her as she had feared for her offering to him.

Her face was luminous. "I have never seen such beauty. Thank you, my darling." Only then did she realize that while he was sparing of endearments, this was the first time she had ever given him one at all. She wondered if the day would ever come when she would be able to tell him that his name alone had been a special word for a very long time.

He took the necklace from her and fastened it around her neck. He put the bracelet on her wrist, and he smiled. She reached up and touched the corner of his mouth, seeing his joy in the words in his eyes.

Jamie saved them by asking, with a shade of worry in his voice, "If Maggie isn't comin' here today, how're we goin' to eat?"

Mary scrambled to her feet. "I'm cooking dinner, and you're going to help, aren't you?"

"Oh, boy! I think I better," he giggled.

New Year's Eve brought its own, different ceremony. During the day, the men took all the now brittle Christmas trees and piled them on the shore above the high tide line, covering the pile with oiled canvas against the drizzling rain. At midnight the islanders gathered there, even the little ones sleepy and bundled against the cold, when the trees were touched with fire and burst into crackling, soaring flame.

"Should auld acquaintance be forgot," David Becam's voice began it, and the others joined in. Mary heard Jason singing the chorus to her as the flames leapt in the darkness, shooting sparks against the mist and dying back to earth.

> And for auld lang syne, my jo,
> For auld lang syne,
> We'll take a cup o' kindness yet,
> For auld lang syne.

"May there be much kindness between us and a brave new year," Jason murmured as the song ended, and he drew her into his arms. She could see the last glow of the fire golden in his eyes, and she whispered, "Always," before he kissed her, tasting tears on her cheeks.

She gave herself up to his kiss, drawing him in, relaxed and warm against him. Lit only by the last embers and dim lanterns, they were covered by darkness.

They drew away from each other, reluctant and dazed, and parted to wish everyone else a happy New Year.

Jamie was wiggly with excitement over being up so late, but he gave Mary a smacking kiss even while he confided that he didn't think "that old Erin" should have kissed him.

"I promise, you'll remember it as something very nice indeed —when you're older," Mary assured him, and that set him off again. She felt a sudden pity for Ellen who had been firm in her refusal to join them, and she wondered again if the woman were ill.

She had no difficulty in identifying the shadowy figure coming toward her since Captain was his advance guard and nearly knocked her down with his greeting. "On some coasts, this would be very profitable, luring ships in to plunder. Happy New Year, Mary Smith," Cade said.

"And to you," she replied and kissed him soundly.

"Whoever you really are, Mary Smith, don't ever leave us. Don't ever leave Jason."

The words were said so softly, she was not sure she had heard them correctly. Cade and Captain were gone.

All the rest of the greetings flowed smoothly in uncomplicated exchanges of good wishes. It was only later that she realized the tears on Constance's cheeks had not been caused by the bitter-sweet joy of the occasion and the chill of her flesh had not been the chill of the winter night.

For now there was a new year; there was Jason and everyone and everything that radiated from him; and there was the dawning of the first belief she had ever had that kindness and kind love could shape life even as cruelty could be absent from it.

CHAPTER
21

*T*he year began as if it would fulfill the wishes made at the New Year's Eve bonfire. Ingrid had her little girl, Grete, and two days later, Else produced Josef. Maggie and Constance helped with the births, and Mary and Jamie helped to keep the children out of the way. Lars and Mogens didn't seem to be much help at all even though they'd both been through this three times before.

Mary made no secret of what was going on to Jamie; she wanted it all to seem as natural as it did to the Nilsen and Olsen children though she'd already warned Jason that she was leaving the specifics of how babies were conceived in the first place up to him. Remembering the episode in the barn and its aftermath, she thought the explanation would be better coming from Jason. For now, she wanted Jamie to know that the babies were coming and the families were happy.

"Is Ingrid sick?" he asked nervously as the first birth drew close. He couldn't remember a time when Ingrid hadn't been up and working, yelling loving threats at her children, and he'd heard scary noises coming from her house.

"No, darling, she's not, but she's working hard to have her baby."

"Is it hurtin' her?"

"Yes," Mary answered honestly, "but she knows what to do, and she has Maggie and Constance to help her. It's more work than hurt, and nothing is as important as the baby and the joy Ingrid will have when she first sees it." She hoped all this was true.

"My mother died, and she left me. Did I kill her?" The stark words were soft and shaky.

Mary drew him tightly against her with a great surge of relief. It was not natural that he never mentioned his mother or asked about her, and she had long suspected it was the worst of the pain and fear he had carried for so long.

"It happens sometimes, and it's not the mother's fault and not the baby's either. It just happens. I know your mother would have stayed forever to love you if she could have, but she couldn't stay. And yet, part of her stayed alive because you are alive. Jamie, did you know that Ben's parents, both of them, died when he was very little? They got sick. They didn't want to leave him either, and he didn't kill them."

She held him a little away from her and watched his face as he confronted death directly for the first time. It was a harsh thing for anyone to face, but she could think of nothing worse than the guilt that he had carried.

"Where did they all go when they died?"

"I don't know, but some people say that God takes people to a wonderful place, to heaven, when they die."

"Sure, I've heard of it. It sounds like a silly place." He sounded disappointed.

"You know, it does to me too, but we can't really know anything about it. Jamie, the only thing you have to think about is this life here, right now. Whatever comes after will come in its own time. Your only job is to live this life as well as you can and to be as kind to others as you can. Your mother was kind to you; she and your father gave you life, and here you are, alive."

He thought about it silently for several long moments, and then the white misery on his face began to ease. Finally, there was a small smile. "I 'spect it will make more sense next year, when I'm older."

Mary laughed and ruffled his hair. "You are a funny person! And now we'd better track down those children."

"Okay, but Daniel's with 'em, so they're all right." Jamie had vast faith in Daniel's quiet abilities.

For the small population of the island, the addition of two new babies was cause for rejoicing and also for some good-natured teasing of Lars and Mogens by the other men.

Mary had never been around babies much nor had she ever been particularly charmed by the ones she'd seen. But Grete and Josef were different because now she was different. She liked their parents and was enchanted by these tiny new persons. She went to visit and hold the babies whenever she could, often finding Ingrid and Else together.

"Ja, is good for de babies to know love from so many," Ingrid declared. "Someday maybe you too have some babies," she added slyly, noting the color rising in Mary's cheeks.

Mary covered her embarrassment by cooing to Grete, but she felt as if Ingrid had read part of her mind, the part that kept proposing that no matter what happened, it would be wonderful to have a child of Jason's. The other part was ruthlessly sensible, reminding her that aside from considerations of illegitimacy, there was far too great a possibility that without Jason, she would be unable to provide for the child.

Jason noticed her preoccupation with the babies, but he didn't want to see it as anything but a normal woman's response. The idea of Mary bearing a child filled him with gut-wrenching fear. It was different with Ingrid and Else and other women. If Mary became pregnant by him, she would die, just like Gaiety. But with so much talk of the new babies, the thought gained power and haunted him beyond his own needs. It mattered now so much more than it had because she mattered more, so much more.

The first few times it happened, she accepted his mumbled excuse that he was tired. It had been true before, and he had reason to be weary now. A visiting ship had passed on the rumor that a treaty was in the making over the final disposition of the San Juan Islands. Jason remained utterly certain that the United

States would be declared the owner, and he was working exhaustively to make sure his claims to Drake's Island would be in order when the time came.

It made sense to Mary that mental fatigue could affect the body—there were many times when she was just as content to curl up and sleep beside Jason as to have him make love to her —and a man's body showed when he was tired much more obviously than a woman's did.

She gave a little laugh in the darkness. It was time to make him forget his tiredness; she wanted him tonight, and she had learned much about how to make him want her too. She moved closer and rubbed her breasts against him as she slid her hands down to hold and stroke him. She felt his startled response, and she laughed again, teasing his neck and chest with her mouth.

"Don't!" The word hissed as his whole body tensed against her.

She sprang back from him as if he'd struck her, and a deep shudder ran through her. This was different from anything before. This was outright disgust and rejection. He was not tired at all, and had not been in the nights before.

It had happened as she had known it would. He knew, finally he knew. Everything she had thought about herself was true. And he must know the truth too. That was the only explanation. Never had she felt so much the whore as she did at this moment and not a very skillful one at that. A cheap harlot Jason didn't want anymore. She felt the light shatter inside; she was as dark as the room. She cringed in her own shadow; hands covering herself from herself, beginning to tear out the bad.

Jason asked her name softly, ruefully, but she didn't hear him. He reached for her, but she pulled away frantically. He swung out of bed and managed to light a lamp.

"Oh, my God, Mary don't! It's all right, I didn't mean it!"

She wasn't making any sound but tears were pouring down her cheeks from wide blank eyes, and she was methodically clawing at her breasts, her belly, her thighs with her fingernails, leaving long red streaks and welling spots of blood.

He grabbed her hands, and when she tried to jerk away, he held her hard against him. Her heart was skipping and fluttering like a wild thing seeking escape. "Please, Mary, stop it! Please, listen! It isn't what you think. I want you, I want you all the time, but with the new babies, I . . . I am suddenly afraid. I lost Gaiety that way; I could not bear to lose you too. I should have . . . I should have been using something to prevent it all along, but I haven't, and there's nothing here to . . . and when you touch me like that or when I'm inside of you, I can't, can't leave you when I should."

The words were pinpricks and then full rays of light flooding her darkness as understanding came. It had nothing to do with rejecting her. It had to do with protecting her and with his fear. He was as afraid as his son had been.

She breathed his name before the sobs overwhelmed her, and she wept against him.

He held her more gently, letting her cry, tears trickling down his own cheeks. He damned himself for being so clumsy. Whatever, whoever, had damaged her before was always waiting in her mind to inflict further wounds, and he had opened the way for it to happen again. Her hold on her belief in herself as a woman was fragile and dependent on him, and the burden of the care that must always be taken was his. He could not erase the image of the nails clawing at flesh as if she had wanted to tear herself from herself and be free.

Her heartbeat slowed, the sobs subsided, and she reached up blindly to touch his face. "What shall we all do if the Tiger weeps?" she whispered brokenly.

"Forgive him when he is clumsy and cruel?" Jason asked, his voice no more steady than hers.

"It was not cruel to worry about me, but you must not!" she cried with sudden fierce strength. "Jason, I never conceived a child before, and I am not pregnant now. Perhaps I am the kind of woman who does not conceive easily. Think of Etta and Clem. They had only one child, and I am sure they would have liked more. And . . ." it was her turn to find the words difficult, "I am doing something about it. Angie . . . well, Angie told me."

Jason kissed her. She held the thought of bearing his child for a moment longer and then let it go.

He left her only to get a basin of water and a soft cloth. He bathed the scratches, shushing her embarrassed protests. Then he loved her with tender care, taking her as if this were the first time ever they had been together, until she cried aloud and they moved in the ways they had long since learned to please each other.

She fell asleep in his arms. He lay awake for hours. He had loved her, not just made love to her. He let the truth of it become the truth for him. He had loved her for a very long time, perhaps even as far back as when she had returned, half frozen, to his house in Seattle, perhaps even further back, to the first night when she had defended him.

She stirred and uttered a soft, sad cry in her sleep. He rubbed her back and murmured to her until she was still and relaxed against him again.

It did not matter when it had begun; what mattered was what he was going to do about it. For him, the bargain was over.

He saw Gaiety with more clarity than he had seen her in all the years since her death. And for the first time he saw clearly the long, poisonous course of his mourning, his inability to relinquish what was gone. He heard the tripping, contagious sound of Gaiety laughing. He saw her pouting though her eyes belied the seriousness of the complaint. He saw her radiance when she had known she was pregnant and had decided she wanted his child more than she had ever wanted anything in her life. He saw the calm white face of her death. "Child of my heart, I did love you so!" The words were only in his head, but he saw Gaiety's quick flashing smile, heard her laughter again, and knew without doubt that she had let him go and wished him well the instant she had died. A monument of sorrow and regret was the most unfitting tribute he could have given her. He let the tears fall, the first he had allowed himself for Gaiety, the last there would ever be for her. He knew she would approve. She had cried easily and as easily stopped. And she had been impatient with his aversion to tears. "My fierce man, tears and rain are the same thing, they're meant to wash you clean and make you grow. If you don't let them out, you'll drown inside." He remembered exactly how she'd wrinkled her nose and laughed with the tears still drying on her cheeks. The lovely last image, last blessing faded to the reality of Mary sleeping in his arms.

This one, this one was tears seldom shed and agony he did not yet understand, but he would in time. In time she would trust him, and in time she would be ready to bear the knowledge of his love and to decide whether or not she could love him in return. Nothing else, he knew now, would do. He would not push her too hard; she would bolt if he did. Love was not part of her vocabulary, had not been part of his for long years. But in time it would be part of a shared life. He planned it as carefully as he had ever planned any business campaign, and he wanted it more than he had ever wanted anything, more even than he had wanted Gaiety. But the reality touched him again as Mary squirmed and protested in her sleep against the sudden discomfort as he held her too tightly.

He eased his hold. "My love, my love," he whispered as he settled into sleep beside her.

Mary awakened to dim light and the familiar sound of rain. She started to stretch but stopped with a sharp gasp. She looked down at the scarlet marks in wonder and then in dawning memory. She squeezed her eyes shut again, but Jason's voice compelled her.

"Look at me." He was on an elbow, watching her. He looked very tired but equally calm and happy. His eyes were kind. "It's all right, sweetheart. You're here and I'm here, and it's all right." He leaned over to kiss her. "And now we'd both better get up or we'll be here all day."

"Did you sleep at all? You look so tired."

"I slept. It's just my old age showing." He made light of it as he got out of bed, but he was pleased by her concern, and he laughed aloud at the surprise of her hand running quickly from the small of his back to the back of his knees. "Doesn't look old from this side," she giggled.

"Slowly, slowly," he cautioned himself, but he had time, they had time, and he would court her into forever; she wouldn't even know what had happened until she was there with him.

Neither one of them would ever forget the sound that signaled the beginning of the long sorrow.

Jamie, Daniel, and the twins had seen the ship putting in and had raced to put the flag up with the smaller blond children straggling behind. It was Gibson's trader, the *Folly,* which was no folly at all since Captain Gibson did a brisk business in barter, message carrying, and outright sales. He was welcome wherever he made port, and his territory was considerable, including the San Juan Islands and many of the lumber mills on Puget Sound.

By the time the sailors had landed, Mary and Jason had ridden down to greet them. The Captain and his men were favorites with the children and always just happened to have pieces of candy that was slightly sticky from the damp even though wrapped in twists of paper. It made it more fun since it took quite a while to pick all the paper off.

The shriek froze everyone in place except for Gabriel who snorted and plunged in alarm where he was tied.

The screaming went on as Constance ran toward them, words —"Ooooooh, Daniel, noooooo"—but mostly just wailing terror. Constance looked completely insane. Jamie backed into Mary, and she put an arm around him. Daniel murmured, "Momma," but couldn't move.

Jason made himself go forward, calling to her softly.

Constance stopped, not seeing him at all, eyes staring blindly past him to the big sailor, Zeke. Her arm came up rigidly as she pointed at him. "It's you. You are the one. Death bringer, child killer!"

"No, ma'am, no! I wouldn't hurt no child, never, never!" Zeke's young, kindly face above the full black beard was twisted with pain and horror. He was a special favorite with the children and despite his bulk, he was infinitely gentle and careful with them.

"That's enough, Constance! Get hold of yourself!" Jason's voice cracked like a whip.

Constance blinked and dazedly shook her head, taking deep gulps of air, trembling.

"Constance?" Now Jason's voice was gentle.

She saw him now, and everyone else. "I'm sorry . . . I . . ." She pressed a hand against her forehead. "I'm sorry," she repeated helplessly. "Not your fault, Zeke, no one's fault. Dear God, no one's fault." Tears ran down her face.

The change frightened Mary even more than the violence had, but it released everyone from his immobility.

"Do you want us to leave?" Captain Gibson asked gruffly, eyeing Constance uneasily.

"Of course not," Jason assured him, but he wasn't about to explain Constance's awful gift. He felt cold dread inside; he had never seen her like this.

"I don't know what it is, but we will all know too soon. There is nothing to be done now, it is done," she said. There was infinite sorrow in her eyes as she looked at her son. She turned away, walking like an old woman. Everyone except Daniel let her go; there was something about her that warned against offering company. Daniel murmured, "Poor Momma," and ran to her side. Hand in hand they disappeared from sight.

Jamie looked up with shock in his eyes. "I never seen her act like that. Is she sick?"

"Sort of, but she'll be all right." Even as she said the words, Mary doubted that anything would ever be all right again.

Jason drew close to them, and the same doubt was in his eyes.

Captain Gibson delivered papers he was carrying for Jason. He and the men who had come ashore with him did stay the night, but it was not a happy visit, and by the time they were ready to leave the next morning, poor Zeke looked quite ill. Mary was sure it was due to Constance's accusation, but when she took his hand to bid him farewell along with the others, she was shocked by the dry heat of his skin. "Why, I believe you have a fever! Perhaps you shouldn't sail just yet."

Zeke protested miserably that he was just fine. She suspected nothing short of tying him down would keep him on the island after what had happened, but she warned Captain Gibson to keep an eye on him.

"Don't you worry none, he's a strong 'un," the Captain assured her.

Within three days, Constance's prophecy was fulfilled. Death came to the island, and it was the children it sought most viciously. They had all had contact with it either directly through Zeke or with each other, and they had the least resistance to it.

The fever and chills took the smallest ones first. Grete and Josef gasped and struggled for life until they were too weak to struggle any more. They died within an hour of each other. Lars

and Ingrid, Mogens and Else settled into a grim war to save their
other children as the disease choked the lungs or caused violent
vomiting and diarrhea depending on the course it took with
each.

No one even knew what the disease was. It was not diphtheria
or scarlet fever or yellow fever or any of the plagues they knew.
And God only knew where Zeke had gotten it. From another
seaman who had sailed from far away? It didn't matter. It was
here.

Mary, Ellen, and Jason waited in dread for Jamie to get it, and
when Mary went to visit Constance as she had been doing every
day, she knew the disease had found Daniel even before she
entered the house.

He was raving with fever and his breathing was difficult. Constance continued to sponge him off with cool water, her hands
moving automatically. Her face was white and pinched, her eyes
without hope.

"Let me do that for a while," Mary said. "You must get just
a little rest."

Constance shook her head. "There will be time, so much time
when he is gone."

"You mustn't give up hope." She knew it was a weak plea.

Constance stared at her. "There is no hope when you can see
too far. Warnings and warnings all of these years, but then I
knew, I knew it was beginning but not exactly how, and I was too
late anyway. I've always been too late."

She turned back to her child, ignoring Mary's presence.

It was a nightmare that seemed without end. The twins were
ill, and then Ben was too, the first adult stricken though he was
not as sick as the children. Maggie's world was slipping away
before her eyes, and she would not allow it. She coaxed them
to drink water and weak broth even though most of it came back
up. She kept them clean and bathed them with cool water when
their fevers rose. She worked tirelessly to save her family until
she was ready to drop. Nate and Jon persuaded her to rest while
they took over the household. They gave her no choice. They
moved with their usual purposeful strength, only their eyes
showing the depth of their horror. Mary could see it, so had they
lost their wives and children to sickness.

Everyone helped and everyone felt helpless, waiting for the next death, counting each day the stricken stayed alive and praying it meant that much more distance from death. Captain Hanson and David Becam, Hayes and Cade made rounds of the households, keeping the fires going, hauling water, feeding livestock, and taking turns as nurses.

Nate was the next victim. Impassively, Jon stayed at the Carters' and added his brother to the patients he and Maggie were caring for.

Mary and Jason helped where they could and slept brief exhausted hours when possible, hardly seeing each other but clinging together for mutual support when they did.

Mary was returning from the Olsen and Nilsen houses. With six children sick and their parents still in shock from the loss of the babies, there was always something to do. She saw Gabriel as she rode in on Dolly, and suddenly she knew, as she had known about Daniel. She raced into the house and saw Ellen at the top of the stairs, her shoulders slumped, one hand to her chest.

"Jason's with him."

Mary ran up the stairs, her one impulse to get to the child, but she was checked by the closer view of Ellen's face. Her skin was gray and tears stood in her eyes despite her efforts at control. "I am too old. Oh, not Jamie!" she wailed.

Without thinking, Mary put her arms around her. "He'll live, he will, we won't let him go! But you, are you ill too?"

Ellen clung to her for a moment, then straightened her spine and pulled away, but her voice was kind. "Thank you, my dear. Go to them now. I am not ill, just old and useless."

She expected the sound even before she entered the room— Jamie's wheezing, gasping struggle for air. His face was beet red; his eyes were half open, showing only red-veined whites; and his hands were working convulsively at the bedclothes. Jason was crooning to him, trying to quiet him as he bathed the hot little body. Jason looked like a hunched old man. Mary could see the involuntary tremors running through him. The room reeked of aromatic herbs steaming in hot water.

She pushed Jason gently away and gathered Jamie up in her arms, holding his head high on her shoulder. "Jason, do as I tell you. Go get the rocking chair from the parlor and bring it here. Do it now."

He obeyed her without question, bringing the chair and settling her and Jamie into it. "Go now, Jason, sleep a few hours if you can and then come back. It won't do him any good if we all collapse at the same time."

Jason kissed her cheek and Jamie's and left without a word, hearing her begin to sing.

She rocked and she sang the "Coventry Carol," "Hushaby," and the "Riddle Song." She sang "Shenandoah," "Cruel War Is Raging," and every other soft-sounding song she knew. And then she sang them all over again. She kept him rigidly upright against her to give his lungs more room to breathe. And when she wasn't singing, she was telling him she was there, telling him to breathe as she had the day of the picnic.

"One at a time, Jamie, just one slow, deep breath at a time. There, sweetling, there, you aren't alone, you'll be all right. Breathe deeply, sweetheart, breathe deeply. It's Mary, Jamie. It's Mary. I'm here with you. I'll always be here with you. I love you."

For hours she rocked him, talked and sang to him and stumbled from the chair with him in her arms when his skin grew too hot, laying him down on the bed and sponging him off before she wrapped him up once again and went back to the chair.

> I gave my love a cherry without any stone,
> I gave my love a chicken without any bone,
> I gave my love a ring without any end,
> I gave my love a baby with no crying.

Jason heard the husky tired voice singing and the raspy struggle of his son before he opened the door. Mary did not protest changing places with him; she doubted she could lift Jamie again without rest.

"He's holding his own, and that's a great deal. Believe it, please believe it!"

He knew she was pleading for her own belief as much as for his, and he managed to say, "I do," as he took the burden of his son from her and listened to her instructions.

She paused in the doorway, leaning against it for support. "Any word on the others?"

His face lightened for a moment. "Hayes was just here. They all seem to be improving." The message passed between them without words—keep them alive long enough, and they would live; keep Jamie alive long enough, and he would live.

"Daniel too?"

He wanted to lie and could not; the space was so small now, so close to the edge, there was no room for falsehood. "No one seems to know except for Constance, and no one wants to know what she knows. Daniel's not in any pain now, and his fever's down, but he," Jason's voice broke, and he steadied it with an effort, "he's just lying there. He doesn't even respond to his mother. The last time he was conscious, he told her he hoped Raven really did know how to be free because he didn't think he'd be there for Raven to come home to any more."

Mary fled before she could add to Jason's pain. She threw herself down on their bed and sobbed.

"There, there, you must sleep now," a voice was crooning to her exactly as she did to Jamie. Hands were loosening her clothes and pulling off her shoes as if she were even younger than Jamie. Dazed, she looked up at Ellen.

"Hush now and sleep. I promise, I'll wake you when it's time," Ellen said, continuing her ministrations.

Mary fell asleep with the conviction that the whole world had indeed gone completely mad.

Ellen continued to ease the way for them. Food appeared regularly and they were urged to eat whether they were hungry or not. Jason and Mary accepted her edicts as to when one would sleep and the other take over. Ellen took short turns with Jamie herself until she admitted that he was too heavy now for her to lift, and she feared not being able to call for help in time if there was a crisis. They had looked at her apprehensively, but she had been firm.

"This is not my time. But I am an old woman and move more slowly now. I do not want to fail Jamie because of my years. Let me make the way easier for you to move swiftly for him."

Dumbly, they had agreed as they agreed to the schedules she

set for them and the food she cooked for them, including the broth she made in endless supply with the insistence that Jamie must be fed a little at a time whenever it was possible, even if it meant nothing more than touching a drop to his lips when he was quiet. Nothing in the world existed except Jamie struggling to live. That he was struggling was a victory in itself.

His fever went up and down; his breathing quieted and then rasped again. He was silent and then he babbled. He talked about his friends, he wanted Cade to show him how to do this or that. He wanted to go to the caves; it was so cool and dark there, but in the next instant he was terrified of them. They were dark and Mary was lost there, his mother was lost there too. Huge rabbits were coming after him, making him choke, but his father would save him, his father loved him. The terrors, fantasies, and truths of the fever went on.

Sometimes it was Cade or Hayes who was there for brief intervals holding Jamie and rocking as if he had held and comforted a thousand children. These two unlikely and dissimilar men were identical in their strength and kind patience. Love bound them all together, touched them all, kept them all going in their small, beleaguered world. Mary realized it dimly, clung to it, and went on.

It had been four long days and longer nights on top of everything that had gone before. Jason felt as if he were a hundred years old. His good leg felt as unsteady as the bad one. When he opened the door to Jamie's room, his eyes went immediately to the rocker and then traveled on from its emptiness to the bed. Jamie was lying very still, and Mary was crying. He felt his heart stop.

Mary saw him then, and he saw her smile before she reached him. "He's all right. He's sleeping. The fever's almost gone, and he's breathing deeply." The tears kept coming, and she brushed at them angrily. "I can't stop, now when there is no more cause to weep for him, I can't stop."

He held her for a moment before he ordered her to bed. "I'll stay with him now. I haven't seen Mother though, will you tell her?"

She knocked at Ellen's door and entered as she was bidden,

voicing the news immediately so that the tears would not frighten Ellen as they had Jason.

But she knew as soon as she saw the woman that here was cause for weeping. Ellen lay on her bed, propped against the pillows and bundled in blankets, blue-tinged as though nothing would ever warm her again.

"You can't, you can't do this!" It was a scream on the verge of hysteria.

For a moment, Ellen's face was as imperious as it had ever been. "Neither you nor I have anything to do with this now. I told you, and it is true. I am old." But then her face softened to the same kindness she had shown these past days. "Jamie is going to live. That is all that matters. Thank you for my grandson, Mary Smith. And now you must go sleep."

Mary shook her head doggedly. "I can't leave you while you're ill."

"You cannot help me. I am not suffering from the fever that has invaded Jason's kingdom. I am suffering from a heart that was old and weary when I was born. It has done well to carry me this far."

Mary knew it was the truth—the sedentary life Ellen led, the tiredness she had noticed before—even if she did not have that evidence she would have known now. Death was in this room, crouched and waiting.

"Why didn't you tell us? Does Jason know?" she could hardly get the words out.

Ellen closed her eyes for a moment. "No, Jason doesn't really know. His father did, and I discovered the double-edged sword of the tyranny of the perpetually sick. I should have known already. My parents, you were right about them." Ellen smiled thinly. "They were honest shopkeepers but they treated me like a princess. I was their only child and a sickly one. They spoiled me, but they also imprisoned me. I was not to do this or that or the other thing. I escaped by running away with Mr. Drake." She paused to draw ragged breaths. "We were really quite happy at first, but then I conceived Jason. I was frightened, angry, and I wanted a settled, proper life. I attacked my husband with the knowledge of my bad heart, and I destroyed the best of what we'd had together. We kept moving anyway. My husband, James, became more like my father than my husband, protective, indulgent. I became his burden, and he carried it alone. He did not tell Jason. He never thought he would die before I did." She sighed wearily, gasping for breath before she went on. "It is discouraging to know we make the same mistakes over and over. I did not protect Jason enough; I drew away from him, and yet, when Jamie came, I smothered him as I had been in my own childhood. I'm glad you came in time, Mary Smith." She drew another shaky breath. "Now go away and let me sleep. I have no intention of dying right this minute."

The world would never be sane again. Ellen had changed before her eyes as she had glimpsed the world from her view, a view far more like Maggie's in its beginnings than like her own. And now there was no time for her and Ellen to be the friends they might have been; the peace treaty they had made was all they would ever share.

CHAPTER

22

"The Lord shall preserve thee from all evil, yea, it is even he that shall keep thy soul. The Lord shall preserve thy going out, and thy coming in, from this time forth for evermore."

Mary wondered how Hayes could keep his voice so steady, and then she saw the muscle twitching furiously in his cheek and knew his struggle. She watched him, willing him to know his gift was recognized. She knew it was cold standing here in the rain; she wondered why she did not feel the cold.

"Unto God's gracious mercy and protection, we commit you. The Lord bless you and keep you. The Lord make his face to shine upon you and be gracious unto you. The Lord lift up his countenance upon you, and give you peace, both now and ever-more."

Two new graves to add to the place that now held the infants, Grete and Josef. The hurried burials of the babies had been bad enough in the midst of the terror that had gripped the island, how could this be worse? But it was.

Ellen had died in her sleep. Mary had found her in the morning. By evening of the same day, Daniel was dead. Small, white, crumpled like a spent windflower, his body had followed the spirit that had already flown.

Would Raven keep coming back to look for him? She couldn't get the question out of her mind. How would they tell Jamie that his grandmother and his friend were gone? He was so much better; Nate was keeping him company right now. None of those who had been ill were at the graveside; the risk of cold weakening them further was not to be taken.

I'm glad the children are not here, Mary thought. I could not bear to see them standing over these dark holes and all that is left of Daniel and Ellen. She could not stop the squirreling leaps of her mind. Did you make a bargain too, Ellen, did you trade yourself for Jamie? Then whom did Daniel die for? Did you leave together? Have you another child to care for now, finally the way you wish it to be?

Strange, pale Daniel was dead. The knowledge coursed through her again in savage waves. The elusive child of such surpassing gentleness. She remembered the first time he had trusted her and had given her that smile. For an instant that gentle look had embraced every outcast anywhere in the universe, had embraced her and had given her the momentary belief that nothing mattered so much as the beauty of the moment.

She did not want to look, yet could not look away from the calm, remote face of his mother. She wondered how Constance could stand upright when she herself wanted to fall to the earth and claw the heavy black mud and scream at the top of her lungs.

The sudden pain in her hand startled her, and she realized that Jason was gripping it fiercely, Jason was beside her, his own face tight and forbidding but his hand telling her that he knew, that he suffered too. She was glad she could feel the physical pain in her hand.

Hayes's voice faltered and finished. He had offered a last tender stream of words, but who could speak well of Ellen when none had known her well and who could capture the essence of a child like Daniel who had lived such a short time and whose effect on others was such a sweet, impossible-to-capture rustle of the wind?

The sound of singing shivered down her spine. Constance smiled, Daniel's smile, and strong and sure, Mary and Constance began the song again, together:

> Amazing grace, how sweet the sound!
> That saved a wretch like me!
> I once was lost, but now am found
> Was blind, but now I see.

By the time they began the second verse, the sound of sorrow and celebration was shared by all of them, rolling away into the dark woods, drifting toward the sea. We sing for joy and we sing for sorrow, Mary thought, and the songs of Christmas, the New Year, and death were all the same in her mind.

It could not be put off forever. Jamie was asking for his grandmother. He was well enough to be bored and restless. Mary and Jason told him together about Ellen and Daniel.

At first he simply shook his head. "I don't think so."

"You don't think what?" Jason asked gently.

"I don't think that's true." Jamie's mouth was set in a determinedly obstinate line, but his chin was beginning to quiver. Mary was sitting beside him with her arms around him, and she prayed he wouldn't have one of his attacks over this, though God knew, he was entitled.

"It is true. It's horrible, and it's sad, and it's true." Jason's face was naked with grief, and Jamie saw it. Mary felt him tremble as he struggled for control. He reached out to his father. "I'm sorry, Papa. Maybe now Mama won't be lonesome."

It was, she saw, the final straw. Jason barely managed agreement before he stumbled out of the room.

"He's very sad and very tired."

"I know," Jamie agreed. "And he helped me get better. I'm glad I didn't die like . . . well, I'm glad I didn't. Is that wrong?"

"No, it's absolutely right! Your father and I, we couldn't have borne to lose you."

She stayed with him until he fell asleep. In time he would weep for what he had lost, now he scarcely knew the truth of it. He could talk about death and wonder about his mother in heaven, but it was not, she was sure, very real to him. It was, after all, scarcely real to her. Its validity would be, for her and for Jamie, ~~in the absence of Ellen and Daniel in the fabric of their~~ days on the island. But for Jason, there seemed to be no cushion against the truth. She went to his study and found the door closed. She heard the sounds coming from within, and she left him alone.

When he fell into bed hours later, he was blind drunk. She took his boots off, undid his clothing, and went back to sleep.

He slept for most of the next day, but when she saw him, she knew it had done little good. His eyes were cold and shuttered. He had loved Daniel dearly, and he had had so little time even to realize that his mother was seriously ill, no time at all to make his peace with her before she died.

"Guilt is useless, and you don't deserve it. You took good care of her. You didn't know she was ill; she didn't want you to know," she told him softly, but she knew the guilt was hers too; guilt for supplanting Ellen, for taking away her power and perhaps her reason for living. And the irony of it was that she knew Ellen had not felt blame toward either of them when she died.

No light moved in his eyes. Jason simply looked away from her, not even bothering to answer. He moved through the rest of the day as if he were still asleep, and then he drank himself into oblivion again.

When Mary awakened the next morning, she knew she had to get out of the house. Her chest hurt from the tears she had shed and the ones she had kept inside. She felt hot and twitchy in her skin. She wanted to be away from Jason's gnawing guilt and her own, away from the memory of death in this house.

Maggie was her salvation. She was here today, insisting that her family was well enough and help was needed here. It was— oh, God, it was!—Mary thought as she watched Jamie eat his breakfast while she drank a cup of coffee, refusing food despite Maggie's insistence.

She managed to smile at Jamie, glad he was strong enough to be downstairs again, glad the memory of death did not seem to be part of this day for him. "I'm going out for a while," she told him, "and I want you to promise that you'll stay inside. It's too cold and rainy for you to go out yet. And besides, Maggie is going to bake cookies, and I'm sure she'll need you to taste them."

He eyed her suspiciously. "Why is it too cold for me an' not for you?"

"Because I haven't been sick, but you have," she retorted.

He gave in because he knew it was useless to argue. Besides, he liked Maggie's cookies very much indeed. He carefully avoided thinking about Grandmother Ellen and Daniel and those babies. But he had another question. "Papa going with you?"

"No, he's still asleep, and he needs that as much as I need to be outside for a while and as much as you need to stay here with Maggie."

Maggie again urged her to eat, and again Mary politely refused. Maggie studied her face and reached out suddenly to touch her forehead, her eyes flaring in alarm when she did.

With her back to Jamie who understood a good deal of the silent language now, Mary signed to Maggie that she was all right and going to see Cade. When Maggie started to protest, Mary cut her off by bidding good-bye and walking out.

The cold air felt wonderful against her face, the rain was a blessing. But she was surprised at the trouble she had lifting the saddle onto Dolly's back. Ben was still at home on Maggie's orders, and Mary kept working doggedly until the job was done. Despite the rain, Dolly was glad to get out and stepped briskly. Mary immediately began to feel better. She hoped fervently that Cade was home; surely he would be in weather like this. She needed his calm, wise presence desperately.

She met no one on her ride, and she kept her eyes averted when she passed the little knoll that now held the island's first dead. She would have passed the schoolhouse too without stopping if Dolly hadn't shied and then stopped. As Mary regained her balance, she heard it too, a horrible wailing cry.

She tied the mare so she couldn't bolt and made her trembling legs take her inside.

The place was a shambles, books and papers torn, furniture overturned, the slate board smashed into large, jagged pieces.

Hayes lurched out of the shadows. He was dressed in a tattered Union uniform, freshly stained by the blood that was dripping from his mouth and chin. He seemed not to notice as he lifted the broken-mouthed jug and took another pull. He was raving drunk.

"Killed my cousin, shot him, my own cou . . . sin, shoot 'im, sot him. Deserter Hayes, at's me, run away, allus run away. An' now dead ones here too, all dead." He gave another bloodcurdling yell.

Rage boiled over in Mary. "Goddamn you, you stupid son of a bitch! With everything else you have to go and do this after you got through the funeral so well! I ought to let you bleed to death! Maybe you will anyway."

She felt too awful herself to offer sympathy. She advanced on him, and he backpedaled, too drunk to see anything except a vague shape coming toward him. He fell backwards and lay still.

Mary bent over him, heart pounding in anger and fear. But he wasn't dead.

He started babbling to someone named Laurel and reached for Mary, twisting from side to side.

"Stop it!" she yelled, batting ineffectually at his flailing hands and trying to hold him down. "I've got to see how badly you're cut."

Finally she pinned him down by straddling him, sitting on him while he bucked beneath her, and gripping his head with both hands. There was a good deal of blood on her now and more dripping on her hands as she tried to get a clear look at the cuts in the poor light.

She screamed in pain and shock as the first blow landed, and then another, streaking fire across her back. She heard his voice, distorted by rage. "No, no, stop, you don't understand!" she cried, but the blows kept falling until she felt the stick break across her, and there was silence except for her own jagged breathing and Hayes's.

Maggie fumed inside, trying to decide what to do. Jason needed to sleep, and Mary needed to get out of the house for a time, unless she was sick. Maggie flinched from the thought after all they'd been through, but she could still feel the heat that had been against her hand when she'd touched Mary. She feared she was not mistaken.

She smiled with false cheerfulness at Jamie and scribbled a note: "Put three cups of flour into bowl. I'll be right back." She pointed to the bowl, gave him the cup, and showed him the flour bin. He nodded, happy to have something to do.

Jason woke with a start, thinking it was Mary shaking him out of sleep. He gazed blankly at Maggie, and then all his senses sharpened as he understood her desperate signs.

Jamie heard him when he came down the stairs. "You stay with Maggie. I've decided to go out riding with Mary." Jason tried to keep the urgency out of his voice.

"You better hurry, Papa. She left a while ago. I'm helpin' Maggie measure things."

Jason cursed his leg for slowing his progress, but at last he was on Gabriel and heading north. He saw Dolly outside the school-house, brought Gabriel to a skidding halt, and threw himself out of the saddle. Why was Mary here? Maggie had said she was going to see Cade, and Maggie had said Mary was ill.

He heard the muffled cries and saw them on the floor beside the big desk, Mary on top, moving with Hayes. He blinked and focused again, but the nightmare that was reality remained— Mary and Hayes went on heaving and groaning together in passion, unaware of his presence.

The last belief, the last hope he had of love exploded. Everything he had tried to deny but had feared was true; all his vague suspicions and sharp bouts of jealousy were focused in the proof before him.

Mary and Hayes. The time she had spent with him in Christmas preparations, and how often had she ridden out before to be with him? The book he had given her, the poem, "The Tyger"—a joke at the Tiger's expense. Her worry about Hayes being alone on Christmas Day. They had so much in common; they had each other in common. Hayes in Jamie's sickroom, another way to be close to Mary. The way Mary had looked at Hayes at the funeral—the tenderness on her face then came back to Jason now.

All the images coalesced with terrifying speed. He wanted to kill them both. He wanted a gun to blow them to hell.

He stomped through the debris, not even conscious of it. He saw the stick on Hayes's desk, the long, smooth pointer. He raised it and brought it down with all of his force on Mary's heaving back and shoulders. Snarling, "How many times, how long?" he kept on until the stick shattered.

He froze, staring at the broken stub of wood in his hand, staring down at Mary crouched and still over Hayes.

"Laurel," Hayes moaned, oblivious to any threat.

The world refocused with horrifying truth for Jason, obliterating the distortion he had believed only seconds before. He heard the cries Mary had ceased to utter. He saw the blood on her and Hayes. He saw the broken jug of whiskey. He saw that Hayes was only semiconscious. He saw the wreckage of the room and the Union uniform. He saw what he himself had done, the demons he had conjured from himself and loosed on Mary.

She was panting hard, and still she couldn't seem to get enough air. She levered herself off of Hayes and rolled to the side.

Jason reached for her, and she cowered away. "Don't touch me! Do not touch me! Hayes has cut himself badly. You make it stop bleeding." Each word was a separate effort of will.

"Mary, oh, my love!" He tried to reach out to her again.

Her lips were pulled back from her teeth, her eyes wild and glittering. "Don't, don't, don't," the word kept coming as she scrambled away from him, struggling to her feet, grabbing hold of anything that might give support, swaying when she finally stood. "You can't leave him to bleed." She kept going until she had gained the door and disappeared from sight. Jason heard the sound of hooves and Gabriel's scream of protest at being left behind.

He turned grimly back to Hayes, manhandling him until he could tell that the cuts were bloody but manageable and not apt to kill him right away. He stuffed a piece of his shirt into Hayes's mouth where the jug had cut the inside of his lip, he used his handkerchief to bind the chin cut tightly, and then he left him.

It was impossible to tell which way Mary had gone by the

tracks. Everything was a blur of mud and rain. But Jason was almost sure she would have gone on, fleeing to Cade rather than going home. Gabriel was sure; he snorted and pulled to be off after Dolly.

Captain had warned him, and Cade recognized Dolly with Mary on her back, coming through the rain. His smile of welcome faded when he saw how hunched she was in the saddle, saw her face.

She whispered his name as she got down laboriously from the mare, and he saw the fear in her eyes before they closed and she continued to sink down to the earth.

He caught her in his arms, and he heard the thunder of Gabriel's hooves as Jason nearly overrode them.

Cade saw the blood diluted by rain, felt the fever, and heard her whimper when he tried to pat her back in comfort. He didn't understand what had happened, but he knew no one but Jason could have broken her like this. He looked up at the man he loved as a son. "Go away. You will not hurt her again. I will kill you before I let you harm her more."

Jason's voice was as deadly as Cade's. "She is mine. Give her to me."

Their eyes locked, neither of them blinking despite the rain splashing into their faces. Captain looked from one to the other and a rumbling growl began to vibrate in his massive throat.

Cade was not in the least intimidated by the advantage Jason had on the stallion's back nor did he bother to notice the lethal hooves dancing dangerously close as the currents of fear and anger touched the beast. His hand was on the hilt of his knife.

"Captain and I, we could make fish bait of you and your idiot horse, and we will if you come any closer." The words were more threatening for having been spoken in such a calm, conversational tone. Cade might have been observing that it was, indeed, raining.

"I did enough, but I didn't do all of it." The words tumbled one over the other as Jason told Cade what had happened, what he had seen, what he had done. "Give her to me. She needs warmth and care. I love her, Cade! Give her back to me!"

The Tiger was broken. Cade lifted Mary up and gave her into his keeping. And then he tied the mare's reins so that she would not fall in following.

He watched Gabriel race away with his double burden, the riderless mare trying to keep pace.

Captain whimpered and sidled close. Cade patted the broad head absently, wondering if he would ever see Mary riding the mare again, praying in rusty, hardly learned and long-forgotten ways that he would, she would.

It was the longest ten miles Jason had ever ridden. It was a struggle to keep Mary's limp weight and himself in the saddle, worse when she stirred and moved convulsively, seeming not to hear his warnings at all, then sinking back into the shadows again.

Jamie and Maggie met him as he came in, their faces sharing a look of horror. Jamie let out a loud wail.

"Not now!" Jason snapped. "I need you to help Maggie. Can you do that?"

Jamie's eyes were round with fear, but he nodded and listened as his father continued up the stairs with Mary in his arms.

Jason stripped off her wet clothes. His stomach lurched at the sight of the bruises and welts he had raised on her back. She looked very fragile, the pale honey legs and arms so slender, the gilt curls in damp disarray, hair as soft as a child's and longer now than when he had first touched it. And she was burning up and beginning to shake with chills at the same time. He put his head against her chest and heard the dreaded rattle.

He wrapped her warmly and held her, murmuring endearments, begging her forgiveness, demanding that she live. She didn't seem to hear him at all. Maggie brought a steaming toddy, and Jamie brought the rocking chair and built up the fire in the room as his father told him. Maggie urged Jamie out with her, and Jamie left without protest; his father looked as scared as Jamie felt, and he didn't want to see that any more.

"Please, just a little at a time, please, Mary, drink it." Jason held the cup against her mouth, but it did no good. Her teeth chattered against it, but she didn't drink.

He laid her down on the bed. "Mary, listen to me, love. I don't know what to do. Wherever you've gone, you've got to care enough to come back, to get well. I can't lose you. You can't leave me this way."

She surfaced slowly from the terror of the place where she had been, hearing the echoes of the hated voice. *You've been a bad girl, can't have that, mustn't, mustn't. This will teach you.* The hands, one thing leading into the next, the twisted way.

But it was Jason talking to her now. Jason calling her "love." Surely not. She moved and the pain in her back made her cry out. Jason had done this. She tried to get up to run away. Jason loomed over her, huge and distorted. She screamed, and the world slipped away.

Jason bowed his head. He would carry her look of terror with him forever. Now he would gladly give her to Hayes, to anyone she chose if she would only live. And she had chosen no one but him; he knew that. It made everything worse.

He lost track of the hours. Mary would lie in a stupor for a while, and then she would whimper and struggle to escape the smothering blankets in a fierce burst of strength. In the next moment, she would be shaking and burrowing for warmth she couldn't find, and the cycle would start all over again.

Jason cared for her as they had cared for the others, sponging her down when the fever rose, then quickly wrapping her against further chill.

He swore and prayed and could not make her fever break.

She opened her eyes and began to talk.

He felt a great surge of relief and then a thousand cold crawling things on his spine. Her eyes were staring blankly, and she was not talking to him at all; it didn't even sound like her voice. But it was, it was her voice, seeming younger, but the voice he knew. At first, the disjointed phrases made no sense, then suddenly they were a single image so shocking, the bile burned his throat, and he had to swallow convulsively to keep from retching. It could not be, but it was.

He knew now who her first lover was. He had wanted to know. Now he wished the truth had stayed buried forever.

Her voice died away to incoherent murmurs and then silence, but her breathing was growing more audible. He lifted her in his arms.

Constance paused in the doorway, swallowing the tears that came so often these days. The sight of Jason rocking with Mary cradled in his arms touched her unbearably. She had never seen agony so deeply etched as it was now on his face.

He looked up at her, surprised, having expected to see Maggie.

"Cade told me she was sick, and Hayes is all right. I've come to help. Cade's taking care of the horses, regardless of his aversion to them." She forced a small smile, anything at all to change the set misery on his face. "He'll stay with Jamie for a while. Maggie needs to rest. You'll need to rest too."

The gentle, insistent practicality of her voice finally penetrated his fogged brain, and he nodded. "But not yet, Constance, I can't leave her yet." He stared at her in sudden sharp demand. "You haven't seen . . . you don't know?"

She didn't pretend to misunderstand. "No, Jason, I have seen nothing at all since . . . since Daniel died." She steadied her voice again. "We've lost too much already; we won't lose Mary too."

Jason drew strength from her and was grateful, yet he knew if Mary started to talk again, he would send Constance away. He could not bear for anyone else to know Mary's past.

But Mary had no air for words and progressively less for breathing. Jason held her, crooned to her, and Constance helped him when he bathed the hot flesh. She gasped in horror when she first saw the marks on Mary. Jason spared himself nothing when he told her what he had done, but he said nothing about the healing scratches, and she did not ask.

"You did hurt her, Jason, but you didn't give her pneumonia. She was worn out, and it's been cold and damp. I don't even believe this is what the others had," Constance said firmly.

"If I destroyed her will to live, I've as good as killed her." His voice brooked no denial.

As the time went on, Constance began to lose her own faith that they could save Mary. The high fever continued, and her lungs were so filled with fluid, she could breathe only in shallow, grating gasps.

It was Constance who heard the change, and for an instant, she tasted the power of it. Jason was so exhausted from his care of Mary and so tortured by the sound of her labored breathing, there was no way on earth he would hear this silence as anything but blessed before it was too late. And she would be here to comfort him.

The temptation vanished as quickly as it had come. "Jason!" she shrieked. "She's stopped breathing!"

He looked up at her, dazed and uncomprehending, Mary's still body in his arms. "Better now, quiet."

Constance slapped him hard, and horrified awareness dawned in his eyes.

"She's drowning!" she screamed, and Jason acted on her words, finding himself on the floor straddling Mary's body and pumping her bruised back with deep, hard pressure, turning her over to force his own breath into her mouth and lungs, over and over.

Her rib cage heaved of its own accord; she coughed violently, and the gasping sound began again, horribly loud, beautiful in place of the death silence.

Jason and Constance worked over her, clearing the putrid matter from her throat and mouth as her body struggled to survive.

Minutes, hours, days, a lifetime—no regular measure of time made any sense in this. Death dictated its own time, waiting hunched, huge, and darker than the other shadows just beyond the light.

Jason could feel it, could smell it, and in one brief respite, he raised his head and stared at it. "You will not take her!" It was a low, feral snarl.

Constance shivered with the power of Jason's words, and acknowledged her understanding with a small nod when his eyes met hers. Neither of them would ever know how long it was before she cried, "It leaves, Jason, it leaves us now! Listen, oh, listen, this quiet is wondrous!"

It was true. Jason shivered with release from the mortal combat, feeling suddenly weak, but the fierce joy in Constance's voice coursed through him as his own. The darker shadow was gone. Nothing lived now within this room except for himself, Constance, and Mary.

The violent struggle for air had ceased. Her chest rose and fell rhythmically with only faint harshness. The fever that had been burning her alive had broken. She was asleep, not drifting away from them in death.

They bathed the sweat from her skin, dressed her in a warm nightgown, laid her on fresh linen, and cleared away the refuse of the battle.

Jason drew Constance into his arms, kissing her on the forehead and holding her close. "Thank you for loving her as much as I do," he said softly. "She would have been taken away before I knew."

She stepped away from him, away from his warmth, but her voice was infinitely gentle. "It was never in my hands, after all. The Tiger would not lose his woman and so he did not."

He didn't flinch from the name. He could hear Mary's voice the times she had dared to use it. He could hear her saying, "And what shall we do if the Tiger weeps?" He wondered if she would ever care again after what he had done. He wondered how he could live with the new knowledge he had of her. He wondered how she had survived the reality of it. But for now, the only thing on earth that mattered was that she was alive.

CHAPTER
23

$\mathcal{M}$ary slept for twenty-four hours, not even waking fully when she was lifted and urged to drink, though she swallowed the water and broth obediently.

When she opened her eyes, she saw Jason asleep in a chair beside the bed. He looked bone weary, his eyes closed in gaunt hollows. She wondered if his leg were hurting him. Why was he asleep in the chair? The mist swirled and closed over her again.

When she opened her eyes the next time, he was watching her. "How do you feel?"

"As if I've been beaten," she whispered ruefully, still totally confused about why she was here, aching all over, and he was there. Her voice sounded strange too.

"Jason, what's wrong?" she gasped as pain suffused his face, and then it all came back—Ellen, Daniel, the babies, all dead, and all the rest, everything up to the time she had collapsed in Cade's arms. And beyond that, she remembered Jason's voice calling her back, demanding, pleading that she live.

"I was mad to beat you!" He could not say the rest, he could not tell her that he had grown to love her all against his will and that jealousy and its phantoms had grown apace. With what he knew now, he didn't know whether he'd ever be able to tell her.

His misery was so clearly etched on his tired face, tenderness and concern for him overwhelmed her. "I didn't mean that! Honestly, I didn't. It was just a foolish expression. Everything is still very blurred." She paused, gathering strength to go on. "You were wrong to attack me when I was trying to help Hayes, but I understand how it must have appeared to you. Had I been you, I might have done the same. Sleep now, beside me." She managed to move one hand slowly to pat the bed. Her eyes closed even as she fought against it, but she smiled when she felt Jason carefully settle down beside her, his arms cradling her gently.

Jamie was allowed to visit her, the terror in his face easing when she took his hand and assured him she was all right, just very tired. Constance and Cade and the other islanders came too, staying only briefly but seeming to need the same visual assurance Jamie did that they had not lost yet another of their own. Special tidbits of food appeared in the house, food prepared to tempt the invalid to the most practical need.

The visit from Hayes was not so effortless. He wore an expression of such abject misery, Mary's heart went out to him. "It's all right, it wasn't your fault," she said firmly, but Hayes shook his head and touched the still healing cut on his chin.

"It wouldn't have happened at all if I hadn't been stinking drunk." His gaze shifted to some point far away. "Nothing is more useless than being unable to leave the past behind where it belongs. I judge myself the worst sort of fool; my past sours my present until I can't stand the stench of it anymore. I cannot bury the dead."

"You needn't tell me," Mary murmured, thinking of her own past and the terrors that rose from it to fill too much of her present. By Hayes's measure, she too was a fool.

"I do need to tell you. Will you listen?" His voice was harsh in its intensity, and she nodded.

"I grew up in New England, in Massachusetts. I grew up believing in the Union. I grew up under the thunder of the abolitionists. But I had ties in the South too, family there in

Virginia, and what they had to sell, my merchant father handled. It was a comfortable, profitable arrangement, until the war. I spent a lot of summers at Burkeland, and my cousin Clayton was the brother I never had. We were just of an age. Lord, the trouble we could manage in just one day! But life was easy and gracious there, and boys were expected to get into a certain amount of mischief."

His face looked so soft and young for a moment, Mary felt tears burn her eyelids. She wanted to ask him to stop; suddenly, she knew she did not want to meet his demons, but she could not deny his need to confess.

"A little brat of a girl, Laurel McGary, tagged along with us whenever she could. She came from a neighboring plantation. She was a year younger than we and a good sport. She could outride and outshoot both of us; she always took her fair share of the blame when we got caught at something; and she hadn't any interest in being a girl, not until her sixteenth summer. I'd just arrived for my visit. I should have known that Clayton was up to something. I asked him about Laurel, and he slipped right by the question with a smile, saying that old Laurel was just the same as ever. I can still hear him laughing when she rode up and I got my first look at her in a year. That year had changed Laurel Katherine McGary from a scruffy child into a young woman. I can still see the green riding habit she was wearing, deep green to match her eyes, and her skin was pale, her hair shining black. 'Why, Master Hayes, haven't you even one kind word for an old friend?' she asked, and I thought maybe she'd become spoiled and full of false airs, but then she burst out laughing, and it was the new Laurel and the best of the old all in one."

The image of the woman was so strong in Hayes, Mary could see her too, beautifully poised on the edge of womanhood.

"I never loved anyone as much as I loved Laurel. It was impossible not to love her. Clayton loved her too. It was a measure of her kindness that she couldn't bear us fighting over her. She told us that unless we treated each other well, she wouldn't have a thing to do with either of us and besides, she had no intention of settling down for years yet.

"And then it all changed. 'Yankee' she'd called me for years,

but the last time I saw her, the word was a curse. Laurel believed
in the South and the South's rights, and she did not believe the
North was truly concerned about the slaves. She believed as
many did, that slavery would end of its own accord eventually
simply because of the cost, but in the meantime, she had grown
up with the peculiar institution; she considered the slaves on her
father's plantation and those at Burkeland to be well-treated;
and most of all, she believed in the South's right to its own
economic system. She and Clayton were twins in their beliefs,
and the strength of theirs clarified my own. I became the pas-
sionate Yankee against the fire of their Southern hearts." There
was no fire in his voice now, only weary sorrow.

"That was my last summer at Burkeland. Laurel was eighteen.
Fort Sumter was the next spring, and by June, Virginia had
seceded from the Union. Some news of the family still came
through. Clayton and Laurel were married that summer. War
was coming swiftly. There weren't any more long, lazy summer
days, no more years to drift through feeling young and alive."

Tears gathered in Hayes's blind-looking eyes and began to
roll down his cheeks. Mary doubted he even knew he wept.

"By the next summer, Clayton was dead. He was just past
twenty-one and so was I. He was dead, and I was alive. And I
was the one who killed him."

She knew it was true. She remembered now his slurred babbling about shooting his cousin, about Laurel. She could barely
breathe past the lump in her throat.

"We didn't know we were on opposite sides of the same
battlefield until we were face to face. It happened very quickly
—and very slowly. He hesitated, I did not. He died. I lived.
When the battle was over, I went back to make sure." He fumbled like a very old man and finally drew something from his
pocket and handed it to Mary. She studied it through her own
tears and weariness, not seeing it clearly at first and then seeing
it too well. It was open, a gold pocket watch, broken chain
dangling, the crystal over the watch face webbed with cracks, but
the other face undamaged, the exquisite miniature of Laurel's
face unmarred.

The artist had caught her perfectly, all the beauty, strength,

and conviction of a green-eyed woman with the scamp of summers past still lurking in the mischievous eyes. She must have
been no more than seventeen or eighteen when the portrait had
been done in its tiny perfection. How had she looked when she
had learned that her husband was dead? How had she looked
when the war had run its course and wounded everyone in its
path? Had she survived at all?

She handed the watch back to Hayes, and his fingers closed
over it convulsively.

"I ran, the next day we were fighting in heavy brush, and I
ran." His voice rolled over her, heavy and unrelenting. "I never
stopped running. At first I was afraid I'd be caught and shot as
a deserter, and then I was afraid I wouldn't be caught, and then
nothing mattered at all. Nothing has mattered very much for a
very long time. But you matter and Jason matters."

Her head was swimming again. She felt flat and leaden against
the bed, unable to respond coherently to the horror of the story.
"Your family?" she finally managed.

"I never told them anything. I'm sure they assumed I died. I
don't know what the army told them. Not all bodies were ac-
counted for; mine could well have been counted as one of the
missing. It was true enough. As good as dead and certainly
missing." His laugh was like claws on slate.

Younger than Jason, he looked much older now. To have let
his family think him dead, it made Mary shudder inside, for by
his words, he came from a loving one. It was as if he had commenced a long and never-resolved suicide. She groped for the
right words.

"Hayes, it was a civil war. Many ran the risk of meeting relatives and friends on the battleground. You endured the reality
of that risk. War is for killing. It might be more convenient to
kill a stranger, but it's no different. The result is the same."

The bleakness in his eyes did not change. "Clayton hesitated.
I did not. I saw Laurel in my mind, and I shot him."

Her logic had not touched him, and now she understood why.
It was the reason he had shot his cousin more than the act itself
that haunted him.

"Did you?" The words hissed out with such vehemence, he

stared at her. "Did you see Laurel before or after you shot
Clayton? Did he really hesitate or were you just faster? Did you
really recognize each other before or was it only after the shooting, in that instant after? Do you really know? Guilt makes its
own memories, and they aren't always true."

He shook his head as if he were half drowned, and his breath
eased out in a long sigh. "I don't know; now, I don't know. And
I never will know anything except that I did kill him." He pulled
the guilt back around him, a shroud too familiar to abandon.

Mary closed her eyes. She was utterly exhausted. It was all so
useless. The past never let go. She heard Hayes's voice some-
where above her moaning, "God, oh, Mary, I'm sorry," and then
Jason's voice, loud and furious, "What the hell . . . damn you,
Hayes," she felt his hand touching her forehead, her cheeks.
"She's got a fever again! Haven't you any sense?"

"I'm all right! Don't fuss!" Her voice sounded feeble even to
her own ears, and when she opened her eyes again, she knew
she'd slept with Jason watching over her for the countless time.
The pattern was disgustingly familiar. She had only been out of
bed for short, dizzy periods that had left her drenched in sweat
from the effort; the brief surge of energy she felt on waking in
the morning quickly gave way to lassitude and more hours of
sleep than of awareness; and the fever, never so dangerously
high as it had been at the crisis of her illness, still returned with
faint, insidious heat that sapped her of energy she could not
spare. And worst of all to her mind was that Jason, Constance,
and everyone else beamed with approval at what they considered her progress.

"Progress, hell!" she swore, and Jason reached out to touch
her forehead in his now familiar gesture. She twitched her head
away from his hand and ground out, "I am not feverish. I am
bored, bored, bored! And if I am, God only knows how you must
be feeling."

"I'm thankful," Jason said quietly. "I'm thankful every minute
of every day that you're alive. Mary, you came so close to dying!
It was a hard battle, and you've got to give yourself time to
heal." Every time he thought of it, he thought of what he knew
about her now, and then he would force his mind to go out of
focus, flinching away from confronting it fully.

Slow tears started down her cheeks, and she was too weak to stop them. His patience and tender care touched her unbearably.

He scooped her up and carried her to the window, settling down in the rocking chair with her in his lap, rocking her against his warmth in wordless comfort while she told him Hayes's story, a story he had not known. And her admission that she had wondered from the first why Hayes seemed so lacking in spirit, somehow broken and less than a whole man, added to his private pain and guilt.

"The poor bastard," he said softly when she was finished. He held her tighter, sad for her misery, Hayes's, and his own.

He watched over her and cared for her as if she were a child, cared for her better than she had ever been cared for as a child, better than he had been. He bathed her, helped her into clean gowns, and brought her meals, seldom letting Maggie or Constance take his place. He read to her and told her what was going on on the island as life began again.

At first it made sense and gave her endless comfort; she was as helpless as a small child and needed the strength Jason gave her. But as she grew stronger, her mind grew sharper, and a vague disquiet began. It was as if Jason preferred playing parent to the child to being lover to the woman.

She warned herself against sick fantasies—the brooding, overreactive sensitivity which came from too much time spent doing nothing except waiting to be well again. But the certainty grew that the problem was not in her mind, but in Jason's. The grave comfort he gave her became a wall higher and wider than ever between them. And she didn't know how to breach it. She owed him so much, even to her life. And he had lost so much—his mother, a child he had loved dearly, the young promise of the new babies, and very nearly his own son. It must all surely be coupled in his mind with his earlier loss of Gaiety. Perhaps it was just that he needed time to heal also, but the treacherous thought intruded that if he found her with Hayes now, he would not lash out in a paroxysm of jealousy as he had before.

She began to test her theory. He still slept beside her at night, but he was armored now against the intrusion of passion. When she moved against him, as if by accident, he did not move away nor did his body respond in the old ways. He would pat her or hold her close, but it was an act without sexuality. Countless times she tried to summon the courage to question him openly about the change, but she could not bring herself to do it, and she knew she feared the answer.

And then she saw it, awakening to see Jason watching her. In the instant he knew she was awake, his expression changed, but she had seen the other—he had looked at once troubled and baffled, and beyond that, he had looked as if he were regarding someone with both distaste and mistrust, as if he wondered how this particular stranger had ever intruded on his life.

The precious new confidence, the soft blossoming that had begun died in her. It was as if spring had never come; she felt herself slipping back into the winter of her soul and heart, and she could not save herself. This time he did know, somehow he knew, and suddenly, she understood how. She remembered Jamie's delirious babbling, the facts and fantasies he had spewed out in his fever. She had done the same thing; she was certain of it. All that she had tried so hard to hide had been uncovered, and Jason was the one who had seen it. She doubted that anyone else had; there was no change in other attitudes toward her, only in Jason's, only in the one that mattered the most.

She did not blame him for his reaction; she marveled at his kindness, marveled that he still let Jamie spend so much time with her, marveled that he did not order her to leave.

Leave she must. There was no choice. And she must leave without making the Tiger part of it, without forcing him to renege on his kindness. What had been between them was over forever. Her reason for being here was gone and she must go with it. She concentrated on growing physically stronger, eating though she had no appetite, making herself get up and exercise more each day until she was strong enough to make her careful way downstairs. Jason beamed with approval as if she were a precocious child.

She felt as if she and Jason were involved in a last, elaborate game, the purpose of each being to spare the other. It took all her self-control to behave normally, as if the new rules between them were a natural product of her illness and all that had happened on the island.

It was a relief when Jason told her haltingly that he had to go to Seattle and wanted to take Jamie with him. "I would take you, too," he assured her, "but you're far from strong, and I don't want you to risk the cold yet."

She smiled brightly and met his eyes. "You're quite right, even though I'd like to see Angie. I'm so glad you're taking Jamie with you. It will be a very special trip for him, and it will be good for him to get away from the island for a while."

"You're sure you don't mind?" he asked suspiciously, his own guilt at wanting a space away from her making it hard to credit her ready acceptance of his plan.

"Of course I mind, but not enough to throw a tantrum. I'll go the next time." The time that will never be, her mind added, and she could feel the smile wavering on her lips. Oh, God, Jason, let us be done with this!

"I could leave Jamie with you. I haven't told him yet."

"For heaven's sake, what a contrary man you are! You've just gotten your way and you can't bear it." The asperity in her voice was genuine, and Jason grinned reluctantly.

Jamie was beside himself with the prospect of the trip, asking endless questions about Seattle and expressing determined opinions about what he would and would not take with him. Mary finally convinced him that his woodcarving tools were not something he would need while he was gone.

"Well, all right, then you can use 'em 'til I get back, only you've got to be careful, else you'll cut yourself."

"I think I'll wait until I'm older; I'll know how to carve wood better then," she told him, and he burst into delighted giggles at their old joke.

Nothing was harder than being with Jamie, and yet, she craved the contact. From their bad beginnings, they had come so far together. She would miss him desperately, and she stored up all the last minute images of him, praying that somehow he would come to understand and forgive her.

Suddenly there was no more time. The *Gaiety* was ready to sail. At Jason's insistence that she not expose herself to the cold, Mary said good-bye to them at the house.

Jamie was glowing with excitement, but he was suddenly serious as he hugged her. "I wish you were comin' with us."

"So do I, sweetheart," she managed. "But it's better this way, and sometimes just you men ought to be able to go off on business."

He was visibly proud. "I'll bring you something pretty from Seattle," he promised.

"Just bring yourself back safely. And know my love goes with you wherever you are, wherever I am." She said the words calmly and hoped he would remember them though now he blushed and ducked his head the way any little boy would at such mushy motherly talk. Having elected himself in charge of the luggage, he dashed away to climb up with Ben on the wagon seat, and the wagon creaked away. A cold, deadly calm enveloped her. It was not going to be so hard after all. The worst was over in saying farewell to Jamie. She felt numb as she faced Jason.

"Say hello to Angie for me and do take Jamie to meet her," she said in a light conversational tone, but Jason regarded her pale face anxiously.

"You will take care of yourself while I'm gone?" He touched her cheek. "I'll expect to see some color here when I return."

"I'll be fine," she replied obediently, child to parent, all changed, all changed in the timbre of his voice and in her response, all changed in the careful concern in his eyes and the unease ebbing and flowing in their depths. He knew, and it had changed his view of her and his need. He no longer saw her as a woman he desired; he put her away from him by protecting her like a child.

"Have a safe journey." For a moment, their eyes met and held, and then his slid away. He kissed her lightly on the forehead, warned her not to stand in the chill air any more and walked away from her, swinging up on Gabriel to follow the wagon down to the shore.

She watched until the *Gaiety* was a flutter of white on the horizon and then nothing. She watched the two people dearest to her in the world sailing away from her. She felt as if the world had suddenly gone silent, as silent as the world of Maggie and Ben, but theirs was full of each other and their children; hers was an empty husk spinning away on the wind.

Maggie and Ben were horrified the next day when she asked that Dolly be saddled. Maggie scolded and pled with her hands; Ben refused to saddle the horse. But they were no match for her. She would saddle the beast herself. She marched out to the barn, and Ben gave in, unable to bear seeing her struggle with the heavy tack. He wanted at least to go with her, but Mary won that point too, threatening to race the whole way if he tried to accompany her.

Maggie clung to Ben as Mary rode out of sight, and the knowledge flowed through both of them that things were going terribly wrong between the Tiger and his woman. He should not have left her, Maggie signed, but there was more sorrow than blame in the gestures, and Ben agreed.

Mary noticed nothing of her surroundings as she rode out to Cade's. She was thankful that no one intercepted her. Maggie and Ben were right; she had no business riding yet. She was drenched in sweat and shaking all over by the time Captain announced her and Cade came into sight. The cold air was more piercing here on the bare point.

Cade took one look at her as she slid from the horse and ordered her into his house, coming to her side to give her his support when he saw her swaying. He dragged Dolly along with them until he could tie her by the house. Once inside, he sat Mary down and poured her a strong cup of coffee laced with rum, all the while watching her with angry concern. When she wrinkled her nose at the brew, Cade snapped, "Drink it! And when your teeth stop chattering, tell me why you're trying to kill yourself so stupidly."

The potency of the drink was welcome as it coursed down and sent exploding heat through her. She warmed her hands on the cup and sipped slowly, buying time and courage. Finally she placed the words one after another with careful precision. "I want to leave the island. Will you help me?"

Cade stared at her in disbelief, then snarled, "What in the hell is wrong with you, girl? Can't you let Jason out of your sight for more than a minute without mewling like a suckling? You are in no condition to have gone with him to Seattle and a fool for coming out here! Can't the man have any time to himself?"

"He can have all the time he wants to himself," she answered quietly, not reacting at all to his accusations. "That's why I'm going to leave."

Cade's rage gave way to puzzlement as he studied her set face and the gray eyes. All light had fled from them, leaving them as dull as tarnished metal. Abruptly he decided he needed a cup of the same medicine he'd given Mary. He inhaled the sweet rum fumes and sighed. "I don't understand. Jason fought Death himself to keep you with him, and now you want to leave him. Why?"

"It's time, it's time for me to go! Jason is too kind to send me away, but believe me, it will be easier for him if I am gone when he and Jamie return."

"I don't believe you! I think your illness has addled your wits. Jason loves you and so does his son, and you mustn't leave them. I know that clear down to my bones."

"You don't know anything! But Jason does, Jason knows about me now. I must have talked with the fever; I'm sure I did. And now he knows, and he can't bear it. Everything is changed between us, everything! And love was never spoken between us, never, but I was his woman and am no longer. Jason is the reason I'm here at all, and he is the reason I must leave." She drew a long breath. "Cade, you are so lucky to be so free of others and what they think."

"Lucky? Free?" His voice was so quiet, it sent shivers down her spine. "I have never lain with a woman who was not paid well to bear my deformity, and no woman will ever bear my child or share my life. My friends are only those who have learned not to see me as I am. I cannot care what people think because what they think is unbearable. I cannot blame them. I would never carve so ugly a creature. Free? I am free only to be alone, and that is no freedom at all."

The tears she had not shed at Jason's departure came now. "Oh, Cade, now I have hurt you out of my own hurt! It is the last thing I intended. But you are beautiful inside, and I am not. I am not! And now Jason knows. I can see it in his eyes, most of all in his eyes. I can see my own image there. I don't want to see it any more; I don't want him to carry it anymore."

Cade felt helpless, but he had to try. "Mary Smith, perhaps you've thought I love you only because I love Jason. But I've loved you for your own sake ever since you defied me and Captain in the woods that day. I knew even then that the Tiger had found his woman even if she did have a bit of growing to do. I still know it. Whatever went before, whatever you think is happening now, I know he loves you. He told me when he came for you that day, and surely he's told you in every way but words. I know you love him too."

"I don't love anyone. I don't know how. Jason deserves better than that. He deserves someone like Gaiety."

"Gaiety is dead!"

"Not for Jason."

Cade wanted to reach out and shake her out of the terrible leaden quality that had invaded her voice and her spirit, but he knew it was useless; in her despair, she was the stronger. "What if I do not help you? What you ask is a betrayal of my friend."

She rose unsteadily to her feet. "Then I will find another way. But you are wrong. It would be no betrayal. My leaving is as close as I can come to an act of love. Jason and Jamie too, will be far better off without me."

Cade bowed his head. He had not lied; he loved her for her own sake, and he could not forsake her now. "There is a ship sailing from Victoria in three days. I know the captain. He'll take you aboard." He could hardly bear the relief in her eyes.

"I can pay the passage."

He nodded curtly. "Be here at dawn the morning after tomorrow. You'll spend the night in Victoria; we ought to be there before dark. Will you tell the others—Hayes, Constance, Maggie —all the people who have come to love you?"

She didn't flinch from his words. "No. It would serve no purpose. They will know soon enough."

She did not resist Maggie's anxious scolding and orders when she arrived back at the house. She undressed and went to bed obediently. She had to be well enough to leave the island in less than forty-eight hours. She wished sleep would come again, but now when she wanted it, she could not gain it.

Constance found her pacing the room restlessly and smiled in sympathy. "I know, it must seem awfully quiet with the two Drakes gone. Now, you be honest. I'd love to visit, but if you could make yourself rest instead, I'll come another day."

"Rest! Oh, Lord, Constance, I'm so tired of resting, I could scream. Please stay." Suddenly she didn't want to be alone.

Constance studied her closely, then sighed in relief. "Well, your ride seems to have done you no harm. Maggie tattled. My dear, you must take care of yourself; Jason would never forgive any of us if you aren't stronger by the time he returns."

Perhaps it would have been better after all if she hadn't stayed to visit, Mary thought, Constance with her eerie perceptions. But she proved herself good and gentle company and immensely brave. She spoke of Daniel with only an occasional break in her voice, remembering the funny things he'd said and done, remembering the special sweetness of her son.

"I've thought of asking Jamie to help with the menagerie when he gets back, with Jason's and your permission, of course, and with care that none of the creatures left will bring on one of Jamie's attacks."

"It's a wonderful idea! He'll be thrilled!" And he'll be busy with new tasks and new loves, she reassured herself. "I'm sure Jason will agree."

The only moment of unease came when Constance was ready to go. "I haven't seen . . . seen anything since . . . since Daniel, and I don't want to, not again! But I feel so sad all of a sudden. It's understandable I guess, under the circumstances. Take care of yourself."

She looked so frail, Mary's heart ached for her, but her fear that the vision of her departure would suddenly come was stronger. "You must take care of yourself too," she ventured softly as she hugged her, searching for words without finality. She wanted to say, "Please, take special care of Jason," as Constance left with promises to return, but she could not bear the thought of the islanders' reactions and the pressure they would exert if they knew her plans.

Their love surrounded her in a veil of warmth, a veil she now had to rend, and it was agony every step of the way. Never before had she run from so much love; it was a thousand times more difficult than fleeing from terror.

She fought with Maggie who had promised Jason she would stay in the house at night during his absence. It was an exhausting battle, Maggie insisting obstinately, backed up by Ben, Mary equally adamant, pointing out that she was perfectly capable of taking care of herself now, that Maggie was taking care of her during the day in any case, and that the twins and Ben needed Maggie at home. She finally won by adding that while she didn't want to hurt anyone's feelings, she did want some time alone, something she hadn't had since she had fallen ill. Maggie reluctantly agreed.

The hours were interminable. She wished she were already miles away. When she lay down in the bed hoping to sleep the night away in oblivion, a rush of longing for Jason swept over her, and she got up again to pace nervously, finally going downstairs to his study and lighting a lamp there. In the soft light, he seemed so close in the ledgers they had worked on together, in the books and the smell of worn leather. Some of the records he had taken with him, but those he had left behind she checked with meticulous care. She touched the things on his desk, stroking the pen he used most often, handling it delicately as if it might shatter. She studied the books in the shelves with more care than ever before, looking for the most worn volumes, looking for his favorites, knowing most of them—how many minute and grand things she knew now about the Tiger—but also finding new facets of his personality. She smiled when she found a book on horticulture and beside it one on pure mathematics, the volumes equally tattered and marked. How like him. Planting on the island took special care, everything in creating a new world took special care, but the mathematics book was for pure enjoyment. How like him to dislike the tedium of accounts and yet enjoy the mental exercise of trying to solve problems based on complex theories.

But the book of Mrs. Browning's poems was a shock. A slim volume, *Sonnets from the Portuguese.* How unlike him. But it was as worn as the others. Perhaps it had been Ellen's. No, not Ellen's. Her hands trembled as she read the inscription: "Dearest Gaiety—I cannot begin to count the ways. My love always, Jason.''

The thick marker in the book was a photograph, scratched and faded and still much too clear. Gaiety. And none of the conventions of the painted backdrop or the set pose took anything from her beauty. Her dress was low cut, showing off her fine shoulders and the swell of her breasts, and the skirt billowed out from her tiny waist. Her hair was piled on top of her head, away from the slender neck, setting off the lovely face.

Mary staggered to Jason's chair and slumped into it. It wasn't the uptilted nose over the teasing mouth or the eyes which shone so brightly despite the flat limits of the picture; it wasn't the features alone which made the woman so beautiful. It was the tremendous force of joy, the sheer exuberance in living that flowed from the image. Gaiety had obviously been looking at Jason, not at the photographer. There was laughter, and promise, teasing and tenderness; all of it for Jason, all of it out of her love for him.

The photograph had surely not been hidden, perhaps it had even been forgotten; surely for all of its vitality, it was only a shadow of the woman, the woman who remained in Jason's heart just as Laurel remained in Hayes's.

With great care, Mary put the portrait back in the book, the book back in its place. She felt old, old and shriveled in body and soul, an ugly crone who had never in her life been like Laurel, like Gaiety. She could hardly bear the thought of having to get through one more day before she left.

When she finally slept, it was under the restless batwings of half-realized nightmares, and she was glad when the misty morning sun awakened her, glad that the weather still held against a storm which would make sailing the skiff difficult.

It was as if the islanders had decided that in addition to the Carters, others must visit her each day that the Tiger was gone. Today it was Ingrid who came with bread still warm from the oven and freshly churned butter.

"Ja, you sleep better ven de Tiger is here," she observed, "but soon he will be back an' my man too, den all sleep vell."

Mary did her best to respond to the twinkle in the blue eyes.

It was not as hard a visit as the one with Constance had been. The sadness of losing the new baby was part of Ingrid, but there was a deep enduring strength in the woman that could not be broken and an acceptance that joy and sorrow were both ingredients in life. Mary had a sudden image of Ingrid kneading her life with the same vigor she applied to her bread dough.

Strange images were part of the day, and Mary clung to reality with a fierce grip, praying she would not betray her agitation. The picture of Gaiety haunted her; the memories of Jason engulfed her; the need to cuddle Jamie was a physical ache.

The day ended finally, and Ben and Maggie left obediently for home. Mary signed carefully, "Thank you for everything," and she said the words aloud, but she had waited until the Carters were gone lest Maggie read the words.

She packed very little; what she did not take, Jason could sell or give away. The widow was long gone, but the blue dancing costume went into the satchel. She took the simplest of her wardrobe and left the rest except for the luxurious gray cloak with the dark fur. It was the warmest garment she had. She held the moonstone jewelry for a long time, feeling the cool weight warming in her hands. She knew it was foolish, but she put them carefully back in the box and left them. They belonged to another time, and to take them with her now would make them what Jason had feared they would appear and had not meant them to be—jewels easily sold, monetary payment for sexual favors. Whatever he thought when he found her gone, she could not bear that. She packed the little wooden tiger from Cade.

She went to Jason's study, intending to leave letters for Jason and Jamie. But first she took out the picture of Gaiety again. She stared at it for a long time before she put it back. She didn't write anything. There was nothing to say. Jason would be relieved. Jamie would not be placated by words on paper; whatever assurance of caring she had to give him had already been given.

There was nothing left to do except wait for the time to pass. She didn't try to sleep. She went to Jamie's room. Everything was in order. Maggie had cleaned it as soon as Jamie had left, but there was still the scent of him, the young earthy fragrance that clung to him in his new and so much more healthy life. That much she had given him, and even without her, surely he would not lose it.

"Sleep well, Jamie," she whispered, just as if he were there.

Next she went to Ellen's room. No effort had been made to leave it as a macabre shrine, but there had not yet been time or energy to change the room's character. "Ellen, I'm sorry. I'm not what you thought. There'll be another Gaiety for Jason, there will be." She felt as hollow as her voice sounded.

She saddled Dolly by lantern light, soothing the horse with soft words as she struggled with the weight of the saddle. She tied her possessions on the back of the saddle and set out in the predawn darkness, hoping she wouldn't be seen by any of the islanders, early risers themselves. She carried no lantern, trusting Dolly to remember the way she had come so many times, and the mare obliged though she was nervous and inclined to shy at stirrings in the brush. A damp mist blew against them.

Cade was waiting for her, his face set and grim. "You will not change your mind?"

"No, and you?"

"I will take you."

Captain mourned because Cade had left him behind this time, and Mary felt as if it were her own howling. She watched Cade's house grow smaller as they sailed west, the freshening wind working in the sails, and then she turned her eyes away from the island, away from the only place where she had ever known any measure of joy.

It was a dismal journey. The wind grew stronger, and the cold wetness of the salt air stung Mary's face. Cade didn't seem the least bit concerned about the cold, but neither was he interested in talking. He had said all he had to say to her. The silence hung between them, more daunting than the gray and windy weather.

A pallid sun broke through late in the morning, and in the late afternoon, they sailed into Victoria's harbor. Jason had once mentioned that he would take her there one day, and had it been under any other circumstances, Mary would have been impressed by her first sight of it. Once, Victoria had been a fortified outpost of the British Empire but it was now a bustling little city boasting quite a few brick structures as well as the Parliament buildings, a strange collection of half-timbered cottages that Cade grudgingly identified as "The Birdcages," their local name.

She was cold and stiff and wanted nothing more than to crawl into a warm bed, but her condition was her own fault and she didn't complain. Cade pointed out the ship he had in mind, and she followed meekly where he led. The English accents were a surprise though she realized they should not have been since they were no longer in United States territory.

Cade headed for a saloon frequented by seamen and found the captain at his favorite table.

The captain rose abruptly when he saw that Cade had a woman with him, but his greeting was polite when he was introduced to Mary Smith, as if it were no unusual occurrence to find a lady in this smoky, dim place and with Cade.

Mary was reassured by Captain Roger Scott's manner and his appearance. He appeared to be around fifty with the same strong body and weathered features as the other sea captains she had met. Though he was British by birth, he had plied the Pacific for years, and the ship under his command now was American owned. It was a good combination as Captain Scott dealt well with both peoples, and his steamship carried goods and some passengers regularly as far north as Vancouver and as far south as San Diego though the strongest commercial ties were between Victoria and San Francisco.

She was glad her face was shadowed by the hood of her cloak as she listened to Cade's story of why she needed passage so urgently.

"Telegram just came by the underwater line to San Juan Island." (She hadn't even known there was such a thing.) "Miss Smith's sister in San Francisco is very ill. I figured you're the best hope she has of arriving there in time."

No extra details to the lie, no mention of the Tiger or of Drake's Island, no explanation of what she had been doing in that wild region in the first place. And she realized that though they had come into a foreign port, Cade had had no trouble with the authorities. Nor did there seem to be any problem in her plans to sail—she could only assume she didn't qualify as smuggled goods.

The captain made appropriate noises of sympathy even while he named the fare. Mary was relieved. Her passage was assured and on a business level. She felt guilty for suspecting Cade would have allowed anything else. Could she be there, please, promptly at seven o'clock the next morning? She could.

Once outside again, Cade said brusquely, "You'll have to spend the night in a hotel." Coins jingled as he pulled out a leather pouch.

"Put it away, though I thank you. I have enough. I expect gold and silver coins are accepted everywhere." She thought of the horse race that had won the money for her; she thought of Owen and Carrie and of Jason, always of Jason.

Cade led her to a brick hotel which looked quite respectable. He put her bags down and nodded toward the entrance. "Go in and make sure they have a room for you. Tell them you're sailing on the *Cristabel* tomorrow."

"What about you? Won't you be staying? It's nearly full dark."

He shook his head, and his voice was curt. "They'll be frantic about you; I'm the only one who can tell them that you're safe. A dark sea is no stranger to me. And in any case, this is not the sort of place I stay in when I'm in the region. You will be better off to go in alone."

She had foolishly hoped Cade had not noticed the curious glances that had been cast their way as they walked along. But he noticed everything, and now he was willing to stand here acting as her porter because he doubted she would get a room in the hotel if the management saw him as anything more than a servant. His appearance would offend more than the fact that he was a smuggler who normally frequented taverns after dark if he ventured into the city at all.

Her face was so austere, her manner so haughty when she asked for a room, the clerk didn't think of refusing her and asked timidly about her baggage. "It is outside, and I do not need assistance with it," she told him, taking her key, turning on her heel, and leaving him to wonder how many more difficult customers he would have to deal with before the day was over.

"There's still time. You could go back with me." Cade's voice pierced her with its sudden velvet after the long, cold day.

"It was all pretend, all stolen, it never was my time there, whatever you think. But it was the best time, stolen and wrong as it was. Care for the Tiger, care for him as you always have, and for Jamie." She drew a deep shuddering breath. "Oh, God, what am I saying? You will care for them because you love them. What I truly want to ask is selfish and impossible, but I ask it anyway. When you can forgive what you think is wrong, think of me with kindness, please, Cade. You are so special to me."

She wanted to but was afraid to touch him; it was his strong arms that drew her close. "I could never think of you with less than kindness, Mary Smith. Fair winds." He released her abruptly and walked away. He did not look back.

The swell of pain was beyond tears. She wanted to be home, on the island, with Jason. But she did not follow or call Cade back.

CHAPTER
24

*I*t had all gone wrong, every step of the way. And the worst of it was that she really did not care anymore. There was still some minimal impulse to survive, but it was no longer the keen-edged, swift-reacting weapon it had been. She had left some vital part of herself on the island.

The voyage from Victoria to San Francisco was a blurred memory of cold misery—cold sea air and a deeper cold within that muffled all feeling. It had been even worse when shafts of clear vision had pierced her—the sudden sound of Jamie's voice and his laughter; Maggie's hands telling her something; and Jason. Sometimes it was as if she had never known him at all, and she could not see him clearly. And then he would invade her mind so completely, pain flooded her from the sharp edges of the image. Odd things became anguishingly important. She had spent days mourning the fact that his birthday had been forgotten in the sadness on the island. She wanted to turn time back. She wondered if she were losing her mind. Thank God for Cade's story—Captain Scott, his crew, and the few other passengers aboard the *Cristabel* had marked her strange aloofness down to worry about her ailing sister.

Everything went wrong in San Francisco, too. Frenchie was gone. Mary had not even considered that possibility, had not known how much she was counting on her being there, a friend to help her back to the old life.

Frenchie had gone away with a man, maybe to San Diego, maybe somewhere else. Maybe she'd be back, maybe not. No one knew and no one cared. Frenchie was Frenchie and could take care of herself.

John Pike, the piano player, was gone too, replaced by someone else, and only one of the dancing girls was known to Mary though the girl hadn't recognized her.

Mary needed her old job back, needed it desperately. She was a fool, she knew, to have left the jewelry and to have refused Cade's coins. The hotel in Victoria and the passage to San Francisco had left her with very little money. She had not thought clearly about anything except the need to leave the island, to leave Jason. But now there was no way to avoid reality. She had barely been able to pay for a week's stay at Mrs. Davies's boardinghouse. She had gone there like a homing pigeon, needing something to be familiar, hoping to find Frenchie there too. But Frenchie was gone, and Mrs. Davies had looked at her without recognition; Mary had not pressed the point of the past. Sewing might help to keep her alive in this expensive city if she were part of a family, part of any group where the costs of existing were shared. But she was alone. The salary of a dancing girl plus the money the men sometimes threw would give her a much better chance of staying alive.

This was not Seattle. She spent three days frantically applying for other jobs without success. Women did the hiring in most households where her work could be used, and they did not want her there as a maid, governess, teacher of French, music, or anything else. She had no references. She was too young, not strong enough. The women made up excuses; they did not admit even to themselves that Mary Smith, even thin and sickly-looking as she was, had too much to tempt their husbands.

Everything she had done before seemed to take twice as much effort. She was trembling now and hoping it didn't show as the man, Hank, looked her over. He was the new owner of the saloon and hired the entertainers. His small, sharp eyes had looked skeptical when she had claimed to have worked here before; he was unimpressed and uninterested in the fact. A squat, pink, nearly hairless man, he had no interest in the girls himself but knew what the customers wanted. His face was impassive as he ordered her to show him what she could do.

She had brought the blue costume with her and she had it on now as she showed him the steps and routines she knew and sang some of the songs they'd used. It was unnerving to be doing it all alone and without the piano to support her, but she kept on, knowing she couldn't afford to fail.

"Stop, that's enough," Hank finally commanded in a bored voice. Mary kept her back straight though all she wanted was to sink down to the floor and rest.

"Girl, you're damn scrawny. You got consumption or somethin' else?"

It was somehow more degrading that there was no leer in his demeanor, no suggestion of anything except doubt about the piece of flesh he might or might not hire.

She could feel the blood burning in her cheeks, but she answered levelly, "I had pneumonia some time ago. But I am fully recovered now."

"Well, you don't look it. And I warn you, you can't keep up, you're out. I need an extra dancer now, but I don't need one bad enough to keep nobody lazy. And I don't need nobody for the men to feel sorry for—sorry don't make money—so you keep color on them cheeks and lips. And you keep that hair shiny silver like, only reason I'm takin' you on is that funny color. I'll pay you half what the others get until you prove yourself."

She didn't bother to tell him that her hair was natural. She thanked him politely for giving her the job and turned away, heading for the back room to change into her street clothes.

"You ain't cut out for this. You'd be smart to go back to your own kind, Mary Smith."

There was no concern in his voice, nothing but a strangely prim disapproval. She kept on going, pretending she hadn't heard him. She bit her lip savagely against hysterical laughter—that was the whole problem; no one was her kind and there was nowhere to return to.

Even though she hadn't practiced with the rest of them, she

performed with the other dancers that night. They were resentful until they discovered she knew most of what they were doing and wouldn't make them look bad. Peggy Sue, the one she recognized from the time before, finally made the connection between the new blonde and the Mary Smith with brown hair, but they hadn't been friends before so it made little difference now. Peggy Sue had no interest in other women unless they were competing with her for the same man. Thinking of her own curves, she saw no threat in pale, skinny Mary. She was sure the gent she was seeing now wouldn't give Mary a second glance. Peggy Sue never stayed with the same man for long and never seemed to acquire one with any money, but she was seldom without an escort, and that suited her fine.

Mary danced and sang with grim determination, facing each night as if it were a high wall she had to climb, thinking only of the money she would be paid at the end of the week. Half pay was better than nothing at all, and perhaps in another week she would be able to prove herself worth more. Maybe some man would get drunk enough to shower the dancers with coins.

At the end of each night, she was shivering with exhaustion and had to wait patiently just to get enough strength back in her legs for the walk to the boardinghouse. It was as if the healthy young woman who had ridden, walked, and made love with Jason on the island had vanished. She tried to eat the boardinghouse food, but too often her appetite failed and her stomach rebelled. She moved through the hours in a haze, thinking of little, caring about less, simply existing, feeling the pieces of her past, the good and the bad, slipping away until there was hardly a person left in her shell.

She was onstage one night when she felt it happening, and she gave a soft cry of protest, but the black spots continued to dance and grow larger until they blotted out the lights and the people, and she spun away into the darkness.

She came to choking on the smoke of a burning feather, a stench guaranteed to rouse all but the dead. She had been carried to the back room, and Hank was regarding her with disapproval. "That's it. You're fired. I ain't payin' for another man's fun."

Mary stared at him uncomprehendingly, and then she shook

her head. "It's not that! It's not! I'm just a little tired. I'll be all right!"

"Not here you won't." There was no chance of appeal. He had a business to run, and he didn't care who worked for him as long as the work was done to his satisfaction. When it was not, the person ceased to be any concern of his.

For two days Mary stayed in her room, curled on the bed, staring blankly at the wall when she wasn't sleeping for fretful interludes. She was awakened from one of these by a rasping voice.

"Now look, dearie, I ain't one to bother a person an' you've paid your bill, you have, but you been in there a long time, an' well, I ain't havin' no dead bodies in my house, makes trouble all around an' I don't need no more 'n I got."

The voice penetrated the fog in Mary's brain, and she roused herself to answer, "You needn't worry, Mrs. Davies. I'm quite all right. I was feeling a bit under the weather, but I'm all right now. I shall be going out soon. Thank you for your concern."

She heard the unconvinced, shuffling sounds of her landlady outside the door and finally the footsteps going away. She started to laugh and then clamped a hand over her mouth, struggling to stop, hearing how wild the sound was. She got up and studied herself in the tarnished mirror over the bureau. She saw the dark rings around the eyes, the drawn face, the unkempt hair—she saw it all quite objectively, and she disliked the foolish woman she saw who had so lost control of her life.

She had no money left at all though she had nearly another week paid for at the boardinghouse, having paid only for the room this time, not having enough for the meals too. She had one thing of value, the fur-trimmed cloak from Jason, but she knew too well how little she would get if she tried to sell it.

She took it in her hands, stroking the soft cloth and the fur that seemed to ripple with silky life against her skin. Jason was a lifetime ago. She stared at the little wooden tiger, wondering why she tortured herself by keeping it in view. Carefully she put it in a drawer.

The treacherous thought had been creeping through her brain for days. She knew *he* was alive. She knew he would take her back despite what she had tried to do. She would be lost, damned as if she had never made any effort to be free, but she would not want for shelter or food; she would have no more decisions to make, no more choices. None of it had anything to do with Jason.

She had already set it in motion. She had returned to this city with all its connections to other cities, to eastern cities. She had returned without disguise, letting the bright beacon of her unique coloring light the way for the trackers. She had put herself at far greater risk than had the chance meeting with Richard Clayton in Seattle.

She doubled over as her empty stomach clenched and bile burned her throat.

This was as low as she could fall. Her self-loathing was boundless. Nothing on earth could be worse than any degree of need to go back to him. She saw it very clearly. It followed that if she wanted to stay alive, anything would be better than going back. She still had something to sell, something to keep her alive. She would not go back to him, and she could not go back to Jason. But she could still sell what the other had had, what the Tiger had been willing to bargain for.

It made perfect sense to her. She washed and carefully applied the rouge she used as the dancing girl. Her dress was simple, but the cloak gave her warmth and a touch of elegance. She felt very light-headed.

Her moods swung between the urge to laugh hysterically and a numbing fear. She didn't know the rules. This was not as it had been with Jason. God in heaven, the oldest profession on earth, and she didn't even know how to begin. She pictured herself finding a brothel and applying for a job. Was that how it was done? "Madame, I would like to work for you. I certainly know the basics." She should have asked Jason for references; she was sure he knew the best whores in town. She remembered the heavy scent of the other woman. The horrible laughter threatened again. Not to think about Jason, not. That way lay sure insanity.

She would do this on her own. There were still more men than women in this city, men willing to pay for what they could not find for free.

Mary wished she'd paid more attention to some of the regular patrons of the saloon, but her lack of interest and current lack of curves had discouraged them from making advances despite her exotic coloring. There wasn't one of them she could recall who would be any use to her.

There was a difference in women who were willing and those who were not, and she concentrated on it, seeing Frenchie on the prowl, Angie when the Captain was there, Carrie with Owen. There was a soft sway to the walk, a softer look to the mouth and eyes, a subtle beckoning, a promise. She wondered suddenly if she had ever looked so to Jason.

It was all changed now, and there was no warmth in her, but surely pretense was possible in this as it had been in so much of her life.

It was a nightmare. Winter dusk was giving way to dark as Mary wandered the streets of the Barbary Coast. The old terror that it showed, that somehow everyone knew about her past, swept over her as she saw the strange reactions of the men, their eyes and bodies shifting away from her. Not even men searching for whores could bear the association with her.

Men looked at her and saw what she could not—a slender young woman who appeared to be too many things at once. The fixed smile and the sway in her walk promised one thing, but the subdued richness of her cloak and more, the wide, haunted silver eyes said something quite different. She made them uneasy; there were certainly safer and easier women on the streets than this one.

She jostled against someone, and a blowsy woman in a dirty red dress with black petticoats showing pushed her away. "Hey, mind where you're goin' an' keep on! This here's my place."

Mary stared at her blankly for a moment, trying to understand what she meant.

"You heard me, sister, keep movin'!" the woman snapped. "Find yer own corner, I ain't sharin' my trade with nobody."

Mary stumbled away, finally comprehending what the woman meant. Rough gasps of laughter escaped before she could stop them. Perhaps she was supposed to file a formal claim to a patch of land for soliciting. What kind of document did one fill out and where did one file it? Perhaps all the best spots were already taken. She noticed other women now, most of them alone but some standing with others, some even with flashily dressed men. She heard one of the men call to a passerby, "Clean, my girls is real clean. Sally here can squeeze your root real good an' she don't use 'er hands."

Blood was pounding in her ears, her skin crawled over her bones as if it were a separate living thing. All of this had been here before, but only now was she seeing it, hearing it, only now because she was part of it.

The man grabbed her so tightly, the air was forced out of her lungs and then blocked completely by his thick, wet mouth covering hers. She stamped on his foot and tried to bring a knee up. It was like trying to batter a mountain, a mountain covered with shifting layers of fat and surprisingly hard muscle. The rank smell of him made her gag, and that did what her puny efforts at defense hadn't accomplished. He drew back from her in alarm, but he kept a tight hold on one of her arms.

"Wazza trouble, sisser, you sellin', I'm buyin'. How mush?"

She stared up at the red face, smeared with sweat, stubbled, the veined eyes nearly lost in rolls of fat, and her revulsion was so strong, she could hardly get the words out. "You're mistaken. I came here to meet someone. Leave me alone."

"I'm somebody. How much?"

He wasn't as drunk as she'd thought. The beady little eyes stripped her clothes away even as he ran one hand roughly down her under the cloak. He wasn't going to let go, and she wasn't strong enough to fight him off. She wondered if anyone would help her if she started to scream; she wondered what he would do if she screamed. She forced herself to take a deep breath, and she opened her mouth.

The cold, soft voice cut across the air, and Mary made no sound at all.

"Ah suggest ya let th' lady go." The order came again in the same near whisper, but the man dropped Mary's arm and swung around, fists clenched, to face the speaker.

The fists unclenched, and the belligerence went out of the big man as if he were a soap bubble pricked by a pin. He started backing away, protesting that he'd meant no harm, sorry, he didn't know she had someone particular in mind, sorry, sorry. His voice seemed to trail after him even when he turned and picked up his pace to a shambling run.

Her attempt to thank her rescuer died as unborn as the scream as she got her first clear look at him. She doubted she had been saved after all. The man was not much taller than she and whipcord thin in his dark clothes. His nose was straight, finely chiseled, his lips perfectly even, his chin firm. Neat black brows arched even over dark, heavily lashed eyes. His golden-olive skin was unblemished and had the sheen of satin. His features were so perfect, so symmetrical, a shade more delicacy would have made him too beautiful for a man.

But he was not beautiful to look upon. He was as deadly as the gun he wore low on his hip, his hand still resting with easy competence near the weapon as he watched the fat man out of sight. His eyes gave him away most of all. They were ageless in the young face. Hard, glittering, filled with a murderous lust as if nothing on earth would give him more pleasure than killing the man.

Not in Jason, not in anyone ever before, had she felt so much violence. She could feel the icy fire of it touching her even though he stood some distance from her. She wanted to run and could not move at all.

The dark eyes shifted attention to her, and an extraordinary thing happened. She felt as if she were seeing dawn hours before it was due. This was just as miraculous. The eyes were suddenly as young as the face, young and full of soft light and a sparkle of humor.

"Ya all right, ma'am?" The voice was still soft, the words still drawled, but the cold menace was gone from this too.

She managed a quavering thank you.

He went on studying her at his leisure. "First time out on th' streets?"

She nodded miserably, not even tempted to lie to him.

"Well, Ah ain't neva done it mahself, but Ah 'spect it's a hard way t' earn yoah keep. How much ya askin'?"

"I don . . . don't know."

"Je-sus! Ya got somethin' t' sell, first thing ya do is put a price on it."

The absurdity of it all washed over her. The laughter that had threatened for hours broke free—a horrible croaking noise she couldn't stop.

The slap landed squarely but without undue force, and she gasped for air, the hysterical sounds ceasing.

"Sorry, ma'am, didn't have no bucket a' water handy," he said matter-of-factly, and he drew her into his arms, holding her head against his shoulder and patting her back with surprisingly deft gentleness.

He smelled clean, young, and male. His body was hard. She could feel his warmth touching her, and she was comforted. She could still see the fat man, could still smell him and feel him against her. This man was infinitely preferable.

He put her away from him. "Ya hungry as ya look?"

"Yes," she admitted, realizing with a shock that she was ravenous.

"How long since ya et?"

"A day or two."

"Or mebbe three an' not too well 'fore that." He shook his head in disapproval. "That's plain dumb. Come on, Ah'm hungry too."

She went with him obediently and found herself in a small restaurant. It was plainly furnished, but clean, and the food smelled delicious. The proprietor who was also the waiter greeted the man by name, his deference tinged with more than a little fear. The other patrons, mostly men, risked only quick glances before they turned their attention back to their plates; the few women dared longer looks, despite the frowns of their escorts.

"Rio is your name?" Mary asked hesitantly.

"Yep, jus' Rio. It'll do. Yoahs?"

"Mary Smith."

"S'pose that'll do too."

Generously laden plates were brought to them, and Mary put all thought of what was yet to come away, thinking of nothing now but the need to assuage her hunger. She ate slowly, carefully, but she ate more than she had since leaving the island, and it stayed down.

Rio didn't rush her or himself nor did he seek to break the

silence between them. For such a slender man, he ate an enormous amount, cleaning his plate and still finding room for a huge slice of pie and a slab of cheese. Finally he settled back in his chair and took up his study of her again.

"'Fore ya get so nervous, ya toss that good dinna, Ah want t' tell ya, Ah ain't neva screwed nothin' Ah had to feed first; that's what gives sheepmen their bad report, an' Ah ain't no sheepman."

She knew she was blushing as the meaning of his words sank in, but she met his eyes squarely, waiting for whatever else he had to say, trying to ignore the sinking feeling that aside from being full of good food, she was right back where she'd started.

"Ah kin buy what ya thought t' sell jus' 'bout any time, anywheres," he said slowly. "Sometimes it's good, sometimes not, sometimes clean, sometimes not, but it ain't scarce. Ah don' want what ya got 'tween yoah legs, Mary Smith. Chances are, it ain't worth havin' nohow. Yoah kind a woman don' give nothin' less they give everythin', an' Ah don' want everythin' from ya even if Ah could have it. Still, ya got somethin' Ah do want."

She hadn't the slightest idea of what he was talking about. She remained silent, still waiting, wondering if he had some strange appetite which would shock her even more than what he had already said. Then she thought of how much indeed she knew about unnatural lusts. But she was reassured by the softness that remained in his eyes and the tone of his voice.

"Whatevah ya was tryin' t' do an' whyevah ya was tryin' t' do it, yo'ah different from them othas. Mah ma was too, an' mah sista, even mah stepma was. Ah miss that. Ah miss bein' 'round women like that."

"Like what?" Mary asked, finding her tongue at last. "Different, that's a strange term for a woman you saved from the arms of a drunk. I deserved to be there. I doubt that your relatives would ever be found in the same place."

"That ain't got nothin' t' do with it, an' ya know it or ya should," he admonished her. "People got a right t' do what they got t' do to stay alive." He paused and searched her face intently before he went on. "Ah'm from Texas, case ya didn' guess. Mah ma was a Mexican, a beautiful lady. She died when Ah was only three, but Ah remember her. Mah pa's an Anglo an' his second wife is too. They started right in an' had four kids, one afta th' otha. Th' oldest is th' only girl. Mah sista, Katie, well, she's less 'n five years younga 'n me, an' she's a beauty, blond with big blue eyes. Ya remind me some a' her. We was real close. She needed protectin' where th' brothas didn'. There's a lot a' space there, but it wasn't enough. Th' Crowls, they had a spread bor- derin' ours, an' Johnny Crowl wouldn' let Katie be.''

He tried to tell it calmly, but he could still see it all too clearly. Katie, only fifteen and trying to be brave and not make trouble but so afraid of Johnny Crowl that she'd quit riding out on the ranch. And Johnny so big, mean, and loud, and so unable to believe that Katie didn't want anything to do with him. Ordering him off the place hadn't done any good.

Rio could almost smell the sun on the river and on the trees near the swimming hole where he'd gone with Katie that day. It was one of her favorite places, and she hadn't gone for a long time because of Johnny. She'd been so happy to be there again, and Rio had left her to the privacy of her swim and had gone off to hunt rabbits. Then he'd heard her scream. He'd raced back to find her trying to kick, bite, and claw while Johnny ignored her struggles and went on tearing at the few clothes she had on.

Rio had pulled him off, had gone for him with his fists, but he'd known instantly that Johnny didn't want a fair fight. He'd known that death was already there, and it was only a question of the victim. He remembered how smooth and ready the weight of his gun had felt. He remembered the look of surprise on Johnny's face; Johnny who had gone for his gun first, got there last, and died by Katie's favorite bend of water.

"Ah left th' next day."

The cold softness had crept back into his voice as he told the story, and his eyes were hard and opaque. Mary shivered inwardly though she tried to keep her voice calm and reasonable.

"But surely no judge or jury would find you guilty. You had no choice."

"Wasn't that. Johnny Crowl had five brothas. Th' shootin' wouldn' a' stopped 'til all a' 'em or all a' us was dead. With me gone, th' woah neva needed t' get goin'. Ah was trailed fer a time by two a' Johnny's brothas, but they neva did catch up with me. Five years ago Ah left, an' Ah ain't been back since. Used t' tell mahself Ah'd go home someday, but 'tain't so. Leastways, Ah know mah family's all right, an' Ah send 'em word time t' time t' let 'em know Ah am too. Katie's married now with two young-uns. Her husband was one a' pa's top hands. He's a good bit olda 'n Katie, but he's a good man. He was kind t' Katie, an' he waited fer her t' grow up 'fore he asked her t' be a woman. An' pa's got mah brothas t' help him run th' place.

"'Spect this is th' most Ah'm eva goin' say 'bout mahself, matta a' fact, most Ah've eva said on th' subject, so listen careful. Johnny Crowl was th' first man Ah kilt, but only th' first. There's been a passel since. Some drew on me jus' 'cuz they wanted t' try it, but most Ah got paid fer killin'. Ah'm a hired gun, Mary Smith, one a' th' best, an' it suits me fine. Ah've been paid t' protect gold, cattle, hosses, an' people, an' sometimes Ah've jus' been hired t' get rid a' this man or that when th' law didn' seem t' be doin' th' job t' mah employa's likin'. Ain't no posta out on me yet, but that don' mean there ain't gonna be one."

He was the loneliest human being she had ever met, lonelier even than she, more desolate than Hayes, more isolated than Cade had ever been. Death did not lurk in some unforeseeable future for Rio. He carried it constantly; he was death and death would consume him long before his strength failed. All that he had ever loved of family and place had been severed from him in his first encounter, no matter how justified the death-dealing had been. She was closer to him than he knew.

"I still don't know what you want of me," she said softly.

She heard his breath escape in a little sigh. "Ah want 'zackly what ya jus' gave me. Ya look sad, but ya ain't scairt, an' ya ain't tol me Ah gotta stop doin' what Ah do. Yo'ah still lookin' square at me. That's what Ah want. Ah want some'un t' talk to an' be with who ain't always skitterin' away from mah shadow. Ah want a woman who ain't jus' spreadin' 'er legs fer pay."

You want Katie back, your sister and your friend, Mary thought, but there was no unease in the idea. Rio had no unnatural inclinations toward his sister; his love for her and his protectiveness had cost him everything, and yet he could still be happy for Katie's joy in her husband and children.

"I'm not Katie. I envy her. I never had a brother, never had a friend like that. But Katie's far away. I'm here. If I'll do in her stead, I'd be honored. It's not just gratitude or need. I like you, whatever you do, even if I've only just met you. But there is one thing you may not be able to accept. You've told me a great deal about yourself, and I'm glad you've trusted me, but I won't return the favor. Can you accept that?"

"Ya ain't scairt a' me, an' ya ain't no whore. Ya need a friend as much as Ah do. Ah reckon there's not anotha thing Ah need t' know 'bout ya."

It was far stranger than the bargain with the Tiger. There was nothing sexual between them, and it was nothing at all like Jason's denial of what had been. Rio had decided from the beginning that he did not want her as his mistress, and Mary felt no physical desire for him, though she could easily see him as a desirable man even had she not had the evidence the avid looks women cast his way. For an instant they saw the glowing perfection of a beautiful young man, and then they saw the illusion and the danger. The combination was irresistible. But their interest was also less than flattering, no more personal than if they were looking at any dangerous beast. For the most part, Rio ignored them, but he was not above glaring with sudden ferocity simply to discomfit them. There was a young and impish side to him that charmed Mary, and she saw more of it each day. Though he read very little aside from newspapers, he loved stage plays and was uncritical in his enjoyment of them. He had a keen eye for horseflesh and went to races and sales and had his own fine bay stallion well cared for in a livery stable. And he was the most observant human being she had ever known. He noticed everything from clothing to facial expressions to the timbre of voices, and he could mimic them perfectly.

Mary giggled helplessly at his rendition of a plump, overdressed woman they had watched preening herself all through a fairly good if truncated version of *Hamlet*. She had patted her hair and her clothing continually and dabbed at her powdered face until Rio had whispered to Mary, "Ain't she goin' look peculiar with 'er face scrubbed plumb blank."

She could forget the dark side of him for long moments, but

it was always there. It was the reason no one ever asked him to remove his gun, not even in places where guns were not usually allowed. It was the reason they could go anywhere in their plain clothes, and no one dared so much as one disdainful look. It was, in fact, the reason he studied people so thoroughly, so automatically: his life depended on knowing what others were planning to do before they did it. And it was the reason he studied the newspapers and listened to the gossip of men.

"What will you find, 'wanted, one fast gun'?" Her voice was sharp, her fear for him suddenly revealed.

Rio understood and took no offense, answering patiently. "They'll be lookin' fer security men or some such, there's lots a' ways t' call it, or there'll be trouble talked 'bout somewheres, sides choosin' up, that sort a' thing. Word gets 'round, sure 'nuff, it does. An' when it's time, Ah'll move on an' take one a' them jobs."

It was a matter that remained delicate between them. The time for Rio to leave would be dictated by his money running out. He gambled when he felt lucky and won more often than he lost, but he was strangely conservative in this, feeling lucky only sporadically and not betting much when he did, as if he needed that restraint to balance the way he earned most of his living. He did not even consider taking some other job nor did she ask him to. It was too late for him to change; as young as he was, it was too late.

He would move on, and she would not go with him. It was understood. But while he wanted to support her totally as long as he had the pleasure of her company, she refused. She couldn't bear the thought that the cost of her keep brought him that much closer to dealing death again or worse, dying himself.

She did not attempt to repeat her disastrous and short-lived career on the street, a plan strictly forbidden by Rio, but she took in sewing, beginning with the girls at the boardinghouse, the number of her customers expanding as the word spread that she did fine work for little money and could make neglected clothes look like new in addition to being able to make elegant new garments out of materials that weren't of the best.

She didn't earn enough to pay for everything, but it was a way to lessen her debt to Rio. After a while, he stopped trying to dissuade her. He had no idea that she was also keeping track of everything he spent on her, determined to pay it back someday.

Rio had eased the corroding loneliness which had so incapacitated her, and with his attention and care of her, she was far stronger mentally and physically than she had been when she collapsed onstage in the saloon. But so far, Hank was not convinced and would not rehire her. She kept trying, sure that soon he would give in due to her persistence. Time enough when that happened to tell Rio; she was not sure he would approve of that any more than of her being on the streets. She had told him only that she had lost her job, not what the job had been. She tried a few other places but had no better luck than she'd had before.

Her friendship with Rio grew more precious to her each day. She would never have considered it possible to have such an intimate and easy relationship with a virile young man and yet have it free of physical joining. Rio's appetites were normal; they were simply not directed toward her.

"Ah always figure a good whore or two in mah budget," he'd told her with a grin, and he never made a secret of where he'd been.

Everyone at the boardinghouse was sure Mary and Rio were lovers, and Mary made no effort to disabuse them of the notion. It was none of their business either way. Rio had kept his own lodgings, but sometimes he spent the night draped in the one chair Mary's room boasted or sleeping quite soundly on the floor. It had happened quite naturally the first time. They had been out very late, and when Rio escorted Mary to her room, he could hardly keep his eyes open. He had simply asked if he might just catch some sleep there, and she had agreed, thinking to herself that if he meant to change the rules now, she would go along with him, she owed him so much. However, he had meant exactly what he'd said and had fallen asleep immediately. But he was no less alert in slumber than awake. She'd dropped a shoe and found herself confronting Rio's gun in the instant.

"Sorry, dahlin', Ah ain't used t' th' noises here yet."

He was as good as his word, and Mary found she didn't have to creep around in terror of making an inadvertent noise—he slept and woke with the knowledge of where he was and who was there.

She liked having him there. She liked the sound of his breathing and the feeling of another body in the room. And she knew why. She had become accustomed to sleeping with Jason, accustomed to being sheltered by the safety of his presence in the dark hours.

Paradoxically, now that she had Rio's companionship, she thought of Jason constantly. It wasn't just when Rio took her somewhere where she had been with Jason, it was as if the Tiger was never far away and yet never close enough to touch. She knew he would come back to San Francisco; sooner or later business would demand it. She wondered if she would feel him closer when he did; she wondered if he would feel that she was here. She reminded herself that it would make no difference. Jason had left her with his knowledge of her past; she had left him physically. It was the reason she had not gone to see Carrie and Owen even when her need was great. Despite what Carrie had said, despite the fact Mary knew that if she went to them, the welcome would be genuine, she could not go. Carrie was part of Owen's life, an important part, and Owen was part of Jason's life, an important part. When Mary had left the island, she had also relinquished whatever right she had had to contact with Jason's friends. She knew it for justice, but that did not prevent the memories of the kind evenings spent with Carrie and Owen, did not prevent the longing for their company. She wondered what she would say, what they would say if she and Rio ran into them accidentally somewhere, but it never happened.

She smiled sadly, thinking about the cozy house, wishing she were there with Jason. She was so far away in her memories, it took her a long moment to recognize the insistent knocking and the voice at the door, particularly because this was one of his announced nights of sin.

"Come 'n now, Mary, please let me in. Ah'm 'bout t' fall down."

Rio was very drunk, but that only made his politeness more exaggerated. The fact that the flimsy door would have given had he applied even a little strength to it was of no interest to him.

When Mary opened the door, he nearly fell headlong into the room. He righted himself with effort and swept a precarious bow.

"Meant go t' mah place, but Ah'm here 'stead. Sleep here?"

"Of course," Mary managed, then burst out laughing. There was no vestige of the killer in his demeanor now. His shirt was buttoned but not accurately, and it wasn't tucked into his trousers very well. His waistcoat had suffered the same mishandling, and his hat was slanted over his left ear.

He peered at her from one eye, obviously not liking the confusion both eyes produced. "Whist Ah could say they put somethin' in th' whis . . . key, but they didndn'." He shook his head positively and nearly tipped over. "Ah jus' put too mush in me, good whis . . . whishiskey, bad me. Put me in 'er too," he beamed like a small boy who had accomplished a great feat, "fastestest, eh, fasterest lova in Fran Sancissisco, t'night anywho."

He appeared to be about to collapse on the floor. Still laughing, Mary led him to the bed and sat him down on it. But when she reached for his gunbelt, his hand snaked out and grabbed her wrist so hard, she gave a yelp of pain. His eyes glittered as coldly as they had the first time she'd seen him.

He blinked at her, and the tenseness flowed out of him even as he let go of her. "Sorry," he mumbled. He unbuckled the belt with great care and handed it to her.

She managed the heavy weight without dropping it, and she kept her hands from trembling as she put the weapon on the bureau. Rio's eyes, both of them now, measured the distance from the bed to the bureau and seemed satisfied that it was not too far, not here where he was safe with Mary.

Sometimes she forgot how dangerous he was, but never for long; the violence was coiled too near the surface. Even far gone in an alcoholic haze, the alertness remained.

Yet now he looked like a tousled little boy. She pulled off his boots, loosened his clothing, and covered him with the quilt just as if he were Jamie.

"Thank ya," Rio mumbled and slept.

Mary sat in the chair watching the sleeping man. And then, very deliberately, she took off her robe and lay down beside him in her night rail. The bed was hardly wide enough for two, and that suited her perfectly. She wanted the warmth of him, the contact with him. She eased herself close to him under the quilt. He shifted her more comfortably against him, murmuring, "Nice, warm," before his breathing deepened again.

She inhaled the scent of him, even the whiskey smell was good, part of his maleness. Oh, God, she was so hungry for a man! The truth of it swept over her in a wave of desolation, and she cursed Jason silently. He had done this; he had changed her so.

At last she slept, and when she awakened in the morning, Rio was gazing at her through red-rimmed eyes.

"Take me, make love to me!" she whispered, her voice husky and urgent.

Rio kissed the tip of her nose and hugged her to him for a moment, but then he shook his head. His voice was at once tender and firm. "Wouldn', not even if Ah didn' have a herd a' cattle trompin' through mah head. It'd spoil things 'tween us. Ah ain't Jason."

She stared at him, eyes wide, and he nodded. "Ya call 'im sometimes at night, sometimes sad, sometimes happy, even angry sometimes, but it's 'im, not me, yo'ah wantin'. If he's still livin', he's a damn fool t've let ya go."

"I left him; I had to."

She buried her head against his chest and sobbed.

"Ah left some'un too, had to, jus' like ya. Th' Crowls had a sista too, jus' like Ah had Katie. Jenny Crowl, only she wasn' no sista t' me. Meant 'er fer mah wife someday." He rocked Mary in his arms, patting her back gently. "There, honey chile, there."

She wept for the days without Jason, the days past and all the days yet to be, and she wept for Rio's loss and for his kindness to her.

CHAPTER
25

*R*io now spent more nights with Mary than he did at his own lodgings, and if she called for Jason in the night, it was Rio who awakened her with soft words and held her in warm comfort. She had felt close to Cade, but not like this. To Cade, she was Jason's woman, no matter what he had said about loving her for her own sake. Rio thought of her only as he knew her, just for now, without past or future. Jason to him was simply a sad loss as his own Jenny was; he was sorry that Mary was haunted by that part of her past, but Jason had nothing to do with him, no more than Jenny had to do with her.

"Mary. Mary Smith!" A woman's voice accompanied by brisk rapping on the door roused them one Sunday morning. They had been out late the night before, and Mary struggled through the layers of sleep to find Rio fully alert. She had not objected to his preference for keeping his gunbelt hung on the bedpost nearest him; the furthest she had ever seen it from him was the night she had put it on the bureau. Patient as he always was with her, he had explained what a commotion it was going to cause if he ever had to leap up from the bed and lunge to the bureau while the door was being kicked in.

The gun was in his hand now, but his voice was calm. "Some-'un ya know?" Rio never worried much about a female knocking at the door, but he liked to be sure there was no man standing beside her.

"Well, it doesn't sound like Mrs. Davies, it sounds like—oh, I wish!" She was suddenly out of the bed, throwing on her robe, jerking open the door.

Frenchie blinked at the blond woman and saw the man in the bed behind her. "I . . . ah, excuse me, I thought . . ." her voice trailed off as she studied Mary's smiling face. "My God, Mary, it is you!"

They reached out simultaneously, laughing and hugging each other tightly.

Frenchie hadn't changed. The sultry curve of her mouth was still belied by the sparkling awareness in her dark eyes, and the contrast between her curling, nearly black hair and her white skin was as striking as ever. Whatever had happened to her in the past year hadn't aged her or dimmed her vivacity.

Mary could see that Rio, far from being unaware of her attractiveness, was regarding her trimly curved figure with open approval. Frenchie grinned at him and turned her attention back to Mary.

"Seems I've interrupted something. I'll come back later."

"Ya'll do nothin' a' th' sort. Ah'll jus' take mahself off so's ya two kin visit, seems t've been a while." He rose from the bed, not the least embarrassed by the scantiness of his attire, and pulled on the rest of his clothes.

Frenchie eyed him appreciatively as he left. "Well, that's a dangerous one if I ever saw it, but pretty, very pretty. I do like men with tight butts. You've changed. I wouldn't have guessed he'd be your style." Her eyes were curious but not demanding, and Mary smiled at her description of Rio.

"He's a good friend, and that's all, though I can see how it would be hard to believe."

Frenchie shrugged. "Lots of things are hard to believe, doesn't make 'em less true. Hard to believe I'm back here, but I am. Got back yesterday. I went with a nice dude to San Diego, thought I'd settle down. His wife died a few years back, and he was lonely. He wasn't that much older'n me, an' he had a nice spread down that way, beautiful house, easy life, no kids. I could've stayed there forever; he even wanted to marry me. But I couldn't stay, just couldn't. I was so bored! I missed the city, and I missed doing my act. No hard feelings—I've got a couple of trinkets to sell if need be. He didn't want me sad, and I didn't want to drive him crazy."

"I went north to Seattle, just as planned," Mary said abruptly. "The man, Jason Drake, the one who spent the night in your room, they call him the Tiger. He lives up there. He went home, and I . . . I went to him. I was with him for almost a year." Suddenly it all poured out, the people on the island, Angie and Captain Tom, the logging camp, the days and nights of Jason, the tragedy of the deaths on the island, everything but the reason she had left Jason and the fact that they had been in San Francisco and she had not visited Frenchie.

Frenchie was wide-eyed, dazed by the story. "So you fell in love with him, loved his son and his people too, loved the life with him, loved it all so much, you left." She shook her head. "Mary Smith, unless I've mistaken something, that doesn't make any sense."

"I didn't say I fell in love with him. We made a bargain. It was time for it to end. He wanted it to end, but he was too kind. So, I ended it for him and for myself."

The look in Mary's eyes stopped Frenchie from pointing out that love didn't have to be announced to exist and that she knew it when she saw it. She was still marveling that this lovely gilt-haired creature had so fooled her and everyone else with her disguise. Though she didn't know why Mary had disguised herself in the first place, she was uneasy that she had ceased to do so now. Without knowing how she knew, Frenchie was sure it was a sign of some kind of surrender. There were twists and turns to Mary that she did not understand; she doubted she ever would, and she had the sense to know that there would be no friendship if she insisted on prying. She turned the conversation to safer ground, asking for more details of Angie's life in Seattle and her sea captain and asking too what Mary had been doing since she'd gotten back to San Francisco, how she'd met Rio.

Mary spoke frankly about this, admitting she'd made a mess of things, telling how Rio had rescued her.

Frenchie tried to keep a straight face, but failed as her laughter bubbled over. "You on the streets! I'm sorry, I know it could have ended badly, nearly did, but Lord, I bet you confounded the men for a month of Sundays! You just aren't the sort they expect to find, my, no!"

She dabbed at her eyes, and the question came swiftly. "You still want your old job back?"

"Yes, I certainly do, but Hank won't hire me. I keep trying, but he's made it very clear."

Frenchie smiled, a satisfied feline smile. "Hank will hire you because I'll tell him to. I'm too good a draw for him to refuse. He took over last summer, and he was damn mad when I left. But he's not stupid; he gave me my job back yesterday, soon as I asked for it. I spent the night in a hotel, but today it was time to go back to being an honest working girl." She made a mockingly demure face. "Mrs. Davies got downright chatty when she found out I was willing to pay for the nicest room in the place —it was her only vacancy and no wonder since she asks too much for it. Anyway, she told me among other things that one of her boarders was a Mary Smith who was being kept by a gunslinger. I swear she fairly blushed with the delight of it, gives her house a little fame. She hasn't made any connection between you and the other Mary Smith who lived here, and it didn't sound like you, but I had to try. I mean, how many Mary Smiths can there be in the world? It's such an unusual name."

They looked at each other and laughed in sheer delight at their reunion.

Hank sputtered and looked grim, but he gave Mary the job. And she was so much stronger than she had been before, it no longer took the terrible toll it had. If the other girls objected to this favoritism, they kept their mouths shut. Mary was a friend of Frenchie's, and Frenchie meant more customers and coins charmed out of pockets by the liveliness she added to the show. They faced the fact that they hadn't had a main performer without her.

Mary used her first salary to buy material for new costumes, and when the other girls saw the results and found that she was willing to sew for them at reasonable rates, they began to regard her as nearly as much of an asset as Frenchie.

Rio was harder to convince. He hadn't even wanted her to take in sewing, but that was easier to accept than this. In spite of the way of their first meeting, Rio didn't think the role of a dancing girl in a saloon was any more fitting for Mary than it would have been for his sister.

When all other arguments failed, Mary used the harshest one, though her voice was gentle. "When you leave, and we both know you will, I'll need the best job I can find, and this one is the best. And Frenchie's there."

He had no defense against the hard truth, but he spent most evenings watching the women perform. Word got around very quickly that the silver blonde was hands off unless a man wanted to have important parts blown off by an accurate bullet, not to mention the very real possibility of dying.

Mary was glad of his protection. She had no wish to fight off amorous drunks, something she knew without vanity was more apt to happen now that she looked so much healthier. But she began to worry when the legend expanded to include Frenchie. Not only was Rio credited with far more violence than any one man could accomplish, he was now judged to be the lover not only of the blonde but of Frenchie and who knew how many other women. It decreased the flow of coins somewhat though Frenchie could always coax a few from the crowd, but more, it put a hex on any chance she had of carrying on her usual flirtations. Strangely, she made no protest. She seemed perfectly content with the arrangement they had.

The three of them were often together. Frequently, they had late supper after work, and Frenchie often joined Rio and Mary for their daytime excursions, which now included picnics not far from the city when the weather showed brief spells of tempting warmth.

One day in mid-April was particularly fine, promising to be free of fog, chill or drizzle for the whole span of the sun. Mary and Frenchie assembled the food, going to favorite restaurants and shops in complete avoidance of anything resembling Mrs. Davies's heavy boardinghouse fare. Rio not only provided the wine but also picked them up in a rented carriage in deference to Frenchie's aversion to riding horseback, something she did well enough but only grudgingly.

They chose a knoll bright with spring grass and settled down to unpack their feast, but the lighthearted mood ended when Rio found the gold piece while he was searching for his pocket-knife.

"Funniest thing, Ah neva put money in that pocket. An' Ah been noticin' Ah seem t've got hold a' a pair a' magic breeches. Lots a' times lately when Ah wear 'em t' th' boardin' house, they come out with extree money in 'em." His voice was lazy, but the softness had a sharp edge, and his eyes glinted as he stared at Mary.

She thought of pleading ignorance, but the blush was already betraying her, and she damned herself for having thought she could fool him when he was so constantly alert. It had seemed such a good plan. He was accustomed to the noises she made moving around the room, and she had thought to pay back what she owed him little by little, tucking the money into his clothes as he slept, knowing he would never accept it openly.

"I owe you so much!"

"Ya don' owe me nothin'! An' I neva take money from no woman. There's a name fer men that do, an' I ain't one a' 'em." He got up and stalked off.

Mary started to follow, but Frenchie stopped her. "Let him go. He doesn't want to be angry with you any more than you want him to. He's just got a little problem with his pride. He'll get over it."

The advice was sensible, and Mary obeyed, but she felt a startling stab of jealousy; there was something proprietary in Frenchie's voice. She regarded her with sudden intensity. Her worst fears were confirmed when Frenchie's eyes slid away from hers.

"You and Rio?" Her voice was small and pinched, and she saw now all the little looks and gestures that had passed between them, their ease together.

"Please, don't look like that! We haven't done anything, honest! We don't want to hurt you. Oh, damn it to hell! It's all so
confusing. I haven't ever cared before what another woman
thought, but I care what you think. And Rio's all wrong for me
and me for him. He doesn't need a woman loving him too much,
and I don't need to love a man who's sure to get killed before
he gets old. I've loved men before, but I've never been in love.
I don't even like it. It makes me feel all foolish and nervous and
plain scared. And now it's worse because you're angry. Damn
and damn again! I'm even two years older than he is!" The
miserable rush of words stopped and there was silence between
them as Frenchie fought her tears.

Mary looked at herself and didn't like what she saw. She wasn't
Rio's lover, she was his friend, and yet she was behaving as if he
belonged to her, feeling terror that she would be alone again.

"Frenchie, I'm ashamed of myself," she admitted. "You can
give Rio something I can't, and I don't just mean sleeping with
him. You're not wrong for him at all, nor he for you, despite all
the risks. And to hell with the age difference; people don't chose
whom they love, it just happens."

As it happened to you with Jason Drake, Frenchie thought,
remembering all the times she'd seen Mary pick up the little
wooden tiger without even knowing she was doing it. But she
didn't say any of it aloud.

Their hands met in a firm shake of understanding, and they
smiled at each other, unutterably glad that the ugly threat to
their friendship had passed.

When Rio reappeared and ambled over to join them, he wore
a sheepish grin. "Sorry, Mary, wasn't no call fer me t' jump on
ya fer doin' what ya thought was right. But Ah don' want t' find
no more stray coins in mah pockets. Ah'd rather see ya gettin'
a betta room an' some pretty clothes. That all right with ya?"

She agreed happily, already planning to talk Frenchie into
taking the money instead. She'd make up a story about saving
for something special if Rio questioned her about not taking his
advice. Frenchie was more practical than Rio, and now Mary
knew she too would do almost anything to extend the time
before he took another job.

"She knows, and it's all right," Frenchie told him softly. Rio beamed, not the least discomfited that the two women had talked. "Mah God, that's a relief! Ah ain't got so many friends Ah kin afford t' lose 'em."

He kissed Mary on the forehead and Frenchie on the lips and opened a bottle of wine, and the picnic took a merry turn.

Rio gave up his own lodgings and moved in with Frenchie, and though there was a brief flurry of gossip and speculation as to how the three could remain friends under the circumstances, the other boarders were too accustomed to strangeness in their own lives to wonder about anyone else's for long. Mrs. Davies didn't care as long as she got her money on time.

Mary was lonesome for Rio's presence at night, and she tried not to be jealous of Frenchie wrapped in his arms. She knew it had nothing to do with them—it was her longing for the nights with Jason conjured by their closeness. And they were close. There was a gentle gravity about their love, an edge of sad knowing, that made the time they had together more precious than if they had trusted that tomorrows would come forever.

But when Mary tried to give them even more time alone together, Frenchie would have none of it. "You keep making excuses, Rio's noticed it too, and you're to quit that right now. We're your friends; we love you; and we like being with you. Why it's because of you we found each other. Mary, Rio and me, we're not children who have to sneak away to hold hands." Her eyes were suddenly devilish. "We hold hands and a lot of other things just as much as we need to."

Mary ceased to make excuses. She was glad to go back to the late suppers and other outings with them. She did not like to think of how alone she was; without them there was no one. Dwelling on it only raised pictures of the friends she had left behind to the north. Jason.

"Ya got some admirer followin' ya 'round?"

The question came casually from Rio one night as the three of them were blissfully stuffing themselves with Chinese food at a little restaurant Rio had discovered. Far from being a beef and beans man, he delighted in tasting foods he had not experienced before. The brothers who owned this place obviously regarded Rio as a peculiar though not exclusively Western phenomenon. The Chinese had their own strong men and feared or lauded them depending on where their activities were directed, but Rio did not belong to that brotherhood and was unfailingly polite and appreciative when he came to the restaurant. In return, he received good food, good service, and more honor than most white men would ever merit.

The atmosphere was so peaceful and obliging, it took Mary a moment to notice that Rio's eyes were anything but casual as he waited for her answer. The piercing glitter was back, but suddenly a glorious possibility occurred to her.

"A tall man, lame, a man with tawny hair and golden light in his eyes . . ." she stopped, hearing the frantic urgency of her voice, seeing the growing sadness in Rio's expression.

"Dahlin', Ah'm sorry, Ah'm so sorry, but this man ain't yoah Jason. He ain't tall an' he ain't lame nor nothin' else ya say. He's medium built, but Ah jus' know he's small an' snively inside. He's got a knife in his boot an' a lady's gun in his pocket alongside whatevah money some'un paid 'im t' follow ya. Cain't tell ya how Ah know, but Ah do."

She didn't doubt what he was saying; he knew too much about this sort of thing to be wrong even while he saw himself as being worlds above the man who was following her. She knew who had hired the man; finally she knew for sure that he was not dead, that she had not killed him. She had asked for it, coming back here, coming back here so visibly. It was only a matter of time.

"It doesn't matter. Don't get involved." Her voice was leaden, her eyes without light, but she saw the look Rio and Frenchie exchanged, and desperate life came back. "I mean it, don't! Frenchie, you can stop him!"

"Don' upset yoahself now, fella ain't done nothin' t' ya yet, so Ah guess he's got a right t' follow a pretty gal if he wants."

She should have been warned by the too easy agreement and placating reasonableness, but because he was so dear to her, she forgot for the moment how very dangerous Rio could be to others.

When they left the restaurant, she glanced around furtively, yet even having been prepared, she was shocked to see the figure leaning against the side of a rickety building. There was little light on the foggy street, but she saw him. He fit Rio's description perfectly.

She said nothing nor did the other two, but they flanked her on the walk back to the boardinghouse, Rio on her right side, leaving his own right arm, his gun hand free.

For once she was glad of her little room at the top of the house; it put that much more distance between her and her pursuer. Rio escorted her all the way up.

"Ain't his style, he won' come up here, don't want no public ruckus," was all he said.

She lay awake for a long time trying to sort out her feelings, but the overwhelming one was crushing disappointment that it was not Jason. She knew how ridiculous it had been to even think it might be, but that didn't make the pain any less.

She tried to think calmly of the skulking man. Did he know who she was for sure or was he still uncertain? If he did know, why was he just following her? Was it because of Rio that he kept his distance or was it because that was what he had been instructed to do? And if that were true, what was the next step? When would he come for her?

Her mind skittered in panic; she was unable to go past the questions to any kind of answer. But she did know one thing; she did not want to flee again. She would not. She had her job and her friends; she would not leave them. But it was so nerve-racking, so unnaturally intimate to have a stranger living his life on her schedule in order to keep track of her movements, she wondered if she would break and run after all.

He never came into the saloon, but he followed her there and back, followed her if she went out during the day. Frenchie and Rio were gently insistent that she go nowhere alone. Within three days, Mary felt as if she were a prisoner in a very small, airless cell. She considered turning on the man and demanding that he leave her alone, but instantly she realized the foolishness of that; even if he let her get close enough, he would never admit anything.

Things could not go on this way indefinitely; something was going to change, something was going to happen. She was sure of it. But when it did, the way of it took her completely by surprise.

She suspected nothing when her friends said they wanted no meal but would go straight back to the boardinghouse from the saloon, unless of course, Mary was hungry. She wasn't. Her appetite had disappeared again.

They walked along as usual, Mary feeling her shadow's eyes on her back. It was worse when they entered a particularly dark stretch of street. Suddenly Rio wasn't beside her anymore, and Frenchie was pulling her arm, whispering fiercely, "Come on, and don't look back!"

When Mary tried to plant her feet and gasped, "What's Rio . . ." Frenchie kept her moving, snapping, "Shut up and keep walking or you'll make it worse!"

Mary obeyed, her heart pounding madly as they made for the better-lighted street ahead. But Frenchie stopped along with Mary when they heard the growl of male voices followed in a split second by a gunshot.

Frenchie's derringer was in her hand as she started back the way they'd come, her voice hissing, "If he's killed Rio, he's a dead man too."

But Rio intercepted them, spinning them around and marching them away. "Even at this hour, some'un's bound t've heard th' shot. Ah'll explain lata."

He held one of the women on each arm and cautioned them to walk normally, not to run. No one hindered their progress; the few people on the street gave no more than the curious glance they would to any man with two beautiful women all to himself.

The man who had been following her was dead, that Mary knew without doubt; otherwise, Rio would never hinder his gun arm by holding on to her with it.

Nothing was said until they were safely in Frenchie's room, and then Rio was very matter-of-fact, ignoring the white tension on the women's faces. The plan had worked perfectly; the man had not been alert enough to hear that three sets of footsteps had become only two on the dark street. He had not been aware of Rio until Rio had stepped out of a sheltering alleyway and grabbed him.

"It was time. Ya was nervous as a cat with its fur rubbed th' wrong way, an' he'd been skulkin' 'nuff t' drive anyone 'round th' bend. But th' man was a damn fool, said he'd talk an' went fer his little piece instead. Some people jus' don' have th' sense t' stay alive. Ah didn' learn a damn thing 'bout where he came from or who was payin' 'im 'ceptin' he was bein' paid real good, an' he didn' trust no bank t' deal 'im fair." Rio dug a bulging pouch out of its tight fit in his coat pocket. "Ain't counted it yet, but Ah figga there's probably betta n' four hundred dollars, an' all a' it in hard coin—thoughty a' 'im, paper's hard t' wash clean."

Mary stared in revulsion at the dark, still damp stains on the leather and the smear of drying blood on Rio's hand.

Rio regarded her coolly and nodded. "Ah don' 'spect ya'd take none a' this, but long as Ah got any a' it, it's yoahs if ya want it. An' now ya won' have t' try an' sneak money t' me through Frenchie. An' ya, Frenchie, mah love, don' ya neva come back t' save me. If Ah've tol' ya t' go, ya keep goin', no matta what. If Ah cain't trust ya t' do that, I cain't stay with ya. Ya promise?"

The women shared the same thought—he never missed anything. Frenchie raised her chin and glared at him defiantly for a moment, then said, "I promise."

Mary was still trying to come to terms with what had happened. There was a body back on that dark street. It was true; she knew it was, and yet, she was having a difficult time grasping the reality of it. "What . . . what will happen about him?"

"He'll be found, but no'un'll have any idea a' what happened t' im 'ceptin' that he was robbed—happens a lot in these big cities. Even th' man that hired 'im won' know no different fer sure, if he eva finds out."

"The man will send someone else." The words were tightly controlled and absolute.

Rio nodded. "'Spect so, but not fer a while, an' I'll see 'im soon enough, whoeva he is, he tries t' botha ya."

This man had killed for her, and his woman had allowed him

to put himself in jeopardy for her, and neither one of them was demanding that she tell them what had brought them all to this. The bile ceased to burn her throat, the metallic taste of fear and horror was gone from her mouth; she was filled with a surging, savage joy. Rio was alive; her stalker was dead. He deserved to be, horrible skulking hireling. She had become far harder than she had ever thought to be, and she gloried in it. Perhaps she would not survive, but she would not go down before a sliding shadow of the dark.

"Bless you, thank you both. I will sleep well and safely tonight because of you." She kissed each of them and left.

"That gal's a lot tougher than ya'd think," Rio said.

"Thank God for that," Frenchie said quietly. She knew she was truly lost. It did not seem strange to her that Rio could view killing as part of his service to God; what was strange was that she could see it in the same light.

She put her arms on his shoulders and tugged. "Stand up just long enough to come to bed with me."

"Ah don' need no urgin' fer that."

Despite his easy grin and ready compliance, she could feel the quick violence of his blood pulsing beneath his skin, aftermath of the killing, and she knew she could and would use it to her own advantage. Well and truly lost.

CHAPTER
26

*I*n the next days, Mary's relief at being free of her follower bordered on euphoria though Rio was still alert to everyone around her. The body of the man had been found but had caused scarcely more than a ripple, the newspapers reporting only that an unknown man had been found shot to death, presumably robbed by an equally unknown assailant. There were no known witnesses and no particular plea for them though there was a prim warning about traveling certain sections of the city late at night.

Even Hank grudgingly praised Mary for the new animation in her dancing and singing, and he hinted that there might be a solo number for her in the future if she kept performing as well as she was now.

It happened as swiftly as the killing, and Mary was as unprepared for it. There was some commotion in the dark near the door of the saloon, but she and the other girls kept dancing. A little trouble wasn't anything new. Hank and the other men could handle it.

"Are you going to come willingly or do I carry you out?" the voice roared at her. She froze, staring down at him. The other girls faltered to a stop, and the piano stopped with them.

Suddenly the saloon couldn't have been quieter had it been empty. This was better than any theatrical offering.

Rio was not paralyzed by what was happening. He had moved smoothly into position so that he had a clear shot, staring intently, his suspicions confirmed when he found Frenchie at his elbow, whispering frantically, "Don't! It's Jason!" He nodded.

Mary knew that everything had been disrupted, the music and the dancing had stopped, everyone was staring, and then she knew nothing at all except that Jason was here.

The fire moved and gleamed in his eyes. The Tiger come to claim what he deemed his own for whatever reason.

"Well, do I come up after you or do you come down?" His voice was soft, deadly now.

She stood frozen for an instant more, and then she climbed down, not even thinking of the stairs at the side of the stage which would have made it easier, hoping her knees wouldn't buckle when she stood before him. There was a beginning murmur from the men like a swarm of bees growing angry and seeking a new direction.

Frenchie had moved quickly, dashing to the back, and now from the stage her voice floated out over the crowd as she tossed Mary's cloak to her. "It ize none of your buziness, mes amis. De lady goes becuz she weeshes. Eh, voilà!" Her false accent had never been so thick or so effective; no one interfered as Jason led Mary out.

"Same damn boardinghouse?" he snapped, and she managed a dazed, "Yes," not resisting as he pulled her along through the misty streets. Just like the first time, the fog coming in, she thought. Her mind seemed incapable of further activity.

The journey up the stairs to her room seemed endless, but when they were finally there, she put as much distance between him and herself as possible in the small space. Her hands shook as she lighted the two lamps.

Jason was so relieved at finding her after waiting so long, he was torn between the desire to attack her for leaving, for the fear that had been building inside him ever since and the urge to fold her into his arms forever. And so he remained standing just inside the doorway, glaring at her.

"I suppose all good thieves must survive as well as you do," he snarled.

Her mouth framed his name silently, and then she found a voice, a small tremor of sound not at all her own. "I didn't take any money. Surely you know I didn't! I used the horse race money. I left the jewelry and most of the clothes."

This was a nightmare, worse than never seeing him again at all. Her hands groped blindly in her sewing basket and came up with a little packet, fumbling to undo it. Coins clinked together.

"I did take the cloak and a few other clothes. I'm sorry." She held the coins out. "These were to pay a debt to someone else, but I don't owe it anymore. You take them. I know it isn't enough, but it's all I can give you now. Tell me what you think I owe, and I'll send it when I have it." Her voice no longer trembled, and her outstretched hand was steady. She felt as if she were formed of cold, heavy metal like the coins. All that had ever been kind between her and Jason had been no more than an illusion, as kindness had always been in her life.

Jason looked around the painfully bare, clean room and at her face, still pale and hollow-eyed compared to the healthy youth she had had on the island before her illness, and he knew what it had cost her to collect the pitiful hoard of coins for whatever debt, knew what her particular code of honor would always cost her. The lump swelled in his throat and made his voice jagged.

"I'm not talking about money or clothes you didn't want when I bought them for you! Goddamn it! You took other things, things I couldn't afford to lose!"

She gazed at him blankly, unable to form a protest at this injustice. He crossed the space between them, gripping her shoulders as she tried to shrink away. "You took my trust. You took the only joy and love I have. You took my heart and more of my soul than a man can spare. Will you send those back too, at your convenience?" He pulled her roughly against him. The coins clattered across the floor.

"I don't understand!" she cried desperately. "How could I have taken what I never had from you? After the fever, even when I was well again, you didn't . . . you were so aloof, kind but so far away. I thought you were finished with me and too kind to send me away, so I did it for you." Her last words were muffled against him because no matter what was coming next, she could not resist leaning against the warmth and strength she had thought never to know again.

Jason groaned softly, but his anger and despair were lifting with the reassuring press of her against him. He sat down, pulling her into his lap. "My fine attempt to be gallant led to this!"

"A polite tiger? The terms contradict. Surely the women you have known have been long on the mend from their complaints." The question was in her voice despite her attempt at lightness.

"It wasn't that nor was it all gallantry," he replied steadily, and he held her more tightly.

"You do know." She was very still in his arms.

"Yes, when your fever was high, you talked." He took a deep breath and steeled himself to say the painful words. "For a long time, I thought I wanted to know who your first lover was in spite of my promise not to pry into your past. Jealousy made me curious. I suppose I wanted to hear you tell me that I was much better than he, that you loved me much more, that you loved me at all, all the things I once thought I'd never want or need to hear again after Gaiety died. I imagined different situations, pictured different men. None of them was true. But now I do know, and part of me wishes I'd never found out. Your words were confused, but I don't think I mistook their meaning. Once I knew, I couldn't bear to hurt you more. I couldn't bear to take any more from you. And yes, I had trouble with my own feelings, my own acceptance. The first man who took you was your father, wasn't he?"

His relief that she did not struggle to be quit of his hold nearly made him miss the low words. "How can you bear to touch me now, knowing what I am?"

He felt as if he'd been kicked hard in the gut. He had suspected her self-loathing from the first and had wanted to banish it, but now, knowing the source and depth of it made it harder. His mind struggled to grasp the tortured way of her self-blame and failed, and he had a horrified instant of wondering if she meant she had seduced her father deliberately. That would not, in Jason's mind, excuse the father, but would implicate her. He was searching for the right thing to say when she began to speak again, the words flowing from the ghastly visions of her past.

"I was a very good little girl, a very proper little girl. Everyone said so. For all the wealth, not spoiled at all." Her voice was strangely prim, as if she were reciting a set piece. "My clothes were well-made but very plain and never too many. It doesn't do for good Christians to flaunt their riches, and we were such good Christians in our house. We went to church every Sunday, and father read the Bible every evening. Tutors came to teach me at the house so that I could be a perfect little lady and so that I would not be tainted by contact with other children who might not be so perfect. And there were servants, but none of them lived in. There were good Christian reasons for that too—not only thrift but also kindness, for didn't the servants have their own lives and families to go home to at night? The ones in our house always did." The primness was gone in the leaden weight of reliving how trapped and helpless she had been.

"It was all so perfect for my father. I never remember a time when he didn't do as he liked with me. Even when I was very little, I remember him holding me on his lap, rubbing against me, and when I was a little older, he started coming to my bedchamber. He would take off his robe and my nightshift and talk about keeping me warm because Papa's little girl was his favorite, and Papa and his little girl had wonderful secrets. He devised his game of touching. He was good at games like that. He made a game of punishments too, spankings for things like dirty hands or dropping something or not doing my lessons well enough, and the spankings always led to something else. And I can't tell you whether I minded or not."

Oh, but you can, you are telling me, Jason thought as she squirmed and flinched in his hold. He knew she was completely unaware of her movements.

"Sometimes he made me feel good and sometimes he hurt me, and later when my mother was dead, when I was nearly twelve, he hurt me a great deal. At least he waited until then for the final consummation. But I didn't make any judgment about it until then because I didn't know any differently. I thought all little girls did the same things with their fathers. Then I knew I had taken what belonged to my mother, maybe I even made her die. But he wouldn't stop, he wouldn't stop, and everyone said wasn't I a devoted little girl to my brave father who had lost his wife."

Jason swallowed hard, fighting the urge to vomit, fighting the urge to scream at her to stop. He knew she had to keep going, lancing the wound that had festered so long. She was quieter in his arms now, and he loosened his hold on her.

"My uncle Tim, my father's brother, he was not like my father. He was called the family black sheep because he was an actor. He had inherited money just like his brother, though not the power because he was younger, but he lost it all in failed theatrical companies. It didn't matter to him, money didn't matter to him, being in the theatrical world was all that was important. He wasn't a very good actor, but he usually managed to get bit parts, character parts here and there, usually with traveling companies.

"My father and Uncle Tim didn't have any use for each other, but I think Father was afraid of him, so he never banned him from the house. Uncle Tim was quick with his fists and his temper. But he and my mother liked each other; he could always make her laugh. But after Mother died, Uncle Tim just stopped coming to visit. Sometimes little gifts and cards came for me, but not Uncle Tim.

"I was fourteen, it was my birthday, and a little bouquet of violets was delivered to the house for me. It was from Uncle Tim. He was back in New York." At last Jason knew where she was from, but he kept still, doing nothing that might interrupt her. "Suddenly I wanted to get away from the house, away from everything, I wanted to so badly, I thought I'd die if I didn't leave. I never had any money—my father always made sure of that—but Uncle Tim was there within reach. I ran to him. I checked all the theaters and music halls until I found him. I didn't tell him anything, I just cried. I don't know for sure whether he knew anything beyond the fact that I was very unhappy, but I think he must have, I think he blackmailed my father. Uncle Tim took me home, and then he waited for my father to come home too. They were locked in the study for a long time. I could hear them shouting but not the words. Everything changed. I spent most of that week with Uncle Tim. I met his friends. I watched him perform at the theater, and then he would take me home and stay at the house for the night. I hardly saw my father at all and only with Uncle Tim present, but I remember. I remember how my father looked at me, as if he wanted to kill me and love me at the same time." The shudder passed through her to Jason. He wondered if she even knew he was holding her; the compulsive words flowed on as if she were talking to herself.

"The next week Uncle Tim escorted me to a young woman's seminary. It was out in the country. It took us a whole day of train and carriage travel to get there. The only other place I'd ever been out of the city was the country estate where we went in the summers, where everything was the same. The school was completely different. Uncle Tim told me to tell the same story the school had been told—my mother had died and my father was going abroad for some time. It was a little bit of the truth, more of a lie, and it made sense to me because everything around me looked like one thing but was another. I was beginning to understand that, and I was willing to do anything, say anything to get away from my father.

"I spent three years at that school. The last year I tutored some of the younger girls in French and music for as many hours as I was a student myself. I liked the work. I felt useful. I didn't fit otherwise. I was never close to any of the other students. I felt so much older. I'd never been around children before. But their giggling and talking, it taught me a lot. It taught me that their lives were not like mine; their fathers were not like mine, and they were not like me. Uncle Tim came to see me a few times, but not my father. I was thankful for that." Her voice was small, sad, and faraway, and Jason's heart ached with the knowledge of how isolated, how abused and abandoned she had been, not just at the school but from the beginning.

The pulse of sound changed, speeding, twisting with anguish.

"Uncle Tim, he died two days before my seventeenth birthday. It was so stupid! He was hit by a dray and killed. I'm sure it really was an accident; my father was too afraid of him to kill him. No violets from Uncle Tim that birthday. Instead my father came for me. There was nothing to do. I thought of screaming for them not to let him take me, but it wouldn't have done any good. He was the one who had paid for everything. They didn't know Uncle Tim made him do it. They didn't know my father had never been abroad at all. They didn't know anything at all except that he was a prominent man. If I'd told them the truth, if they'd believed it, they would have wanted me to leave even faster. Proper young ladies and proper schools don't have anything to do with incest." She spit the word out.

"He took me home, and oh, God, it was as if I'd never left! I screamed all the things at him I couldn't scream at the school. He acted as if nothing had changed, as if I knew nothing more than I had when I was very young, as if he didn't hear me at all. He came to my room in the night. The door was locked, but he had another key; I hadn't even thought of that. He came to me. I tried to run. He caught me; he was too strong. He told me how much he loved me, how much he loved the softness of my skin and the color of my hair—he was dark; my mother and Uncle Tim were the blonds. He told me how darkness and light belonged together, neither whole without the other. His voice was gentle; his body violent. When he had spent himself, I rolled halfway out from under him. It was far enough. My sewing basket was on the table beside the bed. My hand tipped it over, but I got the scissors, big, heavy scissors. I stabbed him in the back. I stabbed him until the blades stuck, and I couldn't pull them out to stab him again."

The words came faster and faster. Her rib cage was heaving as if her heart and lungs were trying to burst through. Jason saw the sweat gleaming on her skin, saw the wide, unnatural shine of her eyes, and knew it was all happening again in her mind, knew it all had to happen again for her to acknowledge what it had done to her.

"He was yowling, cursing, thrashing about, but he couldn't get up, couldn't follow me, then he was quiet. Blood everywhere. I washed the blood off myself. I dressed. I found a little money on the bureau in his room. I took it. I ran. I couldn't think of anyone who would help me except for some of Uncle Tim's theatrical friends. They did help, for his sake and without asking questions. I was out of New York by the next day, disguised, traveling with a group of actors." She took a deep, harsh breath, and the pace slowed. "Eventually I came across the country with the same kind of people. At first I sewed costumes and painted bits of scenery and props, and then I started doing this and that in the performances, filling in for someone who had drunk too much the night before or left the troop without warning. After the first group, there wasn't even any connection with Uncle Tim, there were just people used to helping each other in their profession because no one else would. As long as one could do something to help the troop stay alive, there was a place. But it all fell apart in San Francisco, and everyone went separate ways. I was tired of traveling, tired of running. I stayed here.

"I should have made sure, I should have made sure he was dead! He's not dead! He's looking for me!" The terrified urgency screamed in her voice again.

"If he finds you, he'll find me too, and I will kill him." Jason's voice was flat and calm.

She was out of his arms before he could stop her, standing over him, keening, "Haven't you heard anything I've said? You know what I am, you know! You know I killed my mother and tried to kill my father. You know I was my father's woman! How can you be so insane? You would let me near Jamie again, near your islanders, near your friends, you would take me back knowing what I am?"

Jason stayed where he was, gazing up at her. Depravity beyond anything he had ever imagined before, but nothing mattered except Mary. None of it was her fault. He knew that as absolutely as he knew the beat of his own heart, and he knew he had to make her believe it as he did.

"Mary, my darling," he drew the word out into a long, soft caress. "Your parents were adults, you were a child, only a child. Your father was evil, terribly, terribly evil to use you so. And your mother, Mary, your mother had to have known! She had to have known he did not look on you as a father should look on his daughter, that he was too much with you, away from her at the wrong times. Your mother was as much to blame, she was! And your kind Uncle Tim, he did something for you, but not nearly enough, and maybe he liked your mother too much and made everything worse." And maybe your father did have your uncle killed finally, and maybe your Uncle Tim was in fact the one who fathered you—what a hellish mess! He didn't speculate aloud; there was no use. They were things which would never be known and made no difference. The man who had abused her had known himself as her father.

"No—o!" It was a long, agonized wail of protest even as the denied truth burst on her like the sun, blinding in its clarity, flashing images of her mother as she had truly been, pretty, vain, and spineless, ghosting around the big house in the city or the place in the country, always the same, afraid of everything and everyone except her brother-in-law, dependent on her husband for the social standing she wanted but could not cope with, ignorant of her daughter's existence as a real human being, not ignorant of but ignoring what was being done to the child because to face it was to risk too much, was to risk taking back the role she hated as wife to her husband. How many times had she heard her mother tell her to go do this or that for Papa, that Papa was looking for his little girl, on and on?

"She did know, my mother knew!" It was an unearthly scream of rage and sorrow. Jason prayed that the proprietress wouldn't burst in and ruin Mary's chance of saving herself. When no one came, he thanked God even while he considered it might be Frenchie who deserved the gratitude by now.

Tears poured down Mary's face. "He took it! He took it all. My father took my right to come to you complete, to come to you first, to give you myself. He taught me everything, and it was all wrong. You were the first and not the first."

He reached out and pulled her down to him again. She was too exhausted to struggle against the pull of his warmth. She wept, cursed, pounded her fists against his chest, and clung to him, lost in a maelstrom of long-suppressed and violently conflicting emotions.

He held her and let her rage, crooning softly, "It's all right, all right now. Let it all out, all of it. I love you, love you dearly. I know what you are. You are a splendid woman, against all odds, you are splendid, and you are mine. All the rest is over, over forever!"

He didn't care that she was probably not consciously hearing him; he was certain some part of her heart and mind heard and was drawing comfort. He knew it was true when the tortured sounds finally ceased and her body relaxed and curled a little as she fell asleep in his arms.

He shifted his body slightly to form a more comfortable cradle for her. He didn't even feel the cramping of the muscles in his leg. All the treasure he now wanted in the world, he held in his arms. There was time now if she wanted to tell him more, time now for everything, and time to take her home.

He thought of the days of delay he had spent without her, and he damned himself for the waste, for not being able to face the truth about her squarely, for not being able to admit the depth of his love for her no matter what had been before. He had wanted to kill Cade when he had arrived back to find him waiting to tell him the truth about the aid he had given Mary in her escape. Yet at the same time, he had felt treacherous relief that the need to face her had been taken from his hands. It was over. She was gone. He had worked and ridden desperately, driving himself to exhaustion, curt and closed-faced to everyone dear to him. And he had soon discovered that Mary, though physically gone, was more present than she had ever been, haunting him every waking moment, then haunting his dreams until he awakened calling and searching for her. And Jamie had made it all worse.

Jamie had thrown no tantrums, had had no attacks, had voiced no anger at all. His first bewilderment had been followed by days of his voice softly calling as he searched for Mary, sure somehow that it was all a mistake, that she was still on the island somewhere. And then had come frighteningly adult resignation and a sorrow that made his face grave and quiet. He had not turned to his father for comfort; he had tried to comfort his father. Jason felt tears burn his eyes even now as he thought about it.

"She belongs here with us, Papa, she'll be back, I know she will," Jamie told him, and Jason hadn't the heart to try to dissuade him from his belief. Jamie did all his lessons so well even Hayes was surprised. And he went out of his way to do nothing which might worry his father. He made it a point to tell him where he planned to be, often adding such things as, "in case you need me," or, "maybe you'll want me to do something for you."

His son, in fact, had more than a little to do with Jason's being here now with Mary. Jason had seen him writing busily in the book Hayes had given him for his birthday. Finally, he gave in to the temptation to read what his son had written. He felt guilty about it, but was also worried, worried that all the anger and pain he had expected Jamie to express were somehow bottled up and doing more damage that way. He expected to find some clue as to the depth of them in the book; he found nothing of the sort. He found a little boy's lopsided handwriting recording small and large things indiscriminately, beginning with the birthday party. And Mary's name appeared most often. Mary had taught this or that, told him this or that; he and Mary had done this or that. "I desided" marked Jamie's deepest thinking in the journal.

"I desided Mary is my mother even if she isnt really."

"I desided Danel knos more than almost anybody but Papa and Mary."

"I desided Cade is one of the most best peple and Captin to."

"Magy is good and funy even if she dont make word sonds. I like Ben to and the twins."

The "I desided" passages marked decisions, joys, and sorrows, and they marked Jason so deeply, he would be able to see them clearly in his mind forever.

Granmother and Danel and them littel babys who didnt talk yet are all gone away. They dead like my real mother when I was to littel to talk yet to. But I desided they are just some place else, and they are all togetter with my real mother. It makes me sad. But I am in this place and they are there and that is all.

And after glowing, excited lines about the trip on the *Gaiety* and the visit to Seattle, Jason had found: "Mary is gone away. I miss her. But I dont worry. I desided she will be back. This is her place to." And then: "Papa is so sad. I desided he will go bring Mary back home soon."

Over and over again Jamie had written variations on the theme, sure at least several times a week that his father would soon be on his way to find Mary and bring her back. The passage of one week to the next had not dimmed his certainty, and Jamie's words had become his father's own certainty, misspelled words and all. When he finally faced the knowledge of what she meant to him, faced the need to see her again, to hold her again no matter what had been before, he was awed by the realization of how well his son understood the force and forgiveness of love. Not once had Jamie said or written that he was angry because Mary had left; he was only sad at the separation and sure it would end. The floodgates of love had been opened in Jamie by Mary herself, and love flowed unceasingly from him now.

"Jamie, I'm going to go find Mary and bring her home. Do you want to come with me?"

He had been so sure Jamie would want to come with him, his son's answer stunned him. "No, Papa, you go by yourself. Mary knows I love her, just like I know she loves me. Just tell her I want her to come home." The words unspoken were louder than those he spoke. Jason could hear them clearly: "You love her too, so hurry!"

Once the decision had been made, Jason was in a frenzy to begin the search. The *Gaiety* had never seemed so slow. He had thought of taking passage on a steamer from Victoria or Seattle but had discarded the idea; if he ever found her, he wanted to bring her home on his own ship. The islanders had seen him off, their faces as approving and as sure of his success as Jamie's. Even Cade had beamed as if there were no doubt that Mary would be easily found now that Jason had decided to look. It made him feel particularly lonely; it was as if he were the only one who understood the hopelessness of what he was setting out to do.

The ship Mary had taken had steamed on south from San

Francisco. For all he knew, she had gone with it. Even if she were in San Francisco, he doubted she would be in her old haunts, and worse, he doubted she would be alone if she were there at all. He was only too aware that his relationship with her might well have paved the way for the next. He had packed the best of her clothes—flimsy, foolish talismans—and brought them with him as tangible assurance that he would find her. The scent of spice and roses had haunted him as he folded the garments. He had thought of sending a telegram to Owen, then decided against it. What could he say, "If you know where Mary is, keep her there"? In any case, Owen had sent no word about her. The quest was his own.

Even with the reality of her sleeping in his arms, he could scarcely believe that he had found her so easily. The *Gaiety* had docked late in the afternoon, and once the ship was secure, Jason had gone to Owen's office.

"Have you seen Mary?" he demanded after the barest greeting, and Owen, who was still trying to assimilate the fact that the Tiger was back and acting so oddly, stared at him blankly, which was answer enough. When Jason blurted out the story, Owen shook his head.

" 'The course of true love never did' et cetera. Come home to Carrie with me; she'll think of something sensible."

Jason knew why he agreed. Now that he was in the city, he was even more fearful and hopeless than he had been on the voyage south. There were only three places he knew to look for Mary, and the first one was empty. She had not gone to Carrie and Owen, had not pledged them to silence. That left only the boardinghouse and the saloon. He wasn't sure he wanted to know so soon that they too, were empty for him. But he found the love and concern surrounding him in Owen and Carrie's little house unbearable. He could see it in their eyes—their hearts ached for him because they were more practical than the islanders, more worldly; they doubted he would ever find Mary.

He left as abruptly as he had appeared at Owen's office. When Owen offered to go with him, he refused.

"You'll let us know?" Carrie asked softly, and she kissed him on both cheeks.

When he walked into the saloon, he stopped dead. He thought for a moment he was hallucinating because he wanted to see her so much. But when he blinked and rubbed his eyes, she remained. Then came the surge of anger, relief, and love all mixed, all fierce. He would have killed anyone who tried to come between him and his woman.

He had seen the sleek, economical movements of the man with the gun so near his hand, and he hadn't given a damn.

Now with time to think, he wondered if she knew it consciously. It had been no miracle. Mary had been there, waiting for him to find her if he would, her bright hair uncovered, a lodestar shining in the dark. He shuddered as he thought of what she had risked to do that.

The soft light of dawn crept into the room and then full sun burning away the fog. Mary stirred and awakened, nestling closer for a moment with a little sigh, showing no fear or confusion about where she was.

"It is true. You are here." She looked up into his eyes. "My name was Sarah, Sarah-Mary. I never was called Mary until I ran away, and now I think Sarah is gone. Mary is the one who found you."

Despite the ravages of emotion that had left her face pale and tear-streaked, she looked radiant, and it was for him alone. He kissed her eyelids, the tip of her nose, and then the vulnerable curve of her mouth. Knowing how fragile she was, he kissed her very, very gently, without demand. And then he drew back a little and shook his head.

"To me, you're Sarah-Mary, Sarah and Mary in one. I love them both. I love you. But Sarah isn't gone, thank God! Sarah is the one who has survived. Mary was only the one who hid her." He smiled suddenly. "But you'll have to remind me if I slip and forget my dear Sarah's name. I've just met her, you know, even though I've loved her for a long time."

She thought of being Sarah again, of really being Sarah for the first time. "I am Sarah." She tested it quietly and then with more force. "I am Sarah!"

She traced the angle of his jaw rough with the stubble of his vigil. "Jason Drake, my beloved Tiger, I, Sarah, belong to you as much as anyone can ever belong to anyone else. You gave me back my soul. All I have to give you is my love, but that you have, all of it. It is no gift though and not even new. I never even knew what it was until you taught me, so all you have is your own back again, and that you have had for a very long time even though I could not admit it, to you or to myself. I admit it now, to you, to myself, to anyone who wants to know. I love you, Jason, I'll never stop loving you."

When he bent to kiss her again, she forestalled him, pressing her hand against his mouth. "There are other things I want to tell you, things I must tell you."

He expected to hear more about her father, and he did, but only indirectly. She told him about Rio, everything about Rio from the first meeting. The jealousy he felt was brief, soon overwhelmed by thankfulness that the man had been there to protect her, even to kill for her, when he himself had not.

He trembled with the effort, but he lost the battle. His face twisted, and the tears spilled over, burning down his cheeks. Though she had tried to make light of it, mocking herself for her inept attempt to make a living on the streets, it was the final blow. What had been her life before he met her was hard enough to accept, but that she had been so desperate when he could have prevented it was unbearable.

He bent his head, pressing his face against the soft hollow of her neck. She stroked his thick hair and searched for his mouth with her own, tasting the salt, murmuring between small, gentle kisses, "No, love, don't weep. It's past. And I have just realized what you must know. I did not hide from you. I was waiting, waiting where you could find me if you wanted me back again."

It was so clear now, she marveled that she had been so blind to her own motives, so blind to the reason for her desperate need for the same job back again, her need to be in the most obvious place Jason would look. And she knew now how much she had come to doubt that he would come for her.

Jason answered the increasing demand of her mouth with his own, feeling the life he had thought lost forever flowing back into him from her.

They moved in the chair. She felt him wince and realized how long the hours of her metamorphosis had been. She pulled away and swayed a little as she stood, even her healthy legs cramped.

"My poor darling, I fear I have lamed you more!" she cried. It was all right; all was admitted, understood, and accepted between them now.

Jason smiled at her and didn't protest as she began to massage the knotted muscles of his leg. "As soon as I can walk without falling on my face, I think we ought to make ourselves presentable and find Frenchie and Rio. Frenchie probably saved my life last night. I had only one goal, and it didn't occur to me that anyone would take dangerous exception to it. Even when I spotted him, I didn't care. Seems the bluebird is even more popular than I knew. I'll expect my wife to wear this," he touched the crumpled material of her costume, a new one she had made but still in blue, "only on special occasions and only for me."

She backed away a little and stared at him. "Wife? You don't have to marry me, you can't marry me, he . . ."

Jason stood abruptly, silencing her with his sudden movement. He held onto the chair, struggling for balance, struggling harder to hold his temper. He hated the power her father had over her and willed himself to patience. Step by step he would teach her that the power of love was stronger than the power of fear; it had to be.

His voice was under control when he spoke. "Yes, your father will probably send someone else or come himself. Yes, I believe you. I believe the man Rio killed was hired by your father. But none of it makes any difference. You are not alone; you will never be alone again as long as I live. And I have no intention of being killed by your father or one of his hirelings. The old bargain is over. I don't want you as my mistress; I want you as my wife, and there is only one reason I will accept your refusal. If you don't love me enough, I'll just have to try to understand."

She made one last attempt. "I'm not Gaiety. I'm not, and I'll never be! I found her picture before I left, and once you called out to her when . . . once you called out to her."

"I'm sorry for that," Jason said softly. "But Gaiety died a long time ago. She was lovely, and I loved her. But she is gone and so is the young man who loved her. It's taken me a long time to understand why she came back so strongly in my memory when you came into my life. I do understand now. I hadn't loved anyone, I hadn't even felt alive since Gaiety's death. Life is easier that way, maybe not good, but easier. And then you came into my life and brought it all back—loving again, feeling alive again, having everything at risk again. And I was afraid. Remembering all I'd had with Gaiety, all I'd lost, was a way to keep it from happening again. But it didn't work, and I realized it was time and past to say good-bye to her. More, I realized how sad and angry she would have been that it had taken me so long. The last thing Gaiety would ever have wanted to leave to anyone was sorrow. I should not have waited to tell you I love you; I should have risked your answer, even your fear. My Sarah, once Mary, have I waited too long?"

Her face was very still for a moment, and then she smiled. "No, I would say you are just in time." She was shining, shining so brightly with youth and joy that Jason felt as if he were looking right into the sunrise.

She threw her arms around him and gave him a swift kiss. "That's all you get for now. My heart may be soaring, but the rest of me has some very immediate needs. And once those are attended to, I want a huge, no, a magnificent breakfast!"

"Your priorities are wonderfully correct and fully shared."

They laughed together in the sweet surety of domestic intimacy. Even though there were bright new things between them, they did not have to begin at the beginning. They were a man and a woman who had learned each other well in every way; their separate attempts to refuse the knowledge had been futile. For that failure, they were profoundly grateful.

Sarah~Mary Drake

CHAPTER
27

*J*ason's voice was so strong and calm, she felt it surrounding her in warmth, but she had a moment of panic, and doubted she would be able to speak at all. Then she heard her own voice, as steady as Jason's, as steady as Rio's had been when he gave her into Jason's keeping.

I, Sarah, take thee, Jason, to my wedded Husband, to have and to hold from this day forward, for better, for worse, for richer, for poorer, in sickness and in health, to love and to cherish, till death us do part, according to God's holy ordinance; and thereto I give thee my troth.

The minister's voice drifted over them, "Bless, O Lord, this Ring . . ."

She was Sarah now, Sarah she had never thought to be again and now was so glad to be. How well this man knew her, how well she loved him.

Frenchie and Rio, Carrie and Owen and the crew of the *Gaiety* —she could feel their love filling the flower-decked room of

Owen's house. Lars, Mogens, David Becam, and Captain Hanson would never know how much their obvious approval that she was back with Jason meant to her. It was confirmation of what Jason had told her of the islanders' sorrow at her leaving and hope for her return. She had been touched to tears by his recounting of the entries in Jamie's journal; she would be going home to Jamie's love, not to his anger. It made an enormous difference.

What a strange few days it had been. She had done almost nothing to plan her own wedding. The women had decorated the room, planned the supper to follow, and dressed the bride. Owen and Jason had taken care of all the details of the license and the ceremony. Jason had not pressed her for her surname, fully aware of why she was deliberately withholding it from him. He knew it was a desperate attempt not only to keep her father at bay in her own mind, but to keep the two men from meeting. Jason was too filled with the joy of having her back to spoil it by demanding the last fact from her. And he had a sense of fate that could not be changed or avoided; if Sarah's father continued to pursue her, he would find Jason blocking his path. Jason had not tried to blackmail the name from her for the marriage ceremony; Owen had arranged everything. Sarah-Mary Smith was marrying Jason Drake.

Now, Jason loosed her right hand and took her left. The gold was warm from Owen's careful hold and the minister's blessing.

"With this Ring I thee wed; In the Name of the Father, and of the Son, and of the Holy Ghost. Amen."

The delicately etched circle fit perfectly though it was the first time Mary had seen it. She pressed her fingers against Jason's, acknowledging this added gift. So many gifts from him and depths she was only beginning to understand. It was he who had wanted a minister to perform the ceremony rather than a justice of the peace. Contacts with ministers had been another ugly hypocrisy in her life before, in the Sundays at church with her father, in the contact with men of God who could not see that a child was in trouble or, if they had, had done nothing about it. If he could not change the memories, Jason could at least change the present. The lean-faced elderly man who was performing the ceremony radiated serenity and kindness, his shoulders a little stooped, his eyes deep and knowing as if he had taken on the burdens of his fellows and found himself strong enough to carry them. Owen had suggested him, both delighted and chagrined to admit he knew such a man, when Jason had told him the requirements.

When the minister pronounced the final blessing, Jason bent to kiss Sarah. He smelled the flowers in her hair, saw the golden glowing light in her gray eyes before she closed them, felt her mouth warm and trembling under his own, and forgot there was anyone else in the room.

"See, and no parlor," Owen whispered to Carrie, and the sound reminded Jason that they were not alone. They drew apart, both trembling as they had not during the ceremony.

"Good Lord, a little more of that and none of us would be able to get through supper," Frenchie declared, adding hurriedly amid the burst of laughter, "Oh, excuse me, Reverend."

The minister's eyes twinkled. "No pardon is needed. And now I will take my leave."

"Please, can't you stay for supper?" Sarah asked, going to him.

He shook his head regretfully. "I still have duties tonight, Mrs. Drake." He smiled at being the first to use her new name, then his face sobered. "Less happy ones than this celebration, I fear. A friend of mine is gravely ill. He is an old man and long ailing. I can do nothing to change that, but I can be with him, one old man with another. Now, my dear, I have made you sad, and there is no reason for that. My friend and I, we have lived different lives; he looked for gold while I looked for God, and neither of us is sure of what he found or what he lost in the search, but we both know we have had long, full lives. It is simply that it is kind to have a companion in the time when the hourglass has run its course." He lowered his voice until only she could hear. "You and your Jason, may you be blessed companions for all the hours, for all the years. And you must take good care of him. He is not as strong as you think. He is strong enough to battle Satan himself, yes, but he is not strong enough to war with you. Don't ever shun him, not with your flesh or with your spirit. When you are joyful, let him rejoice with you, and when you are heavy with sorrow, let him weep with you."

"I will, as well as I am able, I will." She barely breathed the words, and yet she felt the vow more binding than the oath she had spoken so clearly in the marriage ceremony.

"I mean to claim my rights. I haven't gotten to kiss the bride yet." Sarah turned at the sound of Owen's voice.

"Go on, child, and may the Lord bless and keep you." The old man patted her hand and went into the little entry hall.

Jason met him there. The minister stared in confusion at the gold coins pressed into his palm. He had only meant to shake hands in polite leave-taking. "You've paid me already," he protested, "and this is a fortune."

Jason smiled. "It's hardly that, and it comes with one condition, one I suspect will be difficult for you. Half of this you may use for any cause you deem worthy; the other half is only for you."

The old man studied the coins with growing dismay.

"I'm not the Devil tempting you to sin," Jason chided. "You have done more for me and Sarah than you know. I see you as a man who habitually does more for others than for himself. It is your calling and it gives you joy, that I understand, but please, understand me. I know few men like you; I would like to think that a little more comfort for you might extend your ability to comfort others for a little longer."

"I think our friend Mr. Trenglyth has a lyrical tongue."

Jason smiled. "Indeed sometimes he does." The story had moved Jason deeply. Owen, with his insatiable interest in what was going on around him, had noticed the old man sitting alone at a table in a saloon. Even when Owen's friends had left after a long while, the old man in his worn suit remained, still nursing his first glass of cheap whiskey. Finally Owen had gone to him, introduced himself, announced his profession, and asked if there was anything he could do to be of assistance. The misery in the old man's face had eased.

"You already have, Mr. Trenglyth. You have made me see my own unpleasant image—an overgrown child sulking because God's plan does not fit with his own."

His attention caught, Owen had urged him to tell the rest of the story.

The Reverend Bartholomew Mapes had told it starkly. He had lost one of his favorite children, a boy scarcely eight years old. The child had been very ill, and the Reverend had cared for him while his parents worked, the other children in the family being even younger, not old enough to help out much. Tommy had seemed to be improving and then quite suddenly he had died, this evening.

"But you see, Mr. Trenglyth, it is not my faith I have lost, it is my temper. I do not approve of what God has done in this instance. So here I am brooding and surely making as much impression on the Creator as if I were an ant biting at the sea."

Owen was awed by the steadfastness of the old man, by his ability to keep faith with the vastness of God, and by the practicality of his mission. This, Owen learned by seeking out sources other than the minister, pursuing the facts as diligently as if it were for a case.

Bartholomew had no church of his own though he sometimes filled in for ministers who did have their own congregations. He spent most of his time working with the poor of the city, finding jobs for them, and spending every penny he was able to spare or beg on their clothing, food, and rent. What little money he had of his own, he earned by tutoring young sons of the newly rich in Latin and Greek so that they might qualify for the universities in the East and in Europe. He moved easily between the two worlds in his shabby clothing. He never asked anything for himself, but he had no shyness about pleading for those in his charge. Owen guessed that more than ten percent of his own practice now included defending Reverend Mapes's people for no fee.

Bartholomew looked again at the coins in his hand. "Would you allow me to keep them if I promised that at least half would be used for something which would give me joy?"

Jason surrendered with a grin. "From Owen, I know exactly what that means, but at least I tried, and maybe you'll allow yourself one or two glasses of whiskey."

"Oh, I should hope not!" he said with a smile. "I only indulge when I am angry with my Maker, and thanks be to Him, that has not been often enough to fill even one bottle in a long life. However, I do have a weakness for beefsteak even when I am at peace with my soul. I promise I will indulge just short of gluttony. The sin of gluttony is always a temptation once one's teeth begin to wobble like the legs; it is hard not to fear that mush will be all, all too soon. And now I truly must take my leave; my friend will be expecting me. But I hope you will have patience for a last word from a meddlesome old man. Your bride, your Sarah, she is shining, but there is also darkness and fear in her. Deal gently with her; even when your patience would end, deal gently.''

Jason towered over the man and yet he felt as if he were small again and being counseled by his father. "I will. Thank you, Reverend." It occurred to him that this man was far more like Constance than like his father; Bartholomew Mapes saw more of the human condition than most could bear to see because he saw it without the protection of divisions between past, present, and future.

He watched the stooped figure disappear into the night before he went back to the party.

Sarah came up to him instantly, and Rio complained, "Owen, mah friend, how come she don' look at us like that?"

"Just as well she doesn't, you've got enough on your hands with me," Frenchie declared in mock anger.

"That Ah do!" Rio gave her a smacking kiss while Lars and Mogens looked on mournfully, missing their wives.

Sarah glowed with the easy happiness flowing from one friend to the other. Her first relief had been when Rio and Jason had met.

"Thank you for keeping her safe," Jason had said gravely.

"It was mah pleasure, but Ah'm glad ya finally got here. She's been lonesome fer ya," Rio had answered, and all was understood between them.

Jason had kissed Frenchie and thanked her too, and Frenchie had grinned up at him. "Would've been a lot easier if you hadn't slept so soundly that first night, wouldn't it?"

And then Owen and Carrie had welcomed introductions to Rio and Frenchie.

"Sarah is a lovely name," Carrie announced calmly. "You must be glad to have it back again."

Sarah was aware of all of them, and she joined in the chatter and laughter during supper, but her attention was really on Jason. She reached out to touch him now and then, reassuring herself that he was really here, here beside her. Often when she turned to look at him, she found him regarding her, bright warm light moving in his eyes.

Suddenly the hunger for him swept through her so strongly, she nearly gasped aloud. She felt the blood touching her cheeks. She couldn't stop the image of his lean hard body from invading her mind. The past days had not only been rushed, they had also been celibate. It hadn't been her choice. It was Jason who had wanted it this way, saying he wanted even the physical loving which had been so much a part of their time together before solemnized and reborn by the marriage. He had moved her out of the boardinghouse immediately—she didn't argue with the unspoken logic; there was no sense in her remaining in a place one pursuer had already marked—but he had taken her to Carrie and Owen, not to his hotel. And here she had remained. Tonight a carriage would take them to his hotel. She had no idea what time it was. How she wished the carriage would come.

Her eyes widened as she wondered whether or not she'd said it aloud.

"You'd better quit looking so ready or I'm liable to make love to you right here." Jason's whisper was husky with wicked laughter tickling her ear. "Only a few more minutes, and we should be on our way."

The rest was a blur. She hoped she'd said the appropriate things, thanked everyone enough, but all she knew for certain was that she was in the carriage with Jason and she was very cold. She clamped her teeth tightly against chattering, but she couldn't stop shivering.

"What is it, sweetheart? The night's not as cold as these." His hands cradled hers, then he drew her against him. "Much is changed, yes, but so much is the same, you know that. You have nothing to fear, Sarah mine."

"Just bridal nerves, I expect," she managed shakily, but she knew it was far more than that. There was a part of her which still could not believe that Jason could know about her, know *her,* and still love her. That he had waited until now to become her lover again was suddenly terrifying. What if it was because he too, doubted his love for her? What if their bodies betrayed the lie when they came together and proved all that had been between them before was lost forever?

She hardly noticed the broad smiles and words of goodwill from the hotel staff, and she didn't mark the difference at all between this outpouring and the restrained manner they had shown when she had been here at the Grand Hotel as Jason's mistress. She clung to the Reverend Mapes's words about Jason and to Rio's whispered advice, "Let 'im love ya, dahlin'. He's been missin' ya jus' as much as ya been missin' 'im."

But when Jason swept her into his arms and carried her over the threshold, she focused sharply on the softly lighted elegance of the the suite Jason had taken. There were red roses everywhere, their sweet scent filling the air. She drew a deep breath. "They're lovely!"

And then when he put her down, she saw the bunch of violets by the bed.

"The difference is that I arrive with the flowers. You're not alone anymore, Sarah-Mary."

He stood behind her, his mouth kissing the soft nape of her neck, his hands undoing the buttons of her dress. The soft rose silk floated to the floor, followed by fine undergarments until she stood naked before him, shivering not with cold now but in response to his delicate touch. Ever so carefully he pulled the pins from her hair, letting it fall in soft waves below her shoulders, running his hands through it, glad she had not cut it again.

He turned her around to face him, kissing her eyelids, the curve of her cheek, her mouth, running his hands down her back and between her legs, teasing with the lightness of the contact.

Her hands were suddenly urgent on his clothing, wanting to be closer to his flesh, wanting him. He helped her with the fastenings, and they fell on the bed, leaving their clothes in a heap on the floor.

It was all right. She knew it in the singing of her blood, could feel it in his response, his muscles flexing sinuously under the skin where her mouth and hands touched.

"Oh, you are beautiful," she whispered. She knelt over him smoothing the sleek, hard lines, tracing the sinews of shoulders and rib cage and flat belly while his hands played with her breasts. She pulled gently at the fur on his chest and leaned over to kiss the scar on his thigh, moving her mouth upward over his flesh until he groaned, "You take me, Sarah, you take me!"

It was another gift. She knew it even as she knelt over him and lowered herself onto him, taking his hard manhood deep, moving on him, glorying in the power of pleasing him and herself. A gift he was giving her—the power of beginning as the agressor, of being in control of her body and his, assurance that she would never be a victim again.

"I love you." They breathed the words together and moved in unison at her command until she lay under Jason.

He held himself still for a moment, gazing down at her wide gray eyes and full soft mouth. He kissed her mouth and the pink roses of her breasts, and he began to move in her, still watching until he lost awareness of anything except the driving thrust of his sex and the rippling welcome of hers, and they cried the triumph in one voice, joined as their bodies were.

They slept, woke, loved again, and laughed as they drank champagne that had grown warm and tickled their throats and noses.

Jason had wanted it to be different for her and for himself— a new beginning. But he had not expected, had not even hoped that it would be this different from what had been.

Not only was there no reluctance in her at all, there was new confidence. She had wanted the lamps to remain lit, and she didn't reach for her wrapper now. She sat on the edge of the bed sipping champagne, her flesh glowing from his lovemaking, her hair tousled around her smiling face.

Not even with Gaiety had Jason found such perfect interweaving of body and spirit. And the need to cherish Sarah was even stronger than his hunger for her body. *"Deal gently with her."* The old minister's words sounded in his mind.

He was intrigued and charmed anew by her day by day. The laughing mischief he had glimpsed so briefly in her before surfaced fully in their honeymoon days in San Francisco. He had business to conduct as he always did whenever he was in the city.

He would have neglected it had she asked, but she did not, nor did she accompany him to every meeting. When she did, though she was careful to present a most demure face, he could see how amused she was by the reactions of men who had once met her as Jason's mistress and were now introduced to Mrs. Drake.

She was full of laughter and brightness, and he found himself observing the world around them as closely as she did and joying in being alive. If she worried that another of her father's men might be stalking her even now, she gave no sign of it.

One night they went with Carrie and Owen to a musical review. What had been billed as exotic dancers from a sultan's harem turned out to be two less-than-young women who wiggled out of tempo with a drum and a screeching flute and wore the blankest expressions imaginable. The only things exotic about them were the bells, beads, and the thin fabric of their costumes. The act was so bad, the foursome struggled to contain the sound of their laughter. But when Jason was alone with Sarah in their hotel, he was treated to a whole new version of it.

Instead of putting on the thin gown she was holding, Sarah began to hum a haunting minor-key melody, and emboldened by the happy evening and the wine they'd had at dinner, she danced.

Her body wove sinuous patterns, arms gracefully tracing patterns in the air with the gossamer gown, slim hips undulating to the strange little tune.

Jason watched in fascinated appreciation as he realized she was dancing a story. He could almost see the old sultan sitting there while the woman entertained him and refused his demands at the same time. Her own hand circled in back of her, suddenly clawlike with age and greed, but the dancer moved away still smiling and teasing. And then she was moving more swiftly, whirling and swaying behind the veil that swirled around her, allowing tantalizing glimpses of pink-tipped breasts, smooth belly and thighs, the slender line of her back and round buttocks.

The laughter died in his throat as Jason realized the dance had changed in purpose. The old sultan and the story had vanished.

She was dancing to excite and entice him and him alone, and it was surely working. His blood raced, his skin prickled, and he felt as if she were touching him everywhere though nothing was touching him physically except the stir of air when she danced close.

He reached out and grabbed her, and she was pliant in his arms, her lips half parted, her eyes gleaming as she leaned back in the safety of his embrace, looking up at him.

He kissed her mouth and nuzzled her throat and breasts, but even as he laid her on the bed and continued his play, he wondered if she knew for all its humor how close to the bone her dance to the invisible old man had been.

Her father and what had been between them would always be part of her. Jason knew that. But day by day he would work to make his own presence in her life stronger than the specter of the past.

CHAPTER

28

*I*t was time to sail north again. Sarah was grateful for the self-indulgent days they had had to begin their marriage, but now she could hardly wait to see the islanders again and Jamie most of all.

They were spending the last evening at Owen and Carrie's. Frenchie and Rio would join them later, after Frenchie's performance. Hank had been none too happy about losing the dancer he hadn't wanted to hire in the first place, but Frenchie had pointed out this paradox and ignored his temper.

Carrie and Sarah had decided this would be a special meal, prepared entirely by them. They laughed and chattered happily in the kitchen until Owen asked plaintively if it would be all right if he and Jason went out for a bit. "We seem to be entirely superfluous to this process."

Carrie agreed. "All we need you for is to eat the food when it's fixed, and that won't be for some time yet. But don't be too late and don't get too drunk."

"I? Never!" Owen protested with a grin.

Sarah saw Jason's anxious look and knew he wouldn't go if she didn't want him to. "I think you'd better go with Owen; the two of you can keep track of each other." In fact, she didn't mind at all. The last thing she wanted him to feel was henpecked, and she knew with confidence and satisfaction that he and Owen had no need for women other than their own. They were heading for their old haunts, but not for all the places they had once frequented.

She and Carrie smiled at the unspoken knowledge between them and went on with their dinner preparations.

But as the time passed, the first doubt began to creep in. Sarah was sure Jason would not be deliberately late.

"Well, maybe they just aren't paying attention to the time or maybe Owen met one of his clients," Carrie offered. Her face brightened when they heard someone at the door.

But it was Rio and Frenchie, not the men. Frenchie hesitated in confusion. "This is the right night, isn't it?"

Sarah hugged her. "Sorry, we must be looking terribly unwelcoming. This is the right night indeed, but we're missing two men who said they'd be back in plenty of time."

Neither of the new arrivals chided her for worrying; the fear in her eyes and the incident they had shared in the past forbade easy words.

"Ya all stay here. Ah'll go look fer 'em. Carrie, where's a likely place?" Rio's calm command steadied them all.

"Well, the Bank Exchange saloon is one of Owen's favorites, and Jason's too, I think," she offered.

"Jus' so we ain't all wanderin' 'round all night long, ya tell Owen an' Jason t' stay put if they show up here." With that admonition, Rio was gone.

When they heard noises at the door again a few moments later, Sarah's spirits rose with the assumption that Rio had met the men nearly on the doorstep and all was well. The first part was true; Rio had seen the hansom cab pull up in front of the house before he had gone more than a little way, but all was not well.

"Goddamn it, I can walk! I don't want Sarah scared to death!"

"Well, you will scare her to death if you collapse at her feet," Owen's voice scolded.

"We're jus' holdin' ya up a mite, we ain't carryin' ya."

Sarah gave one short, sharp scream and froze, afraid even to touch Jason. The corner of his mouth bulged, one eye was nearly shut, his face and clothes were covered with blood, and he was swaying between Owen and Rio. Owen didn't look much better, but he was steady on his feet.

"Sarah, it's all right." Jason's attempt to reassure her failed in the wince of pain speaking caused him.

Carrie was nearly as white as Sarah; it was Frenchie who took over with surprising efficiency.

"Set him down in the kitchen," she ordered briskly. "There's water and cloths there and nothing blood can't be scrubbed off."

The others obeyed her, Carrie providing her with the things she asked for.

Jason sat down with relief and bore her ministrations patiently. His nose and the corner of his battered mouth had stopped bleeding, but the source of most of the gore was a still-dripping gash near the hairline on his left temple. Frenchie washed it thoroughly and dabbed at it with strong whiskey, causing Jason to screw up his face while his eyes watered.

"Needs stitches, just a few. I can do it, but I won't take offense if you want a real doctor," Frenchie announced. Her competence had expanded to include Carrie, who was bathing Owen's face and skinned knuckles and looking relieved to find no major injuries. But Sarah felt helpless, useless, and terrified. It did not comfort her that the head injury, according to Frenchie, looked more serious than it was—the intent had been to bash in Jason's head. A little more force, a little better aim in the blow, and she would now be a widow.

"Go ahead and stitch it." He just wanted it over. His head hurt the most, but he ached everywhere, and the world was still spinning in unpleasant patterns before his eyes. He could hardly see out of one of them at all. He squinted his good eye and focused on Sarah. For a moment she looked like a frightened child—no, not only frightened, canny too, a child looking down on him from somewhere. The strange image faded as he concentrated harder on seeing her clearly and saw the reality of her white face and wide staring eyes. He made the effort to put his hand out, but her name was the only word he managed before he gasped and clamped his jaw tightly as Frenchie pierced his skin with the needle and took the first careful stitch, tying it off as she would each one.

Jason was holding very still. Sarah shuddered, feeling as if the needle were digging into her. Suddenly she dropped to her knees, cradling Jason's hand in both of hers, bending her head over it, kissing the scraped skin gently. Jason felt her warm tears and her cold flesh, and he stroked her head with his free hand, finally managing to whisper, "Sweetheart, it really is all right, and Owen and I won."

She felt a flash of rage at the pride in his voice, but it died quickly as she heard Owen explaining to Carrie. "Darlin', I swear we didn't start it! Damnedest thing. We were leaving the Bank Exchange, wanting to get back here in good time, and one of my clients stopped me. Jason went on, and by the time I caught up with him, he'd been jumped by four men, so I joined in to even up the odds a little. We were lucky; two on their side were sort of puny. A couple of them had guns, but I guess they didn't want to attract attention at first, and they thought they'd picked an easy target but got the Tiger instead. By the time the fight was really on, nobody could've gotten a clear shot, but one of them split Jason's skull with the butt of his pistol. Would've gone after them when they started to run off, but Jason keeled over. Took a while to, er, wake him up and longer to find something besides our own feet to bring us home." Owen hadn't wanted to say that it had taken him a while to be sure Jason wasn't dead, but Sarah heard the unspoken words.

Finished with her stitching and bandaging, Frenchie demanded that Jason stand up, and when he obeyed a trifle unsteadily, she ran her hands over him without embarrassment, asking if this, that hurt. He assured her that everything was in working order and thanked her.

"Good then, I'll wash your beautiful face and those elegant hands, and you'll be almost good as new even if you don't look it." She shook her head. "Lordy, the two of you look some used up."

But when she reached for the cloth to sponge Jason's face, Sarah took it from her. "Frenchie, thank you, I haven't been any use at all, but I can do this." Her hands were steady and tender as she cleaned away the dried blood, but her voice trembled.

Frenchie patted her shoulder and then looked around. "Now where's Rio gone to? Don't think he's the kind to faint at the sight of a little blood."

None of them had noticed when he left, but he reappeared as if conjured by Frenchie's words. He was grinning triumphantly and carrying a stained, paper-wrapped package. "Took me some time t' find a place that'd sell me these this time a' night. Where Ah come from, we use 'em fer all sorts a' things 'sides eatin', includin' shinas." He presented each of the men with a raw beefsteak.

The picture of Rio going from restaurant to restaurant demanding in his Texas drawl to buy raw meat was too much for Frenchie. "My God, by morning it will be all over that among your other talents you're a cannibal!"

"Didn' think it were none a' their business why Ah wanted 'em," Rio replied, feigning hurt, and then they were all laughing, easing the tension.

Under cover of the noise, Jason murmured very low to Sarah, "It had nothing to do with your father. As Owen said, they were just robbers looking for easy prey."

She wanted to scream at him that he couldn't know that for sure, that he didn't know her father at all, that her father was the sort of man who would enjoy having her husband beaten to death. But she controlled the urge and kept her voice as low as his. "I'm so glad we're going home tomorrow."

Trying to act as if nothing had happened, they finally settled down to eat the food Sarah had so carefully planned, but as far as she was concerned, it was a disaster. She hadn't any interest in eating, and Jason's sore mouth prevented him from tasting anything except the soup. He would have left that untouched as well had not Frenchie ordered him sternly to eat it. "I won't have my patient starving to death after I've done all that neat work."

The others praised Sarah's cooking extravagantly, but she hardly heard them. The minutes until they would be safely aboard the *Gaiety* were ticking away in her head.

Carrie suggested that the Drakes spend the night at the house, but she understood their refusal; she could feel Sarah's need to be alone with Jason in the anonymity of the hotel.

Rio went out again to find a cab. Jason's protest that he could walk to the hotel lacked conviction even in his own ears.

They departed amid promises from the others that they'd be there to see the sailing, and Frenchie drew Sarah aside for a moment. "I'm really quite sure he's all right, love, but he was knocked out, and there're a few things you should watch out for. If he hears buzzing or can't see clearly, you'd better get a real doctor. And it's all right for him to sleep, but it'd be better if you wake him up every couple of hours, bother though it is, just to make sure it's a natural sleep. If all is still well by tomorrow, then you needn't worry."

Frenchie had feared that Sarah would panic at her words, but her reaction was quite the contrary; she was glad to have something specific to do. "How did you ever learn so much?" she asked.

Frenchie shrugged. "I've been a lot of places where doctors aren't easily found. You learn because you have to."

"I'm so glad you did," Sarah said.

It was very late by the time they arrived back at the Grand, but there were night clerks on duty who tried to pretend that they saw nothing odd in Mr. Drake's appearance. The failure of the pretense produced such silly, bug-eyed expressions, Sarah had to muffle her laughter in a cough, and Jason gave thanks inwardly for the first color he had seen in her cheeks in hours. But once they were in their suite, the sight of the bed pulled him so irresistibly, he wanted nothing more than to fall down on it fully clothed.

Sarah would have none of it. She sat him down in a chair and pulled off his shoes, and when his fingers fumbled with his clothing, she pushed his hands away and undid everything with quick dispatch.

He sighed in pleasure and closed his eyes when he finally sank down on the bed.

She covered him warmly and kissed his brow beneath the bandage. She rubbed her hands together until they were warm, slipped them under the covers, and began to knead the knotted muscles of his leg. There was so little she could do for him—he was covered with darkening bruises from head to toe—but she knew too well that with any extra strain and certainly in a brawl, the muscles in his bad leg would rebel. The proof was in the tight cords under her hands.

"Ummm, feels good," Jason mumbled, and his breathing became deep and even as he fell asleep.

She moved quietly, packing the last of their belongings, wondering anew at the way Jason spoiled her. He had brought the best of her clothes south with him and yet had still insisted on adding to her wardrobe. Madame Antoine had beamed endlessly once she had learned that Jason had taken her advice to keep this woman further even than she had thought he would. Sarah stored the little wooden tiger among her clothes.

She was afraid to go to sleep, afraid Jason would sleep too long, too dangerously if she did. She listened to his breathing constantly, freezing in terror when the slightest break sounded as he moved and dreamed.

"Jason, wake up, wake up, darling. Do you know who I am?"

He blinked at her out of his good eye. "You're Sarah-Mary Drake, my wife, and you must be crazy unless it's time to get up."

His voice was blurred with sleep, but he was perfectly aware of reality, and she was filled with relief. "It's not. Go back to sleep."

"What the hell are you doing?" he demanded the next time she awakened him, and she confessed Frenchie's instructions.

His swollen mouth smiled even more crookedly than usual. "Aside from one hell of a headache, I assure you my brains are intact, such as they are. Poor love, you haven't slept at all. Come to bed now."

"I'll sleep on the *Gaiety*. It is less than two hours before we should both be up anyway."

He hadn't the strength to argue with her stubbornness, and he was too sleepy to try. It seemed only minutes later she was telling him it was time to get up.

He groaned with the effort of moving and found himself being efficiently managed by his wide-awake wife. He sank into the hot bath and would have fallen asleep again had not Sarah chided him even as she pampered his bruises, drawing the cloth gently over his skin. "I've left out warm clothes for you; the air is chill and will be more so on the *Gaiety* when we board."

"Yes, ma'am," he said meekly. "However, I want you to know that were the stiffness I feel in the right place, we'd miss the tide. We are newly married, after all."

"I expect it to be in the right place before we're too many days out," she replied pertly, dropping a glancing kiss on the uninjured side of his mouth.

He could feel the joy coursing through her as escape drew nearer. She was pale, and her eyes were ringed by shadows, but they were shining with anticipation. He let it be; now was not the time to try to convince her that her father had had nothing to do with what had happened.

Their friends were there as promised to see them off. Owen and Jason burst out laughing at the sight of each other, both wearing multicolored shiners, and their mirth made the moment easier. The only strong undercurrent of sorrow was in parting with Rio; his precarious profession diminished the certainty of seeing him again.

"You'll let me know how things go?" Sarah whispered low to Frenchie. "We do get mail on Drake's Island though it takes a while. And I know Angie would like to hear from you too."

Frenchie nodded, her smile didn't falter, but Sarah saw the well of sadness in her eyes.

She hugged Rio tightly. "There'll never be any way I can thank you for all you've done for me. Take care of yourself." The words quavered, but Rio's answer was easy.

"Why, Ah'd call us even. Jus' like Ah tol' ya before, if Ah hadn' met ya, Ah wouldn' have mah Frenchie now."

Jason had last private words with Owen and Rio, and then quite suddenly there was no more time. The *Gaiety*'s departure was hastened by two little tugs which helped her out until she gained the power of the wind and tide on her own.

Sarah watched the figures of their friends grow smaller and disappear. All at once, the tension and sleeplessness of the past night's vigil swept over her, and she swayed.

"It's a soft bunk for you," Jason said. He put his arms around her, supporting her for a moment before he led her below.

"Are you seasick?" he asked solicitously.

"No, just so sleepy." She mumbled the words and proved the truth of them by falling asleep before he had finished undressing her.

She slept the clock around, stirring only briefly to curl against him when he joined her for the night.

The days aboard the *Gaiety* were a healing time for both of them. The crew respectfully refused to allow Jason to do his usual share of the work until his bruises began to fade, and Jason agreed because his present clumsiness could well be more hindrance than help. However, he insisted on their second night aboard that making love was not work.

Sarah stopped brushing her hair and stared down doubtfully at his body stretched out on the bunk. "You look like a field of violets, and you move like something that rusted in the rain. Don't you think you ought to wait a few days?"

Jason shook his head. His eyes were golden with mischief. "Not if you do all the work. I'll cry 'enough' if it is too much. I'll remind you again in case you've forgotten—we're newly married. That does a lot for a man."

The comparison was never far from her mind no matter how little she wanted to think of it. Her father had kept her in thrall with threats, pain, isolation. Jason, on the other hand, had more of her in his keeping than her father had ever had and kept her close simply with love. She was bound and fettered more tightly than she had ever been, and she felt more freedom than she had ever known before. Even now, though good sense warned against it, Jason was capable of compelling her with nothing more than his eyes and teasing voice, his desire becoming her own, warming her blood. She slipped out of her robe and knelt beside him.

For a long moment she didn't touch him at all though he felt the love in her eyes as if she were etching patterns on his heart, and then she bent down and began to trace even the lightest bruises with her mouth: a stain of darkness on one shoulder spread down to his rib cage, a curve of shadow on his hipbone, a streak of lavender on one shin, a swollen knee, the scar, and finally the shadows marking his thighs and groin.

Despite his laughing enticement, Jason hadn't been any more

sure than Sarah that this was a good idea. He wanted her, but
he wasn't sure his body would cooperate with his desire; it made
him more aware than he had ever been of how much more the
urge to love was seated in the brain than in the flesh. The
beating he'd received before Owen had jumped in to help had
been thorough, worse than any he'd suffered before. He still felt
a continuous ache subject to sharper stabs at the slightest suggestion of quick or unwise movement, and at the moment he felt
the results of a kick that had landed between his legs more
acutely than he felt the gash in his head. But he had no wish to
cry "enough." Sarah was arousing sensations far stronger than
the pain. Though the air was cool in the cabin, he felt a luxurious, spreading heat as if his blood were warming near the surface wherever she touched him, and as he watched her, he felt
the fitness of being called the Tiger as he never had before,
simply because now she was the Tigress. Her touch was delicate
as she bent over him, but her body was taut with concentration,
her eyes wild with the intensity of her loving ministrations.

He felt her mouth drifting over his skin, her tongue laving his
bruises, and he knew how primitive it was—the tigress over her
mate, healing, defending—and he gloried in her fierce power.

He shifted her so that he could tease her with his own mouth,
nibbling gently, thrusting with his tongue until they were both
shuddering with the rising force, and Sarah moved to take him
into herself.

She was the first to rouse herself from the floating lethargy of
the aftermath, propping herself on one elbow so that she could
see Jason's face, bruises and all. "I don't think you should have
done that, but I'm glad you did."

He heard the purr of laughing pleasure in her throat, and he
answered without opening his eyes. "It's a new cure for everything, highly recommended. If we could just bottle it, we could
make a fortune. The label would read, 'make love like a tiger.' "

"As your son would say, you're funny," she giggled, settling
down beside him again, prepared to sleep.

"It wasn't your father's doing. It was too random for that and
too obvious. A lame man looks like easy pickings."

It took her a moment to comprehend what he was saying in

the sudden shift from play to deadly seriousness. When she did understand, rage flashed through her for the broken mood. She started to move away from him, but his arm shot out and stayed her, lightning quick and hard, a bar pinning her down until it was he who now knelt above her, staring down at her.

"He's lost you, Sarah-Mary. I have you. But such fear of him takes from what is mine. He is not God. But you give him power he does not deserve, power over you and over me, when you fear him so. You unman me. And you forget that he abused a child; the woman escaped him."

She turned her head from side to side, tears flowing unchecked. "He's coming after me; I know he is! He'll never give up, never! You don't know him. God help me, I do! And killing you would punish me forever! It is so like him. He would have you beaten to death far sooner than he would have you killed quickly and cleanly."

Her hysterical fear tore at Jason's heart. He drew her up against him, cradling her head against his shoulder, rubbing her back in slow circles. "There, love, there, hush now." He kept murmuring softly to her until she was quiet against him. He willed himself to patience; the day would come when she would be free of the corroding fear. He would do everything in his power to make it so. He was at war with a man he had never seen; the prize was this woman. He had every intention of winning.

The days of intimacy aboard the *Gaiety* were much to his liking. His bruises faded, and it was Sarah who took out his stitches, succumbing to his plaintive insistence that she'd be more careful than one of the crew who never put stitches in or took them out of anything more sensitive than sails. She got the stitches out without undue strain on herself or Jason, and she was immensely pleased with herself, suddenly seeing the possibility of learning the skills of healing as well as Frenchie had.

Jason was even more pleased than she, though he kept the observation to himself. In fact, he could have taken the stitches out himself. He had reasoned it out very carefully, trying to decide which of all that made a child into an adult was most important. He had thought of himself and Jamie, and at first he

remembered such a confusion of events that had impressed him
as a child, there seemed to be no sense in the quest. But when
he finally found what he was looking for, he marveled at its
simplicity. It wasn't the passage of years or the growing knowledge of pain and sorrow, it was growing competence, the ability
to learn and to use the knowledge.

The truth of it spun in an endless profusion of images. The
image of himself each time he had mastered a new skill, and
most of all when he had learned he and his mother would not
starve though his father was dead, had learned that he was able
to fend well for both of them. The images of Jamie learning
independence by learning himself—even the woodcarving set
was a symbol of it, sharp, dangerous blades he was trusted to use
correctly. And the images of Sarah, then Mary, were images
sharper than the blades of Jamie's knives—Sarah hungrily learning everything the islanders had to teach her, learning more
strength than she realized, enough to leave the only safety she
had ever had, enough to leave for the sake of love. It followed
then that the more confidence and self-reliance she gained, the
further she would travel from being a child, from belonging to
her father. Ruefully, he acknowledged his own arrogance; he
could see nothing but good for himself in Sarah's independence
—the more she belonged to herself, the more she would have
to give and take from him.

He taught her more about navigation and sailing, more about
reading the heavens and the sea. He discussed business with her
and listened to her comments. He treated her as an equal partner, which was exactly what he wanted her to be and knew she
was capable of being.

He told her that at last the question of ownership of the
islands was being settled. "The British have been meeting with
our officials in Washington since January. The agreement
they're trying to reach concerns a lot more than the islands, the
whole of Anglo-American relations in fact, including fishing
rights in the waters of the Northeast and the *Alabama* claims."

"Alabama?" Sarah asked in puzzlement. "What could the
British have to do with that state?"

"Not the state in this case, but a ship, one of the privateers built in England for the Confederacy. The *Alabama* was very successful in her raids on Union shipping, so her name was used in the claims made that the British, however indirectly, prolonged the war. The claims are rather grandiose; according to the expansionists, Canada could be given to the United States in payment." He laughed and nodded in agreement with the look on Sarah's face. "Exactly, a preposterous idea. But apart from that, and it is apart because it has to do with clarifying the meaning of the 1846 treaty and not with the war, the San Juan Islands, particularly San Juan Island itself, remain a key factor, and tempers have been high over it. Each side has accused the other of deliberately misreading the old treaty. The question of which strait was meant remains at issue. We've resisted putting the matter before a foreign arbiter mostly because the British have insisted that three choices be given: Rosario Strait, the British claim, Haro Strait, the American claim, or San Juan Channel, as a compromise. And there's the rub because the compromise choice might seem the best to the arbiter but not to us; it would give more of the smaller islands to the United States, but San Juan Island would go to the British. Finally though, there seems to be a change of position on both sides. The United States is agreeing to arbitration as long as only Haro Strait and Rosario are considered, and the British are agreeing to that for the sake of the arbitration itself, which seems the only way to settle the unease and conflicting claims between the two nations. At least, it's already been agreed that whoever gets San Juan Island will not fortify it. One way or another, the garrisons will be leaving."

Sarah regarded him in wonder. "How do you know all this? Sounds as if you've been in Washington."

"I have my sources," Jason said, pretending great mystery then spoiling it with a smile. "Thank heavens for the telegraph and Owen; he's been keeping close track for me. A man of many connections is Owen."

"You seem remarkably happy about the whole thing considering that some foreign power is going to decide the fate of the islands."

"My love, your good old Yankee mistrust is showing. The

arbiter is going to be the emperor of Germany, and of course, he won't make the decision personally, he'll choose judges for the case and among those judges there are bound to be friends of our minister to Germany, George Bancroft. He'll argue our case, and he happens to be on very good terms with Bismarck, the German chancellor, and others. There is some feeling in Germany that the United States is a good balance against the power of Great Britain. I think, in fact, that the British have been had. It's our good fortune that they haven't seen it that way, at least not yet, and once the treaty has been agreed to and signed, the arbitration is binding, and there's no honorable way out."

"It doesn't seem like a very honorable way in," Sarah pointed out.

"Perhaps not, but it is surely better than war."

She had to concede the point, but then she thought of the future ramifications. "What about the British families who must be living on the islands? What will happen to them?"

"Hopefully our government will deal justly with them. It's not as if the islands are overrun with settlers of any nationality. There's room for everyone who can bear the isolation—that's a rare breed." He hugged her for being part of it.

CHAPTER
29

*I*t was a clear afternoon in early June when the *Gaiety* approached Drake's Island.

They've been watching for us," Jason said, handing his spyglass to Sarah. "The flag's up."

She could see it and the tiny figures gathering. She was suddenly nearly as nervous as when she had first come here. "Di-did you send word?"

"And spoil the surprise? Not on your life! And in any case, I'm the only one who doubted I would find you; the rest of them were sure. There would have been no mercy had I come back without you."

The truth of his words was proven in the wave of love that engulfed her the minute they were ashore. The children shouted her name; "Is good, so good you are home!" Ingrid declared, tears streaming down as she let Else have room to hug Sarah; "Welcome home," Constance and Hayes said in unison; Nate and Jon simply smiled and nodded, both weathered faces red with emotion; and Maggie enfolded Sarah in her arms as if she were one of the twins while Ben signed shyly that they had missed her so much.

"Cease and desist," Jason bellowed, but he was laughing. "I would like to present my wife, Sarah-Mary Drake."

There was silence and then the excited babble rose louder than before. "Sarah? A pretty name. Sarah-Mary." "Congratulations!" "Is good, very good!" On and on, but Sarah was looking at Jamie.

He was hanging back on the edge of the children, and for a horrible moment, she was afraid he was not glad after all that she was back and married to his father besides. But then she saw his hesitation as if it were her own. He was at once shy and eager, overwhelmed by his emotions, paralyzed by them now that what he had wanted so desperately had come to pass.

She knelt down and opened her arms, smiling at him even while tears pricked her eyelids. He moved then, throwing himself into her arms with such force, she had to brace herself to keep both of them from toppling over.

"Love you, love you so much, missed you so much, don't go away ever again, Papa was so sad, I was so sad." "I won't, I promise, promise." "Is your name really Sarah?" "Is it really all right that I married your father?" "Would you mind bein' my mama now if I'm not too big to have one?" "You're not, I'd love to, I love you." Their words tumbled over each other in a litany of love.

"Don't I deserve a greeting? After all, I found her and brought her back."

"Oh, you did good, Papa!" Jamie acknowledged, and it caught at Sarah's heart to see how alike they looked as they smiled at each other. Jamie scrambled up, and Jason lifted him in the air for a moment. "Won't be able to do that pretty soon, young man. You're growing awfully fast."

Jamie glowed with the pleasure of his father's attention, and Sarah thought of how far he'd come from the sullen, pasty-faced child of a year ago. The beauty of the bones he'd inherited from both father and mother showed so much more clearly now. He was, indeed, a handsome child.

The one face missing was Cade's, but she knew he would learn of the *Gaiety*'s arrival and come in his own good time. She didn't even want to consider that he might already know and had stayed away. She both longed and feared to see him, wondering if he had forgiven her for her flight, and more, for the way she had used his love for her to force him to help her.

But her only care now was that she was home. Home with her husband and stepson. Home with the islanders who loved her and whom she loved. Home on this beautiful stretch of earth set in the sea. It was hard to believe how much her life had changed, beginning with the night Jason had seen her in the saloon, hard to believe this was really her life now. But the physical reality of Jason, of sharing day and night with him, kept the truth within reach.

She had turned twenty on the voyage home. Jason watched her as her birthday gift was presented—a four-year-old mare out of Dolly and Gabriel. She favored her sire in the darkness of her coat and in her clean, chiseled lines. But she had the look of her dam in the white patch on her forehead and in the large, dark eyes which regarded Sarah with gentle inquisitiveness.

"Dolly's last foal, a good finish I'd say." Jason offered her the reins. "Happy birthday."

Sarah had seen the animal before; it was one of those patiently cared for and trained mostly by Nate and Jon. Jason too had had a hand in the training. As beautifully and as fully schooled as the mare was, she would bring a good price sold off-island.

"Jason, I can't! She's much too valuable, and besides, Dolly's fine for me."

He shook his head. "Dolly's been given to another beginner, a certain young man named Jamie. And I've graduated you to a better mount, so just say 'thank you' like an obedient wife."

"Thank you," she said meekly. She hadn't any defense against his generosity when he not so subtly reminded her that she was his wife and it pleased him to please her. She laughed suddenly. "Now I know why Gabriel and Dolly have so much to discuss; they're talking about their children."

"More likely about how their offspring were begotten," Jason corrected with a leer, joining in her fantasy. She was his fountain of youth, making him feel more carefree and younger by the day.

They rode out together, with Jamie on Dolly. Jamie was proud to show Mary how much he'd learned about riding since she'd been gone, and she was lavish in her praise. He handled the old

mare gently and without fear. Jason had explained to her that
they had discovered that the hay in the barn was more likely to
make Jamie wheeze than the horse itself. He was not allowed to
curry Dolly, as that raised enough dust and hair to make anyone
choke a bit, and he rode with a saddle, never bareback, to keep
his clothing free of mats of horsehair. But once Jason or Ben had
saddled the horse and led her out into the open air, the restrictions ceased to be any bother.

Sarah wondered if the long-ago scene in the barn still haunted
Jamie, then dismissed the thought. Jamie had nothing but approval now for the love between herself and his father even if
the physical side was something he would not fully understand
until he was older.

Gabriel was beside himself not only to have his rider on his
back again, but to be in the company of two mares. Jason's eyes
sparkled with enjoyment as he firmly reminded the stallion that
man was master to the beast, but he was careful to keep him a
good distance from the mares until the antics of kicking and
bucking were over.

Sarah was delighted and relieved to discover her mare had not
inherited her sire's temper. She was young, quick-stepping, and
inclined to shy a little when her alert senses picked up something
new, but she was without malice and responded well to Sarah's
commands.

"What a lovely beast you are," Sarah cooed, patting the glossy
neck. "Jamie, I just thought, I don't even know her name!"

Jamie giggled. "I think you'd better make up a new one. Nate
an' Jon, they aren't very good at names. They called her 'Gabby'
'cuz of her father and mother bein' Gabriel an' Dolly."

"Dear me! That is an awful name for such a pretty mare. Let
me think. Ah-mmmmm, what about 'Sheba'?"

"It's a pretty word, pretty as the horse, but what does it
mean?"

"Have you ever heard of King Solomon?"

He wrinkled his brow, and then beamed in triumph. "I did!
Mr. Burke told us about him an' we read something too. He was
a very wise man, but not one of those three that went to Bethle-
hem when Jesus was born. The king, he lived a long, long time

before that an' he was famous for makin' those ladies behave when they were fightin' over a little baby."

"You're absolutely right." Sarah ignored the snort which came from the rider, not the horse, as Gabriel drew near. She didn't dare look at Jason, fearing his struggle with laughter would become her own if their eyes met. "Well, you see, Sheba was an Arabian country, and the Queen of Sheba heard stories about how wise this King Solomon was, but she found the stories hard to believe, so she went to find out for herself. And when she found out that it was true, that he was very wise indeed, she praised him and his God, and she gave him many gifts of gold, spices, and jewels, and he gave her presents too before she went back to her own country."

"It would be nice to be a king, better than being a president, I think. 'Course, I 'spect kings got to do a lot of work even if they do get lots of presents," Jamie observed thoughtfully. "Anyway, I've decided Sheba is a good name for your horse."

This time Sarah and Jason's eyes did meet, the laughter replaced by tenderness in the shared memory of what Jamie had decided in his journal and how much it had meant to them. Sarah carried a delicately embroidered handkerchief in her pocket for good luck; it was the gift Jamie had brought back for her from Seattle and had had to wait so long to give to her. "I picked it, but Papa paid for it," he had told her honestly.

Their destination was Cade's Cove, and her heart gave a start of both joy and trepidation when she saw his beached boat and Captain's massive form bouncing toward them as he barked. Cade emerged from his cabin, and Sarah slipped from the mare's back and ran toward him. When Jamie would have followed, Jason stayed him.

"They haven't seen each other for a long while. Perhaps it would be better if we gave them a few minutes alone."

Jamie agreed, feeling very grown-up to be part of a "we" which included his father.

Cade looked blessedly the same, but Sarah couldn't read his expression as she approached him. He stood still, watching her in much the same way he had on their first meeting.

Captain however, had no reservations. He recognized a long-missing friend and yipped, cried, and groveled in hysterical welcome.

It was too much even for Cade; his mouth tugged into a reluctant smile. "Captain's got no dignity, none at all."

The dog looked at him guiltily even as he tried to lick Sarah's hand as she petted him.

"I'm still angry, don't think I'm not," Cade declared. "I've done nothing but worry since I helped you leave. And it makes me even angrier that you were right, that leaving was the only way to come home. I assume you and the Tiger are on more than speaking terms."

She followed his glance to her wedding ring and finally realized what he was saying. "You must be Cade," she said, echoing their first encounter. "And I am Sarah-Mary Drake."

He smiled then, the smile distorting his heavily boned face. "Sarah. It fits. Sarah for sunlight and sorrow too. Sarah for all the things that are part of being alive. Sarah, Tiger's woman, welcome home."

She felt as blessed as she had when Reverend Mapes had given her his final advice. "Oh, Cade, I do love him so much!" she whispered as he drew her close. "Just keep on that way," he murmured gruffly, and then he was hailing Jason and Jamie.

"Kind of you to ride out this way, saved me a walk, I just got back this morning."

Sarah's heart sang at this added confirmation—Cade had not stayed away; he had not been on the island at all when the *Gaiety* arrived.

Cade and Jason greeted each other and then exchanged a long look, saying everything without words, both of them smiling. Then Cade turned his attention to Jamie. "I see Gabby is a new member of the family."

Whatever strange currents were passing among the adults were no longer any concern of Jamie's; he was too busy accepting Captain's reaffirmations of undying devotion and explaining why Gabby was now Sheba to think of anything else.

That day of contentment set the pattern for the summer, and it was a season that showed Sarah how profoundly her life had changed with her marriage vows. At first when Jason began to take her to more places, she felt some resentment, wondering if he had judged her unfit to meet some people when she had been his mistress rather than his wife, but the feeling was quickly banished by the truth. It had been solely to protect her from the inevitable slurs, slurs which were no longer forthcoming now that she was Mrs. Drake. She thought the change in attitude shallow and intolerant, but she knew it was the way with too many people.

She paid her first visit to San Juan Island on the Fourth of July. Besides Jamie, they had the twins and the seven-year-olds, Katla Olsen and Alf Nilsen in tow, and were glad that Constance had come along to help keep track of the children. Else and Ingrid stayed at home with the younger children; Maggie and Ben made excuses about chores to be done but were really just too shy to subject themselves to the inevitable staring; Cade, Hayes, Nate, and Jon simply had no interest in such an outing.

"They're going to think they've been invaded by midgets," Jason observed with a grin as he watched the children scrambling over the deck of the *Gaiety*. They were thankful that their luck held and none of the children were seasick.

"They have no idea how fortunate they are!" Sarah said fervently, remembering all too clearly her bouts with that particular malaise.

It was a noisy, exhausting, and delightful day. San Juan Island itself boasted a hundred families, its own school and preacher, and people from other islands had come to San Juan Town to share the day as had those aboard the *Gaiety*. There was an extra edge to the patriotic display this year with settlement of the dispute so near, but there was no violence over it: The British who were observing and even joining in the celebration seemed to take it in good part. The American soldiers did their best to add a touch of dignity, such as it was, to the day, but most of the festivities were simply in honor of having a good time. There were mountains of food, and there was a tug of war, a three-legged race, and many other games that kept the children going all day. Sarah watched Jamie carefully for signs of exhaustion, but he came to no harm and kept bringing newly met children to greet his stepmother, "Only," he explained earnestly to each of them, "I don't call her stepmother; I call her Mama or Sarah."

In fact, all the children from Drake's Island were enjoying this contact with strangers, even Eric and Erin, despite having to put up with some "silly questions about being twins."

Jason introduced Sarah proudly to everyone he knew, and the only comments she overheard were flattering indeed and to the effect that the Tiger's luck had outdone itself this time.

When evening fell, they were allowed to watch the fireworks, and then the tired children were taken back aboard the ship. There were no protests. They all, even Jamie who had done it before, thought it a great adventure to be spending the night aboard the *Gaiety*, especially since they'd been promised that if the night stayed fair enough, they could sleep out on the deck, wrapped in blankets.

Lars and Mogens cheerfully volunteered to stay aboard with the children. "Ingrid, she hear I go dancing vidout her, I vill be in such trouble!" Lars declared, and Mogens agreed that Else's reaction would be the same. But Captain Hanson stayed ashore to swap yarns with other seamen until the early hours, and Jason and Sarah stayed to listen to the lively music of fiddles.

Jason's leg prevented him from dancing, but when Sarah would have sat out with him, he chided her, "Don't be foolish. I like to watch you dance." The gleam in his eyes reminded her of the dance she had performed for him in San Francisco, and she blushed. And the color rose again in her cheeks more than once at the extravagant compliments her partners paid her; yet no man was anything less than proper with her, not even the ones who had had more than a little to drink during the long day. They were all too aware that the Tiger was present and watching.

David Becam and Constance had come to the dance too, and Sarah caught a look that passed between them and nearly lost her footing as she and her partner whirled past the other couple.

"Sorry, ma'am, guess I'm sorta clumsy," the soldier she was dancing with apologized.

"Not a bit of it," she assured him, "my fault. I'm getting just a little weary. I think I'll sit the next one out with my husband." She gave him a smile, not wanting him to think she was bored with his company.

Jason looked at her curiously as she came to him. "What bee's gotten into the bonnet you're not wearing?" He frowned suddenly. "Did someone say something improper to you?"

"My heavens, no! I've never been so properly treated in my life. They're all scared to death of you. But oh, my, I think I've been very stupid! Constance and David, I just saw them, and they were looking at each other, well, like . . ."

"Like you and I look at each other," Jason supplied helpfully, and then he nodded. "Everyone is being very careful not to notice it. David is shy, and Constance has been through so much, but I think they suit, and I hope it works for both of them. Awful, isn't it, how when one is in love, one wants everyone else to be too?"

"Not awful at all." She squeezed his hand, resisting the impulse to kiss him right here in public, and she kept thinking about Constance and David. David was so retiring, it was possible to forget he was there at all, but not when he had the look in his eyes that he'd given Constance. Sarah suddenly saw him more clearly than she ever had before. He was of medium height and compact build with brownish hair, regular features, and blue eyes. Very blue eyes, Sarah thought with an inward smile, at least when he's looking at Constance, and she hoped fiercely that their happiness would continue to grow.

But her own contentment turned to cold dread when she saw Zeke from Captain Gibson's crew. She recognized him instantly; she would never forget Constance's unearthly screaming nor the day that had brought death to the island. The *Folly* had stopped at Drake's Island since, but Zeke, though he had survived the fever, had never been ashore there again.

Sarah realized that though they had seen the captain early in the day, Zeke must have deliberately kept out of their way. And surely he was only here now because he had assumed they were all back aboard the *Gaiety.*

She felt achingly sorry for him. His big shoulders were slumped, his face above his heavy beard a mask of misery. He knew Constance had seen him, and he was waiting for her wrath to fall on him again.

Constance exchanged a quiet word with David, who remained where he was while she walked steadily toward Zeke until she was standing in front of him.

"It was not your fault. It simply happened. I am glad you lived through it. The children have missed you. When the *Folly* comes to the island again, you must come ashore to see them."

Zeke looked as if he were going to weep. Then, very carefully, he took her small hand in his large one and raised it to his lips.

The music which had faltered at the sense of impending drama, resumed and then changed again to a lively jig. Captain Gibson, who had requested the tune, wore a wide smile. Zeke returned it and began to dance, executing the quick steps with skill and grace despite his huge size. People backed away to give him room and began to clap to the beat. Constance, now back with David and knowing the dance was for her, clapped with the rest and smiled in real pleasure at the gift.

"What an absolutely perfect day it's been," Sarah murmured contentedly when she and Jason were finally in their cabin on the *Gaiety* after having circumvented the blanket bundles of the children sleeping under the stars. "But, oh, dear! Where will Constance sleep?" she asked, suddenly worried at the neglect of arrangements.

Jason laughed softly. "With David, as you are with me, I hope, though I think it's a little soon for that. I expect they'll spend the night like the children, on deck, but not sleeping much. Why else do you suppose I refused the gentlemanly part and did not offer this, the best cabin, to you and Constance? And why do you suppose the rest of the crew didn't offer their quarters either?"

"The Tiger, a matchmaker!" She muffled her laughter against his shoulder, then whispered, "We must be very, very quiet."

The next morning while she and Constance helped David prepare breakfast for all aboard, Sarah was still heavy-eyed and feeling lethargic from the exciting day and the love that had followed it. She was inclined to turn rosy every time she looked at her husband, a fact he had noticed with his crooked grin and with a satisfied gleam in his eyes, and indeed, she was seeing everything through a rosy glass. Jason's prophecy had proved correct—Constance and David had been discovered on deck sound asleep, wrapped in a blanket, one head resting against the other, David's arm around Constance. They had slept through the early stirrings of the children and the crew because they had not fallen asleep until the dawn was nearly broken; they had then

slept blissfully on until everyone else was up and about, and
then they had awakened in some confusion and embarrassment.
But no one, not even the children, made anything of it, and the
unease vanished.

Sarah was helping to serve the children their breakfasts, carrying the food carefully because the ship was under way.

"I guess they are dummies," she heard Eric say to Erin.

"Well, I guess so too. They can't hear and they don't talk
either."

All her soft feelings fled as Sarah understood what the twins
were saying. Rage shot through her. She nearly dumped the
plates she was carrying and had to take a few deep breaths
before she even trusted herself to approach the children.

"Where did you hear that word?" She asked the question as
calmly as she could, but there was enough tension in her voice
that the twins looked up at her with puzzled alarm.

"You mean 'dummies'? From Jamie, yesterday," Eric announced.

It was getting worse by the minute. She called Jamie over. He
looked as wary as the twins at the expression in her eyes.

"Jamie, where did you learn the word 'dummies'?"

He thought for a moment, sorting through the jumble of
yesterday's many impressions. "Oh, I remember! I was tellin'
these other kids 'bout all th' people on our island, an' I told 'em
'bout Maggie an' Ben, how they can talk with their hands instead
of their mouths, an' they said that meant they were dummies,
that that was the word for 'em."

She let her breath go in a sigh of relief; the malice lay elsewhere, not in these children. "It is not the word for Maggie or
Ben or anyone else. It is a very cruel word. It's a word that means
that because someone can't hear or speak, they're stupid and
can't think. Do you think that's true about Maggie and Ben?"

Their faces were three mirrors of outrage.

"That's a lie, a dirty lie!" Eric growled furiously. "Mama and
Papa think like everybody else."

"They're smarter than lots of people," Erin chimed in, "they
just don't say it out loud."

"Why would anybody tell me a word like that?" Jamie asked,
as baffled as he was angry.

"Because some people are mean and stupid themselves, and it makes them feel good to be cruel to other people, and they teach their children to be cruel too."

"That is stupid!" Jamie agreed, and the twins nodded.

"I think it would be better if you didn't tell Maggie and Ben about this or the word, don't you?" Sarah suggested gently. It didn't seem that the twins had any memory of the mistreatment of their parents by the outside world, and she was glad, but she knew they would have to learn to deal with it as time went on. The island could not shelter them forever from everything.

What Sarah privately and with amusement termed the Tiger's Royal Progress continued through the days of summer. Jason was determined that her new status should be widely known. She knew there was a darker side to it, but she tried not to dwell on it too much. Jason was establishing a ring of safety for her that would be difficult for an outsider to breach. This was his territory, and she was his wife, a far more acceptable role than mistress, and the more acknowledgment there was of that, the better.

Jamie accompanied them on the trip to Seattle and the logging camp, and his alert enjoyment of everything added much to the journey. When he wasn't intent on learning some new sailing skill from the men, he and Sarah had a running contest to see who could be the first to spot killer whales, porpoises, the little harbor seals, seabirds, other ships, Indian canoes, and anything else that moved within their sight. Many of the days were clear and the temperature was kind, so different from the smothering mugginess of the summers Sarah remembered in the East.

Jason found himself smiling constantly as he watched their play, and he teased Sarah about seeming even younger than Jamie.

He heard their voices now calling out in unison as they marked the symmetry of two killer whales curving along the surface of the water.

"I saw them first!" Again the voices were joined.

"I think you most unkind, Master James," Sarah accused in an affected voice, dabbing at her eyes with an imaginary handkerchief. "I would not have thought you the sort of man who would take a lady's killer whales away from her. Really, it's most ungentlemanly of you! And I happen to know those animals by name as I'm sure you do not, so, of course, they are mine. They're George and Martha Washington Whale, descended from a very distinguished family and personal friends of mine for absolutely years."

Jamie listened to this performance in high glee and burst into peals of laughter. "Oh, that's funny! You can have the whales."

"What say we share them? Old George and Martha wouldn't mind." She reached out and tickled him, and the two of them rolled around on the deck laughing and wrestling, not even hearing the chuckles from Jason and the other men.

But Sarah was always careful to stop such play before Jamie got truly breathless, and he was sensible enough to follow her lead.

They sat on the sun-warm deck, both of them mussed and perfectly happy.

"What's dis . . . er, distinguished? I thought that's what you do to put a fire out."

" 'Extinguish' is the word you're thinking of. 'Distinguished' means that someone is set apart from others by something special, something such as being a well-known doctor or politician or the like. For instance, your father is a distinguished businessman." She heard the chortle from Jason and ignored it; she was having trouble enough controlling her own amusement. But all play was aside in this; she never wanted Jamie to feel embarrassed about searching for more knowledge, but she knew she and Jason would laugh about it later and the two words would be forever linked in her mind.

Jamie was too busy trying out the applications of the new words to notice his father's mirth. He listed something distinguished about nearly everyone he knew, ending with, "And you're a distinguished mother."

"With a distinguished son," she said, dropping a kiss on his tousled hair, loving him and his generous assumption that nearly everyone was important for some reason.

The exchanges between Sarah and his son touched Jason far

beyond laughter though that was so often a part of what he felt, a course of joy Sarah had opened for him and which seemed to stretch on forever, but they also engendered in him a protectiveness that grew more fierce by the day. The protectiveness he had felt in the beginning toward Sarah when she was Mary Smith was a pale shadow to what he felt now. His wife and his son—they were the dearest things his heart possessed, and he had no doubt about his ruthless willingness to destroy anyone who threatened either one of them.

He wasted no time in executing his particular plan for Seattle. The *Lady Ellen,* the renovated steamer, was already plying the waters of Puget Sound and beyond, carrying freight and passengers as far as Victoria just as the well-known *Eliza Anderson* did. Jason had the privilege of naming her since his was the financial means which had enabled the craft to return to work. He and Sarah had chosen the name with both sorrow and amusement. Even though Sarah had once called Ellen Drake "Lady Ellen" in anger, it fit; Ellen had had an indomitable sense of her position in her own world. And Jason's too was the privilege of christening the finished work of Rob Mactavish and his crew at the shipyard. The *Sarah-Mary* was ready for launching, and with Owen's help, Jason already had buyers lined up for the privilege of purchasing shares in the vessel, though he would keep the major interest. The maiden voyage would be to San Francisco, which would be the *Sarah-Mary*'s home port. Rob Mactavish already had a reliable crew ready to take the ship south under sail and steam.

Sarah was overwhelmed, but her feelings were not pure pleasure. They did not speak of it, and she did not challenge it, but she knew the naming was an open declaration of possession. She had seen the gleam in Jason's eyes as he told her; the challenge to her father was there in the boldly painted letters on the graceful craft which would be seen in the waters off the most prominent city on the west coast.

The reception Jason gave at Yesler's Pavilion was ostensibly to celebrate the two ships, but everyone knew that it was, in fact, his way of introducing his wife to Seattle society.

Yesler's Pavilion, a rectangular board building, had replaced the old cookhouse as the scene for festivities in Seattle, and Jason, aided by an exuberant and efficient Angie, spared no expense in organizing a lavish array of food and drink. Sarah helped where she could but felt numbing fear every time she thought of the party. Finally she confessed to Angie.

"What happens if no one comes? Jason will be so angry! Oh, Angie, I think this is a dreadful idea!"

"It's a grand idea, you silly goose!" Angie snapped back. She'd been delighted at Mary's return as Sarah, Jason's wife. It was a wonderful ending to a story she felt she had had some part in, and it gave her a secret satisfaction that the roaming Tiger had been caught by this winsome creature. But she wasn't going to tolerate any faintheartedness. "I'd have thought you knew Seattle better by now. First of all, there aren't very many people who would give up the chance to go to a party that promises good food and drink, an excuse to get dressed up, and a chance to gossip with their friends. And in the second place, and more important, society here isn't like it is in lots of other places. Here it doesn't matter if your ancestors were pilgrims or peddlers. What matters is how successful you are right here and right now. Seattle has a fine respect for money and success—Lord knows the town's been trying to get both since it started—and the Tiger has both. Besides, you're his wife now, so the good people don't have to worry about anything moral anymore, not that they do much anyway—they're nice enough to me, and they were nice enough to you when you were Jason's mistress. I don't want to hear any more stupid worrying from you. Worry about what you're going to wear and how you'll do your hair instead."

They looked at each other for a moment and burst out laughing. "Clothes and hair, those are certainly the important things!" Sarah gasped, but Angie had given her confidence.

The summer night was soft and fair without the slightest drizzle to muddy the streets or splatter the good clothes everyone wore to Jason Drake's party.

Long enough now, Sarah's gilt hair was arranged simply on top of her head, and she wore her rose-colored wedding gown to give her courage. It was at once demure and dramatic, and it was a talisman from the day that had changed her life and committed it to the man who was standing tall and proud beside her as they greeted their guests. And suddenly she realized that what Angie had predicted was true. The last of her nervousness vanished. It was not that there was any lack of sharp-eyed looks as people who had met her before and many who hadn't were introduced to her as Jason's wife. The looks were there, but the curiosity was tempered in almost all cases by approval. It was obvious that the main reason people were here was to have a good time. And whatever she lacked in her knowledge of Seattle, she knew that many of the prominent citizens were here.

Doc Maynard and his wife, Catherine, had been among the early arrivals, and Sarah had more than a little suspicion of why they had been so prompt, since Doc was already tottering with the effects of free whiskey. She felt rather sorry for his wife, who was a formidable looking woman of rather dour countenance until she smiled. Mrs. Maynard's smile had a singular sweetness and more than a little tolerance when she regarded her wayward spouse. Sarah thought Doc's garrulous kindness more than made up for his vices, particularly when she compared him with Henry Yesler. Consummate businessman Yesler might be, even to having built this structure which housed the party, but he was no hand at geniality. His pouched eyes seemed to regard everyone with the suspicion that they were after his money, and his attempts to smile benevolently were less than successful. Arthur Denny, beloved though he still was as one of the founding fathers of the town, was hardly less rigid than Yesler. Mr. Denny conducted himself much like a visiting and not altogether approving preacher, and Sarah had to remind herself of the good things Jason had had to say about him—"an upright man, perhaps a little too upright, but truly concerned about the welfare of his friends, business associates, and Seattle, and absolutely honest in all his dealings." Still, she preferred his wife and his brother and sister-in-law. No wonder there were so many local stories and jokes about how much the Denny men loved Boren women.

John Denny, Arthur and David's father, having lost his first wife, had married the widow Boren back in Illinois, thereby bringing together his four sons and Mrs. Boren's son and two daughters. Arthur and David had eventually married their step-sisters, Mary Ann and Louisa. Mary Ann and Arthur, quite a bit older, had been married back east eight years before the trek west, while Louisa and David had crossed the country in growing friendship which had ripened into Seattle's first marriage.

Sarah had had only a nodding acquaintance with the sisters until this night, having met them and exchanged polite greetings a few times in Seattle's stores, but now she asked them if they would tell her of the early days of the settlement. Even Arthur managed something resembling a fond smile as his wife laughingly admitted the beginning had been dreary indeed. They had been suffering from malaria on and off, the drizzly weather hadn't improved anyone's spirits, and Mary Ann's health had been so reduced, that her newborn son, Roland, had had to subsist on clam juice, which Mary Ann hastened to admit had proved perfectly nourishing for the babe as had the land and the climate for the settlers.

Louisa, the "Sweetbriar Bride," now in her forties and some years older than her husband, was a comely woman with laughing eyes that belied the determined set of her chin. With her husband's voice chiming in, adding and confirming the memories, she told tales of curious Indians and equally curious bears, making light of all the early tribulations but then adding, "It's sad really, the poor Indians, and even the bears, they were all here first, and what we've gained, I fear they've lost in this beautiful land."

It was the essential difference between the two couples, Sarah decided, even as she listened and enjoyed their tales of two decades ago. It was a difference which seemed to be dictated by the dissimilarity in the brothers. Arthur, the upright, was a doer, a man who wanted to see practical results for every ounce and second of energy he expended on a particular task. David was a dreamer; even his eyes were different from his brother's, lacking the sharp focus, they were humorous, tolerant, and seemed to see a long distance even if the practicality of the immediate escaped them. Louisa obviously suited David as they shared the awareness of the Territory's beauty; even as Arthur and Mary Ann were suited to each other, hardy and practical.

Sarah felt a great sense of comfort. They had been through so much together, and they had remained bonded by love and the commitment of their marriages. If they could survive, so could she and Jason—Jason who was midway between the Denny men, part doer, part dreamer, a combination she would not change even were she able. She prayed she would prove an ever more fit mate for him. Her eyes found Jason speaking with a little knot of people not far away. He turned his head and smiled at her. She turned back to find Louisa regarding her kindly. "I still look at my David the same way," she said softly.

Sarah continued to move among the guests, stopping to chat here and there, feeling more confident than she ever had before and feeling Jason's approval touch her warmly even when he was across the room.

Angie had been helping to keep an eye on Jamie, and she found them together now, seated out of the way of the main traffic.

"Angie's been tellin' me stories 'bout Captain Tom an' his ship, real excitin' stories!"

"That's kind of her, isn't it?" Sarah said. "Angie's a good storyteller."

"Jamie's a fine spinner of tales himself," Angie insisted. "He's told me all about Cade and the other people on the island."

"You look a little sleepy, Jamie. Would you like to go home now?" Sarah knew no one would think it impolite if she left early for the sake of the child. But Jamie protested that he wasn't sleepy at all because after all, he was nearly nine years old now, and besides, this was a special stay-up-late night, and he hadn't even had supper yet.

The mention of food was suddenly very inviting. Jason joined the three as they moved toward the buffet table.

Sarah and Jason both sighed in relief to be sitting down after hours of circulating among their guests. She was sure his leg was bothering him, but there was nothing to be done about it now, and in any case, he was obviously immensely pleased with the way the evening had gone and that was all that mattered to him.

Seattle had paid court to the Tiger's woman.

CHAPTER

30

*W*hen the *Gaiety* sailed from Seattle, people were still talking about how much they'd enjoyed the best party of the summer, best party in a long time, matter of fact. Angie saw the Drakes off with promises to send word as soon as she heard from Captain Tom, and the two women already had a pact to share any news of Frenchie and Rio. Angie trusted Sarah's word that Rio was a good man for Frenchie, but she also shared the worry of their friend loving a gunman.

Jamie and Sarah began their game again as the *Gaiety* got under way, but Jamie gave up after spotting a canoe.

"I've got to ask you something."

The intensity of his voice caught her attention immediately. "Ask away."

"Well, I think I heard another bad word, maybe even worse than 'dummies.' "

"Tell me, and I'll tell you if it is," Sarah suggested sensibly, but she wondered why his eyes refused to meet hers.

"This kid, one of the kids I played with back there," his head jerked back toward Seattle. "Well, he said you were Papa's war an' his mother didn't see why Papa had married you when he already had what he wanted, an' I don't really understand what he meant 'cuz wars are bad 'cuz they kill people, an' they mean armies an' you're not an army an' you don't kill people, so I think he meant somethin' different. Was it a bad word?"

"Yes, it is a bad word. He was saying 'whore,' w-h-o-r-e, not 'war.'"

She kept her voice even with an effort; she felt a mixture of anger, sorrow, and an urge to laugh hysterically. After all, she had named herself whore often enough, but she clung to the knowledge that somehow she had to explain this to him well enough so that he was not hurt.

"His mother used that word as a nasty way of naming me because I lived with your father even when I wasn't married to him." She could see no reason to explain that the most common definition of whore was a woman who sold sex for money even though that had, indeed, been close to the center of the old bargain. "Maybe it was wrong for your father and me to be together then and maybe it wasn't—you'll have to decide that for yourself when you're older," she was glad to see his smile, "because Jason and I are part of your life. But that woman had no right to make a judgment about something which has nothing to do with her. What we do or did is none of her business, and it's even worse that she gave her child bad feelings too."

"I should've punched her instead of her kid," Jamie mumbled.

Sarah stared at him, not certain she had heard correctly until she remembered the slight graze under one eye he had sported a few days before. He had mumbled then, too, something about falling down, and she hadn't thought anything about it since Jamie had done far better than she would have expected in finding children to play with. Eyes sparkling, he'd confided to her that he'd met some of them before when he'd first come to Seattle with his father. His voice had trailed off as he remembered that the homecoming of that trip had found her gone.

"But I'm here now, so you needn't think of that anymore," she'd reminded him. She'd entertained the rowdy bunch one afternoon, serving them cookies baked as Jamie liked them while she'd pretended not to hear the admiring comments from his friends—"Boy, is your Mama pretty!" "I never seen hair like that before, all silvery like." Now she felt guilty that she hadn't kept a closer watch on him.

Made nervous by her continued silence, Jamie felt obliged to explain further. "It was the way he said the word. It just made me all mad, and I hit him." He grinned in spite of himself, and the slightly crooked tilt of his mouth was the image of his father's. "I was lucky. He's a little bigger 'n me an' I guess it surprised him that I hit 'im. He tried to hit me back an' hardly touched me, an' then he gave up an' said he was sorry. Maybe he's nicer than his mother or maybe he jus' doesn't like fightin'."

"Do you?" Sarah asked.

Jamie shook his head. "Nope, 'cuz maybe I won't be so lucky if it happens again, an' besides, I felt funny when I did it, good an' bad at the same time, an' I didn't like the feelin'."

"Well, that's a relief! There's usually a better way of settling things than using one's fists, but I can hardly be angry since you were defending my honor." She smiled at him. "Just don't make a habit of it, promise?"

"Promise. Do you want to know who the kid was?"

"No, I truly don't, because then I'd probably know who his mother is, and I might lose my temper the next time I see her."

Jamie laughed at the sudden image he had of Sarah making a fist at the woman, but he suffered another anxious thought. "Do I have to tell Papa?"

"Only if you think you should, but I think it would make your father very angry with the boy and his mother, and I don't see how that would be very useful."

Jamie sighed in relief. He was sure his father wouldn't be angry with him, but that made little difference; he preferred not to see Jason's anger at all.

Jamie enjoyed the visit to the logging camp even more than the time in Seattle. The crew was very kind to him, and he was enthralled by the work they did and torn now between the desire to be a sea captain or a logger, or perhaps even a bull whacker. His eyes glowed every time he heard Bull Fletcher bellowing at his oxen, and he told his parents gravely that he thought it must

be a very good job to be able to yell like that all day and get paid
for it. He considered it a great adventure to sleep in the smelly
bunkhouse with the men, and though this gave Sarah privacy
with Jason in the little cabin, she fretted about Jamie until Jason
chided in the darkness. "Honestly, largely through your efforts,
Jamie is a healthy and independent little boy, and this is a grand
adventure for him, not to mention the fact that Jud and the
others are watching out for him and he's only a little ways away."

She drummed her fists on his chest in mock anger. "If there's
one thing I hate about you, it's your damn reasonableness!"

He pulled her down so he could kiss her. "Then I shall become totally unreasonable just as this bed has become since I
added another person to it."

She settled against him with a little sigh. "I think there's
plenty of room. I like this a lot better than sleeping over there
by myself." She felt the warm length of him against her, with
such absolute contentment, it was as if she were floating in a
warm, kind sea.

"I love you unreasonably much," Jason heard her murmur as
she relaxed against him in sleep.

Though they pretended not to notice, Sarah and Jason
laughed in private at the fond looks the burly loggers had been
giving them ever since they'd learned about the marriage. Even
Mrs. Tomlinson had the grace to look abashed and offered them
fresh loaves of her bread to take up the skid road.

They were back on the island in time to celebrate Jamie's
ninth birthday in grand style, though the ghost of Daniel was a
sadness they acknowledged, even Jamie saying openly, "I miss
'im. I think of 'im lots of times, 'specially when I'm with his
animals."

Jamie had spent much time with Constance while Jason was
gone, and there was a strong bond between them now. Daniel's
menagerie was gradually being returned to the wild, but there
were new cases, and some of the creatures, such as Raven, would
probably always return for food and shelter now and then. Jamie
had proved a willing helper for Constance, though rabbits and
the cat, Tiger, were kept away from him.

Jason normally went to San Francisco at least twice a year. He went not because Owen and his other agents weren't capable men, but simply because his own presence was a reminder that he truly held the power and would demand satisfaction of anyone who mismanaged his business just as he rewarded those who dealt well on his behalf. He was, at the moment, pleased with most of his enterprises; even the redwood logging camp on the Mendocino coast was running more smoothly now that the men were better fed and had a new boss. They had stopped there on the way north, but even with her new assurance as his wife, Sarah had not gone ashore, and Jason hadn't pressed her; it was still a wild crew, more contented or not.

Jason found the focus of his life radically changed, and he was glad of it. It was not that he had lost the zest for empire building, he hadn't, but the order of his priorities had shifted—Sarah and Jamie continued to be more important than anything else. And he judged it better now for Sarah to be at peace on the island for as long as possible; San Francisco could wait until the next year. Owen kept him well-informed by regular reports sent by various channels so that at least one copy reached Jason before too much time had passed. And if there were urgent word to be exchanged, the telegraph could be used, either in Seattle or closer yet, though not as dependable in Jason's experience, on San Juan Island.

The word Owen had sent recently had more than a little to do with Jason's decision to wait until next year to journey south again. Part of the news he had shared with Sarah—Rio had left San Francisco for a job in Nevada, and Frenchie was doing her best to continue as if she had no doubt of his promise to return alive and in one piece. Other news he had kept from his wife. Before he had gone, Rio had reported to Owen that two men had been nosing around, looking for a Mary Smith and for a certain missing man. Rio hadn't killed anyone this time—there was no need with Sarah gone—but he wondered how well her tracks had been covered, if at all. It was no secret that Mary Smith, the dancing girl, had been carted off by the big, lame man. Even the wedding was not much of a secret since Sarah had been introduced to many of Jason's business associates as his

wife. Owen confirmed Rio's fears by writing that Reverend
Mapes had also come to him in some consternation. He had not
been approached directly, but he had heard that many questions
were being asked about the couple he had married, questions
about the gilt-haired girl and the lame man. Questions about
where they had gone, whether they had gone together. The
Reverend had no intention of answering any of those questions,
even if they were asked of him directly. He had no qualms about
lying or evading facts for the sake of Jason and Sarah; they were
part of his flock, two of his scattered children and thus deserving
of every protection, spiritual and temporal, that he could give
them. His unease came from what he had heard of the two men
who had been asking questions. They were not by any report the
sort of people one should have anything to do with. Some sheep,
the old man admitted, had been lost to the wolves for too long
to ever be part of the flock again.

Owen finished the letter by asking if Jason wanted him to take
any action, and if so, what?

For the time being, Jason wanted nothing done. He had no
doubt that Sarah's father would discover, if he didn't know already, that she had married Jason Drake and where Jason Drake
lived for most of the year. Even if the man's spies were bunglers,
the trail was wide and they were bound to find it soon. The ship,
the *Sarah-Mary,* would surely provide one large and visible clue,
and it would also make it clear that Sarah had gone back to her
real name.

Anything that would draw Sarah's father toward him suited
Jason. He wanted the man to know that he had lost, wanted him
to know that his prize possession was no longer his and would
never be his again. Jason had thought fleetingly of beginning an
investigation in New York. Even from so far away, with Owen's
help, it could be done. He knew the date now within one or two
days, and the question would be what prominent citizen had
been stabbed in that time. But he had quickly abandoned the
idea and for more than one reason. He realized the practicality
of it was probably in some doubt. Sarah's background was so
rich and privileged, her father would have had the means and
certainly the desire to cover up what had happened. There was

probably no record at all of the incident wherein Sarah had tried to kill her father. If there had been any public notice of it, it would have been of intruders or an accident. Perhaps that kind of notation in an old newspaper file would have helped to lead Jason to the man's identity, but what he wanted, what he needed, was for Sarah to finally tell him who her father was; he needed the final truth, the final trust, the one thing she had withheld from him in all the misery she had shared. He needed her to believe that he was stronger than her father and therefore capable of defeating him.

He felt no guilt about not sharing these exchanges with Sarah. The longer he could keep her unaware of what was going on, the better. But they did discuss Rio's disappearance with honest and mutual sadness. Sarah had written to Frenchie as soon as she heard, pleading with her for news as soon as she knew anything or even to come to them if her loneliness became intolerable. They were comforted by the fact that she had Owen and Carrie close at hand.

By late October, word had reached the islands that the dispute over ownership had been settled. The news caused not only rejoicing on the part of the Americans and some grumbling across the border to the north but general confusion too, as the anxious settlers sought to prove their land claims legitimate.

Jason didn't worry; he had already taken extraordinary care to make sure the Drake's Island claims were in order, and he accepted the fact that the matter would undoubtedly be a bureaucratic tangle for some time to come. He counted on the reality of possession to decide the outcome eventually.

"It's an important treaty, not just for these islands, but for the other issues, other boundaries and fishing rights. It's better for all of us to have good relations with Canada and England; the last thing either side needs is armed conflict on the borders. And now with British Columbia being part of the Canadian Confederation too, matters will be even more stable to the north." Jason was speaking quite soberly. He looked at Sarah inquiringly as she laughed.

"I suddenly realized why Cade's been so grumpy lately!" she explained. "I'd forgotten all about what this will mean to him. The customs' jurisdictions will be very clear now."

"Knowing Cade, what it will mean is some very stealthy sailing, but his miraculous sheep may indeed cease to bear quite as much wool as they did before."

The evacuation of the British soldiers from San Juan Island was scheduled toward the end of November but took several days longer than expected due to the weather and was not accomplished until a few days after Thanksgiving. The winds seemed to howl from every direction at once, and the temperature dropped below freezing, turning the water whipped from the sea into icy plumes. Jason gave up all plans of sailing the *Gaiety* over to San Juan Island to watch the festivities though he and Sarah did ride out to Cade's Cove to peer from there through the spyglass. They could see very little in the terrible weather, and the few ships they did catch glimpses of were fighting so hard against the elements, running for shelter as fast as they could, Sarah and Jason were infinitely relieved they were on land.

Cade shared the feeling. "Never seen it quite this bad before," he observed, and he scolded them both, "You're idiots to ride out in weather like this. Even if you don't freeze, your poor dumb horses probably will."

He gave them hot spiked coffee and sent them home where they found Jamie there before them, sent home by Constance, whom he had been visiting.

"She said nothing was worth freezing solid for, at least nothin' less 'n Thanksgiving dinner an' we already had that, and I think she's right." He giggled as he looked at them. "The cold made you look like twins."

They looked at each other and laughed along with Jamie. They both had glowing red cheeks and noses from the bitter bite of the wind.

The three of them sat in front of the fire, munching cookies Sarah had baked, reading and talking now and then about nothing in particular, content to be together while the storm howled against the house.

Jason was growing used to it now, this sense of family, but familiarity made it no less precious. The shared Thanksgiving feast had been even better this year than last with all the islanders together, because now Jason was sure of Sarah's part in his

life and of his in hers. He reached down from his chair to where
Sarah and Jamie sat together on the floor, and he touched each
of the bright heads. Jamie flashed him a smile and went back to
his book. Sarah looked up at him, reaching for his hand, pressing it to her lips. "We're really here, my love," she whispered
softly.

When Christmas came, the Drakes were not the only ones who
felt they had much to celebrate. The Olsens and Nilsens had, at
Jason's urging, become American citizens several years before.
His advice was now proved sound as nearly all of the British
heads of households on the islands traveled to the district court
in Port Townsend to apply for American citizenship, fearful that
without it, the rights of homesteading would be denied them.
Rumor had it that only one man on San Juan Island had refused
to give up his allegiance to the queen; for the rest, the need to
own their own land was stronger than old patriotism. The Olsens and Nilsens, having been citizens for some time now, had no
fears that their land claims would be treated any differently from
those of the other inhabitants of Drake's Island. Though much
of the land was Jason's, it was at his insistence that each of the
families owned their own plots of ground. He had known from
the first that there would be problems if any of them sold out
to people who would not cooperate with the others, but he was
willing to take that risk. He had chosen the people who came to
the island carefully; he would trust every one of them with his
life and thus surely with the land.

As they sang "Auld Lang Syne" by the bonfire on the beach
as 1871 became 1872, Daniel, the lost babies, and Ellen were all
in their hearts though no one said their names aloud this night.
And Sarah knew they were all praying that this new year would
not have so disastrous a beginning as the last. She was comforted by Constance's serenity. There was sorrow in the
woman's eyes—there always would be for Daniel's absence—but
there was also a calm acceptance and a growing joy in the company of David Becam. There was no shadow of ominous foretell-
ing.

"It will be a better year, sweetheart, it will," Jason whispered
as he gave her the first kiss of the new year, and later in bed as

she nestled against his warmth, she murmured, "Nothing could be better than this."

They loved each other with slow care, deliberately stretching out the minutes and prolonging the gathering waves of pleasure. Jason stroked the curve of shoulder to breast, waist to hipbone, on and on. "I love this line and this and this," he breathed, and she laughed softly. "I'm truly lost. I love all of you, every single inch." She nuzzled and nipped at his flesh playfully, her husky laughter vibrating against his skin until the sound caught and changed to a long purr of pleasure as he entered her and held himself still and deep before he began to move within her.

"You are mine," Jason said as he held the sleeping Sarah in his arms. But even in these quietest moments of fulfillment and comfort, he had no illusions. There would be no lasting peace until the war with her father was won. Even when he made love to her, he knew it was a battle, the ultimate way of drawing her that much further away from her father's possession of her.

Despite his assurances to Sarah, he wondered what the new year would bring; he wondered what her father would do.

CHAPTER
31

*T*he new year did indeed begin well, bringing reunions and welcome news of beloved friends. Captain Tom hadn't made it back to Seattle in time for Christmas, but he had returned in less than a year, and Angie had no complaints. They came to Drake's Island for a few days during which Captain Tom kept the children entertained after school with tales of exotic places and life on the high seas. Jamie switched his future plans back to sea captain while Tom was there.

"So it's 'Sarah' and 'Mrs. Drake' too," Captain Tom had greeted her, engulfing her hands in his huge ones. "Good fortune to you and to Jason." He seemed to find nothing odd in her changed status, and she was grateful to him. She had forgotten how enormous he was, and she found herself smiling inwardly at the way he dwarfed his surroundings. Even Jason appeared fairly slight when he stood beside him. But the captain had lost none of his skill on the piano and made wonderful music on the instrument Jason had given Sarah for Christmas.

The piano had been carried in the hold of the *Gaiety*, and hidden at Captain Hanson's house. Sarah had known nothing about it until it had appeared at the house on Christmas Eve. It was such a perfect gift, she would have wept had not Jason kissed her and teased her into playing by protesting that he'd far rather hear carols than blubbering.

Jason had not heard Tom play before, and he was impressed. He particularly enjoyed hearing Tom and Sarah play and sing together. Jamie was delighted too and resolved to practice the scales and exercises Sarah had been coaxing him to learn; playing the piano seemed quite acceptable now that he knew a sea captain did it.

The time with Angie and Tom was made even more joyful by a letter that came to the island. Frenchie's happiness and relief came through in spite of the brief scrawl. Rio was back in San Francisco, unharmed, and considerably richer though he would not speak of the job he'd done. That was all right with Frenchie, anything was all right as long as she had him back again.

Sarah could not help thinking about how strange life was. Her own life was now so much more settled than either Angie's or Frenchie's though when she had first met each of the women, her own existence had been in complete confusion. Her new life was all because of Jason. There was so much tenderness in the look she gave him, Jason blinked and then smiled at her, not questioning his good fortune.

When it was time to go south again, again they gave Jamie the choice, and now it appeared even easier for him to make it. He trusted them both to come back, and he was too settled into his life on the island and his schoolwork to want to wander off with them. He was quick to plan to spend part of the time with Constance, part with Maggie, Ben, and the twins, and maybe even a weekend or two with Cade, who had made the offer. But when Jamie told Sarah he was going to the caves shortly before they sailed, she asked gently if she might go with him. She was worried that perhaps he wasn't so sure after all about letting them go off without him. He seldom went to the caves anymore, and she still thought of it as a sign that he was troubled when he did.

He regarded her in amazement. "You wanna go with me?"

"Yes, if it's all right with you, but not if it'll spoil your private place."

"Oh, it won't! I'd like to show you. I jus' never thought you'd wanna go there after . . . well, after the mean trick I played on you.''

She sighed inwardly. She really didn't want to go, not even now, but she should have asked Jamie to take her there long before this. She had been trying to protect his need for privacy and hadn't even considered that he might instead have needed to share his special place with her. She wondered if two people of whatever ages could ever fully understand each other.

"Shall we take some cookies and a jug of milk, just in case we get hungry?"

Jamie thought that was a great idea. They told Maggie where they were going so that Jason, who had ridden out to discuss things with Nate and Jon, would know where they were should he return in time to find them gone. After a surprised look, Maggie smiled at them and wished them a happy time with quick gestures.

The tide was still on its way out and offered them good access to the caves, far better than the day Jason had rescued her. Her heart beat uncomfortably fast at first in memory, but the fear ebbed as Jamie's lantern cast a soft yellow glow and lighted their way easily into his favorite cavern.

Dark spaces in the center of the earth were never going to be her favorite, but Sarah could understand why the place fascinated the child. There was beauty here she hadn't expected. Jamie knew the way well; the twisting tunnel of rock he chose led at last to a large cave, its ceiling and sides vaulted and carved in fantastic shapes by ancient water. There were sandy and pebbled pools near the front—Sarah didn't want to know what, if anything, lived in them—but the slope of the floor went higher toward the back. Here, above the high tide line, it was drier though nothing could be completely dry in this world controlled by water. And there above the floor was Jamie's fort, a generous shelf of rock reached by easy, natural steps in the rock wall.

Jamie went first and held the lantern so Sarah could see her way to the ledge.

"Why, it's splendid!" she exclaimed, and she meant it. She saw it suddenly from a young boy's point of view. Jamie had managed to bring in crates which served as tables and chests for his valuables: stubs of candles and a tin for the matches not secured in the case his father had given him, a cracked cup and a plate, undoubtedly donated by Maggie, a ball of twine and a rusty blade, pebbles and shells, bits and pieces of all sorts. And there was a pile of driftwood and a neat stack of pieces of blanket.

Sarah was thankful that Jamie had not yet, apparently, lit a fire here—there were no charred bits of wood or stains of charcoal on the ledge—but she said nothing about it even though she felt a motherly urge to warn that there was no way of telling whether one could have a fire safely here or not.

Jamie hugged her tightly. "I'm so glad you like it! It is my most special place. I don't even have to come here very much because now I carry it around in my head a lot, and I can visit it almost any time without even coming here." He drew back from her suddenly, studying her face. "Does that sound silly?"

"No," she replied gravely. "It makes very good sense. It's part of growing up. I still do it."

"You really do?"

"Yes, really. I carry the good times, the good places, and the good people in my heart and my mind where I can never lose them." And almost all of them, she thought, almost all of the good memories are of this island and the people on it; how late I came to wanting to remember anything at all.

"Jamie, is it really all right with you not to be going with us?" She felt emboldened to ask the question because of the comfortable feeling between them.

Jamie's face was shadowed and thoughtful in the lantern light, and he hesitated for a long moment before he answered. "I've thought a lot about it. It's not easy to see you and Papa leavin', 'specially when I know it'll be a long time 'til I see you again. But I belong here now more 'n I ever did before, an' that's important too. An' it's not like I'm here all by myself when you're gone. Oh, I love you and Papa best," he assured her, wanting it to be clear, "but now I've got a big family, one I never knew I had until you came, so I'm not all scairt when you're gone. It's hard to explain, but I know that someday I won't be able to be here all the time I want, jus' like Papa said once. I'll have to go away lots too on business things, an' even maybe for sailin' my own ship somewhere, an' I guess that will be okay then, but for now, I like bein' here for most of the time."

"You're a very wise young man," Sarah complimented him, and inwardly she thought of how much she'd like to stay on the island too, where she was safe, where Jason was safe. But he was going and she would go with him. She felt as protective of him as she was of Jamie, and she could not forget the beating Jason had taken in San Francisco. She still could not believe it had been random. Her father knew she was with Jason Drake; she was sure of that and she knew Jason would never be safe again. The old shadows loomed and threatened to overwhelm her, worse now because other people were involved, worse because loving had made her at once stronger and more vulnerable.

Jamie mistook the expression on her face and reached out to pat her hand. "It's all right, really it is. I want to stay here." He grinned impishly, "Well, not 'zackly here, but on the island, an' don't worry 'bout the wood. It's jus' for a 'mergency, an' I don't think there'll be one."

So her anxious looks had not been missed. She managed to smile at him. "Then we'll toast your wisdom with milk and cookies."

Jason was waiting for them when they got back. "Maggie tells me I've missed an underground party."

"It was more like an important meeting," Jamie said seriously, and then his own smile answered his father's. "Only I don't s'pose anything can be very important when you eat cookies. But Mama went into the caves and wasn't scairt at all!"

Sarah was torn between laughter and tears. Her two men were beaming at her with identical expressions of pride as if she were a precocious child, and Jamie was calling her "Mama." He did so easily now, but it never failed to touch her.

They celebrated Jason's birthday before they left the island, and Sarah continued her tradition of giving him clothes she had made with loving skill. Jason teased her about trying to make him the best dressed dandy in the Territory, but he was pleased by her gifts. He had never had clothes quite so finely tailored as those she made, and it gave him particular pleasure to wear the garments, conscious that her hands had worked every stitch. She used cloth spun on the island, some of it now by her own hands, and fine materials she had purchased in San Francisco, in Seattle, and even from Captain Gibson's stock aboard the *Folly.* These fabrics she would spend money for because they were almost all destined to become gifts for someone else, but Jason had not yet been able to convince her that the money he had settled on her at their marriage was hers, renewable, and that he preferred she spend it foolishly rather than wisely. It had exasperated him at first to find that this was something she was simply incapable of doing, so contrary was it to her nature. It gave her great pleasure to buy things for other people, but she had no interest in spending money on herself.

She had protested, "What can I possibly want? You give me everything and are far kinder and more generous to me than I could ever be to myself. I think it is a perfect arrangement—you spoil me, and I'll do my best to spoil you."

She had said them lightly, but her words pulled at his heart. He ceased to chide her. There was still a deep pool of self-doubt in Sarah, a legacy from her father. And he suspected the different ways he and she viewed possessions were also a legacy from the past. He enjoyed being surrounded by fine furnishings and books, though not by clutter, enjoyed it because in the uprootings of his youth, nothing had remained familiar for long. Shabby furnishings gave way to better quality when his father's luck was good, only to be sold off again when business went bad. He was glad he had been able to give his mother a settled and fairly luxurious life for her last years. But Sarah surely saw things differently. She had been surrounded by possessions and trapped in an environment that gave her nothing but pain. No wonder she had no interest in accumulating the trappings of wealth. But he found joy in making her life as comfortable as possible and had every intention of continuing to do so.

Even Cade was there to see them off, complaining gruffly to Sarah that he was sure they were leaving now just to miss the lambing and then ruining the effect of his complaint by whispering to her, "Don't worry about the boy. We love him, and we'll keep him so busy, he'll hardly have time to miss you."

For several days, Sarah wondered whether they'd ever manage the trip south at all. When they set out, the weather was good enough though unstable, the wind fitful, the sea as leaden as the sky and moving in oily-looking swells. Thin shreds of mist thickened to lowering fog, shutting down visibility to dangerous closeness, causing them all to strain for sounds of another vessel even while the *Gaiety*'s bell sounded to warn others of their position. The canvas hung limply, dripping cold streams of water from the fog. And then, when the wind started again, tearing at the fog, Sarah wasn't sure but that being becalmed was preferable. She stayed on deck until the cold drove her below, but she was proud to be able to show Jason that she wasn't sick, despite the frantic pitch and roll of the ship.

"Frightened?" he asked.

"Not as I was in that other storm, no, not really at all, not as long as you and the other men look so pleased with it all." Her voice was tart. Jason grinned sheepishly and didn't deny that he and the crew were enjoying the tussle.

The bad weather on the last edge of winter followed them out of the Strait of Juan de Fuca into the Pacific, the wind buffeting them and rain coming in heavy sheets. Sarah wished more than once that they could manage with the same ease she saw in the gray whales migrating south to their breeding grounds. The leviathans moved with their slow grace, as though unconcerned by the rough dance of the sea. After more than a week of it, even the men admitted they were glad to be free of the stormy weather, and they praised Sarah for having kept her sea legs well enough even to help David keep them fed while they battled with the elements and went short of sleep.

But before they reached San Francisco, Jason did something which unsettled Sarah more than the storm had. He gave her a small wrapped package, heavy for its size. She opened it to find a double-barreled derringer even more elegantly wrought than Frenchie's. She stared at it as if it were going to go off of its own volition and kill one of them.

"You will not go anywhere in the city without this. I still do not believe your father had anything to do with the beating, but I am not so stubborn that I will risk losing you in case he did." He did not mention the trackers who had come after they had left the city.

"And you?" she asked very low.

"I'll be armed too. I know how you feel, sweetheart, honestly I do. It's why I so seldom carry a gun. They breed their own violence. But there isn't much of a choice right now." His voice altered, becoming a deep growl of anger; she had never seen him so much the Tiger as now.

"I have worked hard for what I have, for what I am, and no one, not your father or anyone else is going to take what is mine or keep me from going where I want to go whether it be San Francisco or the gates of Hell. But having you in danger is a weapon against me, a weapon I can't fight against unless you help. Pick it up."

She obeyed him. The deadly little piece felt smooth and seductively comforting in her hands. The image came unbidden. She saw her father's face with a neat hole precisely between his eyes. She was swept by a killing lust so strong, she clenched her jaw against crying out from the force of it.

Jason read it all clearly, hating that it had to be so, even while he silently applauded its existence. Only by being aggressive on her own behalf could Sarah cease to be the victim her father had made her.

"Now let's make sure you know how to use it," he said calmly, and her tension eased with the practical concern.

At her request, Cade had taught her the rudiments of firing a rifle, but those lessons had been the least successful of her attempts to learn everything the islanders could teach. She had continued to hold the weapon with fearful awkwardness. Cade had finally told her that he felt a lot safer when she was armed with a fishing pole. "If a bear ever climbs up on shore, you'd be better off hitting him over the head with that than risking shooting yourself with the rifle. It's hard to do with a barrel that long, but I think you could manage it plus breaking your jaw in the process," he'd said in disgust.

But the derringer was different—small, neat, and necessary

against a danger far more real than mythical bears. She listened carefully to Jason's explanations about the limited range and best use of the gun, and even as she concentrated on his words, she remembered the night Frenchie had loaned her hers, the night it had all begun with Jason.

The last of her distaste vanished as she practiced firing the gun from the deck of the ship. She must learn to do this very well; someday Jason's or Jamie's life might depend on it, not to mention her own.

But once they were in San Francisco, despite whatever danger lurked there, there was joy in being back with their friends. Sarah was so particularly glad to see Rio alive and well she threw her arms around him and hugged him exuberantly, causing him to sputter, "Now, come on, dahlin', Ah kin jus' tell ya don' have no faith in me keepin' mahself alive."

In spite of the camaraderie, there were undertones in the reunion, currents that Sarah sensed among the three men, but she said nothing, waiting for Jason to tell her if it was any of her business.

Part of it certainly was. Jason told her that he had hired Rio to be her bodyguard while they were in the city. "When I'm not with you, he will be." The only argument he'd had with Rio was over the fee; Rio had been insulted that Jason had even thought of offering him money, but Jason had been implacably reasonable. "You've already risked your life for her once, and this is something you do for a living. If you wanted to buy a share in one of my businesses, I would charge you a fair rate, I wouldn't give it to you as a gift. If you will not allow me to hire your services, I simply won't be able to accept them."

Rio had finally agreed, but now noting Sarah's mutinous expression, Jason suspected the worst of the argument was yet to come.

"What about you?" she asked flatly.

"I don't plan to be careless, nor do I plan to be alone most of the time. Most of the time, I plan to be with my wife, who can be very fierce when someone she loves is threatened." When she failed to return his smile, his voice sharpened. "For God's sake, be sensible! You've told me your father is alive and wants you back. I believe you." For more reasons than I'm going to tell you now, he thought. "Think how I would feel if you disappeared. I wouldn't know where to look. You would be lost to me, Sarah-Mary." He drew an audible breath. "I could not bear it. I would go mad."

It was settled by his need; she could not fight against that. And since Rio had no intention of letting his reluctant employment mar a dear friendship, Sarah soon found that she could forget for long moments why Rio was so constantly with her. Indeed, the presence of Frenchie or Carrie or both made the outings joyful. But she couldn't help but feel a little malicious pleasure in noticing how Rio watched over Jason as carefully as he watched over her when they were all together. It afforded her grim amusement to know Jason was aware of it but could hardly protest.

She was not, however, amused by the hours he spent with Owen over business. It was not the time she begrudged, it was the secrecy, and her hurt was greater than her anger. She was sure he was involved in some new scheme, and she waited patiently for him to tell her what it was. But the explanations didn't come, and the ledgers remained blank of new entries. She tried not to think it, but the idea intruded anyway—it seemed that Jason no longer trusted her. If he did not, they had lost something very precious. It had been a unique part of their relationship from the time Jason had realized figures and business made sense to her, could be shared with her, and that had been an early time, indeed, an early bond between them. That knowledge had been one of the few useful things from her past.

She tried to think without panic of why it had changed now. Because she loved him and trusted his love so much, only one theory made any sense to her—he must be contemplating some new venture which would balance his empire even more precariously between glory and disaster. He knew she was more conservative than he, and so he was probably waiting until whatever he was attempting was accomplished. And that meant, in turn, that she must school herself in patience while she waited for him to tell her.

She was completely mistaken. Jason was not involved in a new project; he was grappling with a threat to what he already possessed. There had been no breathing room since his first private meeting with Owen on this trip. Owen had plunged right in.

"I'm glad you're here," he said. "Something's happening, and I don't understand what it means, but it's certainly new. I know how you've always felt about banks out here, and you're right. They're mostly thrown together with no guarantees and short of capital too often from unwise speculation. A lot of people remember how many of the banks went under in '55, and it could happen again. Private financing has always seemed better to you—it has to me too—but Jason, I don't know now. Quite a few of your notes have been sold. That's no problem now; the terms are the same as long as you meet the payments. But I don't know what will be asked when they're renegotiated, as some of them must be before long, unless you intend to pay them off. And I don't know why the men have sold them. You've always been a good investment for them. I feel as if there's something going on, something I don't understand, can't put my finger on. Some of the men, when I asked them, simply refused to tell me why they sold the notes, wouldn't even look squarely at me. And others admitted they'd been offered too good a premium to hold on to them. You know as well as anyone that things are unsettled now, prices going up and down, speculation going wild in land and everything else. Money's tight, President Grant's involvement with the moneymen, there are all sorts of reasons, but I don't understand why this is happening to you. And there's no way to tell what the new terms will be; on some of the notes, you're already paying eighteen percent, but if premiums were paid on them, that must surely indicate higher percentages to come when the loans are renegotiated. Or no renegotiation at all. Your former associates were always willing to reissue the loans because they wanted the interest payments, not your holdings, and they trusted the steady income from you. Perhaps what you actually own, not what you pay to hold on to it, is what's wanted now."

"Is there one name involved?" Jason's voice was steady, but his heartbeat was beginning to accelerate. It had to be Sarah's father; he had no other enemy he knew of who would or could spend so much to gain control of his assets. Perhaps the name would come to him without Sarah's admission, after all. But even before Owen spoke again, Jason knew it was not going to be that easy.

"No. There're several agents involved, men who often handle investments for eastern influences. That's about all I'd be willing to guess—that whoever's trying to buy you out doesn't live here."

Eastern. New York. A perfect fit in Jason's mind. He studied Owen intently. "Trying to buy me. That is what it seems, isn't it?" He wanted the reassurance that someone who knew nothing about Sarah's fears and background could see the same pattern.

Owen nodded. "Yes, buy or ruin you. It's all come up very suddenly, and I can't see any good reason anyone would be willing to pay extra for notes whose payments have never been more than a few days late and are usually on time. It would seem to me that someone is counting on you either failing to make the payments on time or on renegotiating at so high a rate that you'll be forced to surrender your collateral or find other ways of paying off the notes.

"Why, Jason? Why is someone trying to do this? I can see you suspect someone. And I don't see how I can be of any use to you unless I know who and why. Do you plan to tell me?" Aside from the business aspects which were potentially serious indeed, Owen was feeling the betrayal of their friendship.

Jason grimaced, and Owen could not mistake the pain in his eyes. "I'd tell you if I could, if I knew for sure. Until I really know what I'm going to do, I can't talk about it except to ask you to keep on gathering as much information as you can."

Sarah. The name blazed in Owen's mind, but he didn't say it aloud. It was something to do with her. He was absolutely sure of it. He felt a great sadness. He had no doubt of Jason's love for Sarah or of hers for Jason. She glowed, moving in an almost visible aura of light when she was with him. Nor did he doubt that if Sarah could prevent hurt to Jason she would do whatever was necessary. He had proof of it in the knowledge of how she had left Jason and the island. And he would never forget the fear he had sensed in her when he had first met her. Poor Sarah. And poor Jason. Something from Sarah's past, some*one,* was moving to ruin their future.

What had happened so far in Jason's business affairs was not, by itself, that crucial or unusual, but Owen knew how carefully balanced Jason's empire was between failure and success; the overextension he had often worried about could be a lethal weapon in the right hands, especially if the note buying was only the prelude.

Jason saw it in the same way. This was only the beginning. There had to be losses to make the loans more difficult to repay. Nothing else made sense. He had never been so filled with impotent rage. He wanted to kill someone with his bare hands, wanted to kill one man. And he didn't know who he was.

He talked to each of the men who had sold his notes, and learned nothing except that almost to a man they were ashamed and evasive. Greed had been uppermost with many, but not with all. With some, there was fear so strong, he could smell it. He realized with grim self-knowledge that it added to his fury that any man should be more afraid of someone else than he was of crossing the Tiger.

The agents who had served as the intermediaries for buying the notes were of no use. There were three of them, and they all claimed everything had been done properly and that they themselves didn't know the name of the final purchaser; other agents, men from the East, had contacted them. They were superciliously polite to Mr. Drake, but the satisfaction showed —they had been well paid for the work they had done.

A tangle of names leading nowhere. Sarah had claimed her father was a ruthless, powerful man. Now Jason was beginning to believe it. Only one of the men who had sold out gave him any clue to exactly how ruthless the buyer was, but it was enough.

Jason had dealt with Gerald Claxton for several years. Claxton was older than he and had a lovely wife and several children for whom he provided a comfortable life. He was a wise investor, owning several businesses and lending capital carefully to those he judged as astute as himself. That Claxton had sold out his loan shocked Jason more than any of the others.

He had gone to him and asked why. He had seen the tremor running through the spare, gray-haired man. Gerald had answered stiffly and meaninglessly, throwing out such explanations as "consolidating my interests" and "reconsidering my assets." But Jason had watched his eyes and had seen the fear there. Finally, he decided to go back to see him again.

He saw Claxton's immediate unease. This time he allowed no room for evasion. "Blackmail?" he asked very softly.

Gerald flinched violently and stared at him, confirming the guess. Then he nodded wearily. "I owe you that much. There was nothing I could do. I love my wife and my children, and my standing in the city is good. I could not lose it all. Back East, before I came out here, well, I was in some trouble. I made some bad deals, left some bad debts. And my wife, she's well respected here by people who matter to her, but she wouldn't be if they knew her true background."

Jason regarded him in wonder. Though the man had not given him details, he had given him enough to cause himself harm if Jason chose to spread the information around.

Claxton squared his shoulders and nodded. "It's the least I can give you, and I trust you not to use it against me despite what has happened. You have a beautiful young wife, and it's no secret that you love her very much. I expect you would do almost anything to protect her, even to traveling thousands of miles and changing your name, perhaps even to the betrayal of someone else."

"I would," Jason agreed grimly. His anger against the man was gone, replaced by pity. It was no use to protest that blackmail was illegal; the damage would be done as soon as the information was spread around, the new life in the West destroyed. Much could be forgiven, but few would want to do business with a man who had cheated others financially. Sarah too had changed her name and traveled thousands of miles.

"You're facing a formidable enemy," Claxton said. "And I can't even tell you who he is because I don't know, but he is surely someone highly placed in the financial world."

"Of New York?"

Claxton shrugged tiredly. "Perhaps. But my crimes were committed in Philadelphia. It scarcely matters; at a certain level, cities lose their boundaries; money makes its own communities."

The news was another unpleasant shock to Jason, but he hid his reaction and took his leave of Gerald Claxton.

A formidable enemy indeed.

CHAPTER

32

*I*t was the waiting that was worst of all. Rumors of the loan transfers were already on the wind, and Jason had to agree with Owen's cynical observation that few people were above taking satisfaction in seeing the mighty fall. Maybe the Tiger wasn't so lucky after all. Already the word was beginning to filter through the city. Refinancing the loans was out of the question, not only because thousands of dollars were involved, but because now Jason knew that even if he could find someone willing to loan him the money, that man would undoubtedly become the target of blackmail, or if there was no fuel for that, outright threats, God only knew what. Had Jason been able to find such a source, he would not allow anyone else to take the risk that was his.

He had one key, and that was Sarah. Even now, he knew he had enough information to force her to tell him the name. Blackmail, another form of it, but still the same. And for the first time, he realized he was ambivalent about wanting to know. Sarah was right; only violence would come from his knowing her father. And if he killed him, what then? Years in prison, the destruction of his own life, Sarah's, and Jamie's? And beyond that, not in the light but buried deep enough, was his own small but insidious worm of doubt—love and hate could run so close, was Sarah really free of love for her father? She had suffered so much at his hands, and yet, even so, he had been most of her life—was there not some small part of her that beheld him forever as the first and final lover, that would grieve for his death even though she herself had once tried to cause it? It was a thought which never quite left Jason, no matter how hard he tried to deny it.

The confrontation would come. He accepted that. But he eased himself back from the edge of causing it now. *Tell me who he is, Sarah, tell me.* The plea was never far from his mind, but he did not voice it aloud. Let her tell him if she would.

He concentrated his energy on action. Owen quickly realized they were involved in plans for a financial war.

"You've always wished my interests were more consolidated, haven't you? Well, that's what I'm aiming for now."

Owen found to his private dismay that he wasn't nearly as pleased as he once would have thought to be by this new conservatism in the Tiger. It was not just that the loans were to be repaid on time, but there were shares and property to be sold.

"Start with the lot on Fern Hill. I have no plans to build on it and no rent is being paid for it. Sell it for gold or silver. I don't want any paper, nothing but hard money in exchange. It should realize enough to make the next payments due on the loans and perhaps to begin to pay one or two off. And if need be, the next things I want disposed of are my silver shares. They're worth something now with the high grade ore they're beginning to bring out."

Owen's usual calm demeanor deserted him. "But Jason, that property on Fern Hill is worth more by the day! They're beginning to call it Nob Hill because of the rich mansions going up. Hold on to it, and it will be worth ten times, even more, than what you'd get for it now. And it's the same with the silver shares. For God's sake, the mine is just starting to prove itself, just beginning to prove that you and the others were right. But it's not all the way yet, and no one will pay what I'm sure your shares will be worth in a year or two."

"I don't have a year or two, and you're the one who's always pointed out how overextended my businesses are," Jason replied calmly, but his eyes were fierce. "Whoever is trying to ruin me knows a lot about my investments. We already know that. And he's going to be counting on me being short of ready capital; it's the only way I could be forced under. Lumber prices going up and down, cargoes late or not as saleable as they should be, ships needing repair, loans foreclosed, properties confiscated. It's how I'd ruin a man like myself if I wanted to.

"The sales must be as secret as possible. There shouldn't be any problem; I'm the only one who will lose by them."

Owen nodded reluctantly. "I know more vultures than I care to admit, rich vultures at that. But word will get out eventually."

Jason shrugged. "Some will think I'm looking to buy something else; let the others think what they will."

It was Sarah who could not be left to wonder any longer, though the truth was not what he was going to offer her. He had been sleeping badly and knew that his preoccupation was beginning to show. He could see Sarah's concern mirrored in her eyes though she had not pressed him for any explanation.

He was glad to find her now in their suite at the Grand. Rio was with her, teaching her, all too successfully, he claimed, to play poker.

Sarah welcomed Jason with a glad cry, and Rio took his leave immediately, drawling, "Saved by th' husband. She was 'bout to win mah futuah. I 'spect mebbe ya won' need me 'til tomorra." He tried to hide his grin, but Jason smiled openly. "That we won't. Thank you, Rio."

He caught Sarah in his arms and nuzzled her neck as soon as the door closed. "How's my neglected bride?"

"Hungry, hungry for you." She nibbled at his mouth. "You're much more interesting than poker." She searched his face. "Is everything all right?"

He was able to look at her without shadows or doubt. Everything was all right; he was doing the best he could to make it so and to protect her. "Everything will be all right if you come closer and closer yet." He claimed her mouth with his own while his hands worked at her clothing.

"You're much too good at this! Thank heavens!" She was

laughing as they tumbled on the bed, her doubts vanquished by the light in his eyes, by his concentration on her. She had willed herself to patience these past days but it had been so hard! She had gritted her teeth against questions and pleas as she watched him pick at his food during the few meals they shared, as she shared his restless nights which began and ended without him touching her in more than swift, habitual comfort. He spent his energy in tossing, turning, and muttering unintelligible words throughout the night. Even when they had gone out with Carrie, Owen, Rio, and Frenchie, Sarah had known how distant Jason was from them in spite of his show of enjoyment, and she had not failed to notice the worried looks Owen had cast his way. Strangely, Owen's worry had served to reassure her—Owen tended to worry about Jason's financial risk-taking as much as she did, and to regard new ventures dourly.

"I've missed you!"

Jason heard the urgency in the whispered words as he stroked the silken hollow of her throat. No anger or blame, not a hint of the pouting reprimand even Gaiety would have indulged in despite her good nature. It made him even more protective than ever of Sarah.

"I'm back, sweetheart," he murmured, "and I love you, love you, love . . ." the words trailed off as his mouth traced the pattern of his love.

He emptied his mind of everything except her, making love to her with total concentration, and she felt his intensity beyond the touch of his flesh, felt as if she were surrounded, cradled, and rocked in shining warmth. His name was shivering sweet from her throat—the only name she needed to know.

They had late supper in the room, laughing over how good the food tasted, knowing it was because all their senses were sharp and alive to enjoyment tonight.

They had champagne, and when they were back in bed, Jason carefully poured a cold trickle of it between Sarah's breasts.

"Oh, la, la, Madame, I am zo zorry! How verrrrry clumsy of me!" He rolled his eyes and pursed his lips in imitation of a finicky French waiter. "I must clean zis from ze fine garment you arre wearring." He proceeded to follow the trail of champagne, his tongue teasing her skin.

"We are wanton! . . . Lovely!" Sarah gasped through her laughter.

She blushed when she met his eyes on waking, the night's celebrations clear in her mind in the morning light.

"It's all right; we're married," Jason reminded her with a smile, watching in delight as the blush deepened.

It could not be put off forever. That day he gave her the new information to enter in the ledgers.

At first she thought she was mistaken. She read through the brief notations again, looking for some new project, finding none. She looked up at Jason with a puzzled frown. "Am I understanding these correctly? All I find is loan transfers, changes in the names of some of your creditors."

"That's right," he replied calmly.

"This is what you and Owen have been working on? What does it mean?"

This was the time to lie as well as he ever had, before fear and suspicion had a chance to take hold. "Means just what you see there—we now make payments on several of the old loans to different people." He shrugged. "It's done all the time, selling out notes because you suddenly need the money for something else instead of waiting for it to come back in payments, even if you do lose the interest. I must admit, though, that my pride suffered some damage when I discovered that my notes had been sold. Owen and I've spent a good deal of time asking the men why, and they all had good, if different, reasons—new properties, new businesses they have a chance to buy, unwise speculation that's left them with debts of their own to pay off, that sort of thing, all of it giving them a need for capital just as my own need caused me to borrow the money in the first place. I can't blame them. Business in this part of the country is nothing if not changeable."

"But what about the men who bought the notes, do you know them?"

"Not personally, but by reputation. They have money to make this sort of investment, enough money to wait for the payments and collect interest too." The last thing he was going to tell her was that the new names were agents for Eastern interests, but he added a little of the truth. "Of course, there could be problems if the loans aren't paid off before it's time to renegotiate them; the interest could be raised. I might have to sell off a few things to make sure that doesn't happen." He did not mention the possibility of losing the collateral due to no new loan offers; she was accustomed now to the favored treatment he had heretofore enjoyed of new loans being offered almost automatically, and he wanted her to go on thinking that was the case for as long as possible.

He knew he had succeeded. Her brow wrinkled in distress at the thought of the higher interest, but there was no suspicion or fear in her expression.

She gazed around the luxurious room. "Don't you think we ought to move to more modest quarters? And you must not buy me any more clothes or such."

He laughed and patted the top of her head. "We're not in such dire straits as that! And what do you want to do, panic my other business associates? I can just hear them, 'Why, the Tiger can't even keep his woman decently, don't want to do business with him anymore.'" He reflected with private, grim humor that that was indeed exactly what would happen, and more. If this war was going to be as vicious as he suspected, such things as hotel rooms and his wife's clothing would be meaningless considerations.

Sarah could see his logic and accepted his explanation, and she tried not to feel guilty about being so spoiled by him.

It was more important than ever now for Jason to meet with his other associates, with those who were fellow investors in the silver mine, the redwood logging camp, and the *Sarah-Mary.* He had, in fact, the right to sell his shares in any or all of the enterprises to whomever he pleased, but he didn't want to panic the others by making them think their own investments were unsound. Financial panic was far easier to start than to stop. He would have to handle the men delicately, particularly those involved in the silver mine, since those shares he indeed might sell. But that decision was made for him.

He was at Owen's office when he opened the letter. It had arrived there because Owen acted as Jason's business representative in San Francisco. Correspondence was sent to him since Jason's presence or absence in the city was hard to predict.

With a grin, Owen tossed him the dirty envelope. "Here, this just arrived. Do some of your own work. I recognize the scrawl —it's from the mining foreman and undoubtedly contains pleas for more equipment or more miners along with a glowing description of the fortune within reach, all of it written and spelled so badly, you'll be deciphering it out forever."

Owen's smile faded as he watched Jason's face drain of color. It took Jason no time at all to read the letter. He handed it without a word to Owen.

Owen read it once and then again. "Well, it's bad all right, but it could have been a great deal worse. No one was hurt. And the foreman thinks the explosion might even have exposed some high grade ore."

Jason closed his eyes wearily. "It is something to be thankful for, that no one was hurt. But I'm sure whoever caused the explosion didn't care one way or the other."

"Whoever caused . . . ? Jason, it doesn't say one damn thing about anyone causing it. They don't know. They think it might have been a pocket of gas in the mine; that's not unusual."

"But *I* know. I'll try to sell my shares to the other investors. If they don't want them, I'll trust you to find a buyer as soon as possible."

Owen looked at him aghast. "You must be out of your mind! Admittedly it was a bad thing, but you haven't any proof at all that your enemy, whoever he is, had anything to do with it. If you sell now, after this, nobody is going to pay a decent price. The minute you offer the shares, it will be the whole bad-luck story, even to a man who knows it's a good bet. Sure, it's going to take some work and time to dig it out and shore it up again, but it can be done; it will be done! If you back out, it will affect the others. You can't sell now; you don't need to sell now! I already have good possibilities on the Nob Hill property. Go ahead and sell that, but keep the silver."

"I can't keep those shares. The mine may never produce anything at all unless I'm out of it. They don't know what happened. It could have been this, it could have been that. But I know. It was no accident. If I don't get out, someone will be hurt

or killed the next time. And there will be a next time. I don't
know how those miners are, I don't know what they think or feel,
but I do know I don't want them dying for me.

"I thought this would be a clean battle, just between him and
me, my rules, not his. What a fool! I don't know how to fight on
his terms, and I don't want to know. But the least I can do is try
to protect the innocents involved."

"And Sarah, what does she have to do with this, what will you
tell her?" Owen was sorry as soon as the words were out, sorry
even before he saw the rage blazing on Jason's face.

"She has nothing to do with this! I'm not going to tell her a
damn thing about it and neither are you! Do you understand?"

Owen nodded. "God, I'm sorry, Jason! If you'd implied the
same sort of thing about Carrie, I would have punched you in
the mouth. It's just that I don't understand what's going on, and
well, there's no man I'd rather call friend than you. It's hard for
me to know you're in trouble and I can't help."

The anger was gone. "You can help. You can help by doing
as I ask. And someday perhaps I'll be able to explain, though I
can't even promise that." He put his hand out and was glad
Owen took it without hesitation. "Believe me, no matter how it
seems, I do value your friendship and all the work you've done
on my behalf."

They regarded each other gravely, both a little embarrassed
by the revelation. Until now, their friendship had been expressed in good business dealings and boisterous good times
after working hours.

Now Jason had need of Owen's friendship and patience. The
meeting with the other silver mine shareholders went badly.
Owen had already notified the others of the problem at the
mine; writing one letter about it was all the foreman could manage, and in any case, he habitually communicated with Owen
because Jason was one of the major owners and the others had
long since agreed to let correspondence come through Mr.
Trenglyth. This was one instance when Owen and Jason were
devoutly sorry such a tradition existed.

The others were not overly concerned about the mine incident, not until Jason announced quietly that he was going to sell
his shares and was offering them here first.

The hearty reassurances of good ore died into absolute silence as all eyes focused on the Tiger.

It was like distorting the truth, skimming the surface, lying to Sarah, and it was every bit as imperative that he do it quickly and convincingly here.

"Gentlemen, I realize there couldn't be a more inopportune time for my announcement, but I ask you to believe that my decision was made before the news of the explosion reached me. I am selling my shares because of a matter of personal finances, not because I doubt the value of the mine. There is already proof of high grade ore, and I have every confidence that the mine will produce great wealth for many years. It is my loss and my sorrow to be leaving the venture now." His voice hardened. "But I am leaving it, and if you don't purchase the shares, someone else will."

"Tiger maybe isn't so lucky after all. Heard about some of his loans being traded off."

"More likely he's onto something new and better than the mine."

"Tangle a man with a woman, and he loses his ass, not to mention his balls, knew that blond hussy would mean nothing but bad for him for all her shy looks."

"Maybe he knows something about the mine we don't know, maybe he's holding out on us. After all, the letters come to him first."

Too many of the whispered comments were audible, but Jason kept his face impassive, only the golden glitter of his eyes betraying his feelings. He kept reminding himself that the men were speaking as much out of fear as out of any ill will toward him; they had long considered his "luck" their own by association, and now they feared losing it. But the irony of it burned deep—by pulling out of the venture, he was probably insuring its success; at the very least, he was making sure that it would not be destroyed by outside hands.

He bore it until the whispers died to uneasy silence. Then his voice cut across the room, decisive but devoid of resentment. "I think that's enough, gentlemen. In the past you have trusted me, and to my knowledge, I have never played you false. I have told you, and I tell you again that from all the evidence, the mine will soon produce high grade silver ore. The explosion did not make future mining impossible; indeed, the damage may even prove beneficial if hopes of a rich vein uncovered are borne out. That is up to fortune, good or bad, but it no longer has anything to do with me. And why I am selling my interest in the mine has nothing to do with you. The fact is, I am selling, and this is your last chance to buy."

"I'll buy your shares." The voice came bravely before another silence could settle on the assembly.

Jason barely restrained a smile and knew Owen was having the same problem. The little wisp of a man who had spoken was Mr. Bedow, the quietest, meekest member of the group. It was widely known that he was only a moderately successful merchant despite all the opportunities the city offered and that his investment in the silver mine was the only brave risk he had ever taken. His voice had not been among the malicious whispers.

"Your bid will be the only one accepted from this room, Mr. Bedow. Please deal with Mr. Trenglyth; he is empowered to arrange the sale. And should you purchase the shares, I wish you the best fortune from them and think you will have it."

The bedlam was stunning, a mad rush of voices after too much quiet and muttering, voices raised in protests and promises. Meek Mr. Bedow had broken the spell and banished the doubts. Suddenly almost everyone wanted the Tiger's shares.

Jason listened for an instant, his mouth tight in disdain, and then he roared, "Enough! It is finished. Mr. Bedow is the only man in this room who has the right to bargain for my shares. And if I hear one word, one whisper about any one of you applying pressure to him to gain the shares for yourself, I will personally see you ruined."

He walked out on them feeling good about the whole disastrous business, knowing he had reinstated his own myth of power and luck at least in one small group. No matter what they heard, no matter what happened, he doubted any of these men would tamper with Mr. Bedow. Bedow would make a low but reasonable bid, reasonable under the circumstances. Owen would accept it, and all the others would envy little Mr. Bedow from now on. He wondered if they'd yet realized that with his own shares and Jason's, he would control a major part of the company. As soon as the deal was concluded, he would make sure the outcome was made public. He did not fear that Sarah's father would interfere now. The man was after him, and there had to be some limit to the destruction he could undertake. With grim satisfaction, Jason thought of how expensive all this must be—buying loans and hiring thugs and God knew what else. He had met the man only through Sarah's past and through the incidents he judged him to have engineered, but altogether it was enough for him to divine an obsession to the point of madness. It was a weakness Jason had every intention of exploiting; there seemed to him a good chance that if he could hold on long enough, Sarah's father would ruin himself one way or another.

He was taking care now not to shut Sarah out again though he was not encouraging her to accompany him to business meetings, and he was relieved that she was out when he returned to the hotel. It gave him time to catch his breath and decide what he was going to tell her.

In the end he simply told her that he'd decided to sell his silver shares and already had a buyer.

"There are still problems at the mine and probably will be for quite a long time, though I expect there'll be a rich yield eventually. But I've lost interest in it, and I'm glad to get out now."

He was so relieved by her seeming acceptance, he did not realize it had been too easily given.

The loan transfers, Fern Hill (now called Nob Hill by most) property, and now this—Sarah's confidence that all was well evaporated in a wave of unease. Jason was keeping something from her after all, and she wanted to know what it was. He wasn't going to tell her, but Owen might.

It should have been another happy evening since they were all together at Carrie and Owen's house, but Sarah was nervous as a cat, waiting for a chance to speak privately to Owen. She was aided by the fact that the crew of the *Gaiety* was here tonight, invited by Carrie, who was sure they must be lonesome for their own homes. The *Gaiety* was being readied to sail again soon and was well-guarded by seamen Captain Hanson trusted.

At last she saw Owen standing alone, and she went to him, hoping the smile would stay in place on her mouth. "We always have such a good time here," she said softly. "Owen, what's going on? What sort of trouble is it that Jason won't tell me?"

She caught him completely unaware, and the worried look in his dark eyes gave him away before he managed to say, "Nothing but the usual ups and downs of business in the West."

She regarded him sadly. "You're not a very skilled liar."

"Oh, Christ, Sarah!" Though he kept it low, the anguish in his voice was clear. "I don't know much myself, but what little I do know is between Jason and myself. We have a professional relationship as well as friendship between us."

"And he asked you not to tell me anything."

Owen nodded miserably.

"It's all right. Jason needs your loyalty, more now I expect than ever. I'm glad he has it."

He watched her rejoin the party with a good show of enjoyment, but his heart was heavy for both the Drakes, each trying so hard to protect the other. It couldn't go on forever; they would have to share the burden before too long, but he wasn't going to tell Jason about his conversation with Sarah; he owed her loyalty too.

Sarah tried not to disturb Jason, who seemed to be sleeping well. She was now the one tossing restlessly. She hardly slept at all and was glad to see morning come, as weak and gray as it was.

Jason was off early to yet another meeting, this time with the redwood investors, and he was preoccupied with the hope that all would go smoothly despite the rumors the other men had undoubtedly heard by now. He had no intention of selling his interest in the logging camp, for in spite of fluctuating lumber prices, the demand for redwood both here and in the Orient was continuing to grow due to the special properties of the wood.

But even with his mind on business, he didn't fail to notice Sarah's pallor. "Aren't you feeling well?"

She felt his sudden complete concentration on her, and she managed to answer with a smile. "I think I'm getting homesick for Jamie and everyone else. It seems as if we've been here for years instead of weeks."

That made perfect sense to Jason. He was feeling the same way. "I think we can leave by next week. I'm just as anxious as you are. But, please, take it easy today."

She made a face at him. "It's taking it easy that makes me so tired. High time I got back to useful days." *Tell me, let me help, tell me what's going on. Is it he, is it my father?* The words sounded in her head, but she did not give voice to them. "All I plan for today is to bore Rio with useless errands."

"See that you do. Don't go anywhere without him." The warning was a reflex. Rio had seen no sign of anyone following either one of the Drakes, and Jason had gone another step mentally in his assessment of Sarah's father. He was still not going to risk having Sarah grabbed away from him, but he doubted it would happen now. He judged that now that the man knew so much about his business, he would prefer to leave Sarah with her husband long enough for her to witness his downfall. That suited Jason just fine; he had no intention of failing.

"Yes, sir," she agreed with mocking meekness and received a kiss for the rebellious loom in her eyes.

But she did allow Rio to accompany her and was even glad of his escort; the poverty and desperation of the section of the city they visited reminded her only too graphically of her abortive attempt to earn a living on the streets.

"I'd like to visit the Reverend Mapes, the man who performed our marriage ceremony," she'd told Rio. "Do you have any way of finding him?"

"I expect I do," Rio said to her surprise. He looked a little sheepish at the admission since association with men of the cloth wasn't exactly in his line. "He's a good man even if he is a preacher."

In fact, Rio had grown quite fond of the old man. He had first sought him out on Owen's advice simply to find out whether Mapes knew any more about men looking for the Drakes. He had found himself going back to see the Reverend even though the minister had no new information. There was an inner quietness about the old man that Rio knew he would never have in his own life. It was a quality which attracted him, and then he found himself beginning to feel more and more protective of the minister. He had never known anyone else who lived so simply and so much for others as Bartholomew did. And though he kept waiting for a thundering sermon on his bad life, it never came. Bartholomew welcomed him with pleasure whenever he saw him even when he clearly knew that Rio had been away on deadly business.

"I am thankful you have returned safely," was all he'd said.

"When're ya goin' talk t' me 'bout God?" Rio had once demanded, hearing his own childish truculence with amazement.

"Never, unless you wish to talk about Him," Bartholomew had replied promptly, kindness and humor clear in his eyes. "My friend, of all the men I know, I assume you are the closest to knowing your God. I doubt that anything a muddling old man could say would help or hinder what you already know within yourself. I believe it's your move."

Rio had been closer to weeping than he'd ever been since he was a very small child. He'd viewed the checkerboard through a blur of tears and lost the game.

"You see, God may not listen to my major requests, but He does sometimes work in mysterious ways when I'm playing checkers," the Reverend had said gently.

Only Frenchie knew about his visits with the Reverend. "I expect it does you both good," she said casually, seeming to find nothing strange in it at all.

Nor did Sarah now betray that she thought it odd he should know where to find the minister as they threaded their way through garbage-strewn alleyways. Sarah was only thankful that he knew where to look even in the fog-shrouded day.

Rio knew that Bartholomew wouldn't be in his bare room at this time of the morning since he never seemed to sleep late, despite his often obvious tiredness and his advancing years. Later he would probably go to some wealthy household to tutor the heir apparent in the classics, but now he would be wending his way among the poorest of his scattered flock, most especially where there were clusters of children.

Rio finally spotted him, hearing the noise first, then picking out the figure in the dark suit surrounded by a laughing mob of ragtag youngsters. He was performing the magic feat of making a small coin appear and disappear from various ears. The children saw Rio and Sarah before Mapes did.

Some of them knew Rio and smiled shyly at him, awed, regardless of their own street toughness, by what they recognized in him, but Sarah they regarded with round-eyed silence. Though some of the bigger boys, nine and ten years old, had particularly bold comments they normally used to shock posh ladies, none of them were voiced now. It was not only the presence of Rio and the Reverend that stopped them, it was something about the woman herself, the way she smiled at them even though her eyes were sad.

They ducked and smiled back at her as the Reverend Mapes rumbled through the introductions.

Bartholomew was pleased by the unexpected pleasure of seeing Sarah Drake again, and his joy showed on his face and in his greeting. But as quickly as the joy had come, it was gone. He had been in the business of knowing when people were in trouble for too long to mistake Sarah's need. He could feel it as clearly as the cold dampness of the day.

"I'd like to speak to him alone," Sarah whispered to Rio.

He asked no questions, merely pressed her hand briefly and then was suddenly in charge of the children, calling many of them by name, drawling his words even more than he usually did, beginning a highly fanciful yarn about a wild stallion who had stolen over a hundred prize mares.

"Why thet ol' hoss kin jus' steal up quiet like in th' dark a' th' night, an' then he calls jus' once t' them mares, an' off they go, jumpin' th' highest fences, flyin' jus' like birds . . ."

His voice faded out of their hearing as Sarah and the minister moved away.

She had not thought to talk to him in such surroundings—a narrow passageway wreathed in mist and stinking of refuse—but she realized it didn't matter; they were as private here as they would be anywhere, and this was part of his world.

"I'm sorry to interrupt your time with the children," she said, "but I'm desperate for advice. I can't seem to make the decision on my own."

"Before you go any further, Mrs. Drake, I must be certain you understand my limitations." His voice was quiet but firm. "Whatever you say to me or I say to you remains between us. Never doubt that. But do not mistake me. I am not a priest of the Roman Catholic Church. I have never to my knowledge been closeted alone with God though I am ever hopeful that my voice sounds as loudly as the others in the babel. I cannot absolve you of sins or promise you any particular favors in the hereafter. I cannot even promise that I will give you proper advice, only that I will listen."

She regarded him with a puzzled frown until the sense of his words sank in. Then she smiled. "Reverend Mapes, I swear to you, I haven't come to ask forgiveness for betraying Jason. I love him dearly, even more than the day you married us. It is what to do for that love that has me so confused.

"I fled from my father some years ago. I even tried to kill him. I will not tell you why, but you must believe that he is an evil and very powerful man."

Now he understood the shadows he had seen from the first in her and chided himself inwardly for not recognizing their source even then. How many abused children he had seen in the years, children abused in body, mind, and spirit by the very people who should have protected them most fiercely. It sometimes left wounds that never healed.

He listened intently to her short, sharp description of the changes in Jason's business affairs and her own suspicions, and he thought of the men who had come looking for the Drakes.

"I don't want him to know who my father is, I never want him to know! Only violence will come from it. But I'm sure my father knows who Jason is, knows everything about him by now. Is it right for me to continue to withhold his name from my husband? Is there any use in that now?"

Bartholomew closed his eyes for a moment. He had never lost his childlike hope that a voice recognizably divine would speak and break the silent vigil of his faith. But he had not yet heard it nor did it speak now to free him of the burden of counseling Sarah.

Finally he said, "In a way it would be easier to tell him, wouldn't it? Your burden would become his and you would no longer have to fight to keep them apart."

She nodded, saying nothing.

"My dear, I think your instincts are sound; you want to protect Jason above all things. And you don't know whether or not your suspicions are correct. I think you must carry your burden alone for a while longer. I think you will know when you must tell your husband. I fear there will be no way in the end to keep the two men apart no matter what you do if indeed your father is trying to disrupt your new life."

His unhappiness showed. "You see, I am not much good at this."

"But you are! I needed another voice, and yours is a wise one. Thank you." There was peculiar comfort in knowing that someone else saw the inevitability of the conflict as clearly as she did.

Bartholomew made a mental note to ask God's forgiveness when he could find true contrition within himself for his unkind hope that Sarah's father would go to Hell before he ever met Jason. In his mind, Hell needed no pyrotechnics but would be perfectly adequate simply by penning together those souls who had tormented others. They would be without victims and would all themselves be victims of each other. People who tormented children were on the top of Bartholomew's rather short list of those who truly deserved damnation.

CHAPTER

33

Sarah's meeting with the minister meant a great deal to her, and she continued to draw strength from the memory. She would protect Jason for as long as she could, and she would bear the knowledge that there was much he was not sharing with her. The time would come when it was all shared again, a time she dreaded because it would most probably come only when the war between Jason and her father was too intense to deny or hide any longer.

She was so glad to be aboard the *Gaiety* bound for home, she admitted to Jason that she felt like getting down on her knees to kiss the deck.

"That would surely get the crew's attention," he said, his mouth turned up in the familiar crooked grin, his eyes bright and clear. He was as happy as she to be going home, leaving the confusions of San Francisco behind him. He missed Jamie intensely, and he knew they were all safer on the island, particularly Sarah.

Sarah. The depth of his love and need for her was a continuing wonder to him. Despite all the current problems and those yet to be, he was grateful every day that she was with him. And though he neither questioned it nor examined it too closely, he had felt her warmth and concern touching him, enfolding him even more closely in the past days. A wonder indeed.

"You have the most peculiar expression on your face," Sarah said.

"A fine thing to say when I'm thinking about how much I love you," Jason said self-righteously.

The days aboard the *Gaiety* had long since come to symbolize the most private and joyful time they had together, regardless of the presence of the crew. Whatever problems had to be faced could wait until the land was reached again.

Sarah turned twenty-one aboard ship and informed Jason that it was fast becoming a tradition.

"We'll keep it so from now on," he announced. "Even if we're home, we'll sail out for the day. Saree, Sarrrreeee, it's yer eighty-first birthday! Hurry up now, little woman, put on yer specks and come along, we can't miss the tide!"

Sarah gave a peal of delight at his foolish imitation of a very old man, perfect even to the puckering of his mouth, the quavering voice, and the hunch of his shoulders, and yet there was a sharp edge beneath the delight.

"I'll love you then too, Jason. I'll love you even more than I do now," she said softly, and she thought, God grant that we have each other long enough to know what it is to grow old together.

"Even if I'm crotchety and can't remember where I put my slippers?" he teased, but inwardly his thoughts paralleled hers: I'll kill him before he ever has a chance to touch you again.

"Even then." She managed to smile at him. She would not let dark thoughts spoil this day.

David Becam even managed to produce something like a cake, admitting with a grin that his sea-baked goods all tended to be similar to hardtack.

Jason opened champagne for the occasion, and Sarah unwrapped her gifts from him, having no idea what the canvas bundle could be until the finely polished leather was revealed. It was a stockman's saddle made slightly smaller than the normal especially for her so that she could ride astride as she had learned to do from the beginning. With it was a matching bridle and a bright red blanket which would complement Sheba's dark coat.

"Oh, Jason, it's all so beautiful, I can't wait to see how Sheba will look in her new tack!" She threw her arms around him and kissed him. "Thank you, thank you!"

When they were back in the cabin, he reached into his coat pocket and handed her a flat jeweler's box. "This is not for Sheba to wear. It's for you to remember your twenty-first birthday."

She opened the box and gasped. On the dark velvet lay a necklace. Twenty-one small roses intricately wrought in several shades of gold to give the flowers shadows and light were joined by pairs of gold leaves linked in the center to make the collar pliable.

She was torn between laughter and tears, afraid to touch the piece. "Oh, God, Jason it is too much, especially now! You'll have me draped in precious jewels while the rest of your world goes begging."

"Not quite. Now hush and let me fasten this." He took the necklace and put it around her neck. "Didn't you promise to humor me in your marriage vows?"

She had to laugh at that. "Love, honor, and humor? I don't think that's quite the way it went." She reached up to touch the necklace, remembering the roses that had scented their bridal chamber, knowing Jason had remembered too. "It's the loveliest thing I've ever seen," she admitted with a little sigh.

"I'd have to disagree with you there," Jason murmured, his voice turning husky as he began to take the pins out of her hair.

The crew made sure Jason had no watch to stand, no duties on the *Gaiety* that night.

The island was in full and verdant spring by the time they arrived home, and Sarah loved it anew, loved riding out on the island and seeing all her friends again, loved most of all being with Jamie.

Even though he assured them repeatedly that he had missed them, he had an endless list of adventures to recount to them, his shining eyes telling even more clearly than his words how rich the days on the island had been for him. Cade had let him help with the lambing, and he was proud of himself.

"Mostly the ewes, those are the mothers, do all the work themselves," he told them earnestly. "But sometimes they have trouble, or even after they have the baby, they don't want it much. That's when Cade and me helped."

Jason and Sarah exchanged glances of amusement; there was a new competence and maturity about the boy and an acceptance of the natural process of things which any parent should welcome.

Jamie was particularly delighted to share one of his new fascinations with them—the birdlife on the island. "Some of them fly for hundreds, even thousands of miles," he told them in wonder, "building their nests in one place but spending lots of time in other places. And no one knows how the birds know where they're goin', but they do! Cade knows lots of their names and so does Mr. Burke, an' he has a book I've been studyin'."

They went with him to the east side of the island to peer over a cliff edge at a peregrine falcon's nest and then at some distance away, the eyrie of a pair of bald eagles and their still immature young.

The unpopulated east side of the island, with its cliffs, rugged brush, and soil that seemed unfit to grow anything but timber, was ideal for the predators. Sarah and Jason heeded Jamie's warning about the care they must take when they went to observe the birds.

"They can be real mean if they think you're going to hurt their babies, so we have to be quiet and move slow."

After following nothing more than a deer trail through dense growth, they left their horses in the shadow of the trees and walked the rest of the way out to the bare promontory of the cliff, crawling the last bit of the way to the edge.

Sarah had to stifle nervous giggles and her head spun unpleasantly as she looked down to the sea-washed rocks below; it reminded her of the day she had gone over the other cliff face after Jamie. But it was worth it when she finally spotted the birds, using Jason's glass to get a closer look at them.

The young faces still had wisps of down on them and did not look as if they'd ever be as graceful as their parents, one of whom was watching while the young squabbled over the food it had brought while the other was in the air nearby crying, "Kek kek kek ke-ek," in a rasping voice.

They withdrew swiftly from the cliff edge when one of the falcons suddenly soared up to hover over them with angry cries before swooping back down to the nest.

"Brave little bird," Jason whispered.

"Not so little when you see the talons and the beak," Sarah said.

When Jamie pointed out the eagles' eyrie, Sarah blinked in surprise. "My goodness, that's one of the messiest things I've ever seen. It's a wonder it doesn't just fall down."

It looked like a huge bundle of sticks in a fork of one of the tallest trees.

"But it's really made better 'n it looks!" Jamie protested. "Eagles don't build new nests every year, they just add stuff to their old one, but sometimes they have two or three nests and sometimes they just don't lay eggs this year or that, so we're really lucky to be able to see this one with fledglings," he produced the word proudly, "in it. Of course, Cade found these nests, not me, an' he's the one that knows all about 'em. He told me they like fish even more 'n we do an' that they can go right into the water without gettin' soaked and sinkin'. I didn't believe 'im 'til I saw it, but now I know it's true." He was humming with the excitement of his new interest, and it was contagious.

Through Jason's glass they saw first one and then two heads peering out of the nest—dark, fierce eagle faces for all their youth—and then they heard and spotted one of the parents perched on another tall tree close by. The adult bird was splendidly arrayed in the white and dark of full maturity. They slipped away as quietly as possible, united in their wish to leave the birds with the feeling of sanctity in their wild place.

The adventure was made complete for Jamie when his father found and presented him with a long, perfect feather from one of the adult eagles, and they finished the outing with a picnic by the pond under a bright sky.

Sarah and Jason both tried to spend as much time with Jamie as possible, both conscious of the unspoken thought that the more complicated things became, the less time they were likely to have with him, the less able they would be to take him with them, whether he wanted to go or not. However they did take him along to Seattle and the logging camp in July.

In Seattle whatever scandal had been attached to the Drakes was old and tame compared to the buzz still going on over Doc Maynard's first wife turning up from back East. Seems he'd never gotten around to divorcing her, and she'd gotten tired of waiting for him to return or to give her her property rights, which he'd supposedly claimed on her behalf in Seattle. Doc had told his barber that the town was going to witness a sight they'd never seen before, and he was right. He'd gone down to meet the boat with Catherine, his second wife, on one arm and had walked back with Lydia, his first wife, on the other. And God knew how and most respectable people didn't want to consider it too closely, but the amiable doctor and the two wives had managed to live together peacefully for several months while they tried to sort out their business affairs. And then Lydia had departed serenely for home. However, as genial as the human relationships might have been, there was speculation that Doc's business affairs and land claims were now in worse shape than ever. Jason wondered if he himself would end up owning the waterfront lot after all. At present there was a tidy little rent coming in from a ramshackle saloon that sailors and loggers liked to frequent.

The rest of the talk in Seattle that summer seemed still almost wholly concentrated on the railroad. Jamie could hardly wait until it came chugging in from across the country.

"You may have to wait a very long time," his father cautioned him.

"But everyone says it's going to be pretty soon," Jamie pointed out.

"Most people hope it's going to be pretty soon, but that doesn't make it true," Jason corrected gently. "I want it to come as much as everyone else does, but I'll believe it when I see it and not before. The railroad men have a lot of power, and they may not choose Seattle after all for the terminus."

"Do they have more power than you?" Jamie's doubt that that was possible showed in his face.

"Concerning railroads they certainly do. No one is powerful in everything; that's why different people do different things."

The explanation seemed to make sense to him even if he did wish his father was a big railroad man.

Jason wondered for the countless time where Sarah's father's weakness and lack of power lay. No man was invincible in all things.

Waiting to see what happened next grew no easier. Owen had done as Jason had instructed, taking the money in hard coin from the sale of the silver shares to Mr. Bedow and from the sale of the Nob Hill lot and using most of it to meet interest payments and to pay off loans, keeping some back for emergencies. Three major loans remained, paid only up to the next installment with thousands still due, monies which should come in regularly from lumber profits, the rent on the business lot in San Francisco and the one in Seattle, profits from the *Lady Ellen* and the *Sarah-Mary,* and from Jason's share of the cargo the *Moon Chaser* would bring in.

There was nothing wrong with Jason's financial status at the moment, and he wondered how long it would take for Sarah's father to realize that fact.

Jamie's birthday picnic was even happier this year, not only because Owen had shipped the special items by steam packet so that they reached the island in time, but he had also sent word that the *Moon Chaser* had made port in San Francisco and was heavily laden with goods bound to bring high prices. There was a letter from Clem too, and his exuberance over the successful voyage showed through his terse New England style.

Sarah and Jason were overjoyed at the prospect of seeing the Pollards again, and Jamie could hardly wait to hear more of their stories about life on the high seas. He also intended to share his birthday gifts from his parents with the Pollards. He was entranced with the field glasses and the lavishly illustrated bird book he'd received, and was sure that Clem and Etta had seen all sorts of strange birds in their travels.

Sarah and Jason had watched him opening gifts and had shared a moment of extreme tenderness betrayed only by their hands holding with sudden fierceness. At ten years old, Jamie was not a little boy anymore. To be sure, it would be another few years before he started to shoot up in earnest, but he had grown a great deal since Sarah had first met him, and there were already signs that the blurred lines of childhood were giving way to the definition he would have as a man. He carried himself proudly, his shoulders squarely set, his body sturdy, his facial bones beginning to show so clearly, it wasn't difficult to see the handsome man he would be.

He was going to break hearts somewhere, Sarah thought again, but he would never do it knowingly. Gaiety's blood would keep him from being as rugged-looking as his father, but his father's strength would keep him from being too pretty. And he had a special gift for which Jason gave Sarah full credit despite her truthful protest that it had always been there and just needed the chance to come out—Jamie gave to and received from others with equal grace and joy and without selfishness in either process. It was a rare quality, and Sarah prayed he would keep it all his life.

She was thinking of it a few days after the picnic as she and Jamie fished from the beach not far from Nate and Jon's property. The beaches here and there on the island's edges were spectacular, bordered as they were by cliffs or green bluffs, but they were not very comfortable to walk on since what sand there was, was in narrow ridges far back from the water except at high tide and cluttered with driftwood. The rest was deeply pebbled with smooth sea stones that rolled and bruised underfoot. This beach was one of the largest and was easily accessible by a path through the woods. Jamie had a very good reason for wanting to be here.

Loons, ducks, gulls, and various other birds liked the area, even the eagles came for fish washed up on the beach, and Jamie planned to take whatever he and Sarah caught and scatter it, then hide and see what fowl came to feed. He'd decided that fishing to feed the birds was as fair as fishing to feed himself.

It was fine with Sarah. Jamie often preferred to be by himself or had plans which included the other children, and she felt honored that he thought her more qualified for this expedition than they. His father was invited too and had promised to come along later.

"You and Papa are quieter than the kids," he told them. "Daniel could've come too, of course." He spoke of his dead friend matter-of-factly now though the pain of the loss still sounded in his voice, as it did when he spoke of his grandmother. "Constance can be real quiet too with birds and animals, but I think she's making a dinner for Mr. Becam today. I think maybe someday they might be married to each other."

Jason and Sarah had exchanged a glance; so much for hiding things from children.

Sarah and Jamie spent some time competing to see who could coax the most skips from flat rocks shied across the water. Jamie admitted it wasn't a very good way to attract birds. "But it's fun."

Now he announced it really was time for them to fish. Sarah couldn't think of a more unlikely way to go about it than trying to throw lines out in the ripples from the wet pebbled edge, but she went along with it anyway.

Their first efforts to get their hooks out into the water ended in failure and giggles as the lines caught each other. Sarah moved a few paces away, and they tried again.

"Are you sure we can catch anything this way?" she asked after what seemed to her a long time of patient standing.

"'Course we can! Look at those silver an' dark streaks. You know they're fish," Jamie chided.

"Out there, not here," she muttered under her breath, but she jiggled her line and hoped the fish liked the stale cheese Maggie had donated enough to come in for it.

Some birds didn't seem to mind that there were humans about. A little flock Jamie proudly identified as sandpipers ran frantic zigzagging patterns on their thin stick legs near the water's edge. Gulls swooped and scolded, greedy for the possible catch, and a loon wove near and far patterns on the water, his snakelike head turned toward the intruders on the beach.

Sarah grew so interested in the antics of the waterfowl, she forgot what she was doing, and the pull on her line came as a shock.

"You've got somethin', you do, you do, pull 'im in!" Jamie's excited yell sent the sandpipers wheeling away in squeaking alarm.

Sarah saw the silver flash on the water and felt the surprisingly hard pull on the line. She pulled against it. The pole was bending near to breaking, and she stepped forward into the water in a futile attempt to ease the strain, having no more line to give the fish. The line snapped, the pole arched out of her hand, her feet lost purchase so quickly, she had no time to do anything but close her eyes as the water came up to meet her. She expected in that split second to fall flat in shallow water but found instead that she had fallen off a ledge and was in water above her waist. She surfaced sputtering and laughing so hard there would have been a chance of drowning in the icy water despite her ability to swim had her feet not found the bottom.

Jamie went down on his knees, and for a terrified instant Sarah thought he was having one of his old attacks, but then she realized he was simply overcome with laughter.

The day was hot, the water cold but not harmfully so. Sarah swallowed her own mirth as best she could and asked in a deceptively gentle and slightly breathless voice, "Jamie, will you give me a hand out?"

He struggled to his feet immediately, still laughing, and came over to offer his hand. She pulled, catapulting him into the water but holding him high in spite of his weight so that he wouldn't swallow any.

"Serves you right for laughing at me!"

"Feels good! I was gettin' hot. Oh, you did look funny!" he said. He buried his face against her neck. "I do love you, most of all, I decided, 'cuz you make me laugh." His voice was still unsteady with little hiccoughs of amusement.

"That's one of the best reasons I've heard," Sarah agreed, and she held him closer, swirling them both in the water. "I love you for lots of reasons but most of all because you're a special person who makes me glad every single day." He nuzzled against her again, and she felt as complete as she ever had in her life. He was not her child by birth, but now in every way that mattered he was her son. She dropped a light kiss on the tip of his nose. "And now, fellow fisherman, we'd better get out of this before we turn into fish, or more likely, icebergs." She pushed him up on the high ground and scrambled up after him.

They retreated beyond the water's edge and sat on a large, sea-bleached, sun-warm cedar log on the sandspit, feeling the summer heat beginning to dry them immediately.

"I been thinkin', well, learnin' about the birds an' everything, I know now that there's lots of water on the earth, whole other oceans. Mr. Burke told us that lots of times, but now I've really been thinkin' about it, an' I been wonderin' why they don't all run together an' just wash right over the land." There was the smallest shade of fear in his speculation.

"Lordy, I'm not the best person to ask about such things, but if I remember correctly, the sun and the moon pull different ways so tides are constantly coming in and going out but not all together." She understood suddenly that he was beginning to see the vastness of the world, a frightening immensity whenever one discovered it. She chose her words very carefully. "Knowledge doesn't change the world in an instant, though sometimes it might be well if it did. But knowledge allows one to see things more clearly, understand them better. The fact that you now realize there are other oceans on the earth isn't going to change those oceans from their natural courses, whatever those are, and set them rolling toward you. It hasn't happened yet, so it surely won't happen because you know a little more about them. Does that make sense?"

He regarded her solemnly, the golden intentness so like his father's. "I think so. Knowing things can change you but maybe not the things you're knowing about. So, no matter how much I ever know 'bout oceans, they'll just go on their own way. It's nice and scary at the same time, isn't it?"

"It is indeed." She was both glad and sorry to see him leaving childhood behind; surely one of the largest and most complex steps was the shifting of perception of self, the realization that one was not the central controlling force of the universe but only a small part of that universe, a small part that was, paradoxically, important in a different way. She was thankful that Jamie was coming to that stage naturally and in his own good time, whereas she had been forced into it far too early and unnaturally and was still struggling to attain a sense of her self as important and worthy of life. That sense was already part of Jamie, was already tempering the fearful vision of boundless horizons and would grow stronger as he grew older. In this, he would surely be like his father. Sarah had never known anyone so innately aware of his own presence as Jason was, and that awareness made it impossible for other people to ignore his existence. It was not arrogance, though Jason could be arrogant; it was simply an acceptance of the power and responsibility of being himself.

She was so intent on her thoughts of Jason and his son, so filled with the warmth and the presence of Jamie beside her, at first she simply stared at the vessels moving swiftly toward the beach. Then she focused on them sharply, blinking in disbelief. They did not disappear.

"Forget your shoes, forget everything but running. Oh, God, run for the horses!" She jerked Jamie to his feet and tried to pull him toward the path through the woods. "You can go faster than I can. Get help!"

She thought Jamie was frozen in fear when he refused to budge, and then she saw he was smiling and trying to get his arm up to wave despite her fierce grip on him.

"Don't be scairt. I'm sure those Indians are friends. They haven't been here for a long time, but I remember them anyway. Grandmother Ellen didn't want me to get close to 'em," he finally managed to say, having had no chance since Sarah had sighted the canoes. She had spotted them first because he'd been watching the sandpipers and wondering how many oceans they'd seen. "Honest, Mama, they wouldn't have women an' kids with 'em if they were a war party. Everybody knows that. Well, everybody that grew up 'round here," he amended hastily.

"Mind if I join the party? I didn't know you were inviting so many guests," Jason said as he came up beside them.

Sarah was infinitely glad to see him. Her heart was still racing, and she had her knees locked against collapse. "If you laugh at me, I'll throw you into the sea in front of your friends," she muttered, her voice shaking.

"She wanted me to run away from 'em," Jamie announced, trying not to giggle.

"While you fought them off, no doubt," Jason said kindly, touching her face, which was beginning to regain its healthy color. "I'm sorry they gave you such a fright and glad I decided it was time to see what you and Jamie were up to."

He raised his arm in greeting and yelled something unintelligible as the canoes neared the beach. "Even if they can speak English, and a few of Sam's people can, they won't. They'll speak trade jargon, Chinook Jargon; it's a mixture of Chinook, other Indian dialects, English, and French," he explained. "Don't be afraid if they're curious about you; they mean no harm." He went forward to greet them.

There followed some of the oddest moments Sarah had ever experienced, and she pinched herself surreptitiously, sure it was all a mad dream.

The three large canoes, made of red-cedar trees hollowed out and shaped with designs painted on the bow of the largest, were beached, and the people poured out, proving the truth of Jamie's statement as there were indeed women and children in the group. The people were long-armed and sturdy-legged as if wrought by their lives of paddling the canoes. And they did not fit Sarah's idea of Indians. They didn't look at all like those she had seen in crossing the continent; they didn't even look like the ones around Seattle. They were quite tall and light-skinned, certainly not copper-hued, and their eyes were as likely to be a lightish brown as black; many had wavy dark brown hair rather than black, and several of the men sported mustaches or beards. Their features were definitely slanted as if the blood of Asia flowed strongly in their veins. They were dressed in a colorful motley of white man's and Indian clothing. Some of the women wore patterned hats which Sarah later learned were woven of spruce roots, and some of the men had leather aprons with patterns painted on them. What made the traditional clothing more noticeable was the fact that the women in the hats were as apt to be wearing bright calico dresses as they were their own styles of layered and decorated skins, and the men with the aprons tended to have white man's trousers on under them. Later Jason told her that the men were only as fully clothed as they were as an honor to the whites they were visiting. On their own in the summer they sensibly preferred to wear as little as possible. There was also a sprinkling of ornaments Sarah tried not to stare at—labrets in pierced lower lips and nose ornaments, tattoos here and there.

The air was filled with shrieks, laughter, and greetings as they crowded around Jason. One quite plump matriarch walked up to him and gave him a swat on the back, receiving a hearty kiss in return. And suddenly Sarah was surrounded by people who were touching her hair, her face, her clothing. Despite the rank smell of rancid fish oil, she did not pull away. They obviously meant no harm just as Jason had predicted; their touch was gentle and wondering. Even though the words were strange, though some did sound like bastardized French and English, it was clear they were exclaiming over the color of her hair and eyes; their gestures were as readable as Maggie's and Ben's.

Sam, the chief, would have been easy to identify even had he not been the one who had stepped out of the largest canoe first. He spoke mostly to Jason and directed the others. He was a powerfully built man of advanced years, nearly as tall as Jason, and he radiated authority. Sarah saw him gesture toward her. Then he and Jason had an earnest conversation which ended in laughter and backslapping.

When Sarah saw the things being unloaded from the canoes, she realized the Indians had not just dropped by on their way to somewhere else, and when Jason finally made his way back to her side, he informed her that they were in for a "potlatch"— a fine way to end the summer—and that there was no time to waste in letting the other islanders know.

The sense of unreality never quite left Sarah, though the Indians stayed for three very real days of merrymaking. The potlatch, she soon discovered, was Chief Sam's way of honoring Jason by letting Jason honor the Indians, but Jason felt no reluctance. Indeed, he did feel honored by it.

"They're of the Haida people, and they live far to the north,

but their canoes are swift. They used to visit these islands much
more frequently and long before I got here. And when I did,
they could have raided Drake's Island; they still had the power
to do it then. But they didn't. They pointed out shellfish and
berries I hadn't thought to eat and showed me how they prepared them, and in return I gave them some tools and other
trinkets. It was just a lucky chance that we met and that there was
goodwill on both sides. But they haven't been here since Jamie
was quite small, probably four or five years ago, and though they
have traded on the way, they have come this far south now only
because word reached them that the lion man—a rough transla-
tion between the two cultures—has taken in marriage the star
woman. Actually, they came to see you. Chief Sam thinks perhaps you're otter woman too." Jason grinned at her still-damp
clothes. "You hadn't seen them yet, but apparently they saw you
coming out of the sea with Jamie."

"Star woman? And how did they ever know I was here if they
live so far away?" she asked in wonder.

"Stars, 'tsil-tsil,' in the Jargon, and according to them, the
color of your hair. And Indians have seen you even as you
looked at them around Seattle—not the same people, but trade
goes a long way. White traders such as Captain Gibson have
seen you too. It took a while, but word got there. Why, by now,
you may be known as far north as Alaska."

And surely as far east as New York, she thought, then she
banished the thought from her mind by concentrating on the
vivid present.

She learned a great deal about the Haidas in the three days
of their visit. These were not Indians who lived in huts or tents;
their villages were of great timbered houses which often sheltered several families, and "Sam" was no more the Chief's real
name than "Rose" was the name of his wife—the old woman
Jason had kissed. They were simply names of convenience for
the Indians' dealings with the white man. Sam was of the Eagle
clan and Rose was of the Wolf. Alliances and marriages were
carefully arranged between the clans, and most surprising of all
to Sarah was the fact that their society was matriarchal—children
took their names, privileges, and rights from their mother's side

of the family. The women visiting with their men obviously had a very equal share in their married lives even if a man was the chief.

"I expected you'd smile like that when I explained it," Jason teased.

The celebration they were having was not in the strictest sense a potlatch, as those were usually reciprocal intertribal affairs planned months in advance for such occasions as the raising of a totem pole (for the Haidas were one of the peoples to the north who commissioned and valued the high poles), a wedding, a funeral, or the like. If one were of high enough position, one was expected to return the favor by holding one's own potlatch later on. Chief Sam knew very well that Jason was not likely to show up at his village expecting to be royally entertained. But he was, in fact, according the white man an honor as he hailed him not only as friend but as "tyee," chief.

The other islanders joined in the feasting, sharing Jason's opinion that it was a grand way to end the summer. Food was contributed from every household, including the best of what was left of last year's harvest of potatoes, the new crop not yet ready. "Wapatoos" were a great favorite among the Indians and graciously received as the Haidas were not of an agricultural bent and grew no crops of their own, subsisting instead on what the land and the sea offered freely and eating a great deal of grease rather than starch.

That was one aspect of the feasting that was literally hard for Sarah to swallow. The Indians had brought along a supply of their favorite oil made from the eulachon fish. Their preference was to pour it in and over everything in addition to drinking it straight from wooden bowls. Even the "soop-a-lallie," the alcoholic brew they offered, contained the oil, along with soapberries and water. Sarah managed a few sips and then decided it was just as well she didn't like it since it turned out to be heady indeed.

The Indians seemed to take no offense at the token pretense the whites made of eating Haida foods. "They're not stupid," Jason commented softly to Sarah. "The less we eat, the more for them, and in any case, everyone's enjoying the dried salmon, theirs and ours, and the berries, the venison, the chicken, the fresh fish, the potatoes, the bread, the pies, all ours. Besides, I've told them you're a picky eater. Now they know why you're so scrawny."

"Scrawny! Why you . . ."

His hand moved unobtrusively to pat her bottom. "Their opinion, not mine. I'm quite content with what there is of you."

She had never seen anyone eat as much and as continuously as the Indians did, but they worked it off too. They played games of chance with gambling sticks, moving and hooting all the while, and they danced, wearing horrific face-fitting masks and acting out myths and clan stories, singing and playing drums, simple flutes, and rattles.

Only Jason and Cade had any fluency in the Chinook Jargon, the songs and stories weren't even in the Jargon in any case, but the ease of communication was astonishing. And despite the fact that it was a busy work season, the islanders spent as much time as possible at the perpetual party. The island children loved the festivities, the wooden masks, the brightly painted canoe paddles and personal effects of the Indians, and they and the Indian children taught each other games and devised new ones as if there were no language barrier at all. Maggie and Ben communicated with great ease; the Indians were at home with hand and body gestures. Sarah was glad to see that the Indians did not shy away from the deaf couple or from Cade. Cade was obviously held in great regard and moved among the Indians easily, looking very content. Captain, however, had been left at home, due, Cade said, to the fact that he might take one of the dances as an attack and God knew what would happen then.

"It's not only that Cade speaks the Jargon," Jason commented to Sarah, "but he knows a great deal of their lore, and I think they see his shape as something special, mystical, rather than grotesque. It must be because of his knowledge since I doubt that the Haidas are any more lenient than most peoples about deformities."

Even Nate and Jon joined the fun at the camp near the beach, and Hayes wandered around looking young with excitement.

"It's a rare privilege to be able to observe another culture, especially one of such high achievement as this one," he told Sarah, and she rejoiced that regardless of the circumstances which had brought him here, he had such attitudes to teach the children.

The weather was warm, but the Indians erected bark and wood shelters anyway in case of a sudden rain. Sarah was fascinated by the clever and artistic adaptations of their way of life. They did not make clay pots, and even metal ones available from the whites were not much in evidence with this group; what they didn't cook over open fires, they boiled or steamed in greased, watertight wooden boxes to which water and hot stones had been added. They had brought their own carved cooking and eating utensils and platters too, and everything seemed to fit into special boxes which in turn were shaped to fit precisely into the canoes. And everything seemed to be carved or painted with stylized creatures of the earth, sea, and sky.

She understood even better now what Cade had told her and Jamie about the totem pole. The Haidas, like the other peoples with similar lore, put great store in lineage traced back to mythical beginnings and events. The totems and carvings were not objects of worship, though they might include allusions to spiritual incidents; their purpose differed little from the family trees and heraldic devices which gave so much pride to European nobles.

The hardest time for Sarah came when Jason was expected to tell his own history. It was an honor accorded him that the Indians wanted to listen to it even though he was given the necessary courtesy of telling it in his own language, which most of them didn't understand. It didn't matter; a chief had a right and a duty to brag of his history.

It was not that Jason told it badly; in places he was quite poetic and brought a lump to Sarah's throat: "And I married a woman of the sun but she was taken from me as she gave me my child." (She glanced down at Jamie seated beside her and was relieved to see that he was watching his father with wide-eyed wonder, more affected by the storytelling cadence and the whole performance than the words.) It was just the whole unlikely business of Jason standing there before the assemblage reciting that threatened to send her into hysterical laughter.

She had to dig her fingernails into her hands to stifle the sound when he came to her: "And then in an, er . . . an assemblage of people, I saw the star woman singing and dancing to the . . . ah, to the night, and I wanted her. But I was set upon by evil spirits in my quest and was rescued by the star woman herself and yet still could not have her as she disappeared into the dawn . . ."

She noticed he wasn't meeting her eyes, and then she saw that the other island adults were suffering from her problem as well though the children were all spellbound. Even Maggie looked ready to convulse with laughter, and Ben wasn't much better off as his wife was signing the words to him. From then until it was over, Sarah kept her eyes fixed on the ground.

When he was finished, Jason received loud appreciation from the Indians.

"I saw you laughing while they were applauding," Jason accused later, pretending hurt. "Don't you care for my talents as an orator?"

Her answer was to break into gales of laughter. " 'An assemblage of people . . . singing and dancing . . . to the night,' oh, My Lord, Jason, you ought to be a lawyer!"

He laughed with her, admitting that it had been a near thing. "I kept hearing my own voice as an echo, and it sounded so damn ridiculous, I thought if I so much as smiled, I'd start to giggle like an idiot and lose my standing completely. I'd hate to have my 'klootch-man,' my woman, lose her rank because of me."

Replete with food, dance, song, and gifts—highly prized metal tools for working wood, knives, lengths of the island's own wool cloth, a sack of potatoes, some salted meat, and other offerings from the islanders—the Indians prepared to depart on the third day. But before they left, they presented the Drakes with their own gifts—a carved box, a small blanket softer than velvet made of seal skins, and especially for Sarah, a necklace of delicate shells as valuable as money to the Haidas.

With much well-wishing on both sides, the canoes were run into the water, the paddles took up the beat, and the sleek vessels slipped swiftly away from the shore.

"Will they be safe?" Sarah asked in sudden anxiety. "This isn't their territory, red or white."

"They got here, and they'll get home as well. The old wars are over. But I'm afraid those old wars were safer for them just as the old ways without white intervention were. There was no harm done in our potlatch and much joy in it, but the custom has been widely corrupted now and is ruining a great many Indians. White man's influence and especially our diseases have decimated many tribes, and the heritage Chief Sam and his wife are so proud of is beginning to mean less and less even to the far northern tribes as the leaders die. I haven't witnessed it, but I've heard, especially from Cade, that now potlatches are being given with terrible waste, men beggaring themselves and their families in their attempts to gain high rank, to take over the positions left by the dead hereditary leaders."

"Do you think we'll ever see Chief Sam and his people again?" she asked softly.

"I don't know. Not for a long while in any case. But the Chief's a strong, canny leader and well-loved, and that's all to the good."

She, Jason, and Jamie stood together looking out to sea even after the canoes had disappeared from sight, blending into the shadows of other islands, speeding back toward their ancient world.

Jamie talked about the Indians for days after they'd gone, and his parents were amazed by the detailed knowledge he'd gained of some of the Indian children's lives.

"How did you learn all that?" his father asked.

"They told me."

"In English?"

Jamie regarded him blankly for a moment and then shook his head. "'Course not, they don't speak English, and I don't speak Indian." He paused thoughtfully before he went on. "It's funny, I didn't think 'bout it 'til you asked me. But we didn't talk with words much 'cept for tradin' names for this thing or that. We jus' didn't need words. We talked more like Maggie and Ben do, with all of ourselves."

"The world would be a more honest place if people spoke that way more often," Jason told his son with a smile, and the carved box was given to Jamie to hold special treasures.

In the darkness that came upon them, Sarah was to cling to the memory of the festive potlatch days as the last time of pure joy in her new life.

CHAPTER
34

The telegram came by boat from San Juan Island. Jason knew an identical message would arrive in time from Seattle as well, and a letter would follow, forwarded by Rob Mactavish, still a better route than the fledgling postal service to the islands. He and Owen had agreed on the fastest methods of communication despite the costs, and Jason had prearranged delivery from both of the telegraph offices, offering good pay for the service.

But repetition of this information was not necessary; reading the clear message once was enough to last him a lifetime.

He had been out when the telegram arrived, but Sarah had taken it and asked the sailor to wait. Jason had seen the flag signifying the visit of a ship. He had ridden down and been told the message had already been taken to the house.

Sarah had not opened it, but he could see the apprehension in her eyes. He tried to reassure her—"It's the best way Owen can get business news to me"—but he didn't open it in the sailor's presence. He paid the man, thanked him, and offered him refreshment. The sailor declined, obviously anxious to get away from the foreboding atmosphere though the boat would wait for an hour in case Mr. Drake wanted to send a return message.

Jason opened the envelope and read the message. His face was ashen. He didn't utter a sound. He handed the paper to Sarah, turned on his heel, and went to his study, slamming the door.

The words jumped and blurred before her eyes. She stilled her hands and made herself read it all the way through:

> *Moon Chaser* burned last night. Pollards, two hands, dead. Reverend Mapes assaulted, seriously injured. Fire Farley's Mercantile, losses minimal. No suspects. Please advise.
>
> Owen

The bare words were knife blades. Clem and Etta would never sail aboard the *Moon Chaser* again, and Bartholomew was an old man and might well die from his injuries. And despite the "no suspects," Owen obviously knew all the events were connected. Sarah did not doubt it for an instant.

She was trembling so violently, she could barely walk. She clung to the study door, hearing the terrible sounds even before she opened it. Jason sat at his desk, head bowed in his hands, deep wrenching sobs tearing his throat. He didn't even hear her enter.

"His name is Radley Chambers Allen."

Jason raised his head, staring at her blankly, tears trickling down his lean cheeks. He looked as if he'd aged thirty years in the space of minutes.

"I said his name is Radley Chambers Allen. My father. I am Sarah-Mary Allen Drake. I was wrong; Reverend Mapes was wrong. But it is my fault alone. I should have told you long ago." She articulated each word with great clarity even though she was shivering with ever deeper cold.

The name and the trust through violent death. Jason finally comprehended what she was saying. He swallowed hard, trying to erase the nightmarish vision of Clem and Etta burning to death. He took several deep breaths before he could trust his voice.

"No, not even you could know he would go this far. You did the best you could to protect me." He opened his arms, and she came into them, curling into his lap, pressing desperately against him as if she were a child seeking warmth and shelter against the night beasts. She wept hopelessly with very little sound, and his own tears ceased in his concern for her. Her flesh was so cold, it was as if she had just come out of the winter sea. He rocked and warmed her in his arms, stroking her hair.

"Sarah, my love, it's happened. It can't be changed. But now I have what I need to fight back. Now I know who he is. My God, do I know who he is!" A shock ran through him so strongly he could feel it prickling clear to the tips of his fingers, and he gripped Sarah so hard, she winced. He held her away from him so he could see her face.

"I saw you first long before that night in the saloon, didn't I? Or maybe you don't remember, probably you don't, you were so young. But I remember. I almost remembered the night I was beaten up. I saw you as a little girl peering down at me. It didn't make any sense, not much in my head did, and everything was very vague. But not now. You were that little girl. I did see you. I saw you years ago, a little ghost child with gray eyes and silvery hair, looking curious but scared to death even then, even then in the banker's house in New York. No wonder you know so much about business!"

Sarah's tears stopped with the shock of Jason's memory. "I do remember. You smiled at me, and I thought you were the most splendid, no, the only splendid man I'd ever seen. I knew who you were though not your name from the first moment I saw you in the saloon."

Her monotone did nothing to lessen the impact of her revelation. Jason felt strangely adrift from the present, as if the human rationalizations of time had no meaning, as if destiny worked in one omnipresent instant to accomplish all that ever was or would be. Sarah was his destiny, had been even when he had loved Gaiety, had been even before he had seen the child on the stairs, and would be forever. And with Sarah came her father until her father could be beaten and banished from her life. He felt a burst of savage exultation. He knew something already about the man, and he would learn more. The man had his weaknesses. Oh, he did!

"Are you going to kill him?" Sarah asked in the same flat voice as if she already knew the answer and could see Jason with a rope around his neck.

"No." He felt her start of surprise. "No, I'm not going to kill him physically, not unless I have to. But I'm going to ruin him."

"How?" There was life again even in the single word, and apprehension. He suspected she feared that he was going to use his knowledge of the incestuous relationship Radley Allen had had with his daughter. He knew if he told her he had to use it, she would not try to stop him but would bear the looks of fascinated revulsion which would come from public knowledge of it.

He held her close again. "I doubt your father has changed much in his dealings since I knew him. The Allen and Chambers bank had a good reputation, for many I suppose it still does. My father knew it had been established clear back in the days of the Revolution, that Allen must have been your great-great-grandfather, and he and Mr. Chambers established a banking house of great integrity and eventually great wealth."

He thought of how the work had been carried on by the eldest sons of both families during the succeeding generations until her father's time. Her father had come to power in the bank early, and the last male Chambers had had no interest in banking. Sarah's grandfather and her father bought the family out quite legally, though the name Allen and Chambers had been retained.

"Such a venerable institution," he sneered. "My father dealt with them because the further west he moved, the less reliable he found the banking systems, and when his luck was good, he had need of a good bank. When I needed such an institution, I followed suit, despite the distance, because the banks in San Francisco still left much to be desired at the time. Allen and Chambers survived various panics in what seemed to be good shape. But even in my father's time, drafts were sometimes not honored as quickly as they should have been, though the accounts were solvent. That happened to me one too many times, and I started doing a little investigating. Perhaps your father wasn't so bold with his local investors, but the further west his customers, the more chance there was of delay and mix-ups, things which couldn't be blamed solely on the distance. In fact, more than one man told me that he was quite sure that Radley Allen was given to speculating beyond the bounds of propriety with other people's money. God knows he made a fortune doing it even though he ran the risk of being caught short when the depositors wanted their money."

San Francisco banks became more reliable after the panic of 1855 weeded out many of the bad ones, though Jason was still not overly trusting of such institutions in general. He thought of the men he had trusted instead of banks, the men who had sold his notes to Allen, but he said nothing about them.

"Anyway, when a major draft was delayed again and yet again, I made the trip all the way to New York to get the money and close my account there. Your father and I both acted the part of the genial businessmen—he even invited me to his home—but there was little goodwill on either side. Your father delayed as long as he could, and I fumed at the delay. I think he had to do a lot of manipulating to find the money which was rightfully mine."

"You're right!" She remembered now, much too clearly. "He went on and on about uneducated, unprincipled Westerners. He yelled at my mother for nothing, and he . . . he told me I must never have anything to do with men like you, with any man except . . . and he spanked me for nothing . . . and then he said he'd make the hurt go away and . . . Oh, God!"

Her body bucked and twisted in his hold. Jason could barely speak past the lump in his throat. "Sarah-Mary, sweetheart, it's over! Never, never again will he touch you!" His rage against the man was mixed with the pain of Sarah's memory and his knowledge that in that instance he had been the cause of it, no matter how unknowingly.

"It would hurt your father worse than death to lose his holdings, to lose his standing. And he will lose both; I promise it!"

"It can't be done! It's never happened before!"

"I doubt anyone has ever tried to do it to him before, and he is spending a great deal of money at the present to try to ruin me. He's cruel and arrogant, and he has a reputation of a fine old banking house behind him. That can make a man like your father very careless. He's gotten away with illicit dealings before; he's sure to believe he can continue so. But this is a strange time. Speculation is rife in this country, and there's bound to be a fall. With the knowledge you and I have of him and with Owen's help, we're going to make sure your father falls with the rest."

Jason's savage certainty finally penetrated Sarah's despair. It was possible. It might be done. Her father was a gambler, a gambler with other people's money in spite of his conservative, God-fearing banker's façade. And he did not believe he could ever be thwarted for long. But then another thought occurred to her. "What about the others, the bank's customers who are honest and trusting?"

"Some of them will lose too; others will be paid off by the sale of your father's assets." Jason's voice was implacable. It was as if he could already see the auction taking place.

She stayed curled against him, listening to the beat of his heart, knowing what was coming next.

"There's no use in sending a reply to Owen. I'll be on my way south as soon as I can book passage on a steamer from Victoria or Seattle—the *Gaiety*'s too slow for this. Cade usually knows which ships are leaving."

"I have to go with you. I can't bear to be apart from you now." The attempted calm of her voice did not conceal the frantic edge.

He had planned to leave her on the island, the safest place, but now he knew he could not. To her mind, he was the only safety in the world, more so now than ever.

"What are we going to tell Jamie?" His acceptance was in the question.

"Enough of the truth to make him understand that he's helping us by staying here." She drew Jason's head down and kissed him. "I would shatter into a million pieces and die without you," she whispered.

It was grueling to tell the other islanders about the Pollards, hardest of all to tell Jamie.

He looked at his father incredulously. "They're coming here pretty soon, and I'm goin' ask 'em 'bout birds."

"No, Jamie, they'll never be coming here again. Clem and Etta are dead." He ached with sorrow greater for Jamie than for his own loss of dear friends; Jamie had met death too often for one so young, and yet, there was no way to spare him without lies which would soon be revealed for what they were.

"They were killed. They were killed by a very evil man." Sarah startled Jason; he had not thought she would be the one to explain. "That man is my father. He didn't do it himself, but he hired other bad men to do it. I came west because of my father, running away from him, but he found out where I am, and he's making horrible things happen to get even with me."

Jamie's tears stopped as he stared at her, assimilating these startling revelations. Sarah waited patiently for him to make the connection and place the blame for the Pollards' death on her, but he did not. He glanced fearfully around the room. "Will he come here?"

"No, he won't. The island is safe because he could only come here by ship and everyone would know if he did. Besides, he's a coward; he doesn't fight that way."

Jamie looked to his father, their eyes alike in rage as they were in laughter. "Why don't you just find him and shoot him?"

The words were given added, eerie power coming so matter-of-factly in the young voice.

"Because that would be murder, even if he does deserve it," Jason answered with equal calm. "He is a very rich man who likes being rich more than anything else." Anything else except the flesh of his daughter; Jason tried to ignore the thought. "We are going to make sure he loses everything he owns. Then he will know he is beaten."

Jamie didn't ask how they were going to do this; his father had said so, therefore it would be. He threw his arms around him. "I'm lucky to have you for a papa! But, oh, I did so want to see the Captain and his wife again!" The tears began again, and the three of them wept together, holding tightly to each other.

It was a grim shock to all the islanders, not only to hear of the Pollards' deaths but to learn that Sarah's father was most cer-

tainly responsible. And though they were told no more than
Jamie had been, surely one or more of them must have suspected the nature of the man's obsession with his daughter.
Though she did not remind Sarah of it, Constance particularly
remembered the blood and the man she had first seen when she
had met her, and she remembered with even more sorrow the
strange, bright connection she had seen between Sarah and the
Pollards, only now understanding it. Yet far from a lessening of
the warmth Constance and the rest displayed toward Sarah, she
could feel their love now as a tangible force wrapped around
her, shielding her. She found herself on the verge of tears more
often than not during the four days it took before they were on
the steamer bound from Victoria to San Francisco.

Jamie went with them on the *Gaiety* to Victoria. He had never
been on Vancouver Island, and he inspected everything with
bright eyes and listened carefully to the accents. But his courage
faltered visibly when he had to bid good-bye to his parents. For
the first time he feared for their safety, really feared he might not
see them again even though he had been used to his father's
absences long before Sarah had arrived and was now accustomed to both of them being gone sometimes.

"You won't let that man hurt you?" Jamie's mouth quivered,
and his eyes were overly bright now.

"I won't let him hurt me or Sarah," Jason assured him gravely.
He lifted his son into his arms for a moment, holding him close.
"You're being very brave, and I'm very proud of you. I wouldn't
want anyone else in the world for my son."

By the time Jamie came to her, he had squared his shoulders
and was doing his best to play the manly part, a circumstance
which made it even harder for Sarah to control her own emotions.

"I wish you could stay safe with all of us on the island, but I
know you can't. I know you have to go with Papa. It's right for
you to go with him. He's not happy at all without you. You take
care of him, Mama, an' he'll take care of you, an' then you'll both
come home."

"I love you, and we'll be home as soon as we can." It was all
she could manage. As the steamer pulled away, she watched

Jamie waving, his slight figure flanked by the *Gaiety*'s crew. The image blurred and wavered through her tears. Jason patted at her face with his handkerchief. "It really is better this way," he reminded her. "We'd worry about him constantly if we had him with us in the city."

It was odd to be traveling together on a ship other than the *Gaiety*. Their cabin was clean, among the best the ship offered, but very small, causing Jason to curse more than once as he tried to maneuver his large frame in the limited space. They spent a great deal of time walking the decks and talking out of earshot of the crew and the other passengers, mostly businessmen plus a scattering of couples.

The Drakes didn't feel inclined to be sociable; they would have been surprised to know that there was a good deal of speculation about them. Some thought they were newly married; others were sure they were runaway lovers, an idea enhanced by the obvious age difference between the man and the woman. Not one of the gossips guessed that the whispered conversations centered almost entirely on business, banking, and the personal habits of one man.

It was a horrible process, but Jason pursued it grimly, day after day. "Do you remember any of the men your father did business with? Their names, when, what were they involved in? Were there many meetings at your home? How did the men treat your father, how did he treat them? In his personal habits, is he extravagant in any way? Did you ever know him to have unpaid bills for a long period of time? Does he have expensive vices hidden beneath his respectable image?"

That one stopped Sarah dead in her tracks. She looked up at Jason, her face twisted, eyes glittering. "It wasn't expensive, he owned me. Incest, a pretty little vice, costing nothing." She started to laugh hysterically, and Jason pulled her against him, holding her head to his chest to smother the sound before anyone noticed.

"It will cost him everything and still will have cost you more. Darling, I'm here, you're here with me. I love you. I wouldn't hurt you for the world, but I have to know all there is to know about him. Every single thing you can remember will help."

Despite the tenderness, the savagery was in his voice as it always was these days, never far beneath the surface. He was a hunting beast, certain that the careful stalking would end in his victory, his prey torn to pieces and devoured.

Sarah found herself believing more and more that he could defeat her father. The assurance of Jason's unwavering blood-lust was comfort as basic as a heartbeat, as primitive as her own screams in the night.

The hysterical laughter subsided, and even when his hold on her loosened, she kept her face buried against him, breathing the scent of him, listening to his heart. "My beautiful, tawny tiger," she murmured. She felt at once peaceful and infinitely weary, hardly aware that Jason was guiding her, half carrying her back to their cabin.

He knew he could see more clearly than she the toll remembering was taking of her, and he had to steel himself continually to keep asking her for the memories she had tried so hard to forget. The sounds and the rhythm of the steamer were different from those of the *Gaiety* and the bunk uncomfortable, but it was his concern for Sarah that kept Jason on the edge of wakefulness even when he might have slept from sheer exhaustion.

She was not seasick; she was ill of spirit. The terror she tried so valiantly to control during the day swept through her dreams at night, causing her to thrash about in the confining space, whimpering and crying out. It was like their first nights together in Seattle and yet very different. Now he knew the source of the nightmares, and now with love between them, he could awaken her gently and hold her until the rapid beat of her pulse had slowed and the shivering had stopped. And he understood why often and regardless of the cramped space, if she awakened, she wanted him to make love to her, needing the physical reassurance that the old phantom of possession was not the man who held her now.

But finally his own fatigue was so great, he groaned softly against her insistent urging. "Sweetheart, I can't. I love you, but my body's too tired to prove it." He had eased into the bunk with her to hold her when he wakened her from her latest bout with the demons, and he could feel every inch of her moving with increasing insistence, her hands stroking him feverishly.

"Wasn't your father ever too tired?" For an awful instant, he was afraid he'd said the words aloud out of his own frustration. Then knew he had not. He loved Sarah, and he loved making love to her, but not now, not like this, not with her pleading frenzy and his leg hurting like the devil while the rest of him refused to respond.

"I just can't," he protested again tiredly. He moved to bring her surcease with his hands. But suddenly though he couldn't see her in the dark cabin, he felt her come more fully awake. She pushed his hands away.

"My poor love," her voice was low and contrite, "I'm sorry. I feel more than half mad these days, and you're so weary from watching over me."

It was she who gave him comfort, kneading the tight muscles of his leg until she felt them relax and heard his breathing change to the rhythm of sleep. It was the first real rest Jason had had since they boarded the ship, and he awakened late in the morning to find himself still relaxed despite the fact that they had both spent the night in the narrow space and Sarah was still lying half over him.

"Now I can," Jason told her with a grin after they'd performed what morning ablutions the ship allowed, and there was a special healing grace in their wide-awake enjoyment of each other after the sorrows of the night. The Drakes were not seen on deck until the afternoon, and one of the female passengers blushed when she saw them, having told her husband she had heard the most peculiar noises coming from their cabin not only last night but on previous occasions.

By the time they reached San Francisco, Jason had a sheaf of careful notes. As hard as it had been for her, Sarah had managed to give him valuable information as one memory led to another.

They went to Owen's office as soon as they'd checked into the Grand. Jason knew it could only be a difficult meeting.

"I have more than enough to tell him to begin with. You needn't come."

"I do need to," she said without hesitation. "He will surely have questions, and some of them only I can answer."

The reunion with Owen was every bit as bad as Jason had feared. Though the Drakes had arrived as swiftly as they could, the wait had taxed Owen heavily. He had met the Pollards through Jason, and he had been very fond of them in addition to having served as their lawyer for several years. He had seen the terrible glow on the water and had known the *Moon Chaser* had been moored there after her cargo had been unloaded, had known even as he tried to deny it, that she was not going to sail out as planned. His last hope had been that Clem and Etta hadn't been aboard, or if they had, that they had gotten off safely, but somehow he had also known even then, that they were dead. That Reverend Mapes had been attacked and was only now regaining any strength at all was an added goad to an already angry man. He knew that it was all connected with the Drakes, and he knew that they had withheld information from him. It was a sore test of friendship.

His eyes were cold though his words were civil enough as he greeted them after clearing his office of other clients. It might have gone on like that except that Sarah could not bear it. Everything was so raw now, it was intolerable that there be any restraint between the two men, especially since Jason was counting on Owen's help.

"If you will, look at me like that, but not at Jason," she said, standing in front of Owen, confronting him directly. "It's not his fault, it's mine. The man who is causing so much pain is my father, and Jason didn't know who he is until after . . ." she swallowed hard, willing herself not to cry again, "after we found out that Clem and Etta were killed. I waited too long to tell him. How is the Reverend?"

Owen's self-righteous anger deserted him completely. He felt as if he'd just kicked a kitten or set fire to a puppy. Sarah stood before him, her eyes level with his. There was no defiance in her, just patient willingness that he despise her so long as he continued to love Jason. And there was no need for him to convince them that all the violence was related to them. "Killed," she'd said, and "my father."

"Your father." He found himself echoing the word stupidly and then followed it with, "Bartholomew's much better, but he's still very weak. He's been staying with us. Oh, Sarah, everything will be all right!" He didn't know that; he still didn't know what the hell was going on, but he couldn't bear the look in her eyes. All the protectiveness he'd felt when he'd first met her as Mary surged back.

Jason handed him the stack of papers. "His name and what contacts Sarah can remember."

Owen was so stunned by the name heading the documents, he slumped into his chair without asking them to make themselves comfortable. They seated themselves and watched his expression change from disbelief to horror as he read.

Finally he looked up, shaking his head as if he'd been under water for too long. "My God! I know of the man and his bank, and his associates include some of the biggest financial names in this country, including some who have the ear of President Grant. To bring him to trial . . ."

"There won't be any trial!" Jason's voice slashed across Owen's. "Even if we could prove he's responsible for what's happened, there won't be a trial. And I'm not going to be on trial either; I'm not going to blow his brains out, though I'd like to."

The two men's eyes met and held, and the silence was loud between them. It had not been said; it would not be, but suddenly Owen knew. No other reason would account for Jason's furious reluctance to bring Allen to trial or for the primitive terror Owen had sensed in Sarah since first meeting her. She was a strong woman, he knew that now, but she was still afraid. Her father was not a rigid patriarch who wanted his child to grow up and live in the image of a dutiful daughter—that was not cause enough to have engendered the fear in Sarah—he was a madman who lusted after his own child. A trial of any sort would make that public, and even if the man were disgraced, so would Sarah be. Owen no more than Jason, would ever allow that to happen. And to murder such a prominent man as Radley Chambers Allen would almost inevitably lead to the same revelations and also most probably to getting Jason hanged, no matter how just his cause. Jason was not the kind who would hire someone else to do his killing.

Owen was a tough man by experience; he had learned survival early, and he had dealt with the seamier side of life often in his profession. But this turned his stomach and made the blood sing unpleasantly in his ears. That Sarah had survived as well as she had and was capable of loving Jason so much now appeared nothing short of a miracle.

Jason nodded almost imperceptibly, confirming the shared, unspoken knowledge between them, and then Sarah's skirts rustled as she moved, uneasy with their silence.

"What do you plan to do?" Owen asked. He was pleased with the calm reasonableness of the question.

Jason told him, in detail. "And I want you to begin immediately to use any sources you have to find out everything there is to know about Allen's current business affairs. If he could so easily discover mine, his too can be investigated. It will be a little harder than my case—I've never tried to hide my interests once they're established—but surely it can be done. I don't care how much it costs."

Owen's first reaction had been skepticism, but he'd kept his mouth shut. Now he was beginning to share Jason's enthusiasm. It was not only a beautiful plan, it was possible. Now Owen was seeing Radley Allen more clearly, seeing him through Jason's eyes, seeing the man's basic weakness. Allen had had power all his life; there was no way he could understand the possibility of defeat. It was their strongest card; Radley Allen would not realize what was happening until it was too late. And the uncertain climate of the times, the postwar adjustments that had yet to be made even though the war had been over for years, these too were in their favor.

"There are some people in New York who owe me favors. I can't think of a better time to collect them."

But the euphoria they felt for being united in a plan was short-lived as Owen recounted the toll of the night of destruction. The Reverend Mapes would surely have been beaten to death had it not been for some of his ragged children who did not keep the hours of youngsters who had comfortable homes.

In their rough way, they liked the old man and had not hesitated to investigate when they heard strange noises coming from his room. Nor had the fact that they faced two armed men discouraged the five boys. They had burst in screeching; they had kicked, bitten, and had thrown the minister's books at the men, causing such bedlam that the villains had fled, perhaps not unwilling to kill children, but certainly unwilling to be the center of attention in the area.

The old man was unconscious and bleeding. Finally one of the boys had found his mother, and though her work for the night wasn't over, she had given up whatever other customers she might have found to care for the minister. Rio appeared the next morning. He'd come to see if Bartholomew had time for a game of checkers and had instead found his friend close to death. He'd taken him immediately to Owen and Carrie's, and there the minister still was, despite his protests that he was perfectly sound and ready to go back to work.

"It was because he married us, just because of that." Sarah made no effort to check the tears rolling down her cheeks; she didn't even brush them away. Jason doubted she was aware that she wept.

"And Clem and Etta?" he made himself ask.

"You know how they were. They loved that ship and they loved the sea. Their home was aboard the *Moon Chaser* even when they were here in port." With effort, Owen kept his voice steady. "Only one man might know exactly what happened, and he's long gone, apparently leaving no trace. There were four men aboard with the Pollards. You know how careful Clem and Etta were about fires at sea, how careful any competent captain and crew must be if they plan to live for long in wooden vessels floating on cold, deep water. And the fact that two of their hands died trying to save them indicates there must have been some problem even in getting into the cabin. The sailor who survived thinks they might have been drugged, perhaps in the water or the food. He himself felt as if everything was moving very slowly and strangely, but then, the mind reacts in odd ways to disaster. He had served with the Pollards for years, and his is the best guess we have.

"It was customary for Clem to lose a few men in San Francisco and to sign on a few more for the next voyage. The old hand thinks that one of the new men was responsible for the fire. According to him, the man kept to himself, but he was ready enough to talk about ships he'd sailed on and to present his papers, none of which have proved to be genuine. He was the fourth hand on board that night, and the old sailor thinks he poured oil in the hold and set fire to it after he'd made sure Clem and Etta were in a stupor or locked in their cabin. The new man should have been helping to lower the lifeboat or to get the Pollards out, but the survivor is sure he was doing neither of those things. The fire spread very fast and caused total chaos, but the sailor thinks the new man had already abandoned ship. He's sure he heard a splash even over the roar of the fire, sure he saw a rowboat pulling away. If that's true, obviously it means at least one other man was waiting to help the arsonist get away. The survivor cried like a baby between his curses when he told me. He was doing his job trying to get the launch lowered while the others got the Pollards out, but he'll never forgive himself for their deaths. By the time he tried to go below, the flames were too much. His hands and face were burned, and he had to jump overboard. He nearly drowned before a tender from another ship picked him up, and yet, he still feels terrible guilt. He told me everything he could, and he and the crew members who had been ashore during the fire searched the waterfront for days, looking for that other man, finding no trace of him or of the one who picked him up. Poor fellow, I think he's begun to think the fire affected his mind, but I believe him. He's shipped out again, and I hope he finds peace in his new berth."

They sat in silence, each alone in thought. Sarah shuddered, trying not to hear screams, hearing them anyway, praying that somehow Clem and Etta had died before they knew what was happening.

Owen cleared his throat and spoke. "There's something more. Christ, why is there so often such irony in tragedy?" He handed a heavy, slightly yellow sheet of paper to Jason.

Jason was torn between laughter and tears; the irony was at

once terrible and exquisite, and he had the feeling again of all things being connected without time or distance.

The will was short and simple. Having no other kin and being fond of Jason Drake, the Pollards had left everything to him. The will had been written and signed several years before. Jason handed it to Sarah.

"The Pollards were frugal Yankees," Owen said. "They've left you a princely sum plus a house in Wiscasset, Maine. I guess they always planned to go back there someday. I suggest you simply let that continue as it has, rented to a family who pays right on time."

Jason agreed, still dazed.

"As for the rest, some of it, as you know, is invested in other ships and cargoes, some of it is invested in very conservative businesses, and the rest of it is on deposit at various banks."

"If you liquidate all their assets, is it enough to pay off the loans?" The hard edge was back in Jason's voice.

"Yes, it should be. And you still have the cargo. It's hard to understand why the ship wasn't burned while it was still loaded. I'd guess that either the plan was too late or there was no opportunity—*Moon Chaser* was heavily manned and guarded during unloading and the warehouse is always well protected, so perhaps the arsonist had to settle for destroying the ship afterward."

"And killing the Pollards." Sarah said it as if she were commenting on the weather. Her face had a strange, withdrawn look as if she were listening to something they couldn't hear or seeing something beyond their range of vision.

Jason could see the tremors beginning to run through her. He rose abruptly, swaying for a moment as he found his balance, his bad leg protesting the sudden movement. "We can talk about the rest of it later. Sarah and I ought to go back to the hotel now. We have a great deal—no, too much—to think about as it is."

"Jason, may I have a few words alone with your wife?"

Hearing the urgency in the plea, Jason searched Owen's face, measuring his intentions, feeling somehow reassured that it was for the good. He nodded, attempting to smile and knowing it was less than successful. "I'll allow it only because I know you have Carrie."

Owen wondered if she were going to bolt after him behind a screen of inane words. But she didn't. She stayed where she was, her eyes dull as tarnished metal.

"Don't ever leave him," he commanded without preamble. "I can feel you considering it. Don't do it. You'll not only break his heart and his will, but you'll accomplish no good."

"It would accomplish something!" she protested with renewed energy, not even bothering to deny that she was think-ing of leaving her husband. "He's losing everything because of me, not only his businesses, his investments, but people he loves! I don't want to go back! I keep telling myself there are so many reasons not to," her eyes slid away from Owen's, and he hoped she hadn't seen the awareness in his own, "but I keep coming back to the truth—if I go back to my father, Jason will be free and safe. I love him enough to do anything for him, even that."

"I don't doubt it for an instant. But the only thing you can do for him is to stay with him. It's too late to leave him. It's been too late since the minute Jason saw you, wanted you, loved you, from the minute you loved him, maybe even before that. I don't know, but I know it's too late now." Owen turned away, unable to bear the sudden intensity of her gaze, finding it easier to continue without looking at her.

"It is not the same, and yet it is, or at least so damn close as to make no difference. I was up in the high country," Owen went on, "and I heard sounds as if someone were firing a very big gun. I would have gone on thinking it was some firearm had I not been with a good mountain man. There were echoes from all sides, but he knew how to locate the source. When we got close enough to see, I saw two rams, two bighorn sheep, running at each other, leaping to bash their horns and heads together time after time. Animals are more reasonable than humans; the pur-pose was not death but victory. Usually one finally admits defeat, retreats from the scene, and lives to do it all over again someday. The battle starts," he said, more softly now, "with competition over the ewes, but once it begins, the ewes have nothing to do with it. I saw it. Some of the females were grazing here and there, some were wandering away, a few were watching the rams, but for the rams, nothing existed at the moment except each other. And the point of this lesson, if you haven't grasped it already, is that the only difference between those rams and your husband and your father is that the rams have much more civilized rules for their combat. Whatever you do, even if you fled a thousand miles away, your husband and your father will go on fighting until one of them is destroyed. However it started, you are incidental to it now."

He turned, ready to face her again, and he spoke very slowly. "If you leave Jason, there are only two things you will accomplish. You will weaken Jason while you strengthen your father. You will not, *cannot,* lessen the conflict. Don't ever leave your husband."

He had seen the gray eyes darken, and now he saw them going golden again as if the sun were rising with his harsh words.

She leaned forward suddenly to kiss him on the cheek. "Thank you. As long as he wants me, needs me, I'll be there."

"That's forever, long enough. I've got to talk to Carrie again about parlors, or rather the lack of them." Owen wanted to end this tense time as lightly as possible, but he found it impossible, found himself drawing Sarah into his arms, holding her tightly as he murmured, "Sarah-Mary Allen Drake, I don't know what's going to happen, but as God is my witness, with all the trouble and sorrow, no one, not Gaiety and not anyone else has ever made my friend as complete and happy as you have. If I could give the Tiger one gift in all the world, I would give you to him."

"Thank you, Owen, but the gift is to me, always to me," she whispered.

She felt immeasurably weary. She fell asleep against Jason in the cab taking them back to the hotel. She knew there was something wrong about this overpowering need to close her eyes and drift away even as she had known on the steamer bringing them south, but she couldn't fight against it. Even her hands were numb. Jason helped her undress and put her to bed.

"It's not even dark yet, I'm sorry," she murmured, finding the words with great effort and hearing how slurred they sounded.

"It's all right, sleep now, I'm here." Jason traced the line of her jaw and smoothed back the silk of her hair, watching her slip into sleep. He knew it was an escape, and he welcomed it for her. It was going to be a long war; there was more than enough time for her to face it fully.

CHAPTER
35

$\mathcal{J}$ason spent hours with Owen, and more often than not, Sarah was with them. The plan was simple in essence but complex in execution. The most important thing they needed to know was how stable Radley Allen's fortune was. Was he overextended and if so, in what areas? Were his investments all of his own money or did he still have the habit of using other people's funds without their consent and of reaping the benefits for himself? And if he were in trouble, would he be able to count on other moneymen to bail him out? It would take time and careful investigation to find answers, and there were many variables. Jason was counting on the trends he saw in business to lead to another panic sooner rather than later, but he knew he could be completely wrong in this and must not depend entirely on outside events to accomplish his goals. He told himself it didn't matter; no man's resources were inexhaustible, and Sarah's father must already have spent great sums in order to find out about him and to hire henchmen to wreak havoc. Jason planned that the man would spend even more. It was a delicate part of the plan, but given what he already knew of Allen's character, he had no doubt that it would work if done properly. Word would be leaked that the Tiger was interested in investing in this or that, and he might even venture some capital now and again, but he and Owen would make sure that none of the investments was wholly sound. Lord knew there were enough ways offered in the West to lose money—metal shares with nothing to back them; ships with bad reputations, crew troubles, and a constant need for new backers; and lumbering schemes in areas so remote, the cost of getting the timber out would prove to be more than the profits. The trick was to choose the unwise wisely enough so that Allen would be lured into taking the bait, thinking he was taking something from the Tiger.

They depended on Allen's enormous greed and on his obsessive jealousy of Jason; they depended on him to plunge wildly, forsaking caution in order to prevent the Tiger from expanding the empire Allen had set out to ruin. And most of all, they depended on the insane vanity that had allowed Allen to think he could abuse his daughter without fear of reprisal. In light of that, it was easy to trust that it would never occur to him that he was being stalked on his own ground of financial dealings.

The worst of it was that men who had trusted Jason's judgment might also be tempted to take the risks. It would be their own fault if they did, but Jason knew he could hem and haw enough to make them more careful if they came to him directly. If they did not, there was nothing he could do for them without jeopardizing the whole scheme.

And while Allen spent and, they hoped, overspent, Jason would be spending too, spending whatever it cost to ruin the man. At the same time, he would be storing up hard coin for the day when he would be able to begin again to build a kingdom.

He found he had no qualms in this. He felt fierce joy in fighting back, and nothing he owned mattered as much to him as Sarah. It was she who found the process of dismantling his holdings so painful. Her outcry was as loud as Owen's when Jason announced that the next thing he wanted to sell was the lot under Farley's store. "Farley's wanted to own the land for years. Let him have it at a reasonable price."

"There's no need!" Owen thundered. "The fire did very little damage, and Farley's on his guard now. I don't think they'll try again."

"Perhaps not, but he has several large windows and a great deal of flammable material in his store. You needn't remind me that the rent year after year is a better deal for me than a sale. I know that. But if Farley can come up with the price in gold or silver, he can have the property. I don't want him burned out for spite against me."

Sarah paid no attention to his calm. "You can't, you just can't! It's valuable property which will only become more valuable. You don't need the money. All the careful investments of the Pollards, all the things that would have gone on increasing in value through the years, you're turning it all to bullion to pay off the loans. If you go on like this, you will have nothing left!"

"I will have you. And if everything goes well, I will also have some capital to start over. And I will do it my way." He said it without anger, the cold resoluteness brooking no argument.

Sarah exchanged a look with Owen; he was right about the two rams.

For her own sanity, she was beginning to be able to regard her father for longer and longer intervals as totally without connection to herself. He was an evil stranger, someone who must be defeated. It was all a matter of business. And it was a matter of shoving the memories away again. She knew that paradoxically, there was a hint of madness in the process of regaining her balance, but she was also beginning to realize that there were some things in life which were too intolerable ever to be faced fully for long. There was no use in remembering her father's use of her; it brought only pain and grinding terror. The thing to remember was that Jason loved her day by day, and she loved him in return.

The periods of overwhelming lassitude grew less frequent, and as the islanders had offered the strength of their love, so did the friends in San Francisco. They knew now that it was Sarah's father who was causing all the trouble, but if they suspected the full truth of it, they gave no more sign than Owen did.

Carrie said she was glad her family hadn't seemed to mind so much that she'd left them. "But then, they still had a good supply of children left." And Frenchie drew Sarah aside to tell her a dark secret.

For an awful moment, Sarah feared Frenchie was going to confess a background as terrible as her own.

"Not even Rio knows, and don't you dare tell him. But I was glad to see the last of my mother and she the last of me. She was never quite sure who my father was, and I didn't look much like my brothers and sisters, but then, they didn't look much like each other. Anyway, my mother and I never did get along, and she started all the bad feelings the day I was born." Her voice dropped even lower. "The old bitch, she named me Gladys. My real name is Gladys Whipple."

Sarah laughed until her eyes watered and she was gasping for air. Frenchie's offhand recounting of it took the sting out of what must have been a hard childhood, and Sarah could not imagine a more unfitting name for her friend. She was attacked by further ripples of laughter every time she thought of it.

"Please, could I tell Jason, later in private?" she gasped. "I won't if you don't want me to, but he's looking so curious, and he could use some laughter too. Oh, I'm sorry, maybe I shouldn't say that, it is your name!" She was off again.

Frenchie was inordinately pleased to be the cause of such mirth in these grim days. "As long as he doesn't tell Rio," she allowed graciously.

Rio was back on guard duty, pretending it was nothing out of the ordinary, but his eyes betrayed him, flicking continuously from one face to another, from one shadowed alley or doorway to the next, missing nothing. Only when they were safe within the close circle of friends did his vigilance relax. Even then, he was aware of any movement by doors or windows. He felt a deep smoldering rage every time he thought of the men who had battered his friend and might harm Sarah and Jason.

The reunion with Reverend Mapes had been hardest of all for Sarah. His face was still bruised, and he still moved with much less vigor, giving her much too clear a picture of how seriously he had been injured. But his eyes were as aware and kind as they had been and shone brightly at the sight of her.

"My dear, I am so glad to see you again, though I wish it could be under happier circumstance. I grieve for the loss of your friends."

Sarah's throat closed, and she couldn't utter a word.

"There, there, child, weep for your friend if you will, but not for me. I am perfectly all right except that I am being treated like a visiting sultan here and am probably suffering from a weakening of what moral fiber I ever had." He was happy to see the smile he drew from her, but he added softly, "We misjudged the force of the enemy, but that does not make me or you responsible for the evil. You will have to be very strong for your husband now so that your presence in his life keeps him from becoming like his adversary in the battles to come."

Sarah pressed his hand tightly, feeling as she had from her first meeting with the minister, immensely comforted.

Jason had deliberately given Sarah time alone with Bartholomew, and he was relieved to see how peaceful they both looked when he joined them.

He worried about the old man as much as Sarah did. He wouldn't stay with Owen and Carrie for much longer though Carrie vowed he was the kind of priest she'd be pleased to have in her house any day. "But no parlor," she added with an impish grin at Owen.

Jason devised a plan which he trusted would insure the minister's safety when he returned to his own lodgings. Rio had already rewarded the boys who had saved Bartholomew and wouldn't hear of Jason paying him back, but he did agree to hire them for further work. They were to be paid regularly for keeping their eyes on the Reverend. With five of them, they could work it in shifts. Rio was sure of success.

"Ah'll talk t' em, an' there ain't a solitary chance they'll say no. They like money an' they like th' old man too. An' Ah ain't neva seen tougher young-uns in mah life. Jus' one a' them alone kin make noise like a full woah party. Ain't nobody gonna be able t' lay a hand on Bartholomew without everybody fer miles knowin'."

Jason had never been so thankful for good friends as he was now, most of all for the balm they were for Sarah, making her relax, making her smile.

532   CELESTE DE BLASIS

He watched her now as she brushed her hair before going to bed. The shining silk fell to the middle of her back. He loved the feel of it, loved to run his hands through it and twine it around his fingers. He grinned, and she saw it as she turned toward him. "Share it, and I'll share one with you."

"It will just make you vain."

"Good, now you must tell me."

"Well, I was thinking about touching your hair, and just thinking about that set me to thinking about touching other things, and that set off other reactions." Still grinning, he took off his robe and held out his arms to her. "You can see the extraordinary effect just thinking about your hair, let alone the rest of you, has on me."

She nestled against him. "It's lovely to have a lecherous husband as long as I'm the only one you think about that way."

"Believe me, you are! Any more of this, and I wouldn't be able to get out of bed. Now, before we get in, fair's fair, what are you trading?"

Her eyes were brimming with mischief as she let her gown float to the floor and rubbed against him. "Besides this? My, my, you are greedy! But I'll tell you as long as you promise not to tell Rio."

"This must have something to do with you and Frenchie having hysterics together. All right, I promise."

"It's just the small matter of a name." She tried to keep a straight face and failed. "Frenchie's real name is Gladys Whipple."

"Good God!" Jason exclaimed. He exploded with laughter as Sarah had when she heard it. They fell on the bed laughing, Jason drawing enough breath to say, "I can just hear it, ' 'ello, mes amis, my name ize Gla-dyss Whi-pelll.' "

"Beginning with laughter and ending with love," Sarah murmured later, "a perfectly beautiful gift from my perfectly beautiful husband."

"I think I love you because you're the only one mad enough to label me 'perfectly beautiful.' "

"Jamie says he loves me because I amuse him."

"Ummmm, that too. Jamie's very discerning. Gladys Whipple!

Only you could've charmed Frenchie into revealing that." His voice faded with a last little chuckle into sleep.

"You are perfectly beautiful whether you know it or not," Sarah admonished as she settled down beside him.

They both wanted to go home to Jamie, but they did not discuss it. They confined themselves to occasional speculations on how well the various harvests had gone or were going and whether the few horses fully trained and ready for sale had been safely loaded, if indeed, the scheduled ship had come for them.

"I'm not sorry I've missed that; I sincerely hope I have."

"I confess to the same cowardice," Jason said. "We raise and sell few enough horses from the island, but the stock is good and well-trained enough to make those we sell fetch high prices. And don't worry, we're more careful about who buys them than the buyers are about the horses. But still, I hate the process of getting them off the island. No matter how carefully Nate and Jon handle them they're always reluctant and afraid."

"I know just how they feel," Sarah admitted with a rueful smile, and she could feel another unspoken thought between them—the bulk of the sale money went to the Bradleys because they were the ones who cared for the horses and did most of the patient training, but the stock and the contacts for selling the extra stock were Jason's, and some of the profits were his too; more to add to the barrier against Radley Chambers Allen.

It was a matter of waiting until they had evidence that things were beginning to happen the way they wished. With Owen's help, Jason carefully started the rumors of his interest in this and that investment opportunity. One result was that Jason had a visit which both surprised and touched him.

Mr. Bedow looked acutely uncomfortable to be requesting time from what he hastened to say he knew to be Mr. Drake's busy schedule, but if he could have just a few minutes?

"Trouble with the silver mine?" Jason asked kindly, pretending he didn't notice that the man was so nervous, he was crumpling his hat beyond recognition.

"No, ah, Mr. Drake, that's just the point. It was good of you to sell me the shares, and the ore coming out of the mine now has allowed me and my family to feel more secure than ever. I owe you a debt for that."

Jason hid his smile as he read the man's renewed agitation; Mr. Bedow was afraid that his words might be construed to mean he was willing to give or sell the shares back.

"You owe me nothing. You bought the shares fairly."

Mr. Bedow's relief was evident, but he was still ill at ease. "I don't want to be presumptuous, never that, sir. I know what a good businessman you are, but I've . . . that is, there've been rumors that you're interested in Colworth's mining stock and that new Shepson lumber outfit, and I know it's none of my business, but I hope it isn't true because . . . because, well, I've heard that neither one is run as honestly as it could be," he finished miserably.

"I shall certainly consider your advice carefully," Jason told him. "I suspect you're quite right. Thank you for taking the time to tell me. There are most assuredly no debts between us now."

Mr. Bedow beamed as he took his leave, and Jason knew he wouldn't discuss the meeting with anyone; he also knew his words had carried enough warning so that the man would not be tempted to invest any of his new capital in the shaky schemes.

Owen had already begun the arrangements for having a headstone erected in the cemetery in Wiscasset, Maine, as Jason had requested, and he worked to settle the Pollards' estate as quickly as possible though some of the final details would take some months. Enough was already realized to pay off all but part of one of the loans held by Allen's agents. Whatever the agents knew or didn't, it was apparent they had not expected full payment so soon. Nor were they particularly pleased about it, but they had no choice about accepting the money. The last payment would soon be made out of the money expected for the sale of the mercantile lot.

And then there was further cause for celebration.

"I'm afraid you won't be able to invest in a couple of projects you've shown some interest in, Mr. Drake," Owen said, unable to retain his mocking formality for more than the instant. "He took the bait! Two out of four, it's better than we hoped! It has to be him—same agents, same secrecy—and he's too far away to make any improvements. He doesn't own enough to control either business anyway, and both are riddled with very smooth talking crooks. I'll give it six months, nine at the most, before everything tumbles down and the rats leave with what they can grab."

Owen and Jason smiled at each other with the same fierce joy they would have shown if they'd just triumphed in a brawl, and Sarah's joy was no less than theirs.

"It's going to work, it's really going to work!" She didn't suffer even a moment's regret that it was her father's downfall they were celebrating; she only wished it would come as swiftly and as completely as possible.

Best of all was Jason's decision that they could go home now. Owen knew what to do. It was still a matter of waiting, particularly for the report on Allen's financial standing, but they could wait at home. Sarah was in such a fever to depart, Jason asked her if she'd like to swim ahead; he'd catch up with her on the first ship he could find.

"If I could fly, I'd head north just like one of Jamie's birds, but swimming, no, not the way I do it," she replied pertly. "But, oh, darling, I do so long to be with Jamie on the island!"

"Soon, I promise." He handed her two thick pieces of cardboard.

They were first-class tickets on a steamer bound for Seattle the next morning. She threw her arms around him and wept.

"If you're unhappy, I'll tear up the tickets," he teased, pretending to grab them from her.

"Not on your life!" She slipped the tickets into the bodice of her dress and smiled through her tears.

Their friends saw them off on the steamer, and as she bade the Drakes good-bye, Frenchie whispered to Sarah, "Thank Jason for me, and if you don't know why, make him tell you. I love him almost as much as you do right now."

Sarah wasted no time in following Frenchie's advice.

"Tell me why Gladys Whipple would fall in love with you now when she has Rio," she teased. She was astonished to see that Jason looked discomfited.

"It really isn't as a favor to her, it just worked out that way. I've hired Rio to keep an eye on Owen and Carrie, and that will keep Rio in San Francisco, which will in turn please Frenchie. Owen won't like it when he realizes what's going on, but he loves Carrie, and for her sake, I think he'll live with the arrangement. That and the fact that he will soon have gold and silver hidden in his house. My worst argument with him has been over paying him the fees he deserves; I finally threatened to get another lawyer."

"Frenchie has every right to love you, and so do I," Sarah told him. Rio's job could still be dangerous if anyone went after Owen, but at least he would be close to Frenchie. As for the money, it would be well hidden beneath floorboards in the bedroom and great care would be taken to get it to the house unobserved.

It was another part of the plan. Jason didn't want his capital lost in the failure of a bank. He had nominal accounts for current expenses such as payments to the boys, to Rio, to Owen, and for living expenses in the city, but the bulk of the money he was collecting would be with Owen and with himself and Sarah. They had brought all that could be spared with them on this ship, stored in their luggage and in a crate marked "books." It had made their luggage heavier than it should have been, but no questions had been asked.

The *Gaiety* was waiting for them when they arrived in Seattle. Jason had sent telegrams telling them the estimated arrival date of the steamer and saying that Jamie could come with them if he wished.

Sarah, unaware of this, gave a cry of joy when she saw Jamie waving at them, and heedless of her dignity, raced ahead when they docked, leaving Jason to follow at his slower pace.

Jamie was happier than ever about seeing them, having worried so about their safety. "Mr. Burke said this was more important than school, but I did bring my lessons with me," he told them.

"Hayes has moments of real genius," Jason murmured so only Sarah could hear.

Angie was happy to see them, but she felt their tension immediately. She kept her speculations to herself when Jason sketched the story of Sarah's father's vindictiveness, and agreed readily to send word if there were any suspicious inquiries by strangers. She helped Jason to find men willing to keep an eye on the shipyard, the house, and the saloon lot.

"I don't know whether he'll try anything up here, but I don't want innocent people killed in case he does," he told her grimly.

"This is still a very small town; it's harder to cause trouble here without someone knowing than it is in a place like San Francisco," Angie reminded him.

Jason passed the same words of caution to the crew of the *Lady Ellen* and to the loggers and the mill hands when the *Gaiety* stopped there on her way home. Despite the damp climate, this was a world of ships and timber, and fire was the most savage threat of all. The men reacted with barely suppressed fury at the idea that any bastard would so threaten them and their livelihoods. They promised vigilance. He did not tell them it was Sarah's father who was causing all the trouble. He trusted Angie to know, but he didn't want the men to be speculating on why his wife's father would go to such great lengths to destroy her husband.

Jason had never been so glad to be back on the island as he was now, and he thought how much the Pollards' legacy meant, for he had poured thousands of dollars into the island, and what he owned of it was collateral which might have been lost in massive foreclosures. The irony of it never left him that through destruction and murder, Radley Allen had inadvertently given his enemy great help along with great tragedy.

Jason was exhausted and felt as if he'd been breathing some foul miasma for too long, and he knew it had been even harder on Sarah and would continue to be. But here the land and the people gave comfort, and he and Sarah had time, the will, and the space to draw on each other's strength. Even on their first night back in their own bed, Jason could feel her relaxing more than she had since they had left the island what seemed a lifetime ago. And they both slept soundly the whole night through, the creatures of the night held at bay by the magic of the island.

CHAPTER
36

*T*he harvests had been good, and produce had been stored and the excess sold. The horses had been loaded safely. Everyone on the island was well. The days were growing shorter and rain swept in cool waves across the archipelago.

Waking and sleeping, Sarah held to the images of the land and its people, drawing life from them as if she were rooted in the earth like the flora of the island, drawing life most of all from Jason, always Jason.

They waited, and when word came from Owen, they shared it. But Thanksgiving and Christmas had passed and they had seen the dawning of 1873 by the bonfire on the beach before truly important information arrived.

Jason read through the papers and handed them to Sarah who, even before she began to read them for herself, could tell by the fierce look of triumph on his face that the news was good.

It was even better than they had hoped, and it was as if her leaving had made her father ever more reckless in his business dealings since many of the potentially disastrous investments had been made afterward. The arrogance of the man was clear in the report. He had obviously come to see himself as one of the great financiers in the country. He owned mining shares for gold, silver, and coal; he owned shares in ships, factories, and mills; he owned bits of freighting companies, lumber outfits, and land where railroads were supposed to come through; he owned stock in railroads, and ironically, some of his deepest involvement was in the Northern Pacific. He even was reputed—or "ill-reputed" Owen had written—to own a brothel in New York. Some things he owned outright, some demanded payments regularly in order for him to retain them, and all of it was in his own name, not in the name of the bank or of the bank's clients. No, it was Radley Chambers Allen; often it had taken some digging through agents' names to ascertain that, but the final name was always Allen's. And according to Owen's sources, there was no way Allen's private fortune could have financed everything, not even though he had made some good investments over the years. Since there were records of only a few insignificant loans in his own name, Jason concluded that Allen had been using funds not legally his for quite a long time and had in the past few years done so at an ever increasing rate, plunging into one new scheme after another. There had been rumors now and then of his activities, and though they had been quickly squelched, the bank had apparently lost a few customers, but this hadn't seemed to make any difference to Allen.

My friends,
[Sarah could picture the gleam in Owen's dark eyes as he'd written these lines], things could hardly be better for our purposes. The man is grossly overextended and the kindest word applicable is "embezzler." When the time is ripe, merely spreading rumors may well be enough to bring him down. And the time will be ripe within the year, I think. With Grant in for a second term and still listening to the wrong people, and with greed taking the place of common sense, there's bound to be a reckoning. I think our best course is to wait until that begins in the affairs of Radley Allen Chambers and then to do the utmost to speed the process. One truly major loss, and the house of cards, with

a little help, will fold. I doubt very much that even the wealthiest of his associates would make more than a token effort to save him. He is noticeably short of friends.

He had circled major investments he considered unsound in red ink. They danced, a swarm of ruby rings before Sarah's eyes.

"My father has gone quite mad," she whispered.

"He's been mad since he first touched you. I only hope he retains enough sanity to know when he is ruined." Jason's voice was cold and deadly.

There was a postscript from Owen:

Sarah might be interested to know that she is living with distant relatives, distant indeed since they are reported to reside in a manor house not far from London, England. Mr. Allen is glad she had left for her years abroad before his nearly fatal illness—whatever that might have been—from which he fully recovered. One must sometimes wonder what sort of deity is running this universe. Sarah might also like to know how much she enjoys the experience of living abroad though she misses him. The bastard.

"How convenient! His fairy tale provides the perfect explanation, and he believes that not only will he get me back, but that I will tell his lies for him. The dutiful daughter. My God, why didn't I make sure he was dead!"

"Because stabbing someone to death is much harder than one would guess," Jason said calmly. "His time will come." Inwardly he damned them all anew—all the people who might have helped Sarah and had not, people who even now accepted the comfortable story of her stay in England without doing anything at all to check its authenticity. Though he knew it to be true and thought he accepted it, the isolation in which she had lived continued to have the power to shock him.

Jason was between her and her father, and she was here, safe on the island; Sarah regained her balance. "How could Owen discover so much about my father? If so much is known, how can my father go on?"

"Owen has some strange contacts—they vary from powerful politicians to people who sleep in doorways, and he has them not only in San Francisco but back East. They're willing to deal with him because he uses their information, but he doesn't use them. When he said he had favors to collect, he meant just that, not that he was going to blackmail anyone. You know Owen, and we're not the only people who have benefited more than the fees allow from his work and help. Many people obviously know bits of what is contained in this report, otherwise it wouldn't exist, but I expect you, I, and Owen are among a rare few who know the total. And God help us all and this country, even if a considerable number of the most powerful people do know, too many of them are involved in the same things to risk themselves by exposing your father. As Owen says, greed is taking the place of common sense, and I would add that there is no silence more complete than that of shared greed; one voice confessing is all it would take to ruin many. And the time to bring your father down will be when so many are so close to falling, none will be able to reach out to preserve the silence for him or for anyone else."

The men's assessment of the times made sense. Even here in this northwestern corner of the United States, news came to them. Some reform was under way already. The notorious Boss Tweed of Tammany Hall, a powerful political organization, had been sent to the penitentiary last year after three years of corruption that had rivaled any precedents and had defrauded New York City's government of one hundred million dollars. And even during the campaign, Grant's administration had been tarred with major scandal, the bribing of congressmen by railroad interests. Surely not even the President could remain above blame if his associates continued to indulge in illegal and immoral acts. And surely just as Owen and Jason judged, few men would want to be involved with her father should the extent of his corruption become public knowledge. Sarah considered it all, wondering what further damage he would do to them before he was stopped.

Watching her, reading her clearly, Jason said, "We can hold on long enough, my love, I promise we can."

She managed to smile at him. "Your 'I promise' is as absolute as Jamie's 'I decided.' I believe you." Suddenly her eyes widened as another thought struck her, and she started to laugh. "Richard Clayton, he didn't recognize me! The story about England proves it."

"Richard Clayton?" Jason was completely baffled.

"The man in Seattle, the reason I went to you."

"God bless Mr. Clayton!" he breathed fervently. "I hope he had success in whatever brought him to Seattle." He did not venture his own conviction that Mr. Clayton or not, he and Sarah would have gotten together.

In February Jason submitted to having his thirty-sixth birthday celebrated on an icy cold day that had all the islanders rosy-cheeked by the time they arrived at the house.

"I hope everyone enjoys toasting my old age," Jason groaned, "because I certainly don't."

Sarah studied him with such a solemn expression, he had to smile. "I'm sorry, but I just can't see any signs of it. I'll check again in fifty years."

It wasn't entirely true; there were new little lines on his lean face and more gray hair mixing here and there with the golden-tinged brown, but only with great effort could she see him as others did. To her, his image remained the young man she had first seen so many years before, and even that was more the essence than his actual physical appearance. She thought how odd and lovely it was that the more one loved someone, the more impossible objectivity became. She wondered suddenly how very old couples who had been together and loved each other for years on years perceived each other; she doubted very much that they saw the marks of age as they truly were.

"You're wearing a very secret smile; I'll give you a penny for it," Jason offered.

"It's worth a good deal more than that but I'll give it to you free since it's your birthday. I was thinking that when we're both old, it won't be any different from now."

"There's a mysterious logic there that escapes me, but I'll take your word for it, and if I have any brains left to remember with by then, I'll ask if it's true." As he bent down to kiss her, they heard a giggle, and Erin flashed away toward the kitchen.

"Now there's a problem of age," Jason said with a frown, "and I don't know quite what's to be done about it. It's still all right for the little ones to stay on the island, but the twins are growing up awfully fast. They'll be thirteen this year, and it shows."

"I've noticed. Erin is suddenly all blushes and womanly affectations one minute and then back to scraped knees and footraces the next. And Eric won't be able to sing soprano much longer. I heard his voice go down and up the other day, and he looked as surprised as if someone else were speaking from his mouth."

Jason sighed. "It's hard. Maggie and Ben love their children so much, and of course, it's up to them. But in a year or two at the most, I think the twins ought to leave the island for a while to mix with other people. They wouldn't have to go that far away. For them, Seattle would be a big city. We hardly use the house there anymore. I used to stay in it a lot more because I couldn't stand to be here with Jamie and mother for too long, and then you came along and made this home as it had never been before. For the amount of time we spend there, we could use a hotel; they're decent now. But I've decided to keep the house after all so that the twins and later perhaps Jamie will have a place to live, and the Olsen and Nilsen children if they wish to leave here for a while also. By then, hopefully, the university might be offering courses that would further their education."

"I'm glad," she said softly. "I like the Seattle house." She had a clear image of her first time with him, of the patient way that he had made love to her, love even then, even with the mockery. She made herself return to the matter at hand. "But the twins, won't they have to be apart to grow up fully?"

"Eventually, yes, but I think that will be their own decision. Despite being so close, they are very different from each other and becoming more so by the day. It's not that it will be easy for them, and I'm sure there'll be jealousy when they begin forming close attachments to other people, but I think they'll be all right."

Sarah grinned suddenly. "I just remembered. Erin was chattering away the other day, and she informed me that she plans to marry Jamie when they're both old enough. She figures she'll have to wait until she's twenty so that Jamie will be eighteen, but that's all right with her.''

"Well, my son could do worse. Erin's going to be a beautiful woman and a bright one, but I hope to God she keeps her intentions to herself for a while; if Jamie gets wind of it, he'll hide from her for years.''

Sarah understood Maggie's air of abstraction now; she'd seen her watching her children lately with pride and sorrow mixed. Maggie saw the changes in the twins more clearly than anyone else and knew the separation had to come.

"Have you spoken to either of the Carters about your plans?''

"No,'' he admitted. "I've been a coward about it. Besides, it doesn't have to happen right now.''

"But I'm quite sure Maggie's already worrying about it and probably Ben too though he's much more reticent about his feelings than she is. Would you mind if I talked to her?''

"Mind! I'd be grateful. It's nice to know that even cowardice can pay off. And now we'd better mix with our friends or they'll think we haven't even noticed they're here.''

"Planning to go somewhere?'' Cade asked Sarah as she came up to him.

"Why, no, not that I know of.''

His eyes sparkled with mischief under the jutting brows. "Just wondered. Lambing time's coming up pretty soon, and I've yet to get you out there to help. Nate and Jon help with the shearing, can't ask them for a hand in everything.''

"Unless my lord and master has other plans, I'll be there this year,'' she promised. "But it may be to your woe. You haven't any idea of how poor I may be at the work.''

"The ewes do most of the work anyway,'' Cade replied with a grin, "and I've got Jamie trained in any case.''

Sarah moved among the islanders, feeling the security of their love and friendship as a physical force, a protective circle keeping her warm and safe inside. It struck her anew how strange and wonderful it was to have her life so involved with the lives of others, sharing a common past, present, and future in a closeness she could not have imagined before coming to the island.

The parallel broods of the Olsens and Nilsens raced up to

offer her cookies which their mothers had told them they must share. Sarah politely declined, to their delight. She could see the passage of time here as clearly as she could with the other children. The youngest pair would be six years old this year, the oldest nine, and the middle children, Matilda Olsen and Jens Nilsen, would be eight. Three years had made visible changes in all of them, but all were growing into sturdy flaxen copies of their parents, learning all the skills the adults could teach them as they grew. Sarah wondered what their lives would bring. Would the boys go to sea and the girls wait for them? Would the children of the two families who had been raised as one inter-marry like the Borens and Dennys, or would that never occur to them simply because they had been raised together, familiarity precluding romance? She hoped she would be here to witness whatever was to come. She wondered how often now Ingrid and Else thought of the lost babies and whether new additions to their families would be made in the coming years. Seeing them watching over their children and visiting with the other guests, she could feel the contentment radiating from both of them; whatever sorrow they still suffered was not permitted to poison joy.

It was the same with Constance; it made one smile just to look at her these days. In the glow of the New Year's Eve bonfire, Constance and David had announced their intention to marry. They planned it for mid-April in hopes they might find a fair day.

The seasons of the earth and the seasons of man were so closely bound here, Sarah found great reassurance in the rhythm.

She talked to Maggie about the twins shortly after Jason's party. As kindly as possible she told her Jason's plans, finishing with, "Of course, this is only if you and Ben want it to be so."

To her horror, Maggie's eyes filled with tears that spilled over and ran down her cheeks. She buried her face in her hands. The sounds she made were heartbreaking.

"Maggie, please don't, it's nothing you have to . . ." Sarah stopped abruptly realizing that in her agitation she'd forgotten Maggie couldn't hear a word she was saying. She put her arms around her, patting her back until she raised her head, then stepped away so Maggie could see her speak and sign.

"You surely know Jason would never order you to do anything, let alone something to do with your children! It's only something he's thought of to help if you think it's right."

She was so worried at having bungled the whole thing that for a moment, her mind went blank, and she didn't understand Maggie's signs at all. Maggie repeated everything patiently, finger spelling much of it so that there would be no misunderstanding. Finally, Sarah knew what she was saying.

Maggie had only gratitude for Jason's idea. Lately she had been wondering what in the world would become of the twins. They were growing up so quickly! But she had been able to foresee only trouble if she and Ben moved and took the children somewhere else. Jason's solution was perfect; the children would be in a new world but not so far away. Of course there was sorrow; it was very hard to see them growing so far away from the tiny babies they had been.

"A year or two. It is both long time and very little."

Sarah agreed, seeing both the relief and the apprehension in Maggie's eyes, knowing she would feel exactly the same way when Jamie went out to find the world. All the island children must have their chance to choose whether they would come back to live on the island, and the choice could only be made after they'd seen at least a bit of the world beyond.

Constance and David were married as planned in April, and it was as if they were blessed with a God-gift of kind weather after a wet and windy March. Though the air was still a little sharp, there was softness from the sun in a blue sky and new green was showing in bright beginning contrast to the dark of the firs.

The minister had come over from San Juan Island to perform the simple ceremony in Constance's house, and as Sarah listened, she hoped that Constance would always be as clear-eyed and happy as she appeared today with no shadowed images of the future to blur her present.

Of her own present, Sarah was suddenly much less certain. She had tried to ignore it; this was a happy occasion for all the islanders, or should have been, and she wanted to share the joy, but she could feel something quite different in Jason. He was saying all the right things and smiling at the right times, but something was wrong. The smile didn't reach his eyes, and she could feel the tension in him. For one dreadful moment all her old insecurities rushed back as she considered the possibility that he still cared so much for Constance that it pained him to see her marry. She discarded the idea angrily. The only time Jason had looked genuinely happy was when he kissed the bride and congratulated the groom.

He had slept restlessly the night before. Something yesterday. She had spent most of the day with Constance and the other women, putting extra touches of greenery here and there, helping with the cooking. The minister had arrived yesterday and had spent the night as the Drakes' guest. Jason had played the genial host last night at supper, but even then something had been wrong, though Sarah only realized it now. Word from Owen, she was almost sure of it. She felt like going up to Jason now and demanding to know, but she willed herself to patience. Time enough when the wedding party was over.

"First cloud I've seen today is on your face," Cade remarked, catching her so deep in thought, she hadn't even noticed his approach. "Anything I can do?"

She was tempted to share the burden of her suspicion and then realized she could not. "Just wondering how my lambs are doing."

Cade accepted her lead. "I may never let you help again. There are some lambs out there that say 'Saraaaaaa' instead of 'Baaaaa.' "

This time she really smiled at him, sharing the memory of those March days when the ewes had dropped their tiny lambs and only one had been lost despite the cold.

Jamie came up to offer her a piece of cake she and Maggie had baked. "It's very good! An' Maggie told me you did most of the work."

She broke off a piece for Cade and took a bite herself. "Well, I didn't really do most of the work, but at least I didn't spoil it. Ummm, it is good!"

"I'm glad Mr. Becam is going to live in Constance's house now. She's awful lonesome sometimes."

Jamie scampered off to see what other delicacies were offered, and Cade and Sarah chuckled together over Jamie's practical view of the marriage.

But regardless of the joy of the occasion, the day seemed inordinately long to Sarah. She watched Jason carefully, sensing the effort he was putting into appearing happy and at ease. She wanted nothing more than to go home with him and find out what was going on.

But it was dark before they were home and still she had to delay her questions until Jamie had settled down and gone to bed and the minister had had a last cup of tea.

By the time they were alone in their bedroom, she was ready to explode.

"What is it? What's happened?" she demanded.

Jason blinked at her and then shook his head ruefully. "So much for my attempt to spare you bad news until after the wedding. You read me far too well. Bad timing, that's what it was." His face hardened. "The minister brought a telegram from Owen with him. It just happened to arrive on San Juan Island yesterday, so convenient that he was coming here. Yes, indeed, your father has a very nasty temper or maybe he planned to do it anyway."

Sarah steeled herself to hear him out without interruption, knowing he was struggling with his own temper. Some of the news was good. It would not work again surely, but further false leads about Jason's investment plans had resulted in the banker entering into yet two more unstable schemes, and the ruse was beginning to pay off. Two of the four businesses had now gone under just as Jason and Owen had thought they would. Radley Allen had lost thousands of dollars; Jason had lost very little, just the bait money he had advanced for some bad lumber shares.

The rest of the news was devastating. There had been attempted arson at the redwood logging camp. The damage had not been too extensive, since the woods were still wet from the rainy season. The loggers had quickly discovered the fire and put it out. But far worse, the *Sarah-Mary* had been burned beyond salvage.

Owen had sent only the barest lines, full details would follow in a letter.

The beautifully crafted ship Jason had named for her, destroyed by fire—the vision of flames turned Sarah to ice, and she began to shiver uncontrollably.

Jason gathered her into his arms, holding her fiercely against him. "We'll survive this too, we will! He'll lose."

"He's ge-getting . . . clo-closer. I can . . . feel him . . . ge-getting closer!" Her teeth were chattering audibly, adding to the hysteria of her voice.

"He's not," Jason protested sharply. "He's doing the same thing he's been doing since all of this started; he's hiring thugs to do his dirty work. But he's still where he's always been, thousands of miles away, spinning his webs, webs that will soon be too thin to hold him."

Sarah continued to weep and shiver helplessly, and Jason was flooded with a rush of violence that sent tremors through his own body. How he hated the man and the hold he had over Sarah, the terror that never left her! Perhaps the slow, elaborate plan for Allen's destruction was wrong after all, perhaps he should go after him and kill him.

"No!" Sarah cried, an agonized wail. Unknowingly he'd spoken the words aloud. "No, no, you can't, you mustn't!" She was twisting in his arms, clutching at him with frantic hands.

He knew even as he stripped her clothes from her and his own away that he shouldn't touch her now; that there was far more violence than love in him; that he wanted her to know that he was the man who possessed her body, her heart, her soul, no one else; he knew even as he pushed her back on the bed and entered her with savage urgency devoid of care for her readiness. Dimly through the haze of lust, he heard her cry out, but he did not slacken the force of his thrusts until, his hipbones hard against hers, he felt the pulsing release of his seed deep inside of her, and he gave his own cry of triumph.

Sanity returned to him as quickly as it had fled before his lust. He pulled away from her and stared down at her with sick horror. Her eyes were closed, and he wondered if she'd fainted. He touched her face with trembling fingers. "Christ, sweetheart, I'm sorry! Have I hurt you badly? Please, Sarah, look at me!"

Her eyes opened then, and nothing was as he had thought it would be. They were shining golden-gray, and her voice was gentle. "You didn't hurt me, love, I needed you as much as you needed me. I always will."

It was not entirely true; the suddenness of his entry had hurt, but nothing had been as strong as the rushing glory of meeting his act of possession with her own. He had done what he intended; he had diminished the image of her father with his own.

She reached up and touched the scratch on his arm. "Did I hurt you?"

An impish smile curved her mouth, and Jason was suddenly aware of more than one stinging scratch on his back and arms, aware that guilt even in the midst of the blind violence of the act had distorted his perception of her. She had arched in shock at his brutal thrust, but she had not fought him then or afterwards; she had met him in equal passion for whatever its reasons, had clawed at his flesh, had taken him even as he had taken her.

Beyond words, he smoothed the hair back from her face and lightly traced her delicate features with his mouth. He settled down with her in his arms. He held her for a long, long time, and then he loved her again with slow care.

The days and nights that had flowed into weeks and months and now years had surely bred familiarity between them but had just as surely whetted rather than diminished their hunger for each other. And Jason had long since realized that their physical joining was simply the most immediate and pleasurable way they had of expressing all the shades of love that existed between them. He was profoundly grateful that they shared the gift. It would have been so easy for Sarah to go on despising being touched for the rest of her life.

CHAPTER
37

*A*duplicate of the telegram Owen had sent to San Juan Island arrived from Seattle and his letter followed. It seemed that two recently hired men might have been responsible for the fire in the redwoods; at least everything pointed to them since they were nowhere to be found after the event. As for the *Sarah-Mary,* there had been one life lost, undoubtedly the man who had started the fire and most probably the same one responsible for the blaze aboard the *Moon Chaser.* Despite all the precautions, the arsonist had gotten aboard, but he hadn't gotten off. He had miscalculated and been trapped in his own mayhem. One sailor had seen him before all had abandoned ship, and he fit the description of the arsonist on the Pollards' ship. Good riddance, but his death left them with no proof of the man behind the crime. The ship had been tied up by a wharf for loading; it was a miracle that the whole waterfront hadn't gone up.

Owen concluded:

> I presume you want to sell the redwood shares though you know I wish you would not.

Allen is a vindictive son of a bitch, isn't he? I have not
mentioned it before but will now in spite of the insult to my
brawler's pride—thank you for employing one Rio the
Texan on my behalf. I think he knows the rules better than
I do. This isn't exactly my kind of war, nor yours, I know.
But we'll win. Patience, the hardest thing of all under the
circumstances.

Kiss Sarah for me and keep her with you, up there. Can't
see any reason for you to come south at the moment. Bartholomew is well-guarded by his young brigands. Carrie
and Frenchie send love.

Jason sent word not only for Owen to sell the redwood shares
but also for him to pay off the losses of the other shareholders
in the *Sarah-Mary* and to wire him if he didn't have sufficient
funds. "He won't like it, but he'll do it," he said grimly. "And
he ought to have plenty to pay them off with the lumber sale and
the rest of the Pollards' money."

"But yours was the greatest loss!" Sarah protested. "And
you've told me before, losses are shared just as the profits are."

"In most cases, yes, when bad or good luck happens to all.
That isn't true here. The ship was burned because of me. And
though we've all been partially reimbursed by the ship's profits,
not all of her building and operating costs have been paid back.
Those men trusted my luck to make expensive insurance unnecessary. I owe them." He did not add that even now he was
glad he carried no insurance; a good investigator might conceiv-
ably connect all that was happening and expose Sarah's father
and her. It would lead to public knowledge and the end of
Jason's vendetta. Jason had no intention of allowing that to
happen.

Death and destruction, knowing who was responsible, and
still having to wait—as hard as it was for her, Sarah knew how
much harder it was for Jason. He was by nature direct, accustomed to fighting quickly and openly for what he wanted or to
protect what was already his. He was indeed the Tiger now,
penned in a small space, denied his natural prey, pacing and
raging despite his attempts to be patient.

Jamie found a family of raccoons in a hollow tree near the pond and was delighted to take his parents to see them near sunset. Sarah thought them charming, from the four tiny bandits peeking out to the mother who churred and chirped her instructions anxiously as she left them in the den while she went to forage. Jamie whispered that he liked them even if they did eat eggs and even birds, as Cade claimed.

The late May evening was full of the blessings of spring. The scent of growing things was so strong and rich, Sarah found herself pulling in breaths deep enough to make her dizzy, and the scraping, humming, singing sounds of the small lives moving in the gathering dusk seemed loud enough to fill the world with their chorus. There would still be sudden days and nights of cold and wet, but none of them would be strong or long enough to dim the promise of the coming softness of summer.

It was as perfect as any time could be, and with now familiar sadness, Sarah knew it was lost to Jason. He was being patient and kind with Jamie, but he was not enjoying it. He was blind to the beauty he would have seen so easily before. Now he saw nothing except the war that was taking so long to win. It had been the same with her birthday. He had made it a festival celebrated by everyone on the island—everyone except himself. He had played the jovial host to perfection, even insisting the *Gaiety* take them out for a short run simply to keep tradition. Still, she had known he was locked away in his own cold space, the only warmth coming from the protectiveness she could feel surrounding her, often in too white a heat. She remembered only too clearly Reverend Mapes's warning that she must guard Jason against becoming too much like his enemy.

The romantic illusion she had had of seeing him as a young man on his birthday could not be sustained now. His face was becoming more graven and harsh by the day. His limp was more pronounced, his leg more often in rebellion than before. And yet she knew the illusion was still more valid than the visible truth. The deep lines and tense muscles were the marks of his present embattled state, not a sudden toll of years. Only when it was over—dear God, let it be over soon—could he be young again.

The four little masked faces continued to peer from the tree hole in the fading light as the mother raccoon began to hunt along the edge of the pond, unaware that there were other observers.

Jamie was still watching the animals intently. Sarah seized Jason's hand, wondering even as she did if he would know what she was doing, doing it anyway.

"Beautiful here. Jamie and I love you. You love us. Let that be all now."

She finger spelled it once and then again in the palm of his hand, silently, insistently, trusting him to understand because he had known this language so long before she had learned it.

"I cannot." She understood the sad answer he pressed into her hand.

She knew even the missives from Owen were difficult for Jason because Owen, as Jason's agent, was in many ways more in control of what was happening than he was. It was sensible because Owen was capable and had those useful contacts, but that didn't make it any easier to live with. For her part, Sarah was infinitely thankful that he was so involved, a barrier between the meeting of the full rage of the principals.

And then the focus of Sarah's world changed dramatically. At first she refused to credit the evidence for what it was. She missed one monthly course and then another, but she was quite sure it was simply because of all the tension. But by the middle of June, she faced the fact she would not bleed at the end of this month either. Her body's calendar was not off but changed to accommodate the baby growing inside of her.

"Oh, My Lord!" she exclaimed and was instantly glad that Jason had ridden out early—another part of the old pattern of trouble used again for the new—Jason on Gabriel racing over the island at top speed.

She felt so many things at once, she could not have borne to be with another person at the moment, not even Jason. Of course, she was with another person, the curled life growing in her womb. Her laugh sounded peculiar to her, and she stopped abruptly.

She had long since given up Angie's methods of preventing conception, and she had also given up all hope and longing for

having Jason's child, having become more and more convinced
that something was wrong with her, perhaps from her father's
use of her. Jason had never expressed anything but worry over
her getting pregnant; she remembered so long ago assuring him
that since it hadn't happened yet, it was doubtful it ever would.
And they had Jamie. Not once had Jason even hinted that he
wished they could have a child together. After all, he had lost
Gaiety just that way. And now here it was and at a time which
could hardly be worse.

She had not thought she could conceive; therefore, she had
ignored all signs that she had until this moment. And there were
other small signs in addition to the cessation of her cycle. She
inspected her breasts as if they belonged to someone else. They
were indeed a trifle fuller and the aureoles were surely the
slightest bit darker. And she had been feeling strangely queasy
in the morning lately—well, not strange now that she knew, but
it hadn't been the debilitating sickness she knew some women
had, it had been more a matter of feeling slightly off balance.
She supposed she was; she supposed there must be some re-
alignment for the addition. She had felt more tired than usual,
had even stolen some uncharacteristic naps a few afternoons,
but she had marked that down to the general toll the tension was
taking.

She got up and stood nude before the mirror, inspecting
herself critically. Nothing really showed yet. She was, after all,
only two months along. She pushed her stomach out, trying to
imagine how she would look later. And then she blushed. She
knew exactly when she had conceived, remembering the violence she and Jason had shared on that night. With a minister
in the house, no less. She giggled, and the sound was sane.

She was suddenly quite deliriously happy. She hugged herself
while delight surged through her. Good time or not, she was
going to have Jason's child.

"A tiger cub, a perfect one."

But the laughter and the impulse to go find Jason and tell him
the news faded as swiftly as it had come. She suspected that had
he been under less of a strain, he would have noticed her condition before she had, but he hadn't, and she saw more reasons

for keeping the secret as long as possible than for telling him. It would add a thousand times the weight to the heavy burden he already carried. His worry and protectiveness would know no bounds, and it might just be the final end to his patience. She could visualize all too clearly Jason going off to confront her father directly, to kill him or be killed.

The warmth fled, leaving her cold and empty. No, not empty, full of a mystical beginning, a secret she would keep as long as she could.

It was not, she soon discovered, as easy as she had thought it would be. Jason remained oblivious, but she found herself wanting to tell the other women, wanting to ask them questions, wanting to share the experience that above all else made women sisters to each other. And she discovered that that very universality among women was likely to betray her secret whether she wished to or not, particularly with Constance and Maggie.

Constance moved in a haze of joy through her days as David's wife, looking so young and beautiful, it caught at Sarah's heart to see her. And once-shy David was now given to displaying his affection for his wife even when others were present.

"Honestly, what will Sarah think?" Constance chided, laughing.

David was standing behind his wife, his arms wrapped around her, holding her close despite the fact that Sarah, dropping by to visit, had knocked and had been bidden by him to enter.

"Maybe that I love you," he suggested, planting a kiss on her shining hair. "See you later. There's some work to be done on the *Gaiety.*"

Constance watched him leave, then turned to Sarah with a smile. "I dote on him as if I were a sixteen-year-old with her first romance. Hardly dignified, but I don't seem to be able to do anything about it. By the way, there's something different about you. You wouldn't perhaps be pregnant, would you?"

The transition was so smoothly made, Sarah was taken completely unaware, and she nearly blurted out the truth. Instead she managed to lie. "No, but I do hope we have children one day, someday after all the trouble is over."

"My dear, children have a habit of coming at inconvenient

times, and then they make everything possible and impossible at once. Despite the risk and the glory of having another Daniel, I would still like to have David's child someday. I hope it happens." She then changed the subject to how well her flowers were doing in the early summer heat, and Sarah knew she would neither press her further nor tell Jason but that the offer of help and understanding had been made.

Maggie was more direct. She watched Sarah toying with her breakfast one morning but not eating much of it, and as soon as she could get Sarah alone, she proved she'd been noticing more than that morning by asking the question bluntly, her right hand in the crook of her left arm as if she were rocking a baby.

"Maybe someday, not now," Sarah lied again, finding it difficult to meet Maggie's eyes.

Maggie smiled and made the sign for secret. Sarah didn't agree or disagree with her, trusting that even if Maggie were positive, she wouldn't take the privilege of telling Jason from his wife. However, she soon found that that did not stop Maggie from giving her dark looks when she rode out on Sheba or did anything else that appeared strenuous. She was quite sure Maggie had not curtailed her own work during her pregnancy with the twins, but obviously, Sarah was different in her eyes.

She was quite relieved to be going to Seattle and the logging camp, away from Maggie's concern, Constance's knowledge and the scrutiny of Ingrid and Else; if one of them discovered her secret, she doubted it would remain a secret much longer. Ingrid particularly was likely to blurt it out in joyous celebration.

She knew the trip was not solely for business. Jason was growing more and more restless. Owen's contacts in New York would soon start the last of the plan—the spreading of rumors designed to cause a run on the Allen and Chambers bank. They would use the truth—lies weren't needed in the case of Radley Allen—but it must be used wisely and to the greatest effect with the least possible damage to those who would start the rumors. And then there would be more waiting to see if at last Allen could no longer cover his machinations. They were all grimly pleased by the knowledge of the vast sums he must already have spent in his war of destruction.

Jason needed to be doing something more than waiting for news on the island, and Sarah needed to be with him. She was more sure than ever that she had been right not to tell him; she doubted he would have let her accompany him if he knew.

They took Jamie with them. They had talked about it openly. They had no assurance that any place was as safe for them as the island, but Seattle and the logging camp were close-knit communities and part of Jason's territory, as San Francisco had long since ceased to be. And they knew that Jamie needed to be with them as much as he could. They never spoke about it, but he knew the worry of Sarah's bad father was not over, and he continued to fear for them.

The Drakes arrived after the Independence Day celebrations which Seattle citizens were still boasting had been fine indeed. "Wish ol' Doc could've seen it," more than one person claimed. Doc Maynard had died in March, most of the town had turned out for his funeral, and even people who hadn't liked him much while he was alive were now found to have fond memories and anecdotes they were eager to share. He was part of Seattle's short history and as such was already taking on the posthumous burden of being a legend.

And then on July 14, Arthur Denny received a telegram that became the sole interest of the entire population. The telegram was from Mr. Rice and Mr. Ainsworth, the Western Representatives of the Northern Pacific Railroad, and it read: "We have located the terminus on Commencement Bay."

The news spread like the plague, and the town exploded in righteous wrath and grim talk about the corruption riddling the railroad industry. But the fact remained that the Northern Pacific was not going to be coming to Seattle but was going to expand the prospects of a town it already owned. Some of the railroad officials were known to want to bury Seattle in the process.

"Can they do that?" Sarah asked Jason that night. She was enjoying being in the Seattle house again. It was no longer haunted by the ghost of Gaiety; it was more as if Gaiety had deeded it to her with a full heart and blessings for her to take care of Jason and Jamie. She hated the thought of the house and

the town boarded up and sinking into the decay of abandon-
ment.

"It's an end to a great many hopes and dreams. It's an end
before new dreams have had a chance to begin. But, no, the
railroad, or rather lack of it, won't destroy Seattle. Someday
there will be a rail connection from here to the rest of the nation,
maybe not in our lifetime, but someday. And in the meantime,
Seattle will simply go on. There's too much life and too much
pure stubbornness here to allow for anything but survival."

"That sounds as much like us as it does this town," she ventured, and she felt an enormous need to tell him about the baby.

"It is us, and it's most of the people in the town. It's anyone
anywhere who wants to survive." The grim note was back in his
voice, and she was again glad she hadn't told him.

The new ship was being finished at the Mactavish yard, but
Sarah seldom went with Jason on his visits there though Jamie
loved to go. For Sarah it was too vivid a reminder of the loss of
the *Sarah-Mary*. She knew Rob Mactavish was mourning the ship
as if he'd lost a child, and that was too close to the bone for her.

She spent much of her time visiting Angie.

"Well, are you going to tell me when it's due and when you're
going to tell Jason that it's due at all?" Angie demanded the first
time they were alone.

"Honestly, I don't understand! It seems every other woman
knew the minute I did," Sarah complained, finally too exasperated to deny it once again.

"The minute you knew, you started looking different," Angie
replied. "I saw it right off, and so would lots of women. It's sort
of like you're listening to something no one else can hear, and
you've got a private sort of smile when you think no one's
looking." Without a trace of envy, Angie stated these facts as if
they were well-known phenomena. "And I know you haven't
told Jason because he'd look different too, even more than you
do."

Silence stretched between them until Angie nodded. "I see
your point. It's not a good time for Jason to worry about even
one more thing and especially not this."

They both knew they were sharing the thought of how Jason had lost Gaiety.

"You'll be fine." Angie's voice quavered a little, but Sarah's was firm. "I know I will. I'm young and healthy, and I couldn't be happier about it even if I can't tell Jason yet. I'm only three months along, so unless he suddenly sees what you claim is so visible, there's plenty of time."

"He won't; he's not a woman." Angie's smile was definitely superior and more than a little wicked. "He won't notice anything until something feels different to him." She did not say that Jason would probably notice later than most because he wouldn't want it to be true. She wished she didn't know how much this was going to terrify the Tiger when he did know. Sarah is not Gaiety, she thought, wishing again, wishing she could take the thought and put it in Jason's heart and brain.

For her part, Sarah found it comforting to be able to visit with someone to whom she had admitted her secret.

The irony of the fact that Angie had never had children did not escape Sarah, but it didn't matter; she was glad to have a woman friend to talk to honestly. Angie didn't try to coddle her to death but believed as she did that there wasn't any sense in going through a pregnancy with an imaginary case of the vapors when one felt perfectly well. She did, however, insist that Sarah rest when she felt tired.

"It only makes sense," she asserted. "If you start looking droopy, Jason's bound to be upset."

They talked about Frenchie and Rio and Captain Tom whom Angie expected home by early spring next year, but most of all, just like everyone else in Seattle, they talked about the railroad.

"Those bastards! Oh, not the surveyors and the like," a reminiscent smile lighted Angie's face and was gone, "I mean the big men. They want Seattle to go under, but she won't. They'll be buried before she is. They're claiming to own most of Puget Sound and that won't wash either. Just let them try to take all the land they think is theirs. They can have the water but not the land! Whoever dreamed up this land scheme in place of money from Congress ought to be shot."

Sarah kept to herself the personal reason she had for hoping the railroad company would fail, but she felt a fierce pleasure every time she thought of it—her father had a large investment in the success of the Northern Pacific.

Angie looked away from the savage expression on Sarah's face. She guessed the cause of it though not the specifics—she doubted that Sarah's father was ever far from Sarah's mind these days—and she thought better of warning her about what some people were saying about the Tiger. They were saying his luck had fled; they were saying it might even be dangerous to do business with him; they were talking about the *Moon Chaser* and the *Sarah-Mary*; they were speculating that his fair-haired bride had not proven such good fortune for him after all and that perhaps the trouble had come with her. With an inward sigh, Angie admitted to herself that the Drakes were probably already only too aware of the rumors even if neither one had said anything to her about them. Even if they weren't, there wasn't any use in telling them.

Indeed, Sarah and Jason were aware of the subtle shifts which caused them to be regarded with expressions which varied from pity to gloating calculation. But the change was not in the people Jason knew well and cared about nor was there any sign that Jamie was suffering from it, so they ignored it as well as they could.

But Sarah discovered she was doing a better job of that than he when Jason came home one night with scraped knuckles, a bruise along one cheekbone, and a guilty expression.

"I went with the men from the shipyard for a drink at one of the saloons down on the sawdust, and I took exception to something someone said," he explained. "At least Rob and the others weren't involved and no one was seriously hurt." His eyes were anxious, waiting for her reaction, but his mouth was fighting the grin of satisfaction he'd worn all the way home.

She tried to look stern at least for a moment and failed utterly, her mouth curving up in response to his. "You're incorrigible! You won, and you're so proud of it, you're about to burst your buttons." How could she be angry; even though he hadn't told her, she was quite sure the "something" someone had said had been about her. He reminded her of Jamie. "Felt good to punch someone, didn't it? Sometimes I wish I could too."

Jason laughed at her wistful expression and touched the tip of her nose. "Just as well you don't; somebody might break this pretty nose. Yes, it did feel good, but you feel better." He put his arms around her, suddenly needing the contact, trying to forget the filthy names the drunk had called her. The man was lucky to be alive and missing nothing more than a few teeth.

He was as glad as she to sail from Seattle the next day. Jamie had been asleep the night before, but he noticed his father's bruises when he saw him in the morning.

Jason didn't lie nor did he embellish the story. He simply said that someone else had started it and he had finished it; no one had been badly hurt and fighting was never a good idea though sometimes it was unavoidable. He was startled by the complete understanding in his son's eyes and the lack of questions. It gave him the oddest feeling that Jamie was years older than he'd thought, but he did not pursue the subject. He didn't see the fond, conspiratorial look that passed between his wife and his son.

CHAPTER
38

*D*espite her condition, Sarah had not been seasick on the trip to Seattle nor was she on the journey to the logging camp. She felt very pleased with herself, and she talked silently to the baby. "You're going to be a good sailor right from the beginning. Boy or girl, you're going to be like your father in that, not like me!"

"You just missed seein' some seals an' you got a funny look on your face," Jamie accused.

Good Lord, she thought, I'd better be more careful if even Jamie can see it! Aloud she said, "I was thinking of some sewing I'm going to do when we get home."

He wrinkled his nose in disgust. "Oh, girl stuff."

No, baby clothes, she thought mischievously. She reached out and tickled him before he could dodge away. "Just think how cold you'd be sometimes if no one did any sewing."

"I guess so," he admitted, "but it would be kind of nice right now."

Sarah had to agree with him; unlike the wet of early spring, the days had been very hot and dry for the Sound.

Jason came up beside them, and having heard the last of their conversation, he added his own comments. "We're lucky most of the lightning comes during the wet season. Fire's a real hazard in the timber during weather like this. But Jud and his crew are very careful," he added hastily, wishing he'd never mentioned the subject when he saw Sarah's expression.

Talk of fires or not, Sarah found it delightful to be back at the logging camp. Bull Fletcher, Jud, Red, Bart, Fiddler, Willie the crumb-chaser, and Kit the skid-greaser were all still there along with other familiar faces and some new additions. The youngsters Kit and Willie had done some filling out since the first time she'd met them, but Willie was still frail-looking while Kit was muscular and wiry and informed Sarah with shy pride that there was going to be a new skid-greaser soon and he was going to move up to bucker and who knew what after that.

She praised him lavishly even while she marveled that anyone would see a move to such backbreaking labor as a step in the right direction.

Unlike Kit, Fiddler was in a particularly bad temper as he recited the grievous wrongs nature had done him.

"First that goddamn, 'scuse me, goldang polecat went after my chickens an' kilt two of 'em, then he got under th' cookhouse an' let fly. You can still smell it, but I cain tell you it were grievous worse couple a' days back. An' then I jus' got rid of 'im, an' this big black bar come right into th' camp in th' middle a' th' night, bashed things around, an' lit off with a whole side a' meat. Didn't even git no clear shot at 'im. He got away without even gittin' his ass, 'scuse me, tail singed."

As Sarah understood it, a skunk had gotten under the cookhouse—Fiddler was right, the acrid musk was still present—and a bear had stolen meat. She was thankful it was Jason's duty to placate the cook; if she so much as opened her mouth, laughter was going to pour out. Jamie, she saw, was having the same trouble and was staring fixedly at his shoes. Jason's voice had a queer choked sound.

"I'm sure you handled it as well as possible. After all, the skunk and the bear are both gone, and they didn't take that much."

"Wahl, that's true," Fiddler allowed reluctantly. "But I don't aim t' have 'im take nothin' else."

Sarah and Jason were finally able to give full rein to their laughter when they were alone that night. "I can just see Fiddler racing out in his long johns, or maybe nothing at all in this heat, after that bear. And you can be sure the men will accuse him of feeding them polecat for weeks to come," Jason said, and then he was off again. But when they'd finally settled down, he did issue a warning.

"I doubt that bear will cause any more trouble; he's probably long gone from here. But just to be on the safe side, don't you and Jamie wander too far without me and take the rifle with you even if you are close to camp."

"Yes, sir," Sarah agreed promptly, not bothering to point out that shooting bears was something quite out of her experience. She didn't want Jason to worry needlessly. With rueful humor, she remembered Cade saying she'd be better off hitting a bear over the head with a fishing pole than trying to shoot it. She'd become a little better with a rifle since then, but not much. How terrible that she was more skilled with the derringer, a weapon for killing people.

Jason had enough worries as it was. The loss of the *Moon Chaser* was a serious one for the lumber outfit because the ship had been the ideal way of selling the best of the timber. Clem had been highly skilled at getting top prices in trade in the Orient no matter what the fluctuations of the market at home. Jason still had customers who came to the mill and loaded lumber onto their own ships, but that vital link which had been forged by the Pollards was gone, and he had no intention of investing in another lumber ship until the trouble with Sarah's father was over.

He and Jud discussed the business at length, deciding to keep production at full rate.

"There are still a lot of ships that come into the Sound looking for uncontracted loads; once word gets around that we have more lumber than usual, I think they'll stop here more often."

Jud agreed and was not envious of the power Jason was giving to Tomlinson at the mill to bargain for the top price; Jud saw his job as getting the best out of the men and the forest; he'd never had any patience with what he considered "clerking" chores.

He and Jason spent hours deciding what trees would be felled next, trying to make their choices conform not only with the present market but with future demand.

Jason had done the same so often before with Jud, he found the rhythm of the work soothing in spite of the fact that the rough terrain was hard on his bad leg. And he liked having Sarah and Jamie in the camp.

His overall feeling of satisfaction was shattered that night though inadvertently, by his son. As before, Jamie was spending his nights in the bunkhouse, but he was in the little cabin now, playing a game of checkers with Sarah while his father worked on estimates of board feet.

"Will we disturb you?" Sarah had asked anxiously.

"Not at all," Jason had said, and he'd meant it. It was comforting to hear their voices in the background while he worked over the dry figures.

He rubbed his eyes wearily, pausing to listen to what they were saying before he tackled the next round of estimates. And then he froze, focusing on Jamie's words.

Jamie had been chattering about various men on the crew. He had a quick eye and was fascinated by various peculiar traits. He'd noticed this or that way of sharpening an ax; he'd listened to superstitions and tall tales some of the men had told him, "like they don't really believe 'em, but I think maybe they do." Then he came to the subject of short-stake men.

"You know what they are?" he asked and was rather disappointed to learn that Sarah did.

"Well, those two newest ones, Jones and Brown, the other men don't like 'em much. Short-stake men are supposed to be good storytellers and bring news from where they been before, but those two hardly say nothing." Jamie had borrowed an expression of adult disgust which looked as if it had been directly stolen from Red. "And there's something else funny 'bout 'em. You know how th' men are always countin' how much money they got and how much is owed 'em. Well, those two don't even do that much. Red says they either got gold stashed in their socks or they're crazy. They work hard, I seen 'em, but I decided it'll be better when they move on." The pronouncement was definitely more imitation Red than it was Jamie Drake.

Sarah looked up, wondering if Jason had caught it, and she was so shocked and dismayed by his expression, she nearly gasped aloud. His eyes were glittering dangerously, and his face was set in stark planes of tension. He gave a sharp shake of his head, warning her not to let Jamie know.

Let Jamie know what? She hadn't a clue. Jamie had missed the interchange between his parents. He was studying Jud's battered checkerboard carefully for his next move.

Sarah proceeded to play so stupidly, Jamie accused her of letting him win. "You shouldn't do that! I beat you fair and square lots of times!" There was real anger in his voice.

"Jamie, I'm sorry! I really didn't do it on purpose. I just lost track of the game."

"Thinking about sewing again probably," he sniffed with male disdain.

"Probably. I'll beat you next time, but right now I'm sleepy, and it's time for you to go along to bed too."

"I'm the only man in the bunkhouse who has his mother telling him to go to bed," he complained, but he smiled as he said it and gave both of his parents a hug before he left, pausing briefly to gaze across the short distance to the bunkhouse, just to make sure no bear stood between him and his goal.

"What is it?" Sarah asked urgently. "What in the world is wrong? Jamie didn't say anything wrong, and I could hardly keep from laughing. Red's the one he's imitating at the moment, and he's good at it without even knowing he's doing it. Surely you don't mind that."

"It has nothing to do with that!" Jason snapped, and then he clenched his teeth and took a deep breath. "I'm not angry with you or Jamie. But, oh God, I'm afraid he just pointed out something that's very wrong even though he doesn't know it." He started toward the door. "I'm not even sure he should sleep in the bunkhouse."

Sarah's face drained of color. "Jason, please! What are you

talking about. Surely none of the men would harm Jamie!"

Seeing Sarah on the verge of hysterics steadied Jason. "No, you're right. He's probably safer there than with us. It's the short-stake men, Jones and Brown. Such convenient names. I'd hardly noticed them. There're other new faces here too. Short-stake men are a part of every lumber camp and stay as long as they want as long as they do their work. These two do, which is why Jud hasn't any objection to them. But what Jamie said—Sarah, there's no such thing as a short-stake man who doesn't care about money; money is all they care about, the money for moving on. Jones and Brown are working as swampers; no one does that for pleasure. They're stupid to have been so casual about their pay. No wonder the other men don't like them."

"I still don't know what you're talking about." Her voice was high and thin as if she were short of air.

"Two men were responsible for the fire in the redwoods and gone afterwards. And where do you think they went?"

"Go get Jamie, go tell the others!" It was a high-pitched scream.

"Jamie's all right. Jud, Fiddler, and the others would never let anything happen to him." Again her threatened loss of control restored his own. "And there's nothing to be done tonight. Tomorrow morning's soon enough. At the very least they'll be told to go; at the most they might tell me something. I haven't any proof for what I think, and if I go after them now or the other loggers do, there'll be two dead men at the least. Sometimes I think I'm going as mad as your father." He clenched his teeth, fighting the urge to make sure death happened, regardless of guilt or innocence. He wondered how long he'd be able to resist falling to the level of mindless violence Allen employed. He knew the man had already won a grim victory. Never before had he feared his own capacity for destruction, but now he felt it as a too constant urge. It even made him fear for his temper around Sarah and Jamie, the two people he loved above all else in the world. He was terrified that he would turn on them, hurt them before he knew what he was doing. Because of her acceptance of his need and her own, Sarah had never spoken about his act of violence against her nor shown any fear of him because of it, but he feared himself and still winced from the memory of how he had used her.

Sarah's heart ached as she watched him struggling with himself. She didn't understand all of it, but she understood the basics, and in that moment of understanding, she was willing that the men go free and far even if they were arsonists hired by her father, as long as Jason won his inner battle.

"You're right. Come to me now," she whispered, her arms open to him.

He nestled against her blindly, bending his head until his face was hidden against her neck, and she could feel him trembling. Tears filled her eyes as she stroked the rough head and crooned, "My love, my love, you will never be like him."

He did not make love to her, but he held to her through the night on his narrow bunk as if she were the last sanity in his world.

In the morning, Jones and Brown had moved on.

Jamie's eyes were sparkling with the excitement of it. "They left even before Fiddler was up to make breakfast! They didn't even get the money owed 'em. They were crazy! But I know why they left so fast. It was because of you, Papa!" He giggled with delight at this and missed the look on his father's face. "Red told me that last night when I wasn't there, the men started tellin' stories about the Tiger, about how tough and smart he . . . ah, you are, jus' like they were tellin' tall tales, an' I think that made those men leave."

Jamie's obvious pride coaxed a reluctant smile from Jason, despite his lingering worry about the two men. "If those men believed the stories, they deserved to leave without their money," he managed to say.

Sarah decided it was time to get Jamie out of Jason's hair. She knew Jason would want above all else to talk to Jud without interference. "What do you say to begging Fiddler for something we can eat for breakfast in the woods? We can wrap it in a cloth, take it with us, and look for birds on the way to a good picnic spot. That way your father can get on with his business without being distracted by us. We won't go far just in case the bear has ideas, but I'll take the rifle."

"Bears won't bother us if we don't bother them. Red told me," Jamie offered.

Jason was already deep in conversation with Jud, and Sarah felt no guilt in telling Fiddler rather than Jason of their plans to take a little walk. "We're not going far," she hastened to add, as she took the food he handed her.

"Jus' keep yur bearings," Fiddler said and cracked a smile at his own wit. "But th' bar hisself ain't goin' bother you none." He didn't even mention the two men, and she was in fact far more worried about the bear than about them.

She was quite sure why they had left. Jason had no idea of how frightening he could be, and she was certain the loggers had painted him in such exaggerated terms, made valid by enough of the truth to be convincing, that the two men had cleared out with all possible speed. The theory that they were arsonists was a night phantom banished by daylight. They had been in the camp for days and had done nothing harmful. They were simply misfits driven out by the growing animosity of the other men, an animosity so strong even Jamie knew about it. Even their seeming lack of concern about their pay might have been nothing more than a not very subtle way of thumbing their noses at the others who kept such careful track. Lord knew there were some peculiar men who worked the woods. She felt almost sorry for Jones and Brown as she pictured them wandering from camp to camp and never being truly welcome anywhere.

She and Jamie weren't really going far, though the screen of trees gave the illusion of distance. Jamie had chosen the direction because he was sure the fluting song he'd heard was a thrush, and he hoped to get a look at it. It seemed as if the bird were teasing them, staying just out of sight ahead, singing now and then and causing little rustling sounds. They had gone north from the camp, above the skid road, and were now circling a bit back to the east on the rather steep ground which put them in back of the camp and not far from it. They could even hear the muffled thud of the axes from the men working beyond to the south. Sarah decided they'd go back to camp before they got too close to the work area rather than risk appearing in the brush just as a giant tree was crashing down.

She had stopped thinking of the two men though she kept her eyes open for the bear and reminded herself that the rifle was not to be used as a walking stick. She didn't want to think of anything except being in the woods on a glorious summer morning with Jamie and the child yet to be. Even at this early hour it seemed as if the heat were seeping up from the shadows as much as the sun was beginning to search for ways down through the treetop canopy. The filtered light gave everything a green-gold haze. She remembered how she'd felt as if she were drowning the first time Jason had brought her to the tall timber. Now everything was different. Today it was beautiful. Jamie stopped often to peer patiently through his precious binoculars. It didn't seem to bother him that his prey was so elusive.

They stopped in a circle of light to share the food Fiddler had provided, his grumbling belied by the kindness in his eyes and by the amount of food he had given them. Jamie carefully saved the crusts from his bread in case he might find the opportunity to lure a bird closer. The meat and the pie he thought the birds could do without. They sat there for a while after they'd finished, talking about nothing in particular, enjoying the sunshine and the breeze that wound through the trees. Then Jamie put his finger to his lips as the thrush called again with haunting sweetness. They scrambled to their feet and crept silently after the sound. The song ceased abruptly.

They caught sight of the blond Jones and the dark-haired Brown at the same time. But Sarah understood what Jamie did not.

"What . . ." he started to ask. Sarah clamped her hand tightly over his mouth.

"Jamie," she hissed, "you've got to do exactly as I say, no questions and right now! Do you know how to get back to camp?"

He nodded, his eyes beginning to reflect her fear.

"Put the glasses down and run back and get your father or Jud as fast as you can, bring him here." She heard the dreaded whistle that presaged an attack, and she wanted to scream aloud in fear and frustration. "Jamie, for God's sake, those men are going to start a fire any minute! I've got the rifle, I can stop them

for a while, but I need help. You've got to go! You run faster
than I can. Jamie, if you love me, do as I say, now!"

The field glasses fell to the ground, and he spun away from
her, running, thank God, running in the right direction and
without looking back.

Jones and Brown were making too much of their own noise
to hear Jamie's footsteps, but Sarah could see them through the
screen of foliage. It was only a matter of time before one of them
saw her. She moved quickly into the best position she could find,
still partially screened with the rifle propped on a tall stump and
ready to fire. She needed the support for it; her arms were
shaking so, they didn't feel strong enough to hold the weight.
Too bad she'd left the derringer back on the island; she needed
it now to do this properly. These were people, not bears. The
crazy thoughts swirled in her head.

"A little more wind, an' this is goin' go like fury," Jones said,
and then he caught sight of her and froze in shock.

"Stay where you are, both of you, don't move a muscle or I'll
blow you to hell." She was startled by the shrill savagery of her
own voice and the rage that was beginning to overcome her fear.
Her husband, her son, every man and beast in the forest, was in
danger because of these two men, because of her father. How
stupid she had been to dismiss them so easily from her mind.
The scent of kerosene and burning wood came to her, and she
understood how they planned to fire the forest and live. They
had a small fire going with some long dry sticks stacked neatly
close by, and the kerosene had been poured where they wanted
it already. It was all so simple. With the breeze at their backs,
they'd use the sticks as torches and escape while the fire swept
toward the camp.

It was such a strange tableau, everyone frozen in place. Her
mind was inspecting everything as if her eyes had become mag-
nifying lenses that saw everything in hideously enlarged detail
right down to the droplets of sweat and the dirty pores on the
men's faces. At least they didn't have guns, at least not that she
could see.

"Told you we should have just cleared out, told you it was too
late fer this," Brown muttered, breaking the long silence.

"You ever kilt anybody before?" The tone of Jones's question told her he was recovering from the shock of being discovered and was beginning to see her as not much of a threat even with the rifle.

"Twice." She snapped the lie back without hesitation and embellished it, listening in wonder to her gory account. Time, time was what she needed, and sound to lead Jason to where she was. "First one was clean enough. I shot part of his head off so I doubt he even knew it, but the second one, well, I felt a little sorry about that. Not that he didn't deserve it, mind, but he was gut shot, and it took him a long time to die. You know how that is, everything spilling out but the heart still beating." It was surely finer than any performance she had ever given in her short theatrical career. "Most amazing thing, of course the blood is red, but guts, well, they're all different colors, pale pink, dark pink, purple, even green." How did she know that—oh yes, the meat she'd seen butchered on the island and at the lumber camp. It made perfect sense that human entrails would show the same variety. She was feeling more removed from reality with every second, but her gruesome matter-of-factness had had the desired effect on the men. They believed her.

"Trust that Tiger man to have a hellcat for his wife," Brown whined, but neither of the men moved.

"Oh, Jason's killed a lot more people than I have. I'm not nearly as good at it as he is. Did you know the real reason they call him the Tiger? He killed a man by clawing his throat out, ripped everything open with his bare hands."

She saw Jones turn pale, but she knew the standoff wasn't going to go on much longer. Cold sweat was breaking out on her skin, her teeth were beginning to chatter. She swallowed convulsively against the rising bile in her throat. Of all the times to want to throw up; what the baby hadn't done, fear and her own tall tales of blood and guts were swiftly accomplishing. *The baby.* The reality of it swept over her again, damn these men to hell everlasting for threatening even the unborn.

Finally she heard it, the sound of someone coming through the brush—something or someone, the bear or the Tiger, she thought, how peculiar—and she knew her mistake even as she made it, glancing in back of her and seeing the men in front of her begin to move at the same time.

She fired, heard a cry, and saw Brown staggering backwards, but Jones was scuttling out of sight to her right. Frantically, she pumped the lever, fired again and knew she hadn't hit him. And now she couldn't see him.

He grabbed her from the side, and she screamed until the wind was knocked out of her by the impact with the earth as they both fell and the rifle flew out of her hands. A stream of verbal filth poured over her as Jones grabbed her hair and arched her head back, crouching over her as she still struggled for breath.

"Wisht had time to stick you 'tween the legs 'fore I do this."

She saw the gleam of his knife and closed her eyes against watching it descend to slit her throat. Her body bucked violently in a last protest against dying, and the man was thrown to the side. Even as she dug her nails into the wrist of the hand still holding the knife, she heard a horrible snarl and felt herself picked up and thrown. Head reeling and still gasping for air, she opened her eyes truly expecting to see the bear tearing Jones to pieces and saw Jason on top of him instead.

It was all slow motion again, horrifyingly slow. She couldn't see her rifle, but she saw Jason's where he'd dropped it when he couldn't get a clear shot, and she saw Jones trying to stab at Jason with the knife while Jason tried to kill him with his bare hands, his own knife still at his waist. Even as she edged toward the rifle, she saw Jones's knife draw a long curve of crimson on Jason's back. She screamed though it only came out as a dry choking sound. But Jason didn't let go, he kept pressing his thumbs into the man's throat until he saw the eyes bulging, until he felt everything in the throat breaking and the body going limp except for last twitches of death.

When Jason looked at Sarah, the murderous lust was still in his eyes, but she saw it fade as he realized she was all right.

In the next instant whatever they were going to say to each other was swept away by an ominous crackling and hissing underlaid by an eerie mewling minor note.

Brown had fallen too near the fire pit, accomplishing with his own body what he had set out to do without risk. Now, flames had danced from his hair and arms to run swiftly along his outstretched body to the first of the oil-soaked tinder.

The plaintive cry of what they now recognized as the last human agony was gone in the growing roar. It was going much too fast, and Jason knew it was already far beyond any effort they could make to put it out. They were at the apex of a racing triangle of fire.

He grabbed Sarah by the shoulders and moved her in the right direction. "Run, run as fast as you can! Don't go toward the camp, cut across the skid road and find the stream!"

The sudden howling was nothing she had ever heard before, a universal roar punctuated by deafening explosions and volcanic hissing as pockets of pitch caught fire. She stopped dead and looked back despite Jason's efforts to urge her on. She saw flaming suns beginning to streak through the treetops as though intent on destroying as much as possible as swiftly as possible, and she felt the winds of the earth and the winds of the fire coming together to speed the race of death.

She planted her feet, as rooted to the spot as one of the great trees being ravaged, hearing nothing except the almighty voice of the fire, seeing nothing except the doomsday light. She could taste it, could feel the searing power as she breathed, and she felt an overwhelming peace, a willingness to be consumed, to finish now as part of the quick sacrifice of all living things on the forest altar. Jason was with her. They had fought as hard as they could, but this was beyond their power to fight.

In those split seconds, Jason saw and felt her mesmerized resignation. He shook her violently and bellowed in her ear. "Run goddamn it! Run! The water is your only chance!"

The spell was broken by his words. She knew he meant "your" because his lameness would slow him down, undoubtedly more now because of his struggle to get to her and his fight to kill Jones. In her need for him, she had forgotten, why hadn't he sent someone else, why! His willingness to perish while she survived shattered her own resignation, and she screamed, "Not without you, both of us! Jamie, we've got to get to Jamie!"

She veered toward the camp. Jason was with her, pushing her in the direction he intended, knowing now she wouldn't go without him, screaming back at her, "Jamie's with Jud. All right, he's all right!"

They were running, Jason's face set in stark lines of pain and concentration in his efforts not to stumble over tree roots, not to slip on the steep ground and carpet of needles and decomposing vegetation, his mind racing with the knowledge that Sarah wouldn't leave him and the fire was coming too fast for his pace. They were not even to the skid road yet, let alone the stream beyond, and the fire was not only behind them but reaching to either side. Desperately he searched the landscape even as they ran. When he saw it, he jerked Sarah to a stop and pulled her toward it. Sparks and hot ash were swirling all around them, and the noise was deafening, but she obeyed him.

The ground had crumbled away so much on the slope that a tall fir had toppled and lay rotting a short distance from the shallow cavern left by its roots.

Jason pushed Sarah down into the hollow and curled his body over hers. He wondered if she knew that even if the fire did not burn them to death, there was every chance that it would suffocate them just as efficiently. But her body did not struggle under his, and he couldn't tell whether the inner thunder was from his own heart or both their hearts.

Sarah did know as well as he that the fire's enormous appetite for breath could well deprive them of their own. But it didn't matter. The peace had descended on her once again. They had done their best to escape, Jamie was further out of the reach of the fire than they, and she had not left Jason. Even now, his heavy weight pressed down on her, sheltering. The earth smelled of some musky animal, and even though she couldn't see it, she sensed a small burrow leading off from where they were. She wondered with detached interest if even now a fox or some other beast quivered in fear of them and the fire, pressing itself back and staring in the darkness. She recognized the part of herself which had wanted oblivion for a very long time until Jason had pulled her back from the void. It had returned. It was the greater part now, and it was acceptable, this floating fetal sense of helplessness.

"It is not, not, not!" another voice shrieked suddenly in her brain. "It matters, everything matters! You may well survive while Jason dies, covering your body with his own. Is that all right, is it? And the child, is it never to be, is Jason never to know?" She recognized the voice as her own and yet apart, louder than the fire, more insistent than surrender, and she recognized the thick dampness seeping down on her—Jason's blood from the wound in his back.

He felt her struggling wildly, and he raised himself a little away from her in panic, fearing she was suffocating even as he still breathed albeit with difficulty. But in the faint fire glow in her eyes, he saw she was perfectly aware.

"Not you, not you!" she gasped, and the words only made sense to him because she was twisting around and was moving fiercely, trying to pull him under her, trying to change places. He pushed her down again. Her face was pressed against his throat, the words soft but audible against her hair, "Neither one of us, neither one."

"Three of us, sweetheart, three of us right here."

His whole body tensed over her, and she knew he understood. "Christ, Sarah, of all the times to tell me!" It was part curse, part prayer, part laughter, and part weeping.

A lurid false twilight, and then no light at all. Time without meaning, slipping quickly by, stopped? They didn't know. A silence created out of overwhelming sound, the vapors close, thick, suffocating.

Sarah ceased to be aware of anything except Jason. She felt him flinch a little now and then, and she held him closer, felt him holding her, shielding her, and then she knew nothing at all.

CHAPTER
39

"Sarah, love, open your eyes now, it's all right. Wake up now!"

A hoarse voice was calling her, hands pulling at her, patting her shoulders, pushing the hair away from her face.

She looked up at Jason. "We're alive," she ventured, halfway between question and statement.

His face relaxed into a triumphant grin, white against his soot-streaked face. "We are indeed unless the next world consists of burnt wood and a root hole." But the grimness was back as if the smile had never been. "The fire veered and angled past us; if the edge of it had come any closer . . ." He left the statement unfinished and leaned down to kiss her. "Is it true, did I understand?"

"You did." She was shaking with reaction and cramped limbs. Jason helped her to stand upright and kept holding her even when she could stand on her own. The pain of the blood rushing back into her arms and legs was welcome. She stared at the land they had fled, at blackened treetops and glowing embers on the trunks, spouts of flame flying out here and there. Even the pall of smoke did not obscure the faraway fury of the fire hurricane, and the air around them groaned with the voices of the wounded timber. Her voice sounded the same. "Jamie?"

"He had a better chance than we did, and Jud would die before he'd let anything happen to him. I told them to get ready to move; that's why I didn't let anyone come with me. These fires go so fast." Despite his efforts to control it, his voice quavered and broke.

She became aware again of his blood smeared on both of them, and pulling away from him, she saw the pockmarks on his torn shirt, burn holes from the hot ash that had showered them, and she remembered his flinching.

"You shouldn't go any further," she said very calmly. "I'll go find the others, and we'll come back for you." She must not let herself consider the possibility that there were no others left, no Jamie. "Your back, it's still bleeding."

"There's nothing to be done about it now and there's no way on God's earth I would let you go anywhere without me right now. I'm not trusting you out of my sight again, and I'm perfectly capable of going with you, so we won't waste time and energy arguing about it." His voice was absolute, and she set out with him at his direction.

It was a nightmare journey back to a vision of hell. Deer crashed past them, still running blindly in terror, and they heard other frantic rustlings and piteous whimpering. They found the skid road and followed it back toward the camp until smoldering brush on either side of still-burning skids forced them to detour to the west until they came to the edge of the fire line and the beginning of the lush dampness not even the summer heat had leeched from the stream bed and its banks. But even the stream was running dark and sluggish, choked with ash, and visibility was less and less in the smoke-clogged air.

They heard the bellowing of the oxen and the nervous screams of the horses before they saw them. Then Jamie was racing toward them even as they cried his name.

He was covered with soot as they were, and his breathing was an audible wheeze, but he was alive.

"I didn't get sick, I didn't, and I found Papa, I did, but I thought you were both dead, dead . . ." the rasping words tumbled out. His face was still drawn in a rictus of terror as if he didn't believe they were really alive.

Sarah drew him hard against her, bending around him as if she would shield him as Jason had her during the fire. "We're all right, and it's because of you. Your father came in time to save me from those men. He's hurt, but he's not dying." Surely he couldn't have come this far if he were, she thought, striving to maintain her own control as she comforted Jamie.

Jason put his arms around both of them. "Son, I'm so proud of you, and nothing hurts now that I know you're all right too." He wished it weren't quite so true; the searing pain which had kept him alert was dimming and unless he concentrated very hard, everything began to revolve in slow circles. He knew he was still bleeding, and even his leg seemed strangely numb. He wasn't sure who was giving support to whom as the three of them staggered together toward the others.

The fire seemed to be slowing down at the cleared break in the timber where the heaviest logging had been done, but Fiddler and Willie were dead. Jud and Red had singed hair and skin and burn holes like Jason's on their clothing, marks of their journey back when they'd realized the two were missing. They hadn't been able to get close enough to pull the bodies out, but they'd seen them, charred beyond recognition, near the cookhouse.

The agony of loss and self-blame in the survivors was worse than the pain of their burns and more choking than the smoke, even though it had not been their fault. Bull Fletcher had taken Jamie with him as he moved the oxen as far from harm's way as he could manage. Seeing the smoke and fire coming so fast, he'd known the skid road wasn't going to be passable long enough for him to get the animals out, so he'd taken them toward the nearest water. Jud had taken the few horses and had fought their fear at the fire scent the whole way as he hurried to direct the work crew toward the same chance, knowing as well as Bull Fletcher that the fire was coming too fast for them to fight it. Fiddler was an old hand; he'd also seen how swiftly the fire was coming, and everyone had expected he'd get himself and Willie out. But he hadn't. Fiddler had bossed them around for so long, they'd forgotten he was an old man and not so spry; most of all, they'd forgotten how stubborn he was. No one would ever be sure, but Jud, voice going high and low in his efforts to control it, speculated that Fiddler had tarried to free the livestock in his care despite the fact that most of them were destined for slaughter and then had decided he couldn't leave without making sure Willie wasn't up to his usual trick even in all the noise and confusion.

"We all knew Willie liked to sneak away and sleep a little extra during the day. He goes . . . he used to go and crawl under one of the bunks and fall sound asleep right away, but he only does . . . he only did it when Fiddler doesn't . . . Jesus! didn't need him. And the only thing that ever woke him up was Fiddler's yelling. But the look of it . . . of them, Fiddler found Willie and almost got him out."

In spite of the taunts of "belly-robber" and "crumb-chaser," the two had been beloved of their companions, and the grief on all the hard, worn faces caused Sarah to bite her lip savagely to control her own. But she was undone when she saw the tears coursing down Bull Fletcher's face, his great shoulders shaking. Jamie began to cry against her.

Never would she have imagined seeing the massive bull whacker cry, but now he had lost two friends and his cherished beasts were moaning with fear and the pain of scorch wounds on their hides.

"Shouldn't't've yelled at 'em, shouldn't't've, good uns, Fiddler an' Willie, pulled th' load, old 'un an' young 'un, ain't right, good lads," he mumbled.

Sarah pressed against Jason and felt him sway and then brace himself. Suddenly not even the dead mattered as much as giving him some ease. She realized that the men didn't even know that the black smears and stains were Jason's blood because everyone was filthy. Jason had every intention of ignoring his wound while he listened to the men and shared their grief, but Sarah had had enough of it.

"Jones stabbed Jason, the wound needs attention. How shall we best do it?"

All attention was immediately focused on Jason. "It can wait," he insisted, but his voice was hollow, and his impatient gesture ended abruptly as his eyes closed and his knees buckled.

Jud sprang forward in time to help Sarah lower him to the ground. She cradled Jason's head in her lap while Jud carefully checked the damage. The torn shirt was stuck to part of the knife wound and blood was pouring freely from another. The cut was long and ugly, and there were angry red burns as well.

"Needs cleaning up and stitching, but he was using both arms, so I don't think any important muscles been cut." Jud didn't add the obvious—that loss of blood was the most dangerous thing of all. The back of Jason's pants was soaked with blood where it had poured down from his back.

Jud was in command again, and the men followed his instructions briskly, as concerned for Jason as he was. Using branches, shirts, and even suspenders, they rigged a stretcher while Jud pressed bandannas against the wound, trying to staunch the bleeding.

Jamie stood speechless with horror, staring down at his father, too frightened even to cry any more while Sarah tried helplessly to reassure him, hearing the doubt in her own voice. She could have kissed Bull Fletcher for his intervention.

"Come on, Jamie, yur pa's goin' be jus' fine, takes more 'n that t' kill th' Tiger. You come help Kit 'n me get th' team down t' th' mill."

Jamie hesitated only an instant before he went with the big man; he was obviously glad to have work to do like the rest. The sight of Bull Fletcher's tear-streaked face so full of kindness for Jamie started the tears Sarah had been fighting.

"You're crying on my neck," Jason said, and she could feel his muscles tense even before he added, "In a minute, I'll get up."

"You will not!" She held his shoulders gently, but even that was unnecessary because he faded away from her again.

He came to protesting as the men lifted him onto the stretcher, but his words were low and slurred and ended in a groan before he went limp.

Because Jason was so helpless, the journey down to the mill was even worse for Sarah than the journey through fire had been. She walked beside the stretcher where space allowed, wincing as she saw his body jolted.

"He'll be all right," Jud kept assuring her, but she hardly heard him.

Most of the mill hands and the crew of the *Gaiety* intercepted them on their way, but even the addition of familiar faces and the renewed babble of voices and accounts of the fire made little impression on Sarah; she had no space to think of anyone except Jason.

"You must be joking!" she screamed at Jud, unable to believe his request.

He shook his head unhappily. "Fiddler did all our stitching. Maude Tomlinson has never had the stomach for it, an' Tomlinson himself, well, he does it, but his work sure isn't very neat. Please, ma'am. We'll help, but it'd be better if you did the needlework. It's a long cut, needs to be neat so it won't pull when it heals."

Of all the madness of this day, this was the worst. Sarah had assumed that as soon as they got to the mill, Jason would be competently cared for by someone else, surely not by herself. Instead they were having this idiotic argument about sewing as if Jason's flesh were a prize piece of cloth. Damn useless bitch Maude Tomlinson, she thought, wouldn't you know she wouldn't be any more use than I. Fighting her panic, she searched desperately for an alternative.

"Get David Becam!" She'd seen him immediately begin to help the men dress their burns, and she knew he was clever with a needle—he knew how to stitch sails, didn't he?

He did, but he wasn't any good at this, nor were the rest of the crew though they'd do it if she asked. She looked away from the pleading apology in his eyes and remembered how Jason had had her take the stitches out of his head because he'd said the sailors were no good at it. She realized suddenly that it wasn't really that these men weren't familiar with rough-and-ready surgery, it was just that they didn't want to practice it on the Tiger. They had some childish faith that his wife would do a better job.

"Goddamn it to hell! All of this is wasting time. Tell me what to do, and I'll do it." If Frenchie could do it, she could. She'd watched Frenchie, hadn't she? She'd also planned to learn the skills, she remembered grimly.

They'd already tried to dose Jason with whiskey when he was conscious enough to swallow it, but he'd refused. He turned his head, squinting his eyes, trying to see her when he felt her near. "Good, rather have you do it, neater, like my clothes. Don't worry." He gave up the effort of saying anything more and closed his eyes again.

The men had put him face down on a scrubbed table in the mill cookhouse, and five of them were stationed there to hold him. Jud fitted a strip of leather into Jason's mouth to keep him from biting his tongue, and he helped Sarah soak the shirt from the wound before they stripped it off along with the bandannas he'd used to staunch the bleeding. She closed her eyes, refusing to watch while Jud washed the cut with raw whiskey though she couldn't shut out the sound of Jason's body moving on the table as he instinctively tried to avoid the white heat searing the cut and spilling on the burns.

I can't do this! she thought in renewed terror, and then she thought of the very real possibility of Jason's having to bear a stiff shoulder for the rest of his life along with his leg, and she thought of how much she owed him and how much she loved him.

Her hands were very steady when she began. Jones had undoubtedly meant to plunge the knife in deep enough to kill, but instead the blade had slashed from the middle of Jason's right shoulder in a curve down under his arm. The worst part was a deep flap of flesh over the shoulder blade where the knife had cut sideways. She set the individual stitches with great care and precision as Jud kept wiping away the blood. She willed herself to deny that the needle was piercing flesh instead of cloth for as long as she could, even though it took more force to penetrate the skin. She was helped by Jason himself. He'd uttered one choked sound with the first dig of the needle, but since then he'd been still and silent, not needing the burly men to hold him down. She thought he was unconscious until the last stitch was tied off, and Jud said, "Sewing's over, boss, just a little grease on the burns, and we'll let you be." His voice was shaking.

Jason spit out the leather and drew a deep sighing breath. The thick leather was bitten almost through. She stared at it in horrified fascination, not even hearing Jason's whispered thanks. She bolted for the door, leaving the men to do the rest.

Jud was suddenly blocking her way, torn between shaking her hand and hugging her. "It was a fine job you did. He'll be all right."

"I have every hope that he will be, despite my handiwork, if not because of it." She spaced the words with even care. "However, right now, I am not all right. I have for more hours than you can imagine wanted to throw up."

He reached for her, alarmed by her pallor, afraid she was going to fall over, but she bolted past him, falling to her knees outside, continuing to retch helplessly long after her stomach was empty.

"There, dearie, there, take a few deep breaths now. You've been very brave. I couldn't've done it. The men'll do the bandaging. There, there, a cup of strong tea will help."

Incredulously, Sarah recognized the voice of Maude Tomlinson, though not any voice she'd ever heard from her before. The woman was patting her shoulders gently and even had a cool, wet cloth with which she proceeded to bathe Sarah's face and hands as if she were a small child.

It was the last straw. Sarah began to laugh and cry at the same time.

Maude wasn't the least put out by her hysterics; she led her gently into the Tomlinson house, sat her down, and fussed with the making of the promised tea, letting Sarah regain control of herself away from the anxious eyes of the men.

Nothing had ever tasted as good as the strong sweet tea soothing her throat. She sipped it slowly, finally risking her voice to ask, "Jamie?"

"Oh, he's fine, a mite shaken up by all that's happened, but Bull Fletcher has 'im in hand an' your son's bein' th' brave little man, brave jus' like his ma." The iron-gray head ducked shyly. "Miz Drake, ma'am, I know I ain't been very friendly, an' I'd like to say my sorries for that. Don't know what got inta me, plain ol' green jealousy I 'spect, you so young an' pretty an' all. But they tol' me how you tried to stop them men from startin' th' fire, an' then you took real good care of th' Tiger . . . your husband."

Sarah studied the woman's face, red with the effort of saying the difficult words, and then she smiled. "And you took care of me, Mrs. Tomlinson. Thank you very much. I went to pieces."

"Not 'til it made no mind. Call me Maude, if you will."

"Maude it is then, and I'm Sarah. And I'd better get back to my husband. The tea has made me feel much better." And this was the woman I thought would never be my friend, she thought, exploring the wonder of the transformation.

"You take care of yourself too, don't want that baby you're carryin' to come to no hurt. You ain't feeling no pains or nothin', are you?" Maud inquired anxiously.

"No, I'm not." Sarah didn't even ask the woman how she also knew. She wondered if after all he'd gone through, Jason remembered.

A pillow had been placed under his head and blankets slipped over and under him, the men having decided to let him rest for a while before they moved him again. Sarah agreed with the plan to take him aboard the *Gaiety*. It wouldn't be too difficult as the ship was tied up at the loading wharf, and Jason would be much more comfortable aboard than anywhere else.

He'd been dozing, but he heard her talking to Jud, and he called to her, thinking his voice was very loud though she could barely hear it. "Tell everyone to quit fussing. I'll be capable of walking on my own two legs in a little while. I think I might even have the strength to spank you for going off in the woods like that, even if you did save lives."

She smoothed his hair lightly, but her voice was firm. "No, you won't. I refuse to stitch you up again, and you've lost a lot of blood. You'll do exactly as we tell you."

He moved his left hand with an effort and caught one of hers. "Yes, ma'am." It was humiliating to be so helpless, but he knew he hadn't much choice. The clarity of his vision wasn't improving any and the slightest movement was so much work, he doubted he'd do more than fall over if he did manage to stand up. He stiffened suddenly, ignoring the pain it caused, focusing on the thought, remembering. "During the fire, did you really tell . . . are you . . ."

"Pregnant. With child. In 'that condition'—yes, I am." She leaned down and kissed him.

"Are you all right?" The rush of adrenaline in his fear for her made his voice stronger for the instant.

"I'm perfectly fine. It's going to take more than a forest fire to discourage the newest Drake."

He thought of the signs he had ignored. He wanted to say something more and he didn't want to say how frightened he was of her being pregnant, but all he managed was a whispered curse as the black mists closed in again.

He was still unconscious when he was carried aboard ship.

Sarah was glad Jamie had seized so eagerly on the men's invitation for him to stay ashore with them and grateful to them for asking him, especially to Bull Fletcher and Red who were the instigators. It made it easier for her and for Jamie—the sight of his father lying unconscious was terrifying for him.

It was for her too. At first she had been relieved that Jason was beyond pain, but as the minutes ticked into hours and the day faded into night, the relief was replaced by apprehension. He was a strong man and more capable than most of dealing with pain because he'd had more of it to stand than most. She began to suspect that his stupor had far more to do with shock and loss of blood than the pain, and she realized that that was what the men too feared. The crew of the *Gaiety* were waiting to help if she called them, and David had provided her with water with a little salt added and with brandy, but the only way they'd been able to make Jason take any liquid involved turning him over and propping his head up. Even then, he'd choked more than he'd swallowed and only a few sips had gone down.

He'd been lying so still for so long, she jumped when he cried, "Sarah, run!" and then the whole bunk began to shake. She thought he was having convulsions until she heard his teeth chattering and touched him. The cabin was very warm, and he was covered with blankets, but he was freezing cold, his body thrashing in the grip of involuntary tremors. She opened the door, screamed for help, and went back to hold onto him.

"Be still, oh, please be still! You'll tear the stitches, please, listen to me!"

The cabin was suddenly crowded with the big seamen, and Lars and Mogens immediately took over the task of holding Jason.

"It's reaction to all the blood he lost. David, make the strongest coffee you can and fill it with sugar and brandy. We've got to warm him up," Captain Hanson ordered, and David rushed off.

Though they were being as gentle as possible, Sarah turned away, unable to bear the sight of the men lifting Jason and forcing him to drink the brew. His face was gray with blue tinges around his eyes and mouth, and she heard him choking and gasping. She clenched her jaw against screaming at the men to leave him alone.

She turned back as she heard a collective sigh of relief and Lars saying, "Ja, ja, is good. He is not so cold now."

The faintest color was coming back to his face, and the force of his shivering had lessened. The men slipped him back beneath the blankets as tenderly as if he were one of their children.

"He's better, ma'am, but he ought to keep on drinking as much liquid as we can get down him. Best to let him rest for now, but call us if he gets worse." Captain Hanson fell back on formality to aid his own control, and Sarah nodded her thanks, not trusting her voice.

When the men had left, she undressed and got into bed with Jason, moving very carefully to press her warmth against him without jarring him. She felt the little tremors that still rippled through him, and then she felt them diminish and stop as more and more warmth was generated by the contact.

For her, the heat was overwhelming, and she dozed a little, but she felt the change even before he said, "Hello, I think I've been somewhere else. Are you trying to boil me alive?"

His voice was thin and weak but blessedly sane, and just in time she remembered not to throw her arms around him.

"I'm the one who's boiling; you're barely up to room temperature." She was laughing with relief and then she was crying. "I thought he'd won after all. You were so cold, and . . ." Further words were beyond her.

"And then I think I remember being manhandled by Nordic giants and force-fed a hot river of horribly sweet something." The words cost him energy he could ill afford, but they reassured her, and she could see that he was smiling.

She got up faster than he could lodge his protest, and the next thing he knew she was back with another obnoxious brew plus a determined-looking David Becam.

"You know I could fire you," he ventured, and David grinned.

"Yes, sir, you could, but then I'd talk to my wife and she'd talk to yours, and I'd have my job back, so what's the use?"

"Now I know what 'weak as a kitten' feels like," Jason grumbled, but he let the younger man lift him so he could drink the stuff.

"I'm sure even Tigers have their bad days," the once-shy sailor offered cheekily, making no effort to conceal his joy in Jason's improvement.

David left, and Jason felt his eyes drooping as the need to sleep swept over him, but he kept them open and his head turned so that he could see Sarah's face. "I want to sleep more than anything else," he confessed. "But I won't until I know you're resting too. You're pale as a ghost, and you've got rings clear around your eyes. If not for yourself, then for me and the baby."

"Sleep then," she said, settling down beside him again.

By morning he was feverish, but it frightened her far less than the chill because the fever was not dangerously high. His wounds, especially the burns, were weeping, but the seepage was natural and showed no signs of putrefaction. David helped her to change the bandages and tend to Jason, and Jason, knowing he was too weak to do anything for himself, bore their ministrations patiently.

In this quiet wounded state, Jason was even more the wild woods creature, even more the Tiger, curled in on his pain, waiting with innate dignity for it to leave him, for his body to heal. And even seeing the wildness, Sarah saw again the child of the man who had been taunted and silenced for the suffering of his lameness, but she no longer had any anger. She thought of Ellen Drake only with regret, pity, and sorrow now. And though she didn't want to think of him, she couldn't stop the memories of her father sniveling and making life even more miserable than usual for everyone when he had the slightest sign of illness.

"What's that for?" Jason asked drowsily, rousing to the fact that Sarah was not only bathing his face and neck with cool water but was also following the cloth with little kisses.

"That's just because I love you." *And because I almost wish you'd curse or yell when I know we're hurting you because I feel like doing it for you because you won't.* "And a lot of other becauses all the same as the first one," she added aloud.

"I think I like you pregnant; it makes you all soft and silly," he teased, but then his voice sharpened. "I heard David offering you food, but I didn't see you eat. Did you?"

"I certainly did. You slept through my gluttony. I ate everything David fixed plus what Mrs. Tomlinson, no, Maude, sent over especially for me."

Satisfied she was telling the truth, he fell asleep again, smiling at her account of the newly born friendship with Maude Tomlinson.

For the next few days, these short periods of awareness were the best he could offer, and he used them as well as he could.

His trust in Sarah was not misplaced; she answered his questions honestly. The fire had been slowed but not stopped by the cleared area; smoke continued to funnel up to block the sun, and the night darkness had been broken by an orange glow from the earth. The fire had continued to burn on the second day, but by afternoon, the long-absent clouds had begun to roll in, and by nightfall it was raining.

Jason heard the beginning drops as Sarah did. She reached for his hand, and they held tightly to each other, wordless in their joy for what the rain would save even as they continued to mourn so much that was already lost.

She had been honest too, about Jamie when Jason had asked to see him today. "If you really wish it, I'll bring him here. But my descriptions of how well you're doing are much better than you look. And he'll need you more tomorrow when . . . when it all sinks in." She'd said the rest very quickly. "The men are going up to bury Fiddler and Willie this afternoon. Jamie's going with them. He wants to go, and it's his right; he knew them, and he was part of everything that happened. But I know him—he'll be all man today, but tomorrow he'll be Jamie the child again, and there'll be two more deaths to add to the total he still doesn't understand. He'll need you then, and he'll need to know you're really not going to die too."

They thought of the new graves as they listened to the rain. And then Sarah was glad to see that Jason was sleeping again.

"I've been lying flat on my face for long enough," he announced the next morning, and at his insistence, she helped him to move until he was sitting up, his back cushioned by pillows. She gave him a sponge bath and a shave, claiming she could do anything now that she'd stitched him up, and though it took her quite a while, she didn't cut him.

To her, having seen what Jason looked like twenty-four hours before, he looked quite presentable now, but she knew immediately that Jamie didn't share her view. All the color drained from his face until he was nearly as pale as his father, and he checked as if an invisible wall kept him from approaching too closely.

Jason wasn't quite sure what to do, and so Sarah quickly broke the silence. "Jamie, it's only been forty-eight hours since your father was hurt. He lost a lot of blood, and it's going to take a while for his body to make more. But he's doing fine. He hardly has any fever today, and he ate a big breakfast. He's a very strong man."

"I'll do a jig for you in a day or two," Jason offered, and Jamie relaxed. It comforted him to have his mama telling him the truth, and it made sense, and his father's smile looked just the same.

"They dug holes an' buried Fiddler an' Willie up in th' woods," he announced abruptly. "They put wooden markers on th' graves. They said some words, an' they even sang. It sounded good, almost as big as th' woods. Red said maybe there'd always be fiddle music there an' if you listened real hard, you could hear it. An' I heard the thrush singin' again too, maybe jus' for Fiddler an' Willie." The tears started to roll down his face, and he scrubbed at them helplessly.

"Come here," Jason patted the bed, and Jamie went to him. Jason put his arms around him and held him against his chest, ignoring the pain in his back because it was so much less than the pain he felt for his son.

"The men loved Fiddler and Willie, and they'll remember them. Maybe they even will hear that fiddle music from time to time, playing in their memories just like Fiddler played for them when he was alive." Jason's own voice was choked, and Sarah had a lump in her throat so big, she could hardly swallow.

"They didn't bury those men, Jones an' Brown. They said there wasn't much left an' they deserved to be left to th' animals anyway," Jamie mumbled, and then he pulled away, his face blazing with rage. "They do deserve it, they deserve worse! I hate them! Why did they want to kill people?"

"Because they were evil. But they are dead; they can't hurt anyone ever again."

Sarah looked away from the identically grim expressions. Her father had caused all of this pain, physical and otherwise. She wished she could tear his throat away, kill as she had claimed the Tiger had killed. The image did not sicken her at all. She could almost feel the warm blood spurting over her hands as they curled into claws.

CHAPTER
40

*J*ason was up and testing his strength long before Sarah thought he should be, but short of wrestling him back to bed, she had no choice but to let him have his way. And he was more apt to do the wrestling than she.

It was going to be a very long pregnancy if he didn't stop ordering her to eat more, rest more, sleep more, and to not lift that, not do this.

Jason said all the right things about how wonderful it was that they were to have a child, but his fear was uppermost, and it showed. And even though she knew the reason for it, Sarah found herself gritting her teeth at his coddling and wishing she could have kept it a secret right up to delivery.

"Jason," she tried patiently for the countless time. "I feel perfectly well, and I am, but I will go perfectly insane if you continue to treat me as if I were ill. I am not ill; I am perfectly naturally pregnant."

It didn't do any more good than had her other attempts. She sighed and agreed that yes, she'd have a nice cup of tea and a chat with Maude while he went with Jud to survey the damage at the logging camp. Jamie was to be allowed to go along too.

"But if you tear those stitches or do any other damage to yourself, I swear, I'll scare the pants off of you with the worst case of hysterics you've ever seen or heard," she warned Jason, and she told Jamie to keep an eye on his father. "If he looks tired, pretend you are so that he'll stop and rest for a while."

Jason was tired but none the worse for wear when they returned hours later, all of them needing a good wash to rid themselves of soot.

"I did keep a good eye on 'im, an' he's okay, Mama," Jamie assured Sarah, and she thanked him and said she could see that he had. He scampered off to have supper with the men.

Sarah and Jason ate aboard the *Gaiety,* taking supper privately in their cabin as they had since Jason's injury.

Sarah watched him playing with his fork and regarding the food on his plate as if he didn't see it at all, and she wondered at the look of abstraction he had worn ever since his return from the logging camp.

"It would have been better after all if at least one of those men had stayed alive," she said suddenly, and Jason knew she had come to his own realization. "If only we could have followed him. Somewhere, someone was ready to pay those men whatever else was offered for starting the fire. Surely they were not paid the full amount before the act."

"Who knows? I expect one of the agents in San Francisco might be holding the money, but there's no way to prove it. And the agent may not even know what the money is for or may not want to know. He may simply be authorized to pay a certain amount with no reasons given. I expect your father has several sources capable of telling him whether or not the fire happened. Besides, the news is all over the Sound by now. It's hard to miss that much smoke. The ships that have put in to offer aid are proof of that."

Word had been sent via one of those ships to assure the islanders the Drakes had survived the fire since it was probable that news of the disaster had already reached that far.

"I don't expect we'll ever know exactly why they waited over a week to fire the woods, but Jud's explanation seems as plausible as any. He said the loggers didn't like them from the start.

Even the other short-stake men didn't take to them much. They kept a pretty close eye on them so they didn't have that much freedom of movement, and they had to spend some time figuring out the best way to cause the most damage. Every hot day without rain gave them more of a chance of success. They might have waited even longer if we hadn't showed up. But that was obviously something they hadn't counted on, and they had to go ahead with less care than they'd planned. There wouldn't have been any warning at all if you hadn't sneaked off into the woods like that. Jud will never forgive himself; he'd just about convinced me that the men were just rogues like so many others he'd seen. And they were gone. In fact, we were talking about other business when Jamie came running in."

"I was very foolish. I was more afraid of the bear than of the men. I was sure they had gone."

She closed her eyes, feeling suddenly naked and vulnerable. How many enemies were there? Where were they? Who were they? And then she thought, none of them matter. My father is the only one who matters. He's the center of the web. He's the power and the money causing it all to happen. And his luck. Goddamn him!

Her father's luck had been better than the Tiger's for too long now. Nothing led directly back to him. Fires burned and killed, and either his henchmen escaped or they died. She doubted that Radley Allen cared either way. He had already proved that there was no shortage of men willing to do anything for money. Perhaps he did care after all—surely it was more convenient to have the men die as long as particular jobs were finished. She wondered how long Jones and Brown would have been allowed to live had they survived the fire.

She thought of the gold and silver hidden at the house on the island and now in ever increasing amounts, in Carrie and Owen's house. She hated it even more than she had before. Heavy, inert, dead stuff useless where it was. Not the way of the Tiger. His way had been to take it whenever he had it and build something with it, hire men to work for him with it, transform it into something else in a reverse alchemy, gold into timber, and timber into boards for houses, ties for railroads, lumber for ships. And gold to buy or build those ships, ships to carry passengers and cargo. Even the lots he had owned in San Francisco had been valuable only for what would be built upon them; even the mining shares had given work to miners. But the gold and silver itself lay there, serving no purpose except to provide weapons for the present fight and a promise for a future that might never come. So much had he lost for her. Whatever he built again—if he ever had the chance, if her father was ever defeated and if there was anything left when he was—whatever empire Jason ever built again would never balance what he had lost.

"If this camp can go on, if there really is enough timber left, keep it going, keep the crews on, keep them working for you and for themselves!"

Jason stared at her in wonder. He had expected exactly the opposite reaction, had expected she would be fearful that others would come to further destroy the camp and the timber even though he himself believed that the one attempt would be the last here. Even if there was another attempt, the men would make sure it did not succeed this time. He had, in fact, already decided that this place so much nearer to his home than his interest in the south would not be shut down or sold out as long as the men were still willing to work for him. The men here were close to his heart, and though Jud and Tomlinson and the others had fumbled in embarrassment with the words, they had already stated their loyalty; they would stay on if he wanted them to. The fire had moved so swiftly, it had left a great deal of sound timber in its wake, topping the sunbaked tips of the trees and searing off summer-dry branches without rendering the bulk of the wood unsound. Much of it would be nasty work because of the charcoal and congealed globs of pitch, but the men were used to hard work in the woods and were already joking about how the burning of the underbrush had actually been a favor to the swampers.

He had no idea how Sarah had come to her fierce willingness for the work to go on. He would have been surprised had she asked him to follow the transition from gold and silver to logging.

"A splendid idea," he ventured finally. "Jud, Tomlinson, and I agree with you entirely. So does Jamie." He waited for her reaction to his easy acquiescence.

"I'm glad," she said quietly. "What would you have done if I fought against it?" She didn't really want to ask the question but couldn't stop it.

"God help me, if I couldn't have convinced you, I might have shut down the operation and turned the men out."

"Jason, I love you, and I love sharing your life, but don't ever do anything solely because of me. Please don't! My judgment isn't sound enough for that. I would be terrified if I thought I could change what you know is right, what you need to do." *Even if it is to collect piles of gold and silver.*

Her fear was hard to bear, and he tried to lighten the mood. "I thought that was what every wife wants of her husband."

She would not be diverted. "Maybe they do if they're married to stupid men. But I'm not. I'm married to a very intelligent man whose world was much better before I came into it. Since I did, it has been falling apart piece by piece." *Because my father came with me,* she added silently.

"No, it hasn't! It was not all right before. It was empty. I was empty. I didn't even have enough love inside of me to see that my child was dying for lack of it." He cupped her face in his hands, golden eyes blazing. "Don't ever say that again!" His mouth came down on hers, harsh and demanding so that she felt his anger and his love and his need all at once, and she answered with her own urgency.

They sailed the day after Jamie's birthday had been celebrated in rousing style by the loggers and mill hands. "Fiddler and Willie wouldn't've wanted too much mourning," Jud said gruffly. The men went out of their way to treat him as one of their fellows rather than a little boy, and Jamie loved every minute of it. His parents were glad they had shopped for him in Seattle and thus had the gifts with them, but they knew he was every bit as pleased with the makeshift offerings of the loggers which varied from bright biscuit and tobacco tins to carved puzzles as he was with his parents' more elaborate gifts and the promise of new binoculars to replace the ones destroyed in the fire.

His face was still flushed with remembered joy as he and Sarah began to play their now traditional game of spotting any life in the Sound.

There would never be a better time, and she had claimed the right and duty as her own though Jason had offered to do it.

"Jamie, I have something very important to tell you," she began, and then she went on quickly. "Your brother or your sister will be born in January. I know a little baby won't be much use to you, but I hope you'll be a good big brother to him or to her. Whichever it is, the child will need you a lot more than you'll need it in the next few years."

Jamie's eyes were wide with shock as he looked at her and then away. She kept silent, giving him time to assimilate this new knowledge.

The fear came even more swiftly than she had expected. All the blood drained from his face. "My other mother d . . . died that way." He could barely get the words out.

She pulled him close before he could succumb fully to fear. "Darling, that was an accident. It wasn't her fault, and it wasn't yours. It just happened. Remember, we've talked of this before. People can die from falling out of a boat while they're fishing or from a ladder while they're painting a house, but surely that doesn't mean that no one should ever go fishing or paint houses. And if all the mothers who give birth or all the babies who are born died right then, there wouldn't be any people at all on this earth. Surely you can see that. I'm very healthy, and I feel very well, and I plan to present you with a splendid brother or sister who will need you to teach him or her where to look for eagles and raccoons and how to do so many things."

He burrowed against her, and then he was still. Finally he raised his head and pushed a little away from her. "I'll still be scairt. I don't think I can help it. But I'm glad too. I sort of like th' idea of having a brother or sister. Th' other kids on th' island, they all do, an' they complain sometimes, but they're all really happy about it. Even Daniel made brothers an' sisters with th' animals 'cuz he didn't have any real ones of his own."

"Oh, Jamie, you'll always be my first and first-loved child."
Her voice was less steady than his had been. He wasn't offended
by this proof of his father's love for her, and he hadn't even
asked if she would still love him after the new baby came. She
considered it their mutual triumph that neither doubted the
depth of their love for each other. Her words were only confirmation of what they both knew.

Jason saw them clinging together, and he prayed that, if not
for his own sake then for Jamie's, Sarah would be all right. No
matter how he tried, he could not think of the unborn child
without seeing Gaiety dead in a pool of blood. There was so
little he could do to insure the naturally interwoven lives of
mother and child, but he could make sure Sarah's father didn't
harm either one. He was tired of waiting. It was taking too long.
And too much was at risk now. It had come too close. Sarah,
their unborn child, and Jamie could all have died in the fire like
Fiddler and Willie.

Even the letter from Owen which awaited him on the island
did little to change his mind:

> Have patience, not much longer now. The time is ripe, and
> my contacts in New York are hastening the season by
> spreading rumors in high and low places. The run on the
> bank has begun and is gathering speed by the day. Sources
> report that Allen is standing on his head to cover the sud-
> den demand. Country house has been sold, also attempts
> to liquidate other assets. Other moneymen are running
> nearly as scared as he is and are unlikely to help him. I wish
> it were only Allen heading for a fall, but in fact, things are
> becoming shaky all over and businesses are going under.
> Perhaps you weren't so wrong after all to bury the tangibles
> —am following suit as swiftly as possible.
>
> Nasty business, all of this, but all send love as always.

Sarah looked up from reading the letter. It took her a moment
to realize that her own savage joy in the news had no match in
Jason.

It was a stunning blow. Homecoming had held an extra edge

of joy. The islanders had watched for the *Gaiety* and had been assembled—even Cade and Captain had been there—to welcome the Drakes and give thanks that the fire had spared them. And they were insisting on the now traditional birthday picnic for Jamie even if the day had already passed. Sarah knew that every woman except herself and even some of the men were working late tonight to be sure everyone could eat too much tomorrow at the pond. And the news from Owen made it complete for her. But not for Jason.

"Surely it couldn't be better?" she asked.

"It could be over," he snapped, and then hearing himself, he made an effort to smile at her. "You're right. It is good news. I'm just impatient, which is exactly why Owen cautions 'have patience'; he knows me well."

And so do I, Sarah thought. *You mean to smile, but it's more like a death mask. I won't let you go after my father, I won't, not the way I can see you planning to do it now. You will have patience, you will wait.*

As far as Jamie was concerned, the picnic was a great success, and Sarah received her share of smiles and congratulations now that news of the baby was open.

Constance settled down beside her, and her voice was low enough so that only Sarah could hear it. "It's a lovely picnic on a lovely day, and you and Jason are smiling so much, you'll both have to clean the bugs off your teeth tonight. And neither one of you is the least bit happy. Is it because you know the *Gaiety* may sail again soon? Or so David tells me."

"I didn't know, but I surely would have guessed it. Count on David staying here. The *Gaiety*'s not going anywhere now, at least not with Jason on board. Do you see something I ought to know?"

"No, you seem to know far more than I do," Constance admitted. "I'm not keeping anything from you, I promise I'm not. I don't think I'll ever again 'see' anything. Daniel's death ended it. I don't understand it, but I believe it's so. I didn't even see David that way; I only saw him with my heart. Gift or curse, whatever it was, I don't possess it now, and I don't think I ever will again. And to be honest, as much and as often as I hated it,

I feel somehow lost without it. Fully mortal, I guess." Her mouth twisted in a brief, wry smile of acceptance. "What I see in you and Jason today I see only because I love you both. Will you tell me why the *Gaiety* isn't going to sail?"

"Jason has lost patience when it is most important that he keeps it," Sarah said abruptly. "He hasn't told me; he doesn't need to, but despite the fact that things are beginning to go ill for my father even as we planned, they are not going fast enough for Jason. He is ready to go and kill my father outright, whatever the risks and consequences. I expect he's thinking of taking the train from California after meeting with Owen for a last time. I am not going to let him do that. I am shortly to become the most pregnant woman you've ever seen. Because of Gaiety, he's already terrified even though I've told him over and over how well I feel. And I'm going to use his fear against him because it's the only weapon I have."

The silence stretched between them as Constance considered. Then she said, "I think you will probably feel most unwell after the picnic tonight, but you'll bravely claim that it is only because of all you ate. However, by tomorrow you will be forced to admit that morning sickness has finally descended to take its toll. He'll never know it's rather late, and anyway, it's different with every woman and every baby." She looked at Sarah critically. "You look so damn healthy! I'd suggest you use powder, and I'll bring you some purple stain that won't harm your skin. It should do nicely under your eyes and maybe a little in the hollows of your cheeks. Maggie will have to know too, of course, since you'll have to eat more than Jason sees you eating, and actually, I think Ingrid and Else could help too. This is simple compared to the lengths they'd go to keep you and Jason alive and together."

Sarah was torn between laughter and tears and working hard to control both when Constance took her hand and held it hard enough to give her a focus. "My dear, you are not alone in thinking that life is better than death. There's scarcely a woman I know who wouldn't do almost anything to keep her man or her children alive, even if it means being less than honorable. The code of honor is the stuff of men's idle dreams and too much death. And the worst of it is that the very women who know it

is wrong and foolish are the very ones who help to teach their
sons how to die for foolish reasons. At least I never taught
Daniel that and that is not why he died."

"Sarah, are you all right?"

Jason was standing over them, and Constance spoke before
Sarah had a chance. "She's fine, though I'm not sure all the
excitement and food have been just the thing for her and the
baby. I think she'd better just stay quiet for a while."

He looked to Sarah for reassurance, but she closed her eyes
against the intensity of his gaze. "I'm all right, really I am, but
I think I will just rest here for a while. You run along now and
keep track of Jamie." She heard just the right amount of doubt
in her own voice. It had begun. What had been a secret had
become a weapon. The killing of the man Jones with his bare
hands had not satisfied but only whetted Jason's appetite for
revenge. She could feel how much he wanted the chance to put
those same hands to work to kill her father. She was willing to
do anything to prevent that.

The claim of indigestion after the picnic was followed by the
morning sickness she had never had to any real degree, suffered
so overwhelmingly now that she found she could scarcely lift her
head from the pillow, and she whimpered softly while Jason
bathed her face and frantically plied her with the tea and dry
toast Maggie kept assuring him might help. Actually, her appetite was so healthy, it was all she could do to wait until Jason was
out of the way so that she could eat the marvelous food Maggie
had ready for her.

Maggie, Ingrid, and Else had joined the conspiracy just as
Constance had predicted, none of them knowing all the details
but all of them willing to keep the Tiger from foolishly risking
his life and Sarah from suffering the broken heart they knew his
death would bring.

By the afternoons, Sarah made sure she was quite recovered
and by evening petulant in her need for Jason's attention.

"I know just how the Spartan women felt," she accused on this
night. "I'm sure their husbands' habits allowed as little touching
as you give me."

She watched him grit his teeth and struggle for control.

"Sarah," he ground out, "I'm doing the best I can."

"Well, it isn't a very good best," she carped, "or you would see that I feel much better at night than I do in the morning. And I just need you to hold me at a time like this."

She suspected she might have overplayed her hand this time, and she went to him meekly, curling into his lap and hiding her face against his chest. God, this is hard! she thought. She hated the simpering bitch she was acting. In reality she felt so wonderfully full of life, she wanted to share it with him. Worse, she was constantly aware of how she was playing on the fears he still harbored from Gaiety's death. But even as she accepted the blame for that, she remembered it was the best she could do to keep him alive.

It was a difficult best; she'd badgered and scared him so with her complaints and behavior, he was afraid to make love to her, and she had to content herself with being held at night and knowing that his frustration must surely be at least the equal of her own. Her own patience was wearing very thin.

Suddenly she twitched so violently, Jason nearly dumped her from his lap.

"I wasn't sure I felt it before, but now I am!" She grabbed his hand and clamped it against the soft swell of her belly. "Do you feel it? It's like butterflies, lovely fluttering butterflies!"

Jason doubted he'd feel anything at all—he remembered how Gaiety had been six months along before he'd felt what she was talking about and Sarah was only five months now—but he did feel it, not, he was sure, as she did, but still the faintest flutter against his hand as if the most delicate of wings were flexing against his hand. For the first time, the child was as real to him as Sarah.

"I do feel it," he said aloud, and Sarah felt his total absorption as he kissed her. What she had not been able to wrest alone from him, the baby had helped to win.

It was September 18, and a few days later as news began to reach the island, Sarah wondered crazily if the baby had been doing a victory dance.

The news was so enormous and appalling, it was traveling

with the swiftness of shock waves from an earthquake. It seemed that all the fissures and cracks that had been developing in the economy since the war had suddenly become canyons with the failure of Jay Cooke and Company, the best-known banking house in the United States and the principal financer of the Northern Pacific Railroad. The failure was made doubly devastating psychologically by the service Jay Cooke had rendered the Union during the war when he had marketed millions of dollars worth of bonds at almost no profit to himself. But profit-taking, speculation, and poorly financed railroads were taking their toll of everyone, including Jay Cooke. Financial repercussions were being felt as far away as Europe.

It was terrible news for the country, and it was wonderful for the Drakes. They acknowledged the paradox openly even before the telegram came from Owen:

> He is destroyed. Bank closed. All known assets being sold to pay creditors. Rumor of suicide. I hope so. Letter to follow.
>
> Love, Owen.

They laughed until they cried over their speculations about what the telegraph operators must have thought of the message. They acknowledged to each other how selfish their joy was in disaster, but they also knew that it was people like Radley Chambers Allen, not they, who had caused the catastrophe. Without vanity, they knew they were among the millions who would in one way and another build again on the ruins.

But to be certain, Sarah kept her own deception from Jason until Owen's letter arrived. It contained a detailed account of how her father's bank had failed. It listed the failures one by one, showing how speculation had finally ruined even the sound investments and how panicking creditors had clamored for money that wasn't there. The collapse of financing for the Northern Pacific Railroad had been a death blow. But hard as it was to trace, the money Allen had spent in trying to ruin them and on the bad investments Jason had set up for him had surely hastened the fall. Radley Chambers Allen was presumed dead, thought to have drowned in the Hudson River though some said he shot himself first to make sure. The body had not been found but the report was fairly certain. Allen had last been seen heading for the river, and nothing in his house had been disturbed since then. The house, along with his personal effects, was to be sold for the debts he owed. There was some speculation about whether or not his daughter would return from England, but no one had heard from her yet.

> Holy gods, Jason, when next you plan revenge, please let me know. Businesses and banks are failing by the hundreds while you and I—I because of you—are quite capable of surviving. Rationally I know the only thing you really did was to foresee what was coming, but I can't help but be reminded of the story of Samson tearing down the temple. In accord with this, I can only be glad that Samson is my friend as well as my client and that in this version, Samson did not bring the stones down on his own head. This is a far more just telling of the tale.
>
> Hallelujah, my friend! Kiss Sarah hard for me and for yourself. In the midst of the ruins, we have won.

Sarah read the letter again to be sure she understood.

"Owen is so apt. Surely you remember that Samson's hair and his strength were shorn by Delilah. Shorn, isn't it a lovely word! I did it to you too. It was wicked and right. Everything happened as it should have, as you planned, and you won't hang for it." Laughter was overcoming her. "Oh, my love, my love, I don't think I could have borne it much longer! I need to confess!"

Jason hadn't the slightest idea of what she was talking about, and he thought she was having hysterics now that it was over.

She was laughing harder. "Every . . . morning when you're gone, I eat enough for ten people!" She concentrated on controlling the laughter so that she could talk. "I don't feel sick and I don't feel faint. I feel fine and strong, and I feel like loving you. And you can call me what you wish because I know I played on your old fear, but I did it to keep you alive, and I'd do it again. You are alive; he's dead."

Fury shot through him as understanding dawned. All the whining and worse, the fear he'd put up with these past few weeks. He remembered how worried Constance had professed to be.

"Constance knew too," he accused.

"All the women know, and they've all helped," she answered. "Constance is right; women can't afford a man's idea of honor, it costs too much. You can do whatever you want, but you can't make me sorry." Defiance had replaced her mirth.

And tenderness began to replace his anger. In her place, he would have done the same thing. She had fought to keep him safe with the only weapon she had. He grinned ruefully. "Come here."

She nestled against him with a little sigh.

"Duped by a pack of sneaky women, it'll take me a long time to live that down. But am I ever glad you don't feel badly." He ran his hands down her body. "In fact, you feel damn good with that little round belly and certain expansions in other areas." He nuzzled her breasts. "I have an urgent need to go upstairs with my wife."

"No more urgent than hers."

The news from Owen was left lying on the desk, but the knowledge of their total victory went with them.

"Are you sure this is all right?" Jason asked suddenly, trying to control his rising hunger for her.

She giggled and nibbled playfully at his shoulder. "Positive. I think it would be very unhealthy for me to practice any more self-denial."

They melded together with sweet knowing of each other, and Jason found it strangely erotic to know their child lay curled in Sarah's womb. He had never felt this with Gaiety; there was so much he had never felt in his life before Sarah. He sighed her name as he took her.

Jamie was as relieved as his father had been to learn that Sarah had only been pretending to be ill, and he was even quicker to forgive the deception. "That was pretty smart. I'm glad you kept him from gettin' into trouble even if it did worry us."

There was new peace in Jason's face and a brightness in his

eyes as he began to consider various ways to increase his holdings again. He was in no hurry, and they would certainly not go
to San Francisco again until after the baby was born, but the
weight of revenge had been lifted from his shoulders, and there
was time now to consider the future. The logging camp was back
in operation, and Jud had sent word that he had even found a
new cook, a man inappropriately named "Bones" since he was
quite fat, and a new crumb-chaser. The men were doing their
best not to be too hard on them just because they weren't Fiddler and Willie. Via the *Gaiety,* Jason had sent money to Tomlinson for regular and additional operating costs, but he had not
gone on the trip, wanting instead to spend the days with Sarah
on the island.

The soft days of October showed tinges of yellow and gold
against the unchanging evergreens, and Sarah and Jason felt as
if they were seeing it all with new eyes. It was true that the
economic disaster which had overtaken the country would take
years to mend, and a railroad for Seattle was now even further
in the future, but they were alive, together, and expecting a child
who moved more vigorously with each passing day. Jason fussed
over her riding, but she insisted she'd keep Sheba at a sedate
pace and that when she was as big as the horse, she'd stop riding
her.

He gave in because he found it hard to deny her anything
these days, and he knew it was a way of their being together
more. Long walks would simply never be his strong suit.

She awakened suddenly one night and the idyll was over.

She was reassured to feel the warm life of Jason pressed
against her back. Sleepily she wondered why she'd awakened at
all.

The cold came again, an eerie wave as if someone had opened
a door to some dark place underground where the vapors were
always icy. She smiled in the darkness, considering the fantasies
of pregnant women.

Her smile faded. She knew. Somewhere in her mind, she had
known all along. The body. It had not been found. Every time
the thought had wormed into her consciousness, she had denied
it. But the cold had killed the denial.

She had wanted so to believe all the news from Owen, and

most of it was true. But her father wasn't dead. She knew him so well. Whatever unnatural love he had for her, the first and strongest love he had was for himself. He loved himself too much to commit suicide. And because he had lost everything else including the good name he had drawn so carefully over his corruption, she would be even more important to him than before. She could not have known it more clearly had he been standing before her.

She turned over and put her arms around Jason. "Hold me, please hold me!"

Jason awakened with a start to the urgency in her voice. "What is it?"

She controlled her voice with fierce effort. "I'm just being silly and pregnant. It's probably punishment for pretending to suffer the sillies before."

" 'Sillies,' that's an interesting word," he murmured as he fell asleep again, but he had drawn her close, and she concentrated on drawing comfort from the contact even as her mind raced.

She could not tell Jason what she knew. Final justice, the only justice, was for it to finish between her father and her even as it had begun. She could only hope that she would know in time what her father planned to do and that she would be able to keep Jason clear of it. She didn't close her eyes until the gray light of dawn was creeping into the room.

Jason looked down on her with a worried frown, remembering how she'd awakened him during the night. Now she was sleeping exhaustedly with shadows beneath her eyes. He had planned to ride out to Nate and Jon's, but he stayed in his study with the door open, waiting to hear Sarah come downstairs.

She was surprised to see him. "I thought you meant to get an early start this morning."

"I did, but I was concerned about you. You slept so late and you looked so tired; you still do."

She made herself smile at him. "Well, you ought to be reassured that I'm heading straight for the kitchen now to eat an enormous breakfast. I just haven't gotten used to the baby being so active. I think he or she is a night owl."

Believing her, he left, and she was able to convince Maggie too that she was all right without having to eat much. At the moment, the thought of food was enough to cause real nausea.

But she was not going to let her father destroy her child. She would eat and sleep as well as she could, and she would live day by day.

Yet, as the days passed she could not deny the toll it was taking of her to have her father so constantly in her mind again. She felt as tightly wound as a spring. Her temper flared and she burst into tears over nothing. She was restless at night and exhausted during the day; she alternately clung to Jason and turned away from him and found herself apologizing constantly and insisting she was all right.

She was not, and Jason's short-lived confidence that this time would be different fled entirely now. It was harder for him to see her like this and have her denying she felt ill than it had been when she had claimed all sorts of false complaints.

The sky was threatening the first heavy rains that would move in in earnest with November, but no rain had yet fallen.

She felt as expectant as the clouds. She felt like a white slug in eminent danger of being smothered by its own bulk. Her ankles were puffy, her swollen breasts ached, and her belly felt enormous.

"God, a good rain or a good wind, either one, damn it!" she swore harshly, and Jason, startled, dropped the papers he was holding.

His vision of her was the opposite of her own. Her face looked wan and pinched to him, and though it was obvious she was pregnant in the high mount of her belly, she looked tall, slender, and frail, less round than she had been even a couple of weeks before. The fear rustled through him again though he tried to shut it out.

"I'd do anything to make you more comfortable, just tell me what to do!"

She looked at him with a most peculiar expression for a long moment. "Start the wind or bring the rain," she commanded and then on a queer, broken note, "Oh, you would, my poor Tiger, you would if you could. If you could, you would become as fat and ugly as I am and take the task from me. Poor Tiger, poor poor Tiger!" She was gasping by the time the words finished and laughter overcame her.

He was horrified, rushing to stand over her, drawing her head against his chest, feeling his body shaken by hers, and then he realized that it truly was mirth that was causing this storm, amusement tempered by some sudden tenderness for him which he could not understand but felt as strongly as a great wave washing over him.

He picked her up for an instant, settling under her in her chair in the study, holding her on his lap, his hands cradling the bulge of their child. "I would, my love, I would," he whispered against her neck, and a new spasm of laughter rippled through her. "Something embroidered with posies here and there and very, very large for the Tiger," she choked. She pulled his head down and kissed him, her mouth still quivering.

She would never tell him all she had seen; the image was hers forever. She had been so bad-tempered and impatient of late, and this great tawny man, her man, her Tiger had borne it all with patience, would turn the weather round or bear her child were he able, had mewed when she herself would have snarled at such a puling creature.

"The rain will come and the wind and the baby too," she said. "But right now, only two things concern me. I love you dearly, and I'm very hungry."

And I will win when my father comes, and I'll cease to torture you and myself in the meantime, she added silently.

His relieved laughter joined hers. "The first can wait a while, ma'am, but the second can be looked to more directly, if we can just move this combination as far as the kitchen."

They surprised Jamie on a cookie raid, and the look on his face set them off again.

"You really shouldn't eat this late at night," Sarah said when she had the breath for it. "But since we're planning on the same thing, we might as well have a party."

Jamie beamed at her, glad to have the old Sarah back.

Jason was glad too, but he wondered where she had come from. The new calm that continued had come as suddenly as the onslaught of misery. It was beyond him, but then, really knowing what it felt like to be with child was also beyond him. And she had been through so much.

"I know there's not a thing you can do about it, but I hope it's a girl," he announced one night. "I hope she looks just like you."

Sarah stopped brushing her hair in midstroke and turned to smile at him. "I'd like a daughter too, but I hope she looks a great deal like you, a feminine version, of course." She put the brush down and went to him, tracing the hard planes of his face. "It would be a terrible thing for a girl to look exactly like you because, thank the powers that be, you are a most perfect man."

"That's a case of, to use your word, the 'sillies,' but my vanity thanks you and common sense demands that you get some sleep." He tucked her in, tended to the lamps and the fire in the hearth, and joined her. He settled her against him and rubbed her back gently, feeling her fall asleep as they listened to the rain November had brought.

CHAPTER
41

Sarah had waited for what seemed an eternity, had wondered so often how the sign would come and what it would be, she nearly missed it when it did arrive.

Letters forwarded from Seattle by Rob Mactavish—a route Jason still found more trustworthy than any other—letters which arrived this day via Gibson's *Folly*. Jason was at the other end of the island with Cade when Zeke delivered the letters to Lars, refusing the island's hospitality with the explanation that Captain Gibson was in a hurry to make San Juan Island. Lars gave the letters to Ingrid and suggested she go visit Sarah with them and take something good to eat along with her. She brought the letters to Sarah and stayed to share a cup of coffee and the rich butter cake she had made.

"You are going to make me and the baby very fat," Sarah chided her.

"Ja, I hope so! That is vhy Lars sends me vith de letters an' de cake. He tinks ve sit down like dis an' eat. Vise man, my Lars." Ingrid's laughter was infectious, and Ingrid was proud of herself when she left. It had been a good visit, and she had not betrayed to Sarah how worried she and the other women were. There was something wrong when everything should be right, and none of them knew what it was. Sarah's new calm was as strange as her uneven temper had been. They knew she had suffered at the hands of her father, but he was dead now. They waited patiently for her to confide in them, and in the meantime, they did their best not to overwhelm her with their love.

When Ingrid left, Sarah took the letters to Jason's study, sorting through them idly as she went. There was a letter from Rob, one from Owen in San Francisco, two more from names she recognized as former business associates of Jason's. She wondered what new schemes they were proposing. And then her eyes riveted to the last letter.

She returned to the kitchen, and without hesitation and with great care, she steamed the letter open, praying that no one would catch her at it. Jamie was at school, Jason with Cade, and Maggie was at her own house. It should be all right.

The writer, Mr. Alison, was brief and businesslike. He was interested in purchasing a ship from the Mactavish yard and understood that Mr. Drake was the owner. He had in mind either the purchase of the ship now under construction or the commission of one of his own design. He was highly impressed by the skill and care that went into the building of Mactavish ships. He had seen the *Sarah-Mary* before she had been so unfortunately lost. At present he was in Oregon, but he would be coming north soon. He realized it was a terrible imposition, but he would be most honored if Mr. Drake could meet him in Seattle between November 15 and 18. He would be staying at the Arlington House. If this was not convenient, perhaps they could arrange a meeting at a later date when Mr. Alison could again be in Seattle.

Mr. Alison. How clever of him. Alison had been his mother's name, her grandmother's name, a woman dead before Sarah had been born. Alison sounded so close to Allen because she knew, but would Jason know? She tried to think herself into her father's mind.

Had he meant her to know? No, he had not. She remembered how he'd treated her mother. She herself had been forced to listen to more about his great dealings than had her mother. It would never occur to him that Sarah would even see correspondence addressed to her husband. And in any case, he surely knew they thought him dead. What did he plan to do, lure them to Seattle, kill Jason, and take her? It didn't make sense. He must know that Jason had many friends there. It would be harder to cause trouble in Seattle than in San Francisco. What then? She drew a sharp breath. He must indeed be mad. He must be planning to come to the island for her while Jason was decoyed to Seattle. She thought of her mother again. Her father, no matter what evidence he'd had to the contrary in his prying into their lives, would assume that Jason would go without his wife on the business trip to Seattle, and the crew of the *Gaiety* would be with him, removing four of the nine men on the island.

She was absolutely sure of it. And Jason must go. At last she had her chance to finish it. She remembered telling Jamie that her father would never come here. How wrong she had been.

She resealed the letter as carefully as she had opened it, and she made sure she was with Jason that evening when he went through the letters. She dedicated herself to giving a superb performance.

Jason opened Owen's letter first, and she peered over his shoulder. "What does friend Owen have to say?" she asked, nibbling at his ear.

"Besides making his claim to the exalted role of godfather now that he knows we're expecting a child, he's got about four hundred ideas for investments. Here read for yourself." He handed her the letter and went on to open the others.

She pretended interest in Owen's letter until she saw Jason opening the one from Mr. Alison. She dropped Owen's letter on the desk and peered over Jason's shoulder again, leaning against him deliberately.

"Ummm, now that sounds interesting. There can't be anything better for you and Rob than for the shipyard to increase in reputation."

"Maybe so, but I wouldn't think of leaving you now and I certainly wouldn't expect you to sail to Seattle and back."

"But I would think of it, and I wouldn't go with you. Jason, be sensible! It's two months before the baby's due, while the fifteenth is only six days from now. That letter took a while to get here. Maybe it won't work out with this Mr. Alison, but maybe it will. It's time for the new beginnings to begin. I can't make you do it, but I think you ought to go, and I think you ought to take Jamie with you. At the most, you might be gone a week or so, and I'd be fine in the meantime—though probably fatter when you got home than when you left. However, since you'll do exactly as you please, I'll shut up about it." She moved away from him, picking up Owen's letter again, hoping he didn't notice the pages shaking, hoping she hadn't overplayed her hand. She realized she was holding her breath and let it out carefully, concentrating on breathing normally.

Jason paused, thinking about what she'd said. She seemed so much better now and she was right, this was surely a possible time to leave for a few days, whereas in a month's time it would be impossible for any reason. New business and increased reputation for the shipyard could only be for the good. Even though he didn't know this Mr. Alison, the man sounded genuinely interested and must know the costs involved in building a ship. As she said, it was a chance to begin again. Though he didn't intend to sell the new ship completely, he did want other shareholders. And there were other possibilities to inspect in Seattle, particularly the coal lands which were not being much developed even now due to continuing transportation problems and fluctuations in price, but surely there would be a need for coal in many regions for years to come and better ways to get it out and loaded on ships or the elusive railroad. At least it was something to think about. He was thinking more and more of new investments to be made in the Territory rather than far away in California. It had cost a considerable amount to stay in close communication with Owen and with his contacts in the East, to set up bad investments and give up good ones, but for all it had cost, Jason had come out well enough—with enough to begin again—while Allen had lost everything, including his life. Even the lot in Seattle which he might have lost due to a clouded title from Doc Maynard seemed fairly certain to remain in his posses-

sion now, at least for so many years as to turn a profit—a good
omen indeed.

"I'm not sure it's a good idea to take Jamie with me. After all,
he has school now, and I wouldn't think of letting you stay alone
in this house."

He was going to do it! She felt so dizzy with the success of her
plan, she had to dig her nails into her palms to steady herself.
"Nothing's going to go wrong, and even if it did, I certainly
wouldn't want Jamie to bear the burden. He needs to go with
you. He's been through as much as we have. I'll stay with Maggie
and Ben at night so they won't have to disrupt their lives as much
as if Maggie stayed here. My menfolk won't have to worry at all."

"Are you trying to get rid of us?" Jason was only half teasing.

"Frankly, I am. Between the two of you, I feel like some
ridiculous ornament made out of faulty glass. It will be nice to
be off the shelf for a few days, but I promise I won't break
anything."

Constance came to her the next day. "The *Gaiety*'s sailing in
four days. Is it really all right with you?"

"It really is. I'm the one who talked Jason into it. It's a chance
for expanded business for the shipyard, and I think it's important. He and Jamie should be in Seattle by the fifteenth or
sixteenth and headed home within a day or so after. Good grief!
I will begin to scream if people don't stop trying to treat me as
if I were dying. I am not dying. I am wildly alive! And I would
be so thankful to have my son and my husband out of the way
for just a few days; they are absolutely smothering me with their
love."

Constance had to believe her because she knew suddenly how
Daniel's father would have reacted had he known she was pregnant, knew how David would react if it were ever to happen. But
still, there was something so high-strung about Sarah, Constance was uneasy and wished, despite herself, that she could see
the shadows of the future again. And then she remembered—
remembered how odd she'd felt and how oddly she'd reacted to
everything when she was seven months pregnant with Daniel.
Perhaps after all it had not been totally a condition of the tragedy of Daniel's father and her extra sense but something that
happened in varying degrees to many women.

"Well, you know where to find me if you need me," she said in parting. Sarah felt the fierce exultation rising in her. If she could fool Constance, she could fool anyone. Even without the Sight, Constance was very perceptive.

Jamie's excitement over the impending trip was so strong and so filled the days that only as Jason kissed Sarah good-bye did all his doubts rise up again. She was so positive about this trip, so intent that he should go. And she had been nearly euphoric over the possible outcome of the deal.

"It isn't that important, even if it works. You must know that," he murmured, watching her.

"It's a beginning. And that's all we have, all we need now," she returned, meeting his eyes. As Constance had, he believed her and believed that her enthusiasm for the small chance somehow emanated from her sheltering of the small life.

He believed it through that day of sailing and for part of the next when they were finally well on their way to Seattle after having battled contrary winds and weather, and then suddenly he screamed, "Bring her about! We have to make the island by daybreak!"

Jamie and the crew froze, staring at him.

"I haven't run mad! It's her father, he's still alive! He's Mr. Alison! He's near the island, not Seattle! And she knows! Turn the *Gaiety* back!"

Jamie slammed into him and held tight even as the crew followed his orders. They didn't know any more than Jason did how the information had come to him, but they acted on it.

"We'll get back in time," Jason assured Jamie hoarsely, as he pried himself loose from the compulsive grip and rushed to help the crew.

Even as he handled the familiar lines and felt the ship beginning her turn, he thought of what had happened to him. He didn't know how and he accepted that he never would, but he knew the knowledge which had burst upon him was true. More strongly than he had felt Sarah's involvement, he had felt the evil moving toward her as he himself moved away. He had not seen visions he could clearly identify in his brain nor had he heard words; it had been even more peculiar than that, pure knowledge fully realized the instant he was aware of the first sensation, as true a part of him as his heartbeat.

How was it that Constance had not succumbed to total madness while she suffered this? Constance, anyone on the island, hear me! Keep her safe!

His concentration was intense even as he kept working with the crew, but he felt the silence answering him as strongly as he perceived the danger.

Drenched in sweat, Sarah awakened in the strange bedroom. The baby kicked inside of her as if the force which had made her heart pound was causing it the same discomfort. The room was dark, cold, and silent. The rain had stopped. She had slept through all the dark hours last night in this same bedroom in the Carters' house. Maggie had offered to come stay with her in the Drake house, but Sarah had convinced her that she'd rather be in a strange bed than in her own without Jason and that it would be easier all around if she just spent the night at the Carters'. She had fooled Maggie as well as everyone else.

She was not alone. She had not felt him so close since the night she had tried to kill him. It was as she had known it would be.

Jason was far away. Jamie was safely with him. The other islanders were safe in their homes.

He had drawn Jason away from her. Failing all else he had come physically to reclaim her. Despite the dangerous rocks and currents, despite the weather. He was very close. He expected Jason to be in Seattle or at least on the way. It was the fifteenth, and he would see that the *Gaiety* was gone. What he could not know was that she had done everything she could to make sure the ship had sailed.

The baby squirmed and kicked again.

It was hers to end his life, hers to finish what she had begun, hers to protect Jason from him, to protect herself and the unborn if she could, but above all Jason. He had suffered so much, lost so much for her sake and by her father's hand. People had died, killed by her father's unholy love.

Her relief was greater than her fear. It would end now. By her own hand, she would kill him. He would never hurt Jason again.

She got up, lighted a lamp, and dressed in the soft glow. She tried to envision clearly where he was as if she were the Constance of old with images flashing in her brain. But this was no future she was seeing; he was only a short distance away. The hairs on the back of her neck rose and prickled in atavistic response of the prey to the stalker; in response to the primitive fear and the primitive urge to kill before being killed.

She rubbed her hand against the cold wetness of the windowpane and peered through the circle. The darkness was not complete. Close to, she could see the opalescent gray that fog brought even in the darkness. Fog, deep and heavy had settled over the island, over the sea.

She thought about it very calmly. She must meet him alone in the house where he expected her to be. She knew him too well to doubt that he knew where everyone lived on the island; the land claims alone would have told him that if he hadn't gotten the information elsewhere, and they were public knowledge.

Maggie and Ben would not be up for an hour or more at least, and they would not hear her leave, but she must be careful not to wake the twins.

She arranged the bedclothes as well as she could to make it appear as if she still slept, in case anyone looked in on her. She checked the derringer to make absolutely sure it was in firing order. She had kept it with her since Jason had left.

She blew out the lamp and crept out of the house with great care, hearing no sounds of restlessness behind her. She took no lantern. The fog-shrouded darkness wrapped itself around her like a cloak, and she welcomed it and the cold sharpness of the air.

She knew her way well, and though she started a couple of times at rustlings in the brush, she made it back to the house in hardly more time than it would have taken her in daylight. She paused, listening. Sounds carried strangely in the fog, and she wondered if that faint scrape was an oar working in its lock. She tried to think herself into her father's mind again. He would come now, before the dawn, before Ingrid and Else and their children would be up and between him and his goal, before the other islanders roused to begin their daily chores.

She stepped into the house and knew instantly that it was empty. If he were here, she would feel it.

She lighted lamps and set one in a window, a beacon to the sea through the fog, it was more a symbolic act than anything else. And then she waited. There were two rifles in the house, but she would use the derringer; it was designed to kill people.

She saw images of Jason as clearly as if he were with her. She could hear his laughter and his anger and his tenderness. She could feel him touching her, could see the golden intentness of his eyes when he made love to her, could see his eyes in countless shades of feeling.

She didn't know how long she had been seeing him, but suddenly he vanished, and the other image came to her, the hated ghost of her past who was no ghost at all, who was very, very close now.

She heard him enter the house, and she stayed where she was, waiting for him.

"Sarah, my darling Sarah, at last I've come for you, at last we can be together again."

Her calm purpose began to desert her at that moment; everything was as it had been and yet worse now. She had told Jason more than once that her father was mad, but now she was faced with the full extent of it.

His voice was wheedling, coaxing as if he were speaking to a small child, and suddenly he was standing before her, and her breath caught in her throat.

He was still a big man though he seemed somehow shrunken, as if he were caving in on his own bones. His hair, which had been completely dark when she left, was now heavily streaked with silver. A muscle under one eye twitched, drawing her attention, making it hard to look away. And his eyes, far darker than hers, were the most changed of all, glittering as if they were lighted from within by some secret fire.

"Come with me now." The same voice. He took a step closer, holding his arms out to her.

"Stop where you are!" she snarled, all the rage she'd felt

against him flooding her again. "You filthy, incestuous bastard! You'll never touch me again, never! I'll kill you this time. I'll make sure you're dead."

She kept the gun leveled at him.

He peered at her, and tears gathered in his eyes. "I love you. I need you. You belong to me. Your mother, she was never any use, but I taught you so many things. And I've gone to so much trouble to get you back ever since that night the bad people came and attacked me and took you away. You aren't a prisoner here anymore, you can come home with me now."

She stared at him in horrified fascination, unable, despite the evidence of his insanity, to credit that he believed what he was saying. "I tried to kill you. I ran away. I am not a prisoner here. I belong here. I am a married woman soon to bear a child." She touched her belly with her free hand. "I love the father of my child. I love Jason Drake more than anyone else in the world. I belong to him." She wanted her father to know; she wanted the truth to stab somewhere in his madness. She wanted him to bleed to death of it even as he would of bullets in his flesh.

His face twisted as he stared at the bulge of the child. "No!" he hissed. "No, it can't be true! It isn't!"

"It is! And you're a dead man because you tried to destroy the only man I love. Do you hear me? Jason Drake, the only man I love!" she screamed. "I loathe you. I always have. You're a creature unfit for Hell!" Her hand tightened on the derringer. Why couldn't she just do it, end it now? He deserved it; she wanted to do it. She was as mad as he to stand here talking to him.

"Do it!" she cried aloud to herself, and she still couldn't make her hand work properly. The gun was trembling as if it were going to fly away. She clenched her teeth and brought her other hand up to steady it.

"It is true! The cripple touched you! He took my place, took what belongs to me, took my money, he took you, took you, got inside of you, he . . ."

The inhuman howling shattered the air as he lurched toward her, obscenities spilling from his mouth with globs of spittle, his eyes bulging in their sockets.

She broke and ran, knocking against him, sending him sprawling while the derringer clattered uselessly across the floor. She ran out of the house and toward the cliffs, sobbing because the baby made her clumsy and slowed her escape from the demon.

She got to the edge of the cliff just ahead of him and some last shred of her own sanity screamed at her to stop, screamed that women seven months pregnant do not climb down rock walls. She stood poised on the edge seeing everything in slow motion and great detail as she had when she had faced Jones and Brown across the rifle. She realized the world was no longer in darkness but was cupped in a great bowl of gray light as the dawn seeped through the lifting fog and lowering clouds. She felt the tug against her and the damp drops on her cheeks and knew the wind and rain were returning to the island, ripping the fog before they wrought their own blindness. And as visibility increased for the instant, she saw the alien ship that had carried her father riding at anchor as she had expected, and then she saw the *Gaiety* looming out of the fog and nearly overriding the intruder. She knew it was true, knew it was not a figment of her own mad imagination. Jason had come back.

She saw it all so clearly. If she hesitated a second longer, Jason and her father would come face to face in spite of all she had done to prevent it. One last chance to do it herself. She had not been able to shoot him; she was not strong enough to be sure of pushing him off the cliff, but she could lead him as Jamie had once led her down the cliff, and if he didn't fall and kill himself, she could lead him on into the labyrinth of caves. She knew the way now; he did not. The tide was high and the wind would make it higher. Most of the caves would flood.

Everything snapped back into normal speed and faster. Her father was nearly upon her as she turned to him, but he checked at her smile and the sweetness of her voice which fitted neatly into his illusion.

"I have missed you so! Come now, follow me, I have a secret place to share with you, only you."

She tasted metal as she lowered herself carefully over the cliff edge and down, expecting him to grab her and pull her back or throw her over, not knowing that his disordered mind did not allow for quick changes unless they were his own. He stood there grinning for long seconds and babbling to his Sarah before he realized that he couldn't see her anymore and that she meant for him to climb down after her.

"Child under my heart, you are making this very difficult." She kept talking in sobbing gasps to the baby as she dug her hands and kicked her feet into one hold after another. If she looked down, she would surely fall. She might well fall anyway. This was not the same as climbing without the added burden of the baby, and climbing down without it had been hard enough. Now there was no way she could press flat against the cliff. In disgusted self-awareness she realized she was laughing—at last this was going to be the death of her, this tendency to see herself from the outside and then to have hysterics over the absurdity of the image.

Tiny bits of stone fell down on her with the rain before she understood that the sound she heard was not just the rising of the wind. He was following just as she had bid him.

Even without knowing the hand and footholds, he was traveling much faster than she. Finally she risked looking down. Twenty or thirty feet to go. She closed her eyes and dug her hands and feet into the crevices, trying to ignore the trembling weakness that was beginning to invade her body, slowing it down when she wanted only to go faster.

She cried out in protest as much as horror when the cliff slipped from her grasp and she fell. She landed heavily on her back with her left ankle twisted agonizingly underneath her, but the pain did not surprise her as much as the fact that she was alive. She had come down much further than she'd known before she fell. And she hadn't landed on the baby. Savage triumph shot through her. There was still a chance. She struggled to her feet and nearly fell again as her injured ankle buckled. She whimpered in frustration and dug her teeth into her lower lip. The caves were so close, she could still lead him there! He hadn't fallen to his death, and the sound of him coming behind her was the spur to her purpose. She staggered toward the dark opening she wanted. She wasn't talking to herself or the baby anymore, she was saying Jason's name over and over again, the only name that had ever made any sense in her life, the only one worth living and dying for.

Water from the sea and from the sky pelted her, driven by the wind. Quiet, it would be quiet and dark in the cave.

She gained the entrance, turning back to see her father right behind her. "Follow me, follow . . ."

"Don't touch her!" It roared over the wind. "Run, Sarah, get out of the way!"

"No!" She thought she was screaming, but she made no sound at all as she stared at the two men facing each other, frozen in place. In his hatred, Jason looked as insane as her father.

Her father moved first. "Mine, you took mine, you raped . . ." and then Jason was howling as loudly as the other as the two men closed on each other. Two mad beasts, lips drawn back from their teeth, snarling in killing rage.

Sarah fled into the darkness of the earth, pulling herself along, scraping her already bloody hands on the rocks. Safe, she would be safe at Jamie's fort; it was where she had meant to go and so she would. Light and warmth in the darkness; she could find those things in Jamie's place.

Allen was strong, amazingly strong in his madness. Jason just missed having his head crushed with a stone and then grunted and nearly fell over from the impact of a well-aimed kick. He had ordered his crew to take care of the other crew and to hold on to Jamie. This was one to one. No quarter in this, no quarter. One of them was going to die and the other was going to have Sarah. Even though he knew his people would never let Allen off the island with or without Sarah, he couldn't banish the thought of him getting to her first. God! he hated it, he could see the faintest traces of her face in her father's, no matter the age and the insanity. And then he saw nothing but a red haze and black spots as the older man's hands clamped around his neck. He threw his weight against him, knowing they were going to go down anyway, wanting to be on top when they did, wanting to break the stranglehold on his throat before all his senses fled.

He brought his knee up as they fell, and he landed with all his force in that knee driving into Allen's groin. The hands on his throat fell away as the man screamed. Jason ground his knee deeper, harder, even as he slammed his fist into Allen's face, smashing his nose. His head was clearing as the blood and oxygen rushed back,

The man's hands were flailing helplessly now, his body bucking erratically, blood streaming from his broken nose. His opponent was no longer capable of fighting effectively, pain draining his insane strength, but Jason went on thumping his knee into him, battering the face with his fists until all recognizable features were destroyed and then clamping his hands around the throat until no pulse beat in it anymore.

He heard his own snarling deep in his throat, and suddenly he shuddered with the knowledge that he was savaging a corpse. He staggered to his feet, the water lapping around him and blowing over him from the sea and sky. And then he bent down and grabbed the body, dragging it over the stones until he felt the water pulling at it and at him. He let go of it only when he was sure the sea would have no trouble in disposing of it.

She could hear water rattling stones and rustling along passageways, and it seemed she'd been listening to it for hours. And then she heard someone calling—her father? Jason? She didn't care. She'd denied it the first time, but now she bent over gasping and whimpering, sinking down, arms crossed protectively over the swell of her belly. Jamie's fort was so close and yet she could not reach it.

Jason found her there in the dark. She had not answered his hoarse summons, and by the time he heard her cry out, his heart was pounding harder than it had during the fight.

"It's all right. He's dead. He'll never hurt you again."

She stiffened in his arms and then went limp again, moaning, "He's won, the baby, it's too early!"

He picked her up and carried her out of the caves, hardly noticing the wind and water pushing against him. He kept telling her it was all right, the baby would be all right, she would be all right, but he didn't believe it. He was going to lose her just as he had lost Gaiety.

He refused to leave her even when he'd gotten her to the house and the women took over.

"All right then, stay with her, but stop looking like you're at her funeral; you're not! And put on some dry clothes at least," Constance ordered sharply.

She and the others had immediately abandoned the hope that the contractions were a false alarm and would stop—the baby was coming and quickly despite the breech position.

Constance's tone of voice was quite different when she spoke to Sarah. "Now, my dear, just do as I tell you. Many early babies have lived before, but you'll have to help us to make sure this one does."

Sarah pushed and breathed and relaxed as she was told, but she wasn't really conscious of anyone except Jason. She held on to his hands and listened to the tenderness in his voice, clinging to him to save herself from drowning in the terrible things her body was doing to herself and the baby.

"A good loud yell isn't going to hurt anything, and it might help," Jason crooned, but her head twisted from side to side in refusal until finally a bloodcurdling scream was wrenched from her just as Constance said, "Here it comes!"

Sarah went limp, and there was silence in the room.

"Is she dead?" Jason asked it softly, hopelessly, tears blurring his vision.

"Neither 'she' is dead," Constance snapped, voice rough from her effort to hold back her own emotion as she continued to work over the baby, deftly clearing its breathing passages and patting it with gentle insistence. There was a tiny choked cry and then thin mewling, not very strong but definitely angry.

"Your daughter is small, but with care, she'll make it."

She handed the baby to Maggie and went back to work on Sarah, massaging her abdomen to aid in the expulsion of the placenta.

Jason hardly glanced at his child. He stared down at Sarah's motionless, splayed body and all the blood, and his courage broke. He staggered out of the room.

Constance found him later slumped over the desk in his study, his shoulders still heaving with tired sobs. She wiped her own eyes, squared her shoulders, and brought him brandy and a wet towel.

"For God's sake, Jason, a fine one you are! You go through the hardest part and then you fall to pieces. Now clean yourself up, take a swig of this, and listen to me."

His reddened eyes focused on her, and the ghost of a smile curved his mouth at her bossy tone; she wouldn't be acting like this if anything were wrong, would she? Meekly he did as she bade him, concentrating on her words.

"First of all, Sarah is all right. She's lost some blood, but she isn't bleeding now. Her twisted ankle and her scraped hands are going to hurt more than anything else, and she's going to be very tired for a while. She's been through a lot, but she is through it! With rest and care, she'll be as good as new.

"As for the baby, she's fine too and strong enough, I'm sure, to nurse. She'll need good care, but what baby doesn't? She's fully formed and breathing perfectly well. Can't ask for more than that."

Baffled by these female mysteries, Jason asked, "But with the baby coming so early, will Sarah even have milk?"

Constance smiled at him. "Oh, we women are marvelous creatures. Even if it is the wrong time, Sarah's body knows the baby's been delivered as well as you do. Her milk should come in in the next few days, and even if it doesn't, we do have cow's milk. She'll probably sleep for some time, but I know you're the one she'll want to see when she wakes up. And, I swear, I'll lock you out if you wear that mourning face again. It goes particularly badly with your bruises."

"I won't. Thank you. You're a good friend to both me and Sarah. David's a lucky man, as I've told him many times." He kissed her lightly on the forehead. "Is Jamie all right?"

"Yes, Ingrid went to tell him he has a sister and his mother's fine, and I know he believes Sarah is all right and you too because he agreed without a fuss to wait until tomorrow to visit her so that she can sleep. He's going to spend the night with David. Maggie and I will take turns here tonight just in case you need us. Then Ingrid and Else will take over. We have it all scheduled. I'm afraid you're in for an invasion of women."

She hesitated a little before she told him the rest of it. The *Gaiety*'s men had not fought with the crew of the other ship. "They were hired out of Oregon, and they'd been told some wild tale of Allen's daughter being held prisoner here. I'm not sure they ever believed it, and they certainly don't now, but they were well paid. Allen's money was good even if it meant working for a madman."

Jason had been so frantic about Sarah, he'd nearly forgotten the cause of it all. He rubbed his sore throat wearily. "The bastard kept enough to continue the hunt. Sarah knew he was alive. Somehow she knew. I did too finally, but it was almost too late. Have they found the body?"

"No, whatever was left of it after being battered on the rocks must be far out to sea now."

"Tell them not to look for it. I wish the fish the joy of him. And have the men let the other ship leave with a warning to the men aboard that if any of them ever show up here again, they'll be shot with no questions asked."

The flash of rage on his face made Constance glad that he was letting the other men handle it for him; otherwise, there might well be more killing before the day was out.

But Jason wore quite a different expression as he looked down at his daughter, really seeing her and believing in her for the first time. She was very small, but she was perfectly formed from fingers and toes to the soft vulnerability of the head and the tiny shell curves of the ears.

"You'll make it, little one," he whispered. "You must, for your mother and for me."

Maggie nestled the baby beside Sarah and left, feeling ready tears threatening after the hard day at the look of tenderness on the Tiger's battered face.

Sarah opened her eyes to the same expression.

Jason had sat in a chair beside the bed for hours, watching her sleep. He felt more peaceful than he ever had in his life. Though her bandaged hands and the wrapped ankle propped on a pillow gave evidence of her flight down the cliff, and though her face was pale and shadowed, he could already see that the lines of pain, there such a short time ago when she had struggled to give birth, were vanishing, leaving her looking very young. The women had dried and brushed her hair, and it spread in a silver-gold curtain across the pillow. He touched it carefully.

He saw her focusing on him, and then he saw the look of horror beginning as her hand moved down to touch her now flat belly, and he stopped her before she could cry out.

"Shhh, love, it's all right. The baby's alive! You didn't lose her. We have a daughter, a small but very spunky daughter who is sound asleep beside you."

Tears of relief and joy she was too weak to check slid down her cheeks as she turned her head to look at the baby.

"I do love you so much, Sarah-Mary Drake," Jason whispered huskily as he kissed her.

CHAPTER
42

*A*t Sarah's suggestion and with Jason's gratitude and heartfelt agreement, they named her Gaiety Ellen Drake and delighted in what they saw even in her earliest days as her possession of the best traits of both her names—the good nature of Gaiety and the stubbornness of Ellen, though the order of her discovery was the reverse of her names. Having taken her first breath, Gaiety Ellen clung tenaciously to life and thrived, and then, finding the world so nearly denied her to be a place much to her liking, she responded with joyful acceptance to the love showered on her.

She already knew what it was to have a very large family. All the island women had handled her with ease from the first when they had helped Sarah to care for her, but the men had approached the problem later when they were at last granted the privilege of holding her. Lars and Mogens, with three each of their own, had the least trouble with this, but Captain Hanson and David Becam had worn equal expressions of terror as if they might inadvertently squash the tiny bundle. And when his turn had come, Ben had gotten a hand free to tell Maggie with great speed that it had been too long since the twins and would she please take the baby from him. But Sarah remembered the first reactions of the remainder of the men with both sorrow and joy.

Nate and Jon had come by one day in January to talk to Jason, and Sarah and the baby had been with him in the study. "It's time she met you face to face," Sarah had said, and Nate had taken Gaiety and held her with careful skill. His big calloused hands looked so competent and gentle, it had taken Sarah a moment before she had looked at his face. Jon was standing beside his brother, staring down at the baby, and then the men were looking at each other. Without a word, Nate handed the baby back to her mother, and he and Jon shambled out, two big men with bowed shoulders and tears running down their faces.

"I never meant to do that to them!" Sarah cried in distress.

"You didn't, nor did Gaiety. Sometimes memories are stronger than the present. You know that as well as anyone," Jason reminded her gently. "In time, Gaiety will be herself for them and not their own lost children."

The memories of Hayes's and Cade's first direct encounters with Gaiety were much lighter. After anxious and scholarly inquiries as to whether or not he was risking the possibility of having the baby's head fall off while he held her, Hayes had somewhat rigidly mastered what he considered a safe position for both of them, and then had proceeded to enchant Gaiety with a recitation of Hamlet's soliloquy on the nature of man, done in a doting and slightly lisping voice that had both Jason and Sarah convulsed with laughter long before he had finished. He had handed the baby back to her father and had executed a stiff little bow.

"Sir, quite some time ago you engaged me to teach the best of civilization to the offspring of this wilderness. I plan to waste no time with this newest addition. By the time she is two years of age, she will be able to break hearts with Portia's 'Quality of Mercy.' " His eyes were dancing as he struggled to maintain the mockingly prim tone. And he and Gaiety seemed to have established some special understanding as of that first confrontation. Whenever Hayes held the baby, he quoted great works to her, and she responded by cooing and grinning up at him in complete fascination.

Whatever the Laurel of the watchcase had had and even if she had been allowed to survive the devastating war to make a new life, Sarah doubted it had ever held as much love and joy as the "Yankee" would have given her.

Gaiety's fascination with Cade was no less than the one she had for Hayes, though it was even harder to understand. Cade seemed to do far less than the schoolmaster to entertain her. He held her as matter-of-factly as he held new lambs. He didn't coo or make faces. He just held her and talked to her now and then, telling her about things she couldn't possibly understand any better than Hayes's strange renditions of Shakespeare and other poets. But Cade talked to her about more practical things. He told her how to fish for salmon and how to preserve the catch. He told her the best woods for carving and how to gather and cook the tender heads of ferns in the spring. He talked to her about the best smuggling routes in the islands, and sometimes his voice took on the storyteller's cadence and he told her Indian myths, but even his storytelling was something which couldn't possibly make sense to her now. He did all of it without embarrassment, his only explanation being that no one really knew when babies started to learn useful things and he'd leave the useless chatter to others. Whatever his reasons, Gaiety loved her time with Cade. She had not been born with the fictions of trolls and other monsters. She'd regard Cade solemnly for long stretches, and then she'd smile and babble happily as if the latest piece of information held particular interest for her.

"Your daughter surely got her eating habits from you, not from me," Sarah teased as the baby nursed vigorously. "I don't know what you want for your birthday, but I'm sure Gaiety would settle for another breast full of milk."

"Heaven forbid! She can't have it! She's got plenty as it is and plenty nice they are," Jason ran a finger lightly over the breast not engaged by the baby.

He leered at her, and she giggled, which didn't disturb Gaiety in the least. The baby's mouth had gone slack as she sank contentedly back to sleep.

"I'll take her. It's still so early, get some more sleep if you can."

But Sarah didn't sleep, finding it much more rewarding to watch her husband and her daughter through her half-closed lids.

Jason couldn't feed the baby, but he helped with everything else and had since Gaiety had been born. Immobilized by her injured ankle rather than the birth, Sarah had been able to do very little except feed the baby during the first few weeks, and Jason had simply demanded that the women teach him what to do, threatening to develop his own system if they didn't. With a general air of superiority and a good deal of laughter, they had set out to show him how tedious and unfitting the work was for him, but he had turned the tables on them and proved himself as capable and patient in caring for the baby as they were. And they had to grant that perhaps it wasn't so odd an idea after all since it gave him more time with his wife as well as his child. Jamie too had learned at least to hold the baby without fear though he had decided she'd be more interesting when she got bigger.

Sarah watched Jason walking around with Gaiety against his shoulder. He was patting her back gently and humming a little tune to her, and Sarah had to stifle her laughter for fear of hurting his feelings. But it did amuse her mightily to see her tall, muscular husband limping around wearing only a baby on his shoulder.

She felt like that most of the time now, felt like laughing and crowing aloud. It was finally over. It had taken her a long time to accept the fact that she had been unable to kill her father outright when she had had the chance.

She had cried out with the realization of it the day after Gaiety had been born. Jason had been there, as he had been there whenever she needed him through all those first days and since.

"I had him right in front of me, right there, so close! I could have killed him easily. But I didn't, I didn't!"

Before the hysteria was fully born, he had his arms around her, rocking her with the softest of motions where she lay. "No matter what the reason, no matter what, patricide is one of the oldest curses of human history. Do you hear me, love, do you understand? No matter how terrible his sins against you, he was your father. In the end you proved yourself better than he; he was evil, you are not. It was for me to kill him, not for you."

"But I did try," she whispered, feeling confused and broken. "Even when I failed with the gun, I tried to lead him into the caves. I did."

"I know you tried, and I know you did it more to protect me than yourself, but remember, always remember, I killed him, not you."

She did remember and she loved him more every day for it because finally she understood the ancient murder he had kept her from committing.

It was a bitterly cold February day, but it didn't matter. The house would be warm with fires and friends for Jason's thirty-seventh birthday.

She got up as he laid his sleeping daughter in the crib Cade had made for her with Jamie's help.

"I'd love to lie about all day, but a certain husband of mine is having a birthday today, and there's lots to do." Sarah planted a fleeting kiss on his mouth as she sailed past him. "Better put something on or get back in bed before you catch cold."

Jason winced inwardly and wondered if he'd be able to stand the day with good manners. Thirty-seven. Christ, how had he gotten to be that old? It wasn't a new question; he'd been wondering for some time now, but this was the first time the answer had come so clearly to him.

He wasn't that old; he wasn't too old. He was just too old for Sarah. He was thirty-seven this day and she wasn't yet twenty-three. And more than that, her life was just beginning, beginning as if she were even younger. Never before had she had the chance of normal choices, normal freedom. And she hadn't that chance now unless he let her go.

He felt as if a violent earthquake was shaking his world, and he knew it was. It didn't matter that they shared a child; Gaiety Ellen was an accomplished fact and would go with her mother no matter what the cost to him. It was not the baby's hold on her, but his that kept her from knowing what freedom was.

He crawled back into bed, wishing he never had to get up again and certainly not this day.

Sarah, finished with her morning ablutions, discovered him there. "Today you can sleep almost as late as you like unless Gaiety wakes you, which I expect she will before too long. Any time you come downstairs, Maggie and I will make you an enormous breakfast, or yell from the top of the stairs, and we'll bring it to you. Love, I know you're hiding from your birthday, but it really isn't so bad. Just think, all the presents will be for you!" She laughed as she tucked the covers around him and left the room.

The only gifts he wanted were things he could never have. He wanted Sarah's father never to have existed and yet Sarah to have been born and have become exactly the woman she was now. He wanted far fewer than fifteen years to separate them. He wanted the first bargain made in Sarah's desperate need never to have been made at all. He wanted to meet Sarah as a young man and court her in the old ways and have her choose him simply because she preferred him to other suitors, not because she was frantic for protection and had so few options left. He wanted to be her first lover and show her gently from the first what she had learned only after so much pain and degradation —how well a man and a woman could fit together.

Gifts he couldn't have. But that did not mean there were no gifts he could give to her. No matter what he had to do, she would go free and know what it was to be free, know what it was to make choices without fear. No matter what.

He moved through the day's celebrations in a daze, but he prided himself on behaving perfectly. He laughed and responded exactly as everyone expected him to. Wryly he reminded himself that there were some advantages to years of experience; surely he had long practice in behaving as the occasion demanded in order to avoid betraying what he was really thinking.

Even Sarah was fooled that day because she was so busy playing proud hostess, but not long after she challenged Jason with the bits and pieces she'd been collecting.

"Something's wrong, and I'd like to know what it is. You're wonderful with Jamie who adores you; you're wonderful with Gaiety who adores you; and you're wonderful with me who also adores you. You eat and sleep at the right times. You work harder than anyone else on the island, and you're still capable of making love to me when Gaiety hasn't worn us both out too much. And yet with all you're giving, there's something missing, there's part of you that's somewhere else and very sad. Despite your good work, husband mine, that missing part is very important."

"You, wife, are much too observant. You knew long before I how it would be, but now I know as well as you—it's goddamn hard to decide how to build it all again and better than before." He told the lie without guilt but not without pain as he watched her accept his explanation and shoulder the blame. He knew now exactly how she had felt when she had lied about her own health to protect his.

He was glad he knew that women who were nursing their babies seldom conceived another child in the first year. Even if it wasn't so, he doubted that he could have abstained from making love to Sarah. He needed her physically and every other way more than he ever had because the time was coming ever closer when he would have nothing of her at all. He dared not tell her in words what he was feeling, but he could risk pouring his feelings into his body because making love had long been something glorious between them, and she was accustomed to his careful cherishing as much as he was to hers.

February passed into March, bringing a boisterous visit from Captain Tom and Angie to meet the baby. March passed into April, and Jason faced the fact that the time was growing shorter. Gaiety Ellen was gaining strength and weight by the day, and she was the key. Jason could not send Sarah away until he knew that the baby was strong enough to survive a journey. Often when he looked into Gaiety's eyes and saw the golden image of his own staring back at him along with a leafy green all her own, he wondered if he would be able to bear having her gone from him. And Sarah, always Sarah. He refused to think at all of how it was going to be without her.

News spread all over the Sound and beyond of Seattle's plans to start building her own railroad on May 1. Anyone willing to wield a shovel or pick or an ax was welcome to attend the picnic.

"Can they do it?" Sarah asked Jason.

"If they had a hundred years and a lot of money, they might," he answered ruefully. "I predict a lot of blisters and sore backs from enthusiastic but short-lived work and sick stomachs from too much picnic, and almost no track laid. But I admire the spirit of the thing, and if I weren't feeling so old and tired, I'd go and join them, no matter how useless it is."

"Old and tired, my foot!" Sarah giggled as she played with Gaiety on the bed. Kicking her legs vigorously before she grabbed one foot, the baby snorted back in imitation and then pulled herself to sit as Sarah, laughing, grasped her hands.

Old and tired indeed, Jason thought, not long now. Gaiety was active and strong in spite of her precarious beginning, and she was nursing less often as Sarah began to supplement her diet with other foods.

I've got to tell her soon. He thought of it constantly as May began, and it was far more important to him than any attempt Seattle might make to build a railroad, much more difficult too, he judged. It was far more important than any business considerations. He wondered at how much a man could be changed by loving a woman as much as he loved Sarah.

The island was already buzzing with plans for celebrating her birthday when Jason decided it was time to tell her. Somehow he couldn't bear to go through all the festivities and then tell her. And it was only getting more difficult day by day. Telling her was all he could think about; how things would be afterward was hazy, and in that vision, he saw it all as being very civilized as he was being. After her birthday, the *Gaiety* would take her and the baby south to San Francisco.

He felt no guilt in talking to Jamie before he told Sarah. He needed an ally, and Jamie's life was going to be affected as profoundly as his own.

Talking of nothing in particular, they rode out to the beach where the potlatch had been held. Jamie laughed suddenly as they settled down on a sea-polished cedar log. "I was just remberin' how funny Mama looked when she fell in while we were fishin', an' then she pulled me in too 'cuz I was laughin' so hard at her. An' then th' Indians came an' she was gonna hold 'em off while I got away. That was some day!''

"Your mother is some woman, and I need to talk to you about her.''

Jamie wasn't surprised. "I figured there was somethin' special you wanted to tell me. Is it about her birthday? I think everything's planned all right.''

Jason's gaze focused sharply on his son, seeing him with great clarity, and for a moment, his throat closed so that he couldn't speak at all. Jamie got along very well with the other children on the island, indeed, with everyone, but there was and always would be a self-contained quality about him, a wholeness about him that Sarah had brought forth. Jason was more aware than ever of the passing years. Jamie would be twelve this summer and the past year had wrought great changes. He was slender, and it wasn't hard to imagine the lanky height he would acquire in the next few years. Jason saw traces of himself and of Gaiety in his face but more of something uniquely Jamie—a bright intentness, a willingness to find something new to spark his interest and increase his knowledge each day of his life. His bad behavior and most of the symptoms of his terrifying illness had virtually ended as soon as he had been assured that he was loved. There was nothing of the sissy about Jamie. It was simply that he liked being happy and he liked making others happy. Jason doubted that causing trouble on purpose even occurred to him now.

He was humbled by the realization of the rare human being given to him as his son. He cleared his throat and spoke very softly, "You know how much I love Sarah, don't you?''

Jamie nodded.

"I love Gaiety Ellen too," Jason continued. "But I am going to send them both away for a while, and I want you to understand why. I'm telling you first. I'll tell Sarah tonight.''

"There can't be a good reason!'' Jamie burst out. "It's wrong!''

"Perhaps it is,'' Jason agreed, knowing that for his son's sake and his own, he had to explain this as calmly as possible. "But

I'm going to do it anyway. I'm not sure you'll understand, but please try. When Sarah came to me, to us, as Mary, she was running away from her father. You know that, and you know that he finally came here after her and died here. You know that he was an evil man. Jamie, this is the first time in all of Sarah's life that she has been free. Before, she had lived in a cage of fear that was around her wherever she was. And she met me and married me while she was still in that cage, still in a place where every choice she made was based on fear, not on freedom. The cage should be totally gone now, but how can it be if she must live by what she chose when she was a prisoner? Do you understand?"

"I don't want to, but I do." Jamie's voice, when it finally came, was thick with tears he was trying not to shed. "It's like th' animals. Lots of times even when we let 'em out, they just stay there for th' longest time, not knowing that they're free to go. An' what you're sayin' is that we're Mama's . . . Sarah's cage even though we love her an' she loves us."

The conscious correction from "Mama" to "Sarah" tore at Jason's heart. "It's really me, not you, Jamie. She'll always be your mother. It won't be the same, but whatever happens, I'll make sure you spend a good part of the year with her and your sister." Sarah might indeed find that she preferred another and younger husband, but he knew she would never cease to love Jamie as her first son.

"Raven was set free, but he came back! He still comes back lookin' for Daniel." Jamie tried to make his point with great conviction, but he failed as the tears overcame him.

They clung to each other until the first fierce sorrow had passed. It was as if she had already left them.

Sarah didn't see them until supper, and she knew immediately that something was wrong. Jamie's eyes didn't quite meet hers and he looked pale as he moved the food she'd prepared so carefully around the plate.

She felt his forehead. "Are you feeling all right?"

It was more than he could bear. "Fine, just played too hard," he mumbled. "Can I be excused?"

"May I," Sarah corrected gently, but Jamie was already out of his chair and nearly running from the room as his father gave quick permission.

Sarah looked at Jason. "What's going on? He's breathing normally, and I don't think he has a fever, but he's certainly acting strangely. Did 'that old Erin' push her plans for marriage ahead of schedule?" No smile met her own.

"Jamie's upset because I told him that you and the baby are going away."

"Well, no wonder! Now it's different. If we're all going somewhere, he ought to come with . . ." she stopped as the reality of what he had said sank in. She felt as if all the air had been sucked out of the room.

"I'm sending you and the baby to San Francisco. Jamie and I will stay here. In six months time, we'll sail south. Whatever you've decided, you'll see Jamie. I'll never keep him from you." Jason spoke very quickly.

Sarah's mouth was so dry, she had trouble getting the words out. "Whatever I decide about what? I don't understand one thing you're saying."

He looked away from the fear darkening her eyes. "You are free for the first time in your life, but you don't know it and you never will as long as you stay with me. I'm a forced choice out of your past. I'm Mary's choice. Sarah may choose someone very different and should if that's best for her, for you. There's no question about the children. Gaiety shouldn't and won't be separated from you no matter what you decide, though I would hope I'll always be able to see my daughter and will, of course, support her and you. And it would break Jamie's heart if he didn't spend a good part of the next few years at least with you. But all of that can be arranged."

"Please, let's pretend none of this has been said. It's all so silly, maybe I'm just imagining it anyway." The sound was so metallic and high-pitched, Jason had to listen very carefully to understand.

"You didn't imagine it, and you will leave for at least a while." His voice was cold and hard because if he allowed anything else, he would weep as Jamie had. "I'm nearly forty years old and you are scarcely twenty. Are you so sure you didn't chose me because you were looking for a kinder father than your own?"

He saw the cruel spike piercing her even as it had torn him. He still didn't know whether it was true or not, but he watched her pride and her knowledge of her own worth rise in angry self-defense, and silently he applauded her.

"However oddly you do your sums, there are fewer than fifteen years between us, and they do not matter to me at all. And you must have been most promiscuous to think that you could have fathered me at thirteen, and you are most presumptuous to assume that having suffered my own father, I would want another in that role. I made a bargain with you. I became your mistress, not your daughter. And then I became your lover, not your daughter. And then I became your wife, *not your daughter.* That is how it was for me, but not for you, I find. Tell me, did you enjoy making love to the daughter you created? Did you enjoy it as my father did?" She spat the words out as she rose unsteadily to her feet. "I presume you meant all of this to be decent and civilized. Well, it isn't decent; it's as mad as anything my father ever thought of, and I won't be civilized about it! I want to leave on the fastest ship you can find as soon as you can find it, not on the *Gaiety.* And I don't know what you're planning, but if you so much as try to touch me before I leave, I'll slit your throat, or at least I'll make a good attempt at it." Her smile was ghastly. "As you know, I'm not the best of executioners, but I've had some practice. I'll surely get it right someday."

"I thought you could stay until after your birthday." Jason knew how stupid that sounded even as he said it.

"You thought wrong. You're wrong about everything. However we began, I love you as a woman loves a man. But I swear, I'll learn how not to love you. I'm very adaptable, as you know." With that she was gone.

Jason bowed his head and sank his teeth into his fist to keep from calling her back. He had accomplished what he'd set out to do, but he hadn't known how intense the pain was going to be, hadn't faced how savage he was going to have to be to make her go or how savage she would be in return.

Sarah undressed slowly. Gaiety was still sound asleep. The fire crackled merrily, warding off the night chill of spring. Perhaps it would rain tomorrow. Odd, but next month even though it might be warmer, there would be more clouds. Odd. Everything was odd. She stretched her arm out and moved her fingers slowly, watching them move, not particularly reassured that they did. She pinched one arm, hard. The pain was real. Everything was real.

The baby stirred and whimpered, and Sarah used it as an excuse to pick her up, needing the warm weight of her for reassurance.

She crossed her arms and held her ribs as she started to rock back and forth, back and forth, on and on, mesmerizing herself with the motion even as she soothed Gaiety Ellen in her arms. She heard Jason's uneven steps approach the door, stop, and depart again, and she went on rocking.

"Well, daughter mine, nothing stays the same, all things change, all things."

Gaiety smiled without fully waking, reassured by the warm security and the soft sound of her mother's voice.

Sarah put her carefully back in her nest of blankets. She had heard the softness in her own voice even more clearly than the baby had.

Where had the anger gone? She searched diligently and could find no trace of it remaining. And without the wall it provided, everything else rushed in.

How many times had she wondered how Jason could go on with so much love and so much loyalty to her when all was being shattered around him because of her? Countless times. How much had he lost because of her? So much. How much had he risked for her? Everything. The long scar on his back would be there for as long as he lived, a reminder of how close he had come to dying for her.

"How do I love thee? Let me count the ways."

She remembered the book of Mrs. Browning's sonnets Jason had given to Gaiety. And yet he and Gaiety had loved each other simply without shadows until the sudden, final darkness. It was she herself who had received so much from him. Gaiety Ellen was only one gift of one way of his loving; he had loved her in so many ways.

She thought of the book of Blake's poems Hayes had given

her. "Tyger, tyger, burning bright/ In the forests of the night," and those other lines: "Did He smile His work to see?/ Did He who made the lamb make thee?"

Surely in Jason were met the natures of both, the gentle and the fierce, and he had shared both sides of himself with her.

She went in search of him and found him in his study. There were books open before him, but he wasn't reading. He was staring at nothing, so lost in his thought, he didn't hear her come in and started at the sound of her voice.

"I've changed my mind about slitting your throat. Come to bed now, darling."

He didn't understand the change unless she meant to try to charm him out of his decision, but he went with her as if he were a sleepwalker and wondered if indeed he were dreaming.

With gentle insistence she made love to him, ministering to him, taking her pleasure as she gave him his, stroking, kissing, cradling his flesh with her own.

And in the morning he discovered she was not going to use her power over his body to change his mind. She asked only that he find a ship as soon as possible.

She moved through the next few days in a fog, packing clothes for herself and the baby, feeling somehow cushioned beyond feeling. She was neither happy nor sad; she simply was.

The islanders thought Jason was crazy, and they showed their anger and bafflement openly, but they soon found that Sarah did not want their sympathy and would not listen to anything said against her husband.

"He has his reasons. Both of us have been through a great deal because of my father. It is best if we have a little time apart."

Constance had confined herself to looking sad, but Maggie displayed her displeasure in signs so sharp, it was as if she were screeching aloud.

"Best for what?" Cade had demanded harshly. "This isn't like the time before when you left. The two of you have a child now. This doesn't make any sense."

"Best for Jason," she had answered quietly, refusing to say anything more about it. Cade appeared before she left with a new supply of wooden toys for the baby—toys too smooth to cut and too large to swallow, toys Gaiety would love and handle as she had the others from him.

Her dread had been of facing Jamie, but she found him as accepting as he was sad. Obviously whatever his father had said had made sense to him.

"We will see each other again. He promised."

"I know, and I wouldn't let it be any other way." Sarah held him close for a moment and heard him whisper, "He wants you to come home like Raven, just because you want to."

She forbore to mention that she didn't want to leave in the first place; she would not try to use Jamie as a weapon against his father. Only grief would come from that.

The *Gaiety* took her and the baby to Victoria to catch a steamship scheduled to leave from there. It was all very smoothly done. The islanders wept as they bade Sarah farewell. She shed no tears, not even when she said good-bye to Jamie in Victoria. She felt very little at all.

Jason kept giving her instructions about finances and where she might find good lodgings if she didn't want to spend the whole time with Carrie and Owen, though he knew they'd love to have her and the baby. He kept reminding her that he didn't want her to work because there wasn't any need. He kept talking about everything except the fact that he didn't know how he was going to live without her. She hadn't said one angry word since she had found him that night in the study, and her calm control over the past days should have made everything easier, but it hadn't; it had had the opposite effect on him, making him want to shake the polite stranger to find out if Sarah were hidden somewhere inside. He hadn't even wanted to touch her since that morning that had brought the realization that she wasn't going to fight his decision; it would have been far worse than the first time he had taken her for the bargain.

Suddenly he wanted to quit repeating his useless advice, wanted to shout that it was a hideously stupid idea after all. And then he reminded himself that if he did not force this separation now, neither he nor she would ever know if she would have freely chosen him. And she would never know the power of guiding her own life. She had a right and a duty to that, whether or not she wanted it.

When he had given her the choice of coming back to him or not on that first night in Seattle, he had not known she was so captive. Now, even as he had explained to Jamie, he had to force her to realize that the old walls were gone, that nothing barred her way in the wide world. And if freedom carried her far from him forever, he would have to learn to survive in his own ghostly prison built of his love for her.

Her voice, patient and colorless, broke into his thoughts. "I think you ought to leave the ship now. Jamie's waiting for you. We're very close to leaving. They've called several times for nonpassengers to depart." She gave him a light, glancing kiss as if he were a distant relative, the baby in her arms between them, and then she turned away.

"Six months." His voice was strangled.

"Yes, of course," she said over her shoulder, but she didn't look back.

He carried the double images of his wife and his daughter clearly before his eyes.

Jamie turned away from the naked pain on his father's face and watched the steamer leave the harbor.

CHAPTER
43

Sarah dined that night with the captain.

The ship was the *Cristabel* and a private joke of fate Sarah had not shared with Jason. Roger Scott, the captain, had not seen her come aboard, but he saw her when she came to dine with Gaiety Ellen snugly ensconced in the big basket Constance had made for her with the sealskin blanket from the Indians to keep her warm. His eyes were still full of surprise and curiosity when the steward who had extended the captain's compliments brought her to the table. The steward carried the baby in the basket as if it might explode in his hands.

"Mrs. Drake, you do me great honor, you and your," he studied Gaiety's sleeping face for a moment, "daughter." Sarah's nod confirmed his guess. "I have heard of your husband."

"Many people have," she said, and then she surrendered to the devilish impulse to tell the truth. "My name was never Mary Smith, and I've never had a sister. When last I sailed on your ship, I was not Mrs. Drake and I was leaving Jason Drake because I thought he would be better off without me. He disagreed. He came after me, and we were married in San Francisco. My name is Sarah-Mary Drake. Gaiety Ellen is our daughter. This time I am sailing with you because my husband has decided I was right the first time, and he is better off without me, for six months at least. Six months is a good beginning for an ending, wouldn't you say?"

She felt suddenly brittle and defiant, wanting to see the shock on the weathered face of the Englishman. But she had under-estimated him. He hadn't survived for more than fifty years and most of them at sea, without learning that the conventional was scarcely adequate, even in conventional places, and that half of the truth was often less acceptable than a lie.

"I know so little I wouldn't say anything of the sort. I did not see you come aboard, but I saw your husband leaving because he was pointed out to me. I had no idea then of why it should be, and I still don't know, but I have seen less pain on the faces of dying men. So whatever has happened and whatever you think, you must not believe it was easy for him to send you and your daughter away."

He was suddenly very ruddy-faced. "I beg your pardon, ma'am. I sound as if I'm your father."

"Indeed you do not! You do yourself a grave injustice. My father never had a kind intention in his life, and I know yours are kind." She changed the subject smoothly, asking how he found the life under steam different from life under sail.

Even as he talked easily about a subject which interested him greatly—he had seen long since that sail was romance and steam was efficient work—he considered the riddle of Sarah-Mary Drake, alias Mary Smith. She was at once very young and very old. She was intelligent and very beautiful, as beautiful as any woman he had ever seen, far more than most, and she was outwardly very controlled and inwardly violent.

Captain Scott realized abruptly that he'd stopped in midsen-tence and hadn't the slightest idea of where that was.

"And so you see England as holding her lead in these iron-hulled steamships for years to come?" Sarah politely gave him his bearing. As he took it, and heard himself droning on, he suspected there was laughter in her eyes and found he didn't care.

It was not only foolish, it was dangerous to his peace of mind
—it had been a very long time since Roger Scott had lost his
dignity over a woman—but he found himself doing the least
required of him to please the other passengers while he did his
utmost to please Sarah Drake. He suffered the badly concealed
smirks of his crew and the offended air of some of the passengers even though he knew that all he would ever have of Sarah
was their conversations and the privilege of holding the baby.
He didn't care if more than one person aboard the *Cristabel*
labeled him an old fool; it was worth it. He found himself enchanted only slightly less by the baby than he was by her mother;
the two of them gave him a sense of family he had long since
relinquished. It did not matter that it was transitory. Sarah was
an extraordinary woman. He did not tell her, but he thought that
the man they called the Tiger was an idiot to put so much at risk,
particularly if it were true that his reputation for luck had been
so tarnished by loss in the past two years. And then he had to
admit to himself that perhaps Jason Drake's luck still held—
there was something about Sarah which, even more than the
presence of the child with her, warned against going too far,
warned that she was spoken for.

For her part, Sarah enjoyed the Captain's company. He was
an interesting man. It was a new and odd experience to feel so
at ease with someone on such short acquaintance. She had no
intention of telling him who her father had been, but there was
no longer any reason to hide the fact that she had come from
New York, no longer any reason to fear that she would be
discovered and word would go back. It might be uncomfortable
to meet someone who had known her back East, but it wouldn't
be dangerous.

Whatever Jason thought, she certainly hadn't left him. Gaiety
Ellen, with her eyes becoming daily more like a feminine version
of her father's, was a constant reminder of him. Gaiety adapted
very well to life on board the steamer, accepting the noise and
bustle and fussing very little. Sometimes holding her or playing
with her, Sarah felt her control wavering, felt fissures in the calm
that enveloped her, and she would make herself remember that
it was his wish and something she had to do for him. Six months.

The friends in San Francisco had expected a bereft Sarah and found instead a very self-possessed woman. Jason's telegram to Owen had been brief, but it had told them that Sarah and the baby were on their way, that it was his wish that it be so, and that he trusted his friends to watch out for them. His friends thought he was crazy.

"Seems to me that choices have already been made," Owen said, bouncing Gaiety on his lap.

But they soon discovered that Sarah didn't want to hear anything against Jason. Nor did she want to crowd Owen and Carrie in their little house. Jason had suggested that she take a suite at the Grand if she wished, but she had no intention of going back there without him. With Owen's reluctant help, she found lodgings with Mrs. Pennington, a widow who needed the extra money to keep the house her husband had built for her. She was plump, easygoing, and delighted to have Gaiety in the house. Sarah admitted honestly that she was neither a widow nor divorced though she might well be the latter before the year was out. Mrs. Pennington clucked in sympathy but did not demand more information. Owen Trenglyth had vouched for the woman and that was enough for the widow.

Sarah had turned twenty-three aboard the *Cristabel,* and she felt at once older and younger than when she had first come to San Francisco five years before. Having a growing child was a reminder of her matronly status, but sometimes she felt so green, it was a wonder to her that she did have the child. She didn't wear the ring she had found in the little box among the belongings she had packed in the trunk, but never opened during the voyage. The intricate gold band was set with four stones —a ruby, an emerald, a diamond, and a sapphire. There was no note but she knew the stones symbolized the four of them— Jason, Jamie, Gaiety Ellen, and herself. The jeweler's box was from Victoria, and she wondered when she couldn't stop the thought how long ago Jason had ordered this for her birthday and how he could have been cruel enough to send it with her. But she didn't sell it or give it away. She kept it in a drawer with the other pieces of jewelry Jason had given her. She had not left them behind this time. And with those pieces were the shell necklace from the Indians and the carved tiger given to her long ago by Cade. All the items were of equal pain and equal value in her eyes, and as much as she wished to be free of them, she kept them close and sometimes found herself taking them out and touching them one by one late at night while the baby slept. So many memories, so much life, so much lost in such small inanimate objects.

While Mrs. Pennington cared for Gaiety, Captain Scott escorted Sarah out on several occasions before his ship left for San Diego, and she found herself enjoying the city as if she had never been there before. In a way it was true; she no longer searched faces and dark alleyways for pursuit. It didn't even matter that agents and henchmen of her father still lived; they were no threat to her without him.

And when Captain Scott sailed, Sarah went out with a young lawyer she had met at Owen's office. Owen had to struggle with himself to keep his mouth shut. He felt like sending a wire to Jason telling him that if he'd meant to lose his wife to another man, he was well on his way to success.

But it wasn't so. Sarah enjoyed the young man's company, but she felt no love for him at all, and he knew it. He did not press his suit but settled for the privilege of her company. He felt the same distance as had Captain Scott.

Sarah felt as if she were floating from one day to the next. She took care of the baby, wrote letters to Jamie (there didn't seem any point in writing to Jason), and visited with her friends, particularly with Frenchie, who was showing worry lines on her lovely face though she was trying not to burden everyone with how desperately she missed Rio. He was gone again on some mysterious job.

"It's not even as if he needs the money. Jason paid him well through all that time of guarding Carrie and Owen, and I'm still working. Rio just needs the damn risk!"

Sarah had seen Frenchie bring herself under control with visible effort after that outburst, and she wondered at her own lack of emotion. She knew it was there somewhere inside of her, but she couldn't touch it anymore. Even when she went to bed and felt the absence of Jason for yet another night, even then she shed no tears.

She had been there for six weeks when the letter from Jamie came. She noticed with detached interest that her hands were beginning to shake as she opened it. He had received her first letter and was glad because she didn't seem so far away when he looked at her writing. Though he didn't write at great length, Jamie, the longtime journal keeper, did include some vivid descriptions of the islanders' doings. He had finished writing the letter in Seattle after a trip to the logging camp where he was quite sure he had heard the fiddle playing.

There it was, the first mention of Jason:

> Papa got into some trouble here, but he's all right now. We all miss you an awful lot.
>
> Love, Jamie.
P. S. Love to
Gaiety Ellen
too.

What kind of trouble? Surely, if it were serious, she would have been notified. *Oh, Jamie, I know you meant well, but couldn't you have told me more, told me how your father looks, how he's faring without me?* Her own pleas filled her mind.

What was she doing here leading this useless existence? What was she doing here passing from day to day with such cold purposelessness?

She heard the great gulping sobs and knew them for her own. All the tears she hadn't shed before seemed to want to pour out at once. Gaiety wailed in fright, but Sarah went on crying until she was spent and calm enough to comfort the baby.

Suddenly she wanted to get out of these alien rooms. She sponged her face with cold water, covered the tear marks as well as she could, and dressed the baby. Mrs. Pennington was out, so she would have to take her daughter with her, but Frenchie wouldn't mind; Frenchie loved Gaiety. Frenchie was the one Sarah wanted to see. Even though she showed it in different ways, Frenchie loved Rio every bit as much as Sarah loved Jason.

"Oh, yes, Sarah does love Jason," she crooned to Gaiety.

Frenchie's look of pleasure at her visitors quickly changed to speculation as she studied Sarah's face. "Something happen with that young fellow you've been seeing?"

"No, something happened to me. I can't go on this way. I've been pretending everything is all right, but it isn't. I miss Jason so much, I think I could die of it. My God! People did die because Jason and I were together. But there're months and months to go before I'll even see him again, and I don't know what he'll want then. I can't bear it!" She swallowed the tears that threatened again.

"I don't care what Jason wants!" Frenchie snapped. "He's crazy. You don't want to be away from him, and he doesn't want you to be away from him—that much I'm sure of—and here you are, hundreds of miles apart. That is mad!" She got up abruptly to prowl around the room, her hands unerringly finding little bits and pieces associated with Rio—the glass he most often used, a towel, a handkerchief.

Sarah watched her, seeing it all too clearly. Rio was a man of so few worldly possessions, even his hold on his own life was as tenuous as it was fierce. Frenchie didn't even have extra clothes left in the closet to assure her he was coming back. All she had were common things he'd touched and used and her memories.

Gaiety chortled and grinned in delight at the swirl of Frenchie's dress, reaching with chubby fists as if to catch the moving color in her hands. And Sarah watching her, knew how much more of Jason she had than Frenchie had of Rio.

"If Rio comes back, he is never going to leave again without me," Frenchie said, her voice as quiet and solemn as if she were making a vow. "Too much time is wasted this way. I don't care if he has to hide me in the bushes somewhere. I will go with him. I don't need a wedding ring or his children, but I do need to be with him." Her eyes bored into Sarah's. "And I don't think you and I are so different in that. You have the ring and the child, but what you really need is to be with Jason. Like I said, it's crazy to be away from him when you could be with him."

The tension left her, and she gave a tired shrug. "Ah, hell! Who am I to tell anyone how to live?"

"You're my friend and Jason's besides all the other things you are. Will you be even more of a friend and watch Gaiety for me for a while? I want to go see Reverend Mapes. I shouldn't be long."

"I'd love to. Gaiety Ellen and I get along just fine. I've been teaching her some of my act on the sly. We'll just take up where we left off." Frenchie grinned at the baby who smiled back and tried a few of her special sounds. "You see, she speaks French every bit as well as I do," Frenchie declared.

Sarah was still laughing when she left the two together after providing Frenchie with dry toast to keep Gaiety busy should she get hungry.

She was glad Reverend Mapes was a man of such disciplined habits; she found him right where he should have been, finishing the day's lessons with his band of brigands before he went on to other tasks.

The minister now saw the violence which had nearly ended his life as a godsend. The boys had found themselves beginning their schooling in earnest to please the old man and then continuing because it pleased them, though the minister, to save pride for them, kept up the fiction that it was a favor to him.

The boys greeted her respectfully and slipped away, and Bartholomew tried unsuccessfully to hide his disappointment that she hadn't brought the baby with her. He'd christened her during her first week in the city and had made Owen godfather, and he felt that entitled him to see Gaiety Ellen as often as possible.

But studying Sarah's face, he knew what she had come for without her saying a word about it. He took a deep breath and plunged in. "I didn't counsel you very well the last time, and I may again be wrong. But still I say, follow your heart, go home. Forget your husband's ideas of granting you freedom if it is not freedom as you see it. Three score and ten years, that is considered a full share of years for a human being, yet in all the ages that have gone before and those that will come after, it is a very small time. And of that, even if one is very quick-witted, at least the first twenty are spent in learning how to live and how to love and the last twenty are spent in learning how to die and how to relinquish loved ones and the pleasures of this earth one by one no matter what is to come after. By my reckoning, that leaves at the most and with a great deal of luck thirty years, a very short time indeed for the best chance of loving fully and sharing your life with someone else. Don't waste time, Sarah Drake. You know whom you love, and he loves you, loves you enough to set you free. There are few men who ever love enough to do that. And your daughter, young as she is, needs to see more of her father than the tears you shed for him. I didn't witness your marriage to see you hundreds of miles apart."

The old man took out a handkerchief, mopped his face, and smiled sheepishly at her. "You see what a terrible thing it would be if I had my own pulpit. I've been wanting to thunder away at you since the day you came back, but you weren't ready."

Sarah kissed him very quickly on both cheeks. "I may not see you before I leave, but we'll be back, all of us. I can't wait for you to meet my son Jamie. Thank you."

She was gone, leaving Bartholomew with the faint scent of spice and roses and the after-brightness of her hair. He heaved a sigh and gathered up the books he'd need for the rest of his day's tutoring, hoping that God would make one Jason Drake truly grateful. He thought of his own Anne, dead these many years. He never spoke of her, but he would never forget her either. They had had so little time together and yet it had been perfect time. He prayed that the God who had seen fit to take his own love from him would mercifully grant more time to the Drakes for theirs.

When she discovered how much they all approved of her decision to return to the island, Sarah would have been angry with her friends had she not realized they had held their tongues out of love for her and for Jason, believing that the Drakes must make their own decision about their marriage. They had confined their comments to the unsuitability of Jason's plan, not betraying how much they thought she ought to go home until the silence was broken. Frenchie had broken it because of her own longing for Rio and Sarah's confessed need. Bartholomew had followed suit because at last Sarah had come to him, and with that Owen and Carrie joined in with great relief. Carrie was at Sarah's immediate disposal to help with the packing, and

Owen admitted with a grin that he'd been keeping track of ship schedules almost from the day she'd arrived. Then his eyes sobered.

"Jason wasn't entirely wrong, you know. I thought he was, and I do think half a year is a long time in the circumstances, but you're different from when you came here. Have you noticed? It's what he wanted."

She started to deny it and then stopped, seeing herself very clearly. She no longer flinched away from strangers, no longer searched faces desperately, fearful of seeing someone familiar from her past. Her life now belonged to her. She owed no explanations to anyone. The evil was gone, washed away by Jason's hands and the sea. But she had known all this for a long time now and could have learned it as well with Jason beside her.

She would have to live with her memories of her father for the rest of her life. But that was all they were, fading further into the past with every second. First she had learned to love Jason, and then he taught her to love being alive. But he had failed in one crucial way. She had no doubt that he believed in his love for her, but he was not invincible; his courage and his belief had faltered when he considered her love for him. Having set her free from the demon of her past, he expected freedom would take her far from himself too.

"My poor Tiger," she said softly, and Owen busied himself with his schedules, pretending not to have heard.

Her luck held for her purpose. In two days, she and the baby were on a steamer bound for Seattle, and when it made port, Sarah went to Angie. She had no intention of being in the Seattle house without Jason; it was an unbearable idea now in the face of her hunger for him.

Angie greeted her with love and not a little scolding. "Good God, is it ever time and past for you to be home! The Tiger's been on a rampage ever since you left."

"He sent me away," Sarah corrected.

"Well, whatever. Thought that old temper of Jason's was gone, but it isn't. Oh, he's all right," she added hastily, seeing Sarah's face pale, "and so's Jamie. Jamie understands more of what his father is feeling than Jason does. Last time Jason was here, he really tied one on, cleared out two saloons with his fists. Took Jamie and me twenty-four hours to pour enough coffee down Jason to make him really miserable. Men from the ship-yard and the logging camp are complaining too. They say they can't get near the Tiger without risking getting something bitten off."

Sarah shook her head, anger mixed with her love, understanding now the cryptic note in Jamie's letter. "That idiot! He shouldn't have involved Jamie in it. I'm glad Jamie had you to turn to."

"I told you, it's all right. Because of you, Jamie and Jason are very close. Jamie's not afraid of his father anymore; he's just sad for him. So the trick now is to get you and this little one to the island as fast as can be." Gaiety at the moment was sitting happily on Angie's lap.

Angie had them on a ship bound for San Juan Island with a promise to stop at Drake's Island before Seattle awakened fully to the fact that Sarah Drake had returned.

To Sarah, it seemed the longest voyage of her life. Every minute stretched into hours now that she was so close to her goal.

She saw the *Gaiety* riding at anchor, and her heart began to pound. Jason must be here! She'd wondered how she could bear it if he were not on the island. She saw the dusky red bark of the madrona trees and the deep green of the firs under a clear sky. She saw the flag indicating a ship had been sighted, and she saw the figures beginning to gather to watch.

The sailors settled her and the baby carefully into the tender and rowed them in, and she saw the figures on shore freeze as they realized who she was.

By the time they landed, the air was full of glad cries, and Sarah and Gaiety were swept into the arms of the Nilsens and Olsens. David was there, too, and Constance, who had been visiting Ingrid.

Jamie was fine, off somewhere with Cade as the rest of the islanders were about their business, not knowing a ship had come in. Ingrid and Else were crying with joy at the reunion, and

Constance wasn't doing much better, but she saw the wild searching in Sarah's eyes and answered the unspoken question.

"He's all right, but he and Gabriel had one of their arguments last week, and this time Gabriel won. Served Jason right; he'd been riding around this island like a madman. At least it slowed him down. He's got a couple of cracked ribs and a bad knee to go with his bad leg. Don't look like that! He's healing nicely, and it won't make him any more lame than he is. Ah, your chariot arrives!

"As much as Sarah loves us, she has someone she loves more and wants to see," Constance announced to the others.

The wagon was creaking down the hill, Ben, having sighted the flag and the ships, was coming to see if goods or people were to be transported. His face split in a wide grin as he caught sight of Sarah. And the luggage was forgotten for the time as he drove his passengers swiftly back to the house, getting more speed out of the team than he had in years.

She found Maggie in the kitchen. Maggie froze in wonderment, then tears flooded her eyes as she clasped Sarah and Gaiety against her. And then she got control of herself and signed that Jason was in his study.

Sarah handed the baby to Maggie and made her way to the study. Now that she was so close, she was shaking so hard, she wasn't sure her legs would support her. She opened the door, went in, and then stopped short at Jason's expression. He looked up and smiled ruefully, but the smile was quickly replaced by confusion and alarm.

"It really is you! My God, how did you . . . Gaiety Ellen, is it the baby, where is she?"

She understood then, understood that he had seen her often and everywhere since she'd been gone, that he'd grown accustomed to being haunted by the apparition.

"Gaiety is perfectly fine. She's in the kitchen with Maggie." Her voice was sharp, and she chose defiance because her heart was breaking for him. He looked so gaunt and tired with pain shadowing his eyes, and he was reaching for a stout cane as he struggled to get to his feet.

"Stay where you are! I've got two perfectly good legs because

I don't make it a habit to argue with bad-tempered horses. I'm not going to argue with you either. I'm going to tell you that if you send me away again, it will be forever. No more trial separations. There are years between us, but they matter to you, not to me. I've lived through too much to want a man of my own age who knows nothing at all. If you don't want me, I'm going to have to learn to live without you, and I'll do it, too. But I'll never love another man of any age as I love you, never as long as I live. I lived without love before; I can learn to do it again, if that's what you want."

"What I want . . ." the words were barely audible, but so full of longing, she ran to him, unable to resist the need to touch him.

"You are a prize idiot, Jason Drake, so gallant and so stupid! I was totally free the moment you killed my father, but I had chosen freely to love you long before that, or at least as freely as love as strong as this ever allows. The only freedom I need or ever will is to be able to love you and our children, but God help me, most of all you."

He saw that she was wearing the birthday ring and her wedding ring, and he pulled her into his lap, ignoring her protest that she might hurt him, ignoring the pain in his ribs and everything else except the reality of the scent, weight, and warm life of her pressed against him. He saw again the gilt-haired child peering at him from the stairs; he saw the dancing girl that night in San Francisco and Mary Smith in Seattle when he had first taken her as a woman; and he saw the Sarah-Mary of all these days and felt again the pattern which had begun before he knew.

"It's been so empty, everything empty! Oh, God, I love you so much!" The husky words poured over her with her tears and his own.

Time enough for him to see Gaiety Ellen, time enough for her to find Jamie, time enough for the news from San Francisco and everything else, but time now for the gold to dawn fiercely in his eyes as the Tiger gazed down at his woman and bent his head to seal their final bargain with a kiss.